TD £6/10/-

MATHEMATICAL PLANNING OF STRUCTURAL DECISIONS

CONTRIBUTIONS TO ECONOMIC ANALYSIS

45

Edited by

J. JOHNSTON

J. SANDEE

R. H. STROTZ

J. TINBERGEN

P. J. VERDOORN

1967

NORTH-HOLLAND PUBLISHING COMPANY
AMSTERDAM

MATHEMATICAL PLANNING OF STRUCTURAL DECISIONS

by

JÁNOS KORNAI

Computing Centre of the Hungarian Academy of Sciences, Budapest

with contributions by

THOMAS LIPTÁK *and* PÉTER WELLISCH

1967

NORTH-HOLLAND PUBLISHING COMPANY
AMSTERDAM

This book was originally published under the title
„A gazdasági szerkezet matematikai tervezése”
by Közgazdasági és Jogi Könyvkiadó, Budapest 1965

Translated by
JÓZSEF HATVANY *and* PÁL MORVAY

Joint edition published
by North-Holland Publishing Company
and Akadémiai Kiadó
Publishing House of the Hungarian Academy of Sciences

PRINTED IN HUNGARY

INTRODUCTION TO THE SERIES

This series consists of a number of studies, which are introduced by the editors in the belief that they represent fresh contributions to economic science.

The term *economic analysis* as used in the title of the series has been adopted because it covers both the activities of the theoretical economist and the research worker.

Although the analytical methods used by the various contributors are not the same, they are nevertheless conditioned by the common origin of thier studies, namely theoretical problems encountered in practical research. Since for this reason, business cycle research and national accounting, research work on behalf of economic policy, and problems of planning are the main sources of the subjects dealt with, they necessarily determine the manner of approach adopted by the authors. Their methods tend to be "practical" in the sense of not being too remote from application to actual economic conditions. In addition they are quantitative rather than qualitative.

It is the hope of the editors that the publications of these studies will help to stimulate the exchange of scientific information and to reinforce international cooperation in the field of economics.

THE EDITORS

PREFACE TO THE ENGLISH EDITION

Some decades hence, it will be natural and self-evident in Hungary to use mathematical methods in preparing long-term plans. Electronic computers will pour forth columns of figures for the planners. For us, however, who took part in the linear programming of the five-year investment plan for the Hungarian cotton fabrics industry, the assignment of being the first in our country to elaborate a long-term plan with the help of mathematical methods and an electronic computer, was fraught with the excitement of novelty and of a pioneering venture.

Since that time two further projects – both embracing a whole sector – have been completed: the fifteen-year development plan of the Hungarian man-made fibres industry has been worked out by means of the non-linear programming method, and a similar project was carried out for the bauxite–aluminium industry. At present, mathematical programming projects for the 1966–1970 plans are in preparation in forty sectors, based on the experiences of the three completed sectoral calculations.

On the basis of the first, favourable experiences with programming for sectors of industry, the scope of research has been extended and a mathematical model for economy-wide long-term planning has been set up. The first experimental calculations are now being carried out.

The present work treats of the experiences gained in the course of these researches. It is a composite of three different forms, containing as it does *case studies* of the experiences gained in a number of concrete projects in operations research; *theoretical analysis* of some general problems of socialist planning; and a *survey* of some characteristic features of the actual practice of Hungarian long-term planning.

I am well aware that as regards precision of the exposition, strict logic and the level of pure theory, my work will not compete with those presented to the world by eminent mathematical economists in the course of the past decade or two. But the close connection which exists between our mathematical calculations on the one hand and planning *practice* on the other, may compensate for the shortcomings. I have not tried to elaborate refined and "elegant" models. Concessions were often made with respect to what was considered the ideal model, where the latter might have proved too complicated, the figures could possibly not be substantiated, or the problem technically computed. The aim was rather that the conception formulated should be practicable and usable even with the present planning, statistical and computing facilities. It is felt that the authenticity of the information in the book is due precisely to the fact that the methods described have actually been tested (or are for the smaller part now being tested) and that the conditions for their practical application are already extant.

When the heads of the National Planning Board or of the industrial ministries gave us assignments to prepare recommendations for their long-term plans by certain dead-lines, we could not argue that numerous theoretical problems had not yet been elucidated. We could not wait for the ultimate theoretical conclusions, but had to make do with temporary solutions in order that the calculations should be completed in time for them to be usable in practice. The standard we set ourselves was that the principles and methods of calculation that we used, should be at least one degree better than the usual. For until the open questions of the economic theory of long-run planning and of investments have been clarified, it is an achievement even to take one step forward with respect to the present practice. This will surely promote theoretical development too, for in the course of solving the computing problems set by practice and spurred by the requirements of economic life, the difficult problems of theory will also be more easily elucidated.

The present volume is based on experiences gained in Hungary. I am none the less confident that it will be of interest to the reader abroad as well.

It is, first and foremost, the *planners* who might be interested in our experiences. The contents of this book will, of course, be of most direct use to economists living, as ourselves, in a country with a socialist planned economy. But keen interest in basing long-term plans and decisions on mathematical models is arising in several countries. Experiments in working out and employing long-term economy-wide mathematical models are being carried out in the Netherlands and Norway as well as in India, Egypt and other countries of recent independence. Such endeavours will necessarily lead to problems similar to those dealt with in this volume.

The author's primary objective is to assist in their training those who, though regularly engaged in economic planning work, have so far had no experience in mathematical planning methods. With this objective it is inevitable that some chapters of the book should deal in greater detail with certain notions and relationships which will be familiar to the professional reader well versed in both theory and practice of mathematical methods. The author hopes, however, that even this class of reader will not find the rest of the chapters without interest.

We have a number of methodological problems in common with *those engaged in operation research and the economic application of mathematical methods* – even if their domains are other than long-term planning or taking economic decisions on the national or sector level. Many of these problems will be discussed in these pages.

It is but natural that my book should at several points touch on the subjects that engage the interest of *theoretical* economists. In the course of the exposition I have tried to confront from several points of view the propositions of theory (e.g. of the theory of interest, decision theory, welfare economics, etc.) with the practice of socialist planning.

The subject-matter of the book may finally interest also those *engaged in the study of the socialist economy*. They will be able to draw both on the parts which describe non-mathematical planning methods, and on those discussing the achievements and difficulties in introducing the mathematical methods, which give an account of a new phenomenon of outstanding importance in the development and transformation of socialist planning.

After this general outline of the subject, I will now proceed to delineate the subject-matter of the present work, adding a few preliminary remarks on its structure as well as on the method of exposition.

(1) The book deals with the targets relating to the s t r u c t u r e* of production and foreign trade: what should reasonably be produced, how much of it, and by means of what techniques, inputs and combinations of resources; what investment projects will it be desirable to carry out; how much of what should be exported and where to; how much of what should be imported and where from. The decisions which answer these questions will be called in the following s t r u c t u r a l d e c i s i o n s.

Long-term planning not only provides an answer to the above questions but covers also the *time sequence*, the scheduling of economic activity as

* The concepts here to be newly introduced or used in a special sense, will be l e t t e r - s p a c e d and defined where they first occur. The concepts used in a special sense are arranged in alphabetical order in the Subject Index, where references will be found to the place of the definition and the first explanation.

The majority of these concepts are actually generally used in the literature of mathematical programming or of socialist planning, while a smaller part have been construed for the purposes of the author's own arguments.

well as the determination of its *place*. However, apart from one or two chapters, I will not go into the details of planning for the dynamics of economic activity and will not deal at all with the question of regional planning.

(2) Little space will be devoted in this volume to the critical evaluation of the literature published up to the present on the subject of long-term planning. I will, as a general rule, confine myself to references to the literary sources from which I have drawn, without entering into their detailed analysis.

(There is a single exception made to this rule: in one of the appendices, a short survey and evaluation is given of the recent debate relating to the rental on capital.)

(3) The book will not impose any high demands on the mathematical equipment of the reader, as it requires no more than some knowledge of vector and matrix operations, as well as of the rudiments of linear algebra, calculus and probability theory. To facilitate the task of the non-mathematical reader, the verbal explanation and economic interpretation of each mathematical formula is given wherever possible.

Apart from some instances, the book does not aim to present the mathematics (the theorems, their proofs, the technique of numerical computation, etc.) of the programming procedures, but rather to promote the adoption of a *mathematical approach*. It is primarily the economist's task to set up a mathematical-economic model, while the elaboration of the methods for solving the model is mainly the mathematician's job. The author's aim has been to help accomplish the first of these, to offer advice to the economist on how to set up mathematical-economic models to substantiate long-run plans, structural decisions. To do this, he must of course be fully aware what models can be treated mathematically, lest he build castles in the air, instead of models. Some information on these aspects has therefore also been included.

(4) A few words, finally, on the structure of the book. It was my endeavour to proceed from the simpler notions towards the more intricate ones. In the initial parts, the reader will meet with simpler economic problems, less mathematical difficulties and models that are easier to grasp, and will then be led gradually to the investigation of more complex problems.

The book is complemented with a whole range of appendices: discussions of a mathematical and computing-technical character, compilations of statistical data, surveys of the literature pertaining to some individual problems, etc. The appendices generally contain material which differs in character from the main line of exposition in the book or the treatment of which would interrupt the work's unified argument. The main ideas of the work will be conveyed to the reader without the study of the appendices; the latter are thus meant rather for the reader who is interested in the problems of a more special character.

In conclusion, I wish to express my gratitude to all those who have assisted in my research work.

My first acknowledgements are due to my two collaborators, mathematicians Thomas Lipták (Computing Centre of the Building Industry) and Péter Wellisch (Research Institute for the Textile Industry). Without their creative cooperation my investigations would have failed to achieve their goal. They assisted me in the mathematical formulation of certain relationships and in carrying out numerical calculations; they were most helpful in their criticism of the manuscript. In certain parts of the book their cooperation went even farther than that. Th. Lipták and P. Wellisch figure as *co-authors* in the surveys of research projects where they have already actively participated in working out the model and the theoretical bases of the investigations. Moreover, Th. Lipták is the *author* of two, P. Wellisch of one of the appendices.

I am also much indebted to B. Martos (Institute for Economics of the Hungarian Academy of Sciences) and to Dr. M. Augustinovics (National Planning Board) for their reading the original manuscript and suggesting numerous modifications. In the different phases of the work, Dr. A. Bródy (Institute for Economics of the Hungarian Academy of Sciences), Dr. Gy. Cukor (Institute for Economics of the Hungarian Academy of Sciences), Dr. A. Nagy (Institute for Market Research) and Dr. T. Nagy (Institute for Economics of the Hungarian Academy of Sciences) were also most helpful with their comments concerning the surveys on the individual partial research projects as well as the earlier and actual version of the book.

I have to thank my translators J. Hatvany and P. Morvay for the care they devoted to the difficult task of translating the work into English. My thanks are due to C. J. Bliss (Cambridge, England) who read the English-language manuscript and whose remarks concerning its correction were a most valuable help.

Finally, the author wishes to express his gratitude to the North-Holland Publishing Company and the Publishing House of the Hungarian Academy of Sciences for the English-language edition of his book.

Budapest, 1965 J. KORNAI

CONTENTS

Introduction to the series . . . v
Preface to the English edition . . . vii
List of tables . . . xxi
Signs and symbols . . . xxiii

PART 1: TRADITIONAL METHODS AND INPUT–OUTPUT TABLES

Chapter 1

The traditional plan index system . . . 5
- 1.1. The main groups of indices . . . 5
- 1.2. The consistency of the index system . . . 11
- 1.3. The plan as an equation system . . . 13
- 1.4. Plan coordination . . . 17

Chapter 2

The traditional investment efficiency calculations . . . 22
- 2.1. Central permits for the main investments . . . 22
- 2.2. The index g_n . . . 23

Chapter 3

Input—output tables . . . 28
- 3.1. Main definitions . . . 28
- 3.2. Total contents calculations . . . 30
- 3.3. The characteristics of the breakdown by sectors . . . 32
- 3.4. The "chessboard" balance broken down by authorities . . . 34
- 3.5. Interbranch balances . . . 37
- 3.6. Balance based on breakdown by products . . . 38
- 3.7. Checking the consistency of the plan . . . 40
- 3.8. Other input—output tables . . . 42

Chapter 4

The "footholds" of mathematical planning . . . 43

PART 2: SECTORAL PROGRAMMING MODELS

Chapter 5

THE CHOICE BETWEEN TECHNOLOGICAL ALTERNATIVES. THE MODEL FOR THE COTTON INDUSTRY . . . 51
- 5.1. Decision problems . . . 51
- 5.2. The scope of programming . . . 52
- 5.3. Activities, the variables of the model . . . 55
- 5.4. External constraints . . . 58
- 5.5. Internal constraints . . . 62
- 5.6. The objective function . . . 64
- 5.7. The mathematical summary of the problem . . . 67
- 5.8. The practical results of programming in the cotton industry . . . 68

Chapter 6

THE PROPORTIONS OF PRODUCTION, EXPORTS AND IMPORTS. THE MODEL OF THE MAN-MADE FIBRES INDUSTRY . . . 74
- 6.1. Decision problems . . . 74
- 6.2. The scope of programming . . . 76
- 6.3. The activities . . . 78
- 6.4. The constraints . . . 79
- 6.5. The objective function . . . 82
- 6.6. The practical results of programming in the man-made fibres industry . . . 83

Chapter 7

COSTS AS A FUNCTION OF THE ACTIVITY LEVEL . . . 85
- 7.1. The subject and arrangement of the treatment . . . 85
- 7.2. Common simplifying assumptions . . . 86
- 7.3. The classification of cost functions from the mathematical and computational point of view . . . 89
- 7.4. The characteristic development of costs for various types of activity 96
- 7.5. The consideration of the advantages of mass production in the man-made fibres industry . . . 100
- 7.6. Determination of the parameters of the function . . . 107

Chapter 8

FIRST COMPARISON WITH THE TRADITIONAL METHODS . . . 109
- 8.1. Broader opportunities for choices . . . 109
- 8.2. Choice based on simple ranking . . . 113
- 8.3. The balance method and the requirement of economic efficiency 116
- 8.4. The connection between the sector programming model and the traditional plan index system . . . 118
- 8.5. The computing-technical limitations . . . 120

PART 3: THE TREATMENT OF UNCERTAIN DATA

Chapter 9

THE DIFFICULTIES OF DETERMINING TECHNICAL AND COST DATA 127
9.1. The mechanism of data supply 127
9.2. Random and tendentious errors in estimation 129
9.3. Promoting unbiased work 136

Chapter 10

SENSITIVITY ANALYSIS. PARAMETRIC PROGRAMMING 140
10.1. Serial calculations 140
10.2. Parametric programming 141
10.3. Some practical examples 144
10.4. The "neighbourhood" of the optimum 148
10.5. The significance of sensitivity analysis 149

Chapter 11

"PESSIMISTIC" AND "OPTIMISTIC" RANKING 150
11.1. The problem of decisions with uncertain consequences 150
11.2. The "from-to" form of estimation 151
11.3. Ranking in the man-made fibres industry 153
11.4. First selection 156
11.5. The safety ranking of alternatives 157
11.6. The deficiencies of the procedure 160

Chapter 12

SAFETY PROGRAMMING (*Co-author:* TH. LIPTÁK) 162
12.1. Survey of the exposition 162
12.2. The justification for applying probabilistic methods 162
12.3. Uncertainty and probability 166
12.4. The model of safety programming 170
12.5. The economic interpretation of safety programming 172

Chapter 13

SAFETY AND RISKTAKING 177
13.1. A diagrammatic representation of safety strategy 177
13.2. Executives interviewed 178
13.3. The justification for risk-aversion 183

Chapter 14

STOCHASTIC CALCULATIONS IN PRACTICE 188
14.1. Supplementary assumptions 188
14.2. The problem narrowed down 189

14.3. The most important calculations 191
14.4. The effects of the concentration of activities 195
14.5. A methodological remark 197

Chapter 15

SECOND COMPARISON WITH THE TRADITIONAL METHODS 199

PART 4: COMPUTATIONAL EVALUATIONS

Chapter 16

THE GENERAL ACCOUNTING PRINCIPLES OF THE COMPUTATIONAL PRICE SYSTEM 207
16.1. The role of the accounting principles 207
16.2. The general formula of the computational price 208
16.3. The sphere of application of foreign-trade prices 211
16.4. The treatment of the dynamics of inputs 214
16.5. The further course of the exposition 217

Chapter 17

DETERMINATION OF TOTAL PRODUCTION-FUND REQUIREMENTS AND OF TOTAL WAGE CONTENTS 218
17.1. An outline of the problem 218
17.2. The use of input–output tables 219
17.3. Simplifying assumptions concerning input–output tables 222
17.4. Partial "tracing back" 227
17.5. The traditional method of "real cost calculation" 229
17.6. The official methodology of investment efficiency calculations . . 232

Chapter 18

ATTEMPTS AT THE DETERMINATION OF THE COMPUTATIONAL RENTAL ON CAPITAL AND OF THE COMPUTATIONAL WAGE FACTOR 234
18.1. Objective of the analysis 234
18.2. The aggregate production function of the national economy . . . 236
18.3. The definition and feasibility of the rational computational rental on capital and wage rate 241
18.4. On the ratio of the rental on capital and the wage rate 247
18.5. First experiment: Observation of the "capital market" 248
18.6. Second experiment: Conclusion from plan-variants 253
18.7. Third experiment: Conclusion from the distribution of national income 255
18.8. Fourth experiment: Conclusion drawn from the growth rate of the national economy. Description of the model 258
18.9. Fourth experiment: Conclusion from the growth rate of the national economy. The propositions 263
18.10. Fifth experiment: Statistical investigation 266

18.11. Sixth experiment: The determination of computational evaluations through mathematical programming 269
18.12. Accounting principles 270
18.13. General conclusions 273
18.14. Sensitivity analyses 274

Chapter 19

IMPORT MATERIAL COSTS. FOREIGN TRADE PRICES 279
19.1. The problem surveyed 279
19.2. What should be regarded as a foreign trade price? 280
19.3. Characteristic trends of price movements 282
19.4. Price trends of new commodity types 283
19.5. The forms and bases of estimation 292
19.6. The indirect import material costs 300

Chapter 20

THE COMPUTATIONAL FOREIGN EXCHANGE RATE 301
20.1. The necessity of uniform foreign exchange rates 301
20.2. The economic contents of the rate of exchange 304
20.3. Determination of foreign exchange rates by means of the input–output table 305
20.4. The program's foreign exchange-rate sensitivity 307

Chapter 21

THIRD COMPARISON WITH THE TRADITIONAL METHODS 310
21.1. Divergences from the actual prices 310
21.2. The rational relationship between computational and actual prices 314

PART 5: CONNECTING ECONOMY-WIDE AND SECTORAL PROGRAMMING

Chapter 22

THE CENTRAL PLAN FIGURE AS A PARAMETER 321
22.1. Some practical examples from the material of the sectoral programming projects 321
22.2. Economic experimentation 328
22.3. Survey of the sensitivity tests carried out in sector programming 330

Chapter 23

IMPROVING ON THE PLAN OF THE NATIONAL ECONOMY 335
23.1. Consistency analysis 335
23.2. The redistribution of resources between two sectors 336

Chapter 24

THE MODEL OF "TWO-LEVEL PLANNING" *(Co-author:* TH. LIPTÁK) 343
24.1. The course of the discussion 343
24.2. Imitation of the usual course of planning 345
24.3. The central model 346
24.4. The primal sector model 348
24.5. The dual sector model 353
24.6. The course of programming 355
24.7. Detailed description of the algorithm 358
24.8. Interpretation of the problem in terms of the theory of games . . 366
24.9. The treatment of investments in the model 368

Chapter 25

THE FUTURE OF MULTI-LEVEL PLANNING 371
25.1. Aspects of the model of two-level planning 371
25.2. Computation-technical properties of the algorithm 371
25.3. The first experimental calculation 374
25.4. The "pyramidal" network of programming models 375
25.5. Multi-level programming as a simulation of economic planning 381

Chapter 26

THE SHADOW PRICES 385
26.1. The equalization of shadow prices 385
26.2. The relative character of the optimality of shadow prices 386
26.3. The use of shadow prices outside the model 387
26.4. The rental on capital and the rate of interest 389

Chapter 27

THE OPTIMALITY CRITERION 392
27.1. Serving the aims of the economic policy 392
27.2. "Weights" and "absolute target" 397
27.3. The planning process and the model 402
27.4. The "tightness" of targets of economic policy 403
27.5. Checking the feasibility of the targets 408
27.6. Efficient programs 409
27.7. Are there revealed preferences on the part of higher economic administration? 412
27.8. Economico-politically admissible programs 416
27.9. The surplus creating role of the objective function 421
27.10. Is programming really worth while? 425

APPENDICES

Appendix A

APPROXIMATION OF THE CONCAVE MINIMIZATION PROBLEM 429

A.1. The problem outlined 429
A.2. The method of "progress at random" 430
A.3. The "curving" of the objective function 431

Appendix B

FROM THE MATERIAL OF THE PROGRAMMING PROJECT FOR THE MAN-MADE FIBRES INDUSTRY 434

B.1. Some examples of forecasting the trend of world-market prices 434
B.2. Correlation estimates 438
B.3. Expected value and standard deviation of the stochastic cost function 440

Appendix C

THE EFFECTS OF THE CONCENTRATION AND THE SCATTERING OF THE ACTIVITIES (*by* TH. LIPTÁK) 444

Appendix D

COMPOUND INTEREST FORMULAE 447

D.1. The rental formula 447
D.2. Investment cost with interest added 447
D.3. Costs discounted 449
D.4. The rate of interest used in compound interest formulae 450

Appendix E

PROOFS OF THE PROPOSITIONS RELATING TO THE RENTAL ON CAPITAL (*by* P. WELLISCH) 453

Appendix F

THE STATISTICAL EXAMINATION OF MACROECONOMIC GROWTH PROCESSES (*Co-author:* P. WELLISCH) 457

F.1. Aim of the examination 457
F.2. The growth of national income, of the production fund and the labour force 458
F.3. The more important production ratio figures 462
F.4. The time series relating to the utilization of the national income 465
F.5. Regression analysis 468
F.6. Estimation of the parameters of the production function . . . 474

Appendix G

A SURVEY ON THE DISPUTE ON THE RENTAL ON CAPITAL 477
G.1. Character of the survey 477
G.2. The views connected with the production of national income . . 478
G.3. The views connected with the distribution of national income 481
G.4. Distribution and optimality 482
G.5. Other questions under debate 484

Appendix H

THE GENERAL MODEL OF "TWO-LEVEL PLANNING": "TWO-LEVEL PROGRAMMING" (*by* TH. LIPTÁK) 487
H.1. Introduction 487
H.2. The overall central information problem 488
H.3. Sector partitioning 489
H.4. Evaluable central programs 490
H.5. Generator sets 491
H.6. The two-level problem 493
H.7. Derived polyhedral game 495
H.8. Regularity 498
H.9. Fictitious play 500
H.10. The termination of the iteration: δ-optimal solution 502
H.11. The "equalization" of the shadow prices 503
H.12. A general decomposition and embedding technique for solving an arbitrary solvable linear programming problem by the use of the method of two-level programming 504

REFERENCES 507
AUTHOR INDEX 519
SUBJECT INDEX 523

LIST OF TABLES

Table		Page
1.1.	Diagram of the specified balances of the traditional plan index system	7
3.1.	The Hungarian input–output tables	40–41
5.1.	Proportion of machinery and building investments in the cotton industry	69
5.2.	Dressing carried out by modern machinery in the cotton industry	70
5.3.	Modernization of the stock of looms in the cotton industry	71
5.4.	Dressing shop capacity as a percentage of weaving mill requirements in the cotton industry	72
7.1.	Classification of cost function types	90
7.2.	The exponents of degression in the man-made fibres industry	102
7.3.	Effect of the concentration of production in the man-made fibres industry	104
8.1.	Investment variants in the cotton fabric industry	112
8.2.	The selection of investment proposals in the light industry	117
9.1.	Permit paper estimates and their realization	131
9.2.	Realization coefficients and their frequency distribution	133
10.1.	Critical r.p.m. of the bobbin-changing loom	147
11.1.	Ranking according to mean	154
11.2.	Ranking according to "pessimistic value"	155
11.3.	Ranking according to "optimistic value"	156
13.1.	Problems of choice between certain and uncertain alternatives	179
13.2.	Results of interviews concerning decisions with uncertain consequences	180
13.3.	Inferences concerning the safety level	181
14.1.	Ranking of programs according to expected value in the man-made fibres industry	191
14.2.	Safety values of programs in the man-made fibres industry	192
14.3.	Programs ranked according to standard deviation in the man-made fibres industry	196
18.1.	Branch averages of the g_n indices	251
18.2.	Utilization of the investment credit quota for which interest was charged	252
18.3.	Parametric programming in the cotton industry with the rental on capital as a parameter	275

18.4. Parallel programming in the cotton industry with two kinds of rental on capital 277
19.1. Time series of price indices of plastics and man-made fibres . 286–287
19.2. Time series of price indices of some pharmaceutical products 291
20.1. Actual foreign exchange rates for main commodity groups 301
20.2. Deviations of sectoral exchange rates from national average 302
20.3. Parametric programming in the man-made fibres industry with the dollar rate of exchange as a parameter 308
21.1. Average change of prices of sectors in the case of "two-channel" prices 311
21.2. Divergencies between the actual price system and the computational evaluations 312–313
22.1. Parametric programming in the cotton industry with the output obligation as a parameter 323
22.2. Objective function value as a function of output obligation in the cotton industry 325
22.3. The consequences of plan modification in the cotton industry 327
22.4. Sensitivity tests with the cotton industry model. Deviations from the basic model 331
22.5. Sensitivity tests with the man-made fibres industry model . . . 332–333
B.1. Trends in benzol prices 435
B.2. Trends in terylene prices 435
B.3. Trends in acrylonitrile prices 436
B.4. Price forecasts 438
B.5. Correlation estimates 439
F.1. Time series of the national income, the production fund and the labour force 458–459
F.2. Time series of the more important production ratios 460–461
F.3. Stock of investments not put into operation 463
F.4. Effect of changes in the product pattern 464
F.5. Extensive utilization of industrial fixed capital 465
F.6. Time series of the accumulation share and the index of real wages 467
F.7. The accumulation share in capitalist countries 468
F.8. Parameters of the regression functions 471
F.9. Means and coefficients of variation of the efficiency of the production fund 472
F.10. Regression equations of the changes in real wages 473
F.11. Parameters of the production function 476

SIGNS AND SYMBOLS

The Principles of Notation

(1) The system of notation employed in this work is aimed at facilitating the recognition of the economic content of symbols. Identical or similar symbols are, accordingly, used throughout the volume to denote identical or related economic concepts. Even so, the same symbol will not always cover the same concept: e.g. r_j would denote, sometimes total operation costs, sometimes proportional operation costs; the concrete definition would then be given in the text. In such cases, the remark "type genus" (for short: t. g.) in the list of symbols will indicate the fact that we were dealing here with a mathematical symbol used to denote a whole group of not entirely identical but none the less closely related economic concepts.

The purpose of facilitating the recognition of the economic content of symbols is further served by the practice of using in certain cases abbreviations as a special suffix, e.g. "nat" in the case of data measured in terms of natural units; "$" in the case of data measured in terms of dollars, etc.

(2) The system of notation adheres, within the limits of possibility, to the notational conventions more or less firmly established in mathematical and mathematical-economic literature.

The two aims outlined above are to a certain extent contradictory. It was therefore sometimes necessary to use the same symbol to denote several, economically independent concepts. Care was, however, taken to avoid this happening within the same chapter.

General Notation

Vectors and matrices. Latin letters in italics as well as Greek letters denote scalars. Bold-type small letters denote vectors. Vectors without a distinguishing sign are always column vectors; row vectors are the transposes of the corresponding column vectors and are distinguished by a prime beside the original symbol. (E.g. the transpose of column vector $\mathbf{c}$ will be row vector $\mathbf{c}'$.) Bold-type capital letters – such as e.g. $\mathbf{A}$ –

indicate matrices. The list of the principal symbols below gives only the general component of the vectors and the general element of the matrices. These are denoted by italicized small letters; the *same* letter (small or capital letter) in bold-type indicates the corresponding vector or matrix.

Random variables. The random variables are denoted by *sans-serif type* letters, their respective expected values by the *printed* type of the same letter. The symbol of the standard deviation of a variable is σ; the symbol of the expected value will, for the sake of differentiation, appear in the suffix. (E.g. Q_j, Q_j, σ_{Q_j}). The list of principal symbols below contains only those referring to the expected value of the random variables.

Sets. As a general rule sets are denoted by capital letters in *script type.* (E.g. $\mathscr{F}$.) An exception is Appendix H, where the sets are denoted by capital letters in sans-serif type. (E.g. X.)

Lower and upper limits. If a variable may vary between two limits, the symbol denoting the variable and 0 as a lower suffix will indicate the lower limit, the symbol denoting the variable and 0 as an upper suffix the upper limit (e.g. $Z_0 \leqq Z \leqq Z^0$).

Optimality. An asterisk as the upper suffix of a symbol will denote optimality (e.g. x_j^*).

Leontief's inverse. $\check{\mathbf{G}} = (\mathbf{E} - \mathbf{G})^{-1}$, where $\mathbf{G}$ denotes the inner square of the technological matrix in the Leontief input–output model. The vectors and matrices obtained by means of multiplication with matrix $\check{\mathbf{G}}$ will be given the same sign $\check{}$ (e.g. $\check{\mathbf{u}}' = \mathbf{u}'\check{\mathbf{G}}$).

Principal Symbols

a_{ij}	=	the coefficient of the *j*th variable in the *i*th constraint
b_i	=	the *i*th constraint constant
c_j, C_j, C	=	cost (t.g.)
C_P	=	*P* quantile of random variable C
d_i	=	external output of the *i*th commodity (t.g.)
D_{Rbl}, $D_{\$}$	=	the rate of foreign exchange (rouble/forint; dollar/forint)
$\mathbf{E}$	=	the unit matrix
f_{ij}	=	output coefficient; the amount of output of the *i*th commodity produced by one unit of the *j*th activity (t.g.)
$\mathscr{F}$	=	the set of feasible programs
g_{ij}	=	material input coefficient; the amount of the *i*th material utilized by one unit of the *j*th activity
$\mathscr{G}$	=	the set of efficient programs
h_{ij}	=	resource input coefficient; the amount of the *i*th resource utilized by the *j*th activity

$\mathscr{H}$ = the set of economico-politically admissible programs
H_i = the ith capacity constraint (t.g.)
i = the rate of interest
k = the technical equipment of labour
K = the volume of the production fund
$\mathscr{K}$ = the set of possible programs
L = the labour force
m, M, n, N = the number of variables, activities, constraints, etc. (t.g.)
p_j, P_j, P = investment cost; production fund requirement (t.g.)
P = safety level
q_j, Q_j, Q = wages cost (t.g.)
r_j, R_j, R = operation cost (t.g.)
s_j, S_j, S = price; revenue (t.g.)
t = time as a variable
T = the length of a time period (t.g.)
u_{ij} = the amount of the ith external input utilized by the jth sector (t.g.)
v_{ij} = the (gross) output of the ith commodity produced by the jth activity; output target (t.g.)
w_i, W = resource quota; primary input (t.g.)
w = the actual wage rate
x_j = the level of the jth activity; program component (t.g.)
x = documented plan figure
y = the productivity of labour
y = auxiliary plan figure
Y = national income
Y_K = the marginal efficiency of the production fund
Y_L = the marginal productivity of the labour force
z_{ij} = material quota of the ith material allocated to the jth user (t.g.)
z_i = the ith effect of economic policy
α = accumulation share
β = elasticity of national income with respect to production fund
γ = the rental on capital
δ = the permitted deviation of the value of the objective function from the optimal value
ζ_i = the shadow price of the ith material quota
η = the elasticity of national income with respect to the labour force
ϑ = safety level (in the non-stochastic model)

θ_P = safety factor with safety level P (in the stochastic model)
$\varkappa_i$ = the shadow price of the upper constraint of the ith supply task
λ = the growth rate of the labour force
λ = the parameter in parametric programming
μ = the quality parameter of the technical level
ν_i = the shadow price of the ith supply task
π_j = the degression exponent of the investment cost of the jth activity
ρ = the growth rate of national income
ρ_{ij} = the coefficient of correlation between the ith and the jth price
σ = standard deviation
σ_i = the shadow price of the ith special sector constraint
Ψ_j = the degression exponent of the wages cost of the jth activity
ϕ_i = shadow price
χ = the efficiency of the production fund
ω = the computational wages rate; the shadow price of the manpower quota
Ω = the computational wage factor

PART 1

TRADITIONAL METHODS AND INPUT–OUTPUT TABLES

Introduction

The application of mathematical methods to long-term planning is in Hungary still in the stage that technical research calls "pilot-plant operation". It is beyond the purely paper phase, more than a "laboratory experiment" conducted amid special, artificially created circumstances – it has several times successfully been tested in practice. A real "full-scale application", the everyday mass use of the method has, however, not yet taken place. In most facets of the everyday work of long-term planning methods which do *not* utilize the tools of higher mathematics are still dominant. These pre-mathematical planning procedures will be referred to as the traditional methods of planning.

It is not the aim of this book to enter into a detailed analysis of these methods. Nevertheless it will occasionally be necessary to compare the traditional and the mathematical methods and to explain the relation between them. In order to facilitate this, it is proposed at the outset briefly to treat some of the characteristic features of the traditional planning methods.

There are no cut and dried methods for long-term planning. The procedure is changed from one plan to the next, and is not fully identical for the various sectors of the economy and different industries even within the space of one particular planning period. Nevertheless there are some outstanding features which may – at least in general terms – be regarded as permanent. It is mainly the latter that will be discussed in the following chapters.

In ch. 1 the traditional index system of long-term planning will be described, with the primary emphasis laid on the so-called system of balances.

Chapter 2 will deal with the traditional methods of investment efficiency calculation.

In ch. 3 the input–output tables will be dealt with. In Hungary, these methods have only been applied in the last few years. Input–output tables cannot be classed with the "traditional" methods, constituting as they do mathematical tools (although the simplest and most elementary ones) of planning. However, as the present work proposes to deal in the first place with mathematical programming as a more advanced planning method, it appears reasonable that input–output tables which represent an earlier stage of development should be discussed in Part 1 already. As a matter of fact these tables must – together with the methods described in chs. 1 and 2 – be considered historically as the precursors of programming and belong thus to the "environment" in which the first programming models made their appearance. Their discussion in Part 1 is further motivated by the fact that in subsequent parts of the book the mathematical programming models will be linked in various ways with the input–output tables.

Finally, ch. 4 will deal with the relationship between the traditional and mathematical methods of planning.

CHAPTER 1

THE TRADITIONAL PLAN INDEX SYSTEM

1.1. The Main Groups of Indices

As a start let us get acquainted with the set of plan figures, or, in our own terminology, with the index-system of the traditional economy-wide planning.

In the following survey I will often use the term balance. The balance counts the flow of a product or a resource, for a given time-period; contrasting total resources with total uses. One of the central problems of socialist planning is to assure that the general equilibrium of all the balances is obtained. From the mathematical point of view every balance is a simple equation:

$$\sum_i R_i = \sum_j U_j, \tag{1.1}$$

where

R_i = the ith resource
U_j = the jth use.

The balance aggregates both the resources and the expenditures in absolute sums.

We have seven main index groups.

The first group: synthetic balances. To mention only the most characteristic ones:

– Production of, and expenditure on the gross national product. How much the different branches of the economy produce and how it is divided between productive and final use, within the latter how much goes to consumption by the population and by the public bodies; how much to exports, investments, renewals, etc.

– Production of, and expenditure on the national income. How much do the different economic branches contribute to the national income; how is the national income divided between investment and consumption, etc.

– Balance of international payments. Connected with it, some synthetic, aggregate targets of the plan of foreign trade.

– Aggregating forecasts of the state budget which form the balance of the money revenues and expenditures of the state.

– Balance of the money revenues and expenditures of the population. In this connection above all the equilibrium of the purchasing power of the population and of the commodity funds is studied.

The second group of the plan indices: the product balances. Such balances are drawn up for the most important fuels, materials, finished products, machines and transport services. Now the new Five Year Plan covering the period 1966–70 is being drawn up in which 650–700 product balances are worked out. The products for which balances are drawn up by the National Planning Board (NPB) are called priority products. The scope of the priority products does not cover the whole social production. Let us plot the diagram of the product balance system (see table 1.1).

The rows of the balance are the resources of, and the expenditures on an individual product. The term "product" may exceptionally mean one single specific product: e.g. electric power. More frequently, however, it means a whole group of products, an aggregate formed of many kinds of commodities of physical manufactures. E.g. the balance of pumps, or the cement balance – which obviously aggregate many types of pumps, and many sorts of cement in one balance each.

Whenever it is feasible the balance is given in physical units of measurement (e.g. cement in tons, timber in cubic meters, etc.). Whenever such a unit of measurement cannot apply (e.g. in general in the case of machines) the balance will be drawn up at current prices. But the bulk of balances drawn up in natural units are in parallel drawn up also in forints, which is the Hungarian currency*. Thus our table which I have shown contains more rows than products.

Let us look at the interpretation of the columns. We wrote in the headings of the first columns: 1st addressee, ..., *N*th addressee. In planning terminology the different supervising authorities of economic life, especially the ministries in charge of the different spheres of the economy (e.g. Ministry of Building, Ministry of Light Industry, etc.) as well as other institutions who from this point of view have rights equal to theirs (e.g. the Centre of Cooperative Trade, the Centre of Cooperative Small Crafts), are called addressees. The government "addresses" the "plan instructions" to these supervising authorities; the head of the

* The abbreviation of the Hungarian currency unit forint is Ft. On the evaluation of foreign currencies in Ft see ch. 20.

TABLE 1.1

Diagram of the specified balances of the traditional plan index system

		1st producer addressee	. . .	*N*th producer addressee	Ministry of Foreign Trade			Domestic trade	Public bodies	Investment and renewal	Changes of stocks	Other uses
					1st market	. . .	*R*th market					
Product balances	Balance of the 1st product											
	. . .											
	Balance of the *n*th product											
Investment balances	Distribution of the global investment fund											
	. . .											
Manpower balances	Global manpower balance											
	. . .											
Cost and profitability figures	Material costs											
	. . .											
Foreign trade figures	Export targets											
	Mixed import quotas											

supervising authority is personally responsible for the execution of the government instructions. One of the fundamental principles of socialist planning is the "addressee" character of the plan instructions. It logically follows from the fact that the plan does not only give the future forecast but serves as a basis for government instructions.

In the plans which are now being worked out there are some 60–70 addressees of plan directives relating to production and productive utilization. This, of course, does not mean that there are in fact 60–70 ministries or other authorities of the same importance. The great number of addressees is explained by the fact that their breakdown differs from balance to balance. E.g. in one of the balances the addressee may be a ministry (let us say, the Ministry of Heavy Industry), in another one, only a sector under this ministry (let us say, the chemical industry). For the sake of greater lucidity, in the schema of table 1.1 each of the 60–70 addressees was given a separate column.

Let us consider in our balance the sources with positive signs and the expenditures with negative signs. Let us take e.g. the anthracite balance. It is produced by the "addressee" called "Ministry of Heavy Industry, Mining Section". Also the column of the Ministry of Foreign Trade contains a positive item because we have a certain import of it. In almost all the other columns of the row in question the items we find are negative items. In the column of "changes of stocks" we find positive or negative items according to whether a decrease or an increase is planned.

The product balances are drawn up so that as far as possible the requirements of the main users, of the principal consumers should appear in concrete form. The consumption of small items is not planned concretely in the balance, only in aggregate form in the column "other uses". E.g. in the rolled steel balances among the priority consumers we find the engineering and the building industries and transports. Therefore we find concretely planned negative items in the rows of the addressees. No doubt, Light Industry also consumes a certain amount of rolled steel but it is slight. Therefore in the column of the Ministry of Light Industry, in this place, we do not find this small item but zero – the rolled steel consumption of the Ministry of Light Industry will appear, together with similar small requirements, in aggregate form in the residual column called "other uses".

I have already stated in connection with the rows of the system of product balances that the scope of the priority products does not cover the whole of the social production. Now I have to add something similar in connection with the breakdown by columns: the concretely planned items indicate only the main utilizations; those of smaller significance are expressed only globally, in aggregate form in the residual column: "other uses".

The balances of investment goods include also another column: consumption for investment purposes. Thus e.g. the machine-tool to be installed in the engineering workshop of the new plant of the light industry will not figure in the column of the Ministry of Light Industry but in the investment column. In fact the consumption broken down by addressees represents the productive consumption for *current* production, whereas the utilization for investment purposes is indicated in the separate investment column.

Table 1.1 shows not only the product balances, but the third, fourth, fifth and sixth groups of plan indices as well.

The *third group:* the distribution of investment funds. The planners usually do not call it a balance. However, on the basis of the above schema, this may also be considered a balance, since it serves to distribute the available resources among the addressees. There are several investment balances, such as:

– the distribution of the global investment fund, containing the full amount of investments;

– the priority items of the former: the quotas of construction, machinery of domestic origin, machinery imported from socialist and from capitalist countries;

– the distribution of the global renewal fund; (renewal meaning here the complete overhaul or replacement of machinery, equipment and buildings);

– the priority items of renewals, such as the quotas of construction or import machinery for renewal purposes, etc.

The *fourth group* of the traditional plan index system is composed of the manpower balances. These will partly distribute global manpower, but contain also further rows of a more detailed breakdown, according to sex, qualification, etc.

The *fifth group* contains the estimates of production cost and profitability. These, too, are fixed for every addressee. According to the latest instructions, the estimates should be worked out under 38 headings, which means 38 further rows in our schema. A few headings will be pointed out here for the sake of illustration only.

Material costs
Wage costs
Taxes
Payroll tax

Depreciation allowance
Contribution to technical development funds
Plant operation profits
Producers' sales tax, etc.

The *sixth group* of the plan indices contains the estimates of the foreign-trade plan. Part of these may be inserted in schema 1.1 without any difficulty:

– The export and import estimates of the priority commodities. These are given not only in global form but also in a breakdown to principal markets and relations. The schema will, therefore, contain, instead of a single addressee (the Ministry of Foreign Trade) as many columns as there are foreign-trading relations planned.

– Each addressee is given a global export target. This is one row in the schema.

– Each addressee is given a quota for "sundry imports". This determines the importable quantity of non-priority commodities, those not distributed in the product balances. This means a further row for our schema.

Besides the above mentioned indices the foreign trade chapter of the plan contains several figures, which appear only in the synthetic balances.

Let us from now on call the second, third, fourth, fifth and sixth groups of indices specified balances to distinguish them from the synthetic balances. The specified balances have the common feature that certain output tasks or input quotas are broken down in them by "addressees" (they may refer to resources or the consumption of products or forecasts relating to the use of aggregated costs).

Table 1.1 gives a comprehensive survey of the specified balances. As shown in the schema, these balances can be presented in a single table – or, for that matter, in a single matrix. However, the schema is given here for the sake of greater lucidity (and for its analogy to the later mathematical models) only; in the actual plan documents a separate note or table is drawn up for each individual balance or group of balances.

All synthetic and specified balances are prepared for the terminal year of the long-term plan. Several of the balances – especially the product balances – are worked out for the intervening years as well.

The following *seventh group* of indices differs fundamentally in its character from the former one, for it is connected with the individual approval of certain specified investment *actions*. E.g. a new artificial fertilizer factory with an annual capacity of 30 000 tons must be constructed, or a certain existing machine factory must be reconstructed, etc. Here not only the action itself is described but some of its most important technical and cost-parameters: the date when the investment should begin and when it should be completed, some characteristics of investment and operating costs, etc. Also in this chapter of planning we find "addressees": for each investment action a certain specified, supervising authority is responsible.

We must see clearly in what respect this part of the plan differs, e.g. from the earlier mentioned investment fund-balance. That balance indicates what investment funds the Ministry of Light Industry should have in 1966, another how much it should have in 1967, etc. The Ministry will spend its funds on several kinds of investment actions. In the national plan, however, some are singled out from among these. They are the biggest, the most important ones and in the plan they are prescribed also individually, as priority investments*.

Besides the seven most important groups of the traditional plan index system, we have also other plan figures: e.g. production targets for priority products for which no balance is drawn up, or forecasts of technical development, etc. I do not wish to discuss them now in detail because they have a lesser importance.

1.2. The Consistency of the Index System

The traditional plan index system has some general characteristics.

The architects of the index system have set two objectives: they want to cover the *whole*, the total of social production, turnover and consumption. At the same time they wish to "handle", to plan also individually, in specified form, some sectors of the social production, turnover and consumption, deemed to be particularly important. Also they wish to treat in this way the flow of some especially important products and resources (in the most characteristic sectors of utilization, of consumption), some especially significant investment actions, etc.

Both aims are only too easy to understand. They take account of the fact that it is impossible to survey and to plan every part-process of economic life from one single centre. Therefore they wish to plan the

* The list of individually approved investment projects is called by the planners the "limit list". The name indicates the fact that we are here concerned with major investments exceeding a certain limit value. The approval of individual investment projects will be discussed again in ch. 2.

total, global interconnections and the most important partial connections, and do not wish to plan unimportant or less important partial interconnections.

At the same time this dual endeavour involves certain contradictions. The collection of plan indices I have discussed does not form a *strictly* interconnected system. Let me illustrate this with some examples. In the product balances, among the items "addressed" to the Ministry of Foreign Trade we shall find the major import and export forecasts, but not the total exports and imports. Therefore we cannot directly infer from the set of balances of products to the synthetic foreign trade balance since this is also influenced by the export and the import of non-priority products not singled out in product balances. Similarly the sum of the items "addressed" in the product balances to the Ministry of Home Trade indicates an important part of, but not the total consumption of the population. Therefore we cannot conclude from it directly how far the population's purchasing power is in equilibrium with the commodity fund. To obtain such an estimate we would also need to take into account certain time lags, the money stocks and the bank deposits of the population and the commodity stocks of trading companies.

We can say: since the specific balances do not cover the total social production, turnover and consumption, the summarized items of the specific balance system do not exactly tally with the analogous items of the synthetic balances but they contain also undefined, un-planned residuals. Such un-planned residuals can be quite large.

To some extent the situation is similar in respect of product balances and resource balances. The resource balances include e.g. the quota of domestic machines allocated to the different "addressees". This, however, is more than the sum of items envisaged for investment purposes in the concrete machine balances.

The situation is similar with the interconnection between the seventh group of the plan index system, i.e. the concrete forecasts and the balances relating to priority investments. As mentioned: the amount of the investment requirements of the priority investment actions obligatorily prescribed for the Ministry of Light Industry is lower than the total investment fund prescribed for that Ministry. We find here also a residual which is not completely planned.

Moreover, the different items of the traditional index system do not fit precisely together. The different chapters of the plan, its different parts do not use quite identical concepts and categories. They use indices of different coverage for the same processes; e.g. the permit paper by which a priority investment action is started, indicates the most important machines to be installed in the new project in a breakdown different from that used in the machine balances. Therefore it is a figure not suitable for direct use when the machine balances are drawn up. Similarly, this same document indicates the material requirements after the new project is put into operation. But again the breakdown of this material requirement may differ from the breakdowns of the relative material balances: it may be more or, on the contrary, less aggregated.

I would like to stress this point: the problem raised here is not whether or not the plan itself is in equilibrium. This depends on what figures we write into the different tables of the plan index system. Now, however, I have not written about this; rather, I have said that the traditional structure of planning does not constitute a sufficiently consistent system – independently of what figures we write in the different places of the model.

1.3. The Plan as an Equation System

Let us introduce the following symbols for our further discussions:

$x_1, \ldots, x_m$ = the documented plan figures. These include all the forecasts of the traditional plan index system; all the plan figures to be documented by the planners: to be drawn up in the tables and forms prescribed by the NPB in its precise regulations. We can safely say: all the figures that appear in the plan document are unknown variables at the time of planning. Even such an apparently "exogenous" figure as e.g. the labour-force of the whole country, is variable as it can be influenced by several tools of economic policy (e.g. by wages).

$y_1, \ldots, y_n$ = the auxiliary plan figures. These include all the data, which do not appear in the officially prescribed documents, but play a part in the relations expressed by the plan.

Auxiliary plan figures are for instance the different residual quantities filling up the gap between the aggregate and the more detailed priority plan figures (e.g. the investment cost requirements of the non-priority investment actions for every addressee).

To the category of variables type y belong, furthermore, e.g. different technological coefficients which have to be taken into account when determining the product balances. At the moment of planning these are unknown variables too, because they have not a prefixed magnitude. Their magnitude is determined by the planners, based on some technical and economic considerations. But they are auxiliary variables as they cannot be found among the obligatory documented indices.

Type y also includes a special kind of the auxiliary plan figures: there are quantified representatives of economic activities whose implementation would be possible in the plan period and has actually been suggested in some stage of planning – eventually however they were rejected and thus their quantified representatives have not been included among the documented plan figures (e.g. forecasts in rejected investment projects, etc.).

Some auxiliary plan figures are, put down in writing, on the desk of some planner. (The planners call it "supplementary calculation".) Some of them have not been put down in writing at all, they live only in the planners' minds – in a more or less precise form. Whether these figures are put down or not usually depends upon the arbitrary decision of the planner whose job it is to work with the auxiliary plan figure in question. It is not compulsory to document the auxiliary plan figures.

$b_1, \ldots, b_s$ = exogenous bounds of the planned activities, regarded as constant. They are quantitative parameters of exogenous characteristics whose magnitudes do not depend on the planners but are given to them from outside, e.g. the capacity of an existing plant with a given number of shifts or: the total cultivable land area available.

Now the plan can be conceived as a system of simultaneous equations with two main types of equation.

The first type is constituted by the documented plan equations. All synthetic and specified balances belong to this group.

In order to be able to write down the balances in the form of a system of simultaneous equations – a system where *every* variable is contained in *every* equation – coefficients have been assigned to the variables. The coefficients α_{ij} and β_{ij} can have only three values: $+1$ whenever the variable in question does actually figure in the equation, denoting a resource; -1 whenever the variable in question does actually figure in the equation, denoting a user; and 0 whenever the variable in question does not play a role in the equation.

The documented equations may be written down in the following mathematical form:

$$\begin{aligned} \alpha_{11}x_1 + \ldots + \alpha_{1m}x_m + \beta_{11}y_1 + \ldots + \beta_{1n}y_n &= 0 \\ \cdots\cdots\cdots\cdots\cdots\cdots\cdots\cdots\cdots \\ \alpha_{r1}x_1 + \ldots + \alpha_{rm}x_m + \beta_{r1}y_1 + \ldots + \beta_{rn}y_n &= 0. \end{aligned} \qquad (1.2)$$

In the documented plan equations, the coefficients $\beta_{ij} = +1$ or $\beta_{ij} = -1$ are assigned to the y-type variables of residual character which fill out the "gap" between the various global and detailed plan directives.

Let me call the second type of equation an auxiliary plan equation. To begin with let me give some examples.

Let e.g. documented plan figure No. 100 be the cotton cloth production in 1966, in sq. metres, and plan figure No. 101 be the cotton cloth production in 1966, in forint value. These two documented plan figures are each included in a documented plan equation, in the cotton cloth balance expressed in physical units and in the cotton cloth balance expressed in forints respectively. These two plan figures, however, are linked together to form a non-documented auxiliary plan equation:

$$x_{101} = y_{50}\, x_{100}, \tag{1.3}$$

where y_{50} is an auxiliary plan figure: the unit price of cotton cloth. It is not a figure exogenously given as a constant but a variable since even in case of fixed prices it depends on the proportion of the different types of cotton cloth in their relation to each other within the product group of cotton cloth. The average prices applied in the balances are actually planned by the planners but they do not form part of the fundamental documentation. This simple price equation is one type of the auxiliary plan equations.

Consider another example. The documented plan figures include prescriptions relating to priority investment actions. Let e.g. x_{201} be the cost requirement of one of the priority investment actions of the Ministry of Light Industry in 1967, x_{202}, x_{203} and x_{204} a second, a third and a fourth cost requirement respectively. Let x_{300} be the total investment fund of the Ministry of Light Industry in 1967. So we get the following auxiliary equation:

$$x_{201} + x_{202} + x_{203} + x_{204} + y_{300} = x_{300}, \tag{1.4}$$

where y_{300} represents the cost requirements of the non-priority investments of the Ministry of Light Industry in 1967. Thus this equation links one item (x_{300}) of the investment balance to the plan figures relating to the priority investment actions.

Consider a further example. The items of the product balance include the quantity handed over to the Ministry of Home Trade. This in fact is meant to cover the population's demand. At the same time the cost figures also include the total planned wages and salaries. It is clear that there exists a relation between them. Let us suppose for simplicity's sake that, with prices fixed, the demand for shoes, for clothes, for furniture and so on are power functions of the total wages and salaries. Let e.g. x_{400} be the quantity of shoes sold to the population in 1968 and x_{500} the total income of the population in 1968. In this case our demand function will be:

$$x_{400} = a + bx_{500}^{E}, \tag{1.5}$$

where E is the income elasticity of the demand for shoes. This set of demand functions is a part of the auxiliary equations.

Finally, we come to the last example. The products cannot be sold abroad in unlimited quantities. The demand for Hungarian furniture offered on foreign markets depends on the sales price and on the market situation, with a given quality and assortment of products; it may have its upper limits, etc.

All these are but illustrative, very simple examples. There are a number of interconnections between the different plan figures, not expressed in the documented plan equations but still not to be disregarded in the course of planning. The consideration of these interconnections will in its turn widen the scope of the auxiliary plan figures of the variables type y as shown in the earlier examples.

In their mathematical character the auxiliary plan equations are rather different. We have seen linear and power functions among the simple examples but they may also include other types of functions too. Since we do not wish to discuss here in full detail their mathematical characteristics we are going to sum up only in absolutely general form:

$$\begin{aligned} f_1(x_1, \ldots, x_m, y_1, \ldots, y_n) &= b_1 \\ \cdots\cdots\cdots\cdots\cdots\cdots \\ f_s(x_1, \ldots, x_m, y_1, \ldots, y_n) &= b_s. \end{aligned} \tag{1.6}$$

In some of the equations (1.6) the constant b_j on the right side may as well be zero.

Most of the auxiliary plan equations type (1.6) are not put down in writing by the planners; accordingly they do not put these interconnections into precise, exact mathematical equations. These interdependences and especially those we could express only in a more involved mathematical form live in the planners' minds only in rough, approximative form. E.g. they are aware of a certain connection between the export price and the export sales; this, however, they do not express in the form of demand functions. Or: they know there exists a certain connection between the volume produced and the costs of production and also that in many cases this connection is not linear but the planners do not express it in the form of a cost function. In connection with some auxiliary equations of this type the planners make actual and thorough preliminary studies. (E.g. for the demographic foundation of man-power balances or for the interconnections between demand and income: in this connection use is made of the results of science, in the given example of demography, of up-to-date market research, of demand analysis, etc.) There are some other auxiliary equations about which the planners have only an inkling. Yet even though there may be differences among the degrees of preparation, wisdom and information, the precision of the quantification of the connection, it is beyond doubt that the planners have also these auxiliary plan equations in mind.

To sum up the above, the more concise vector form can be applied*:

$$\mathbf{x} = \begin{bmatrix} x_1 \\ \cdot \\ \cdot \\ \cdot \\ x_m \end{bmatrix}, \quad \mathbf{y} = \begin{bmatrix} y_1 \\ \cdot \\ \cdot \\ \cdot \\ y_n \end{bmatrix}$$

$$\boldsymbol{\alpha}'_i = [\alpha_{i1} \dots \alpha_{im}], \quad \boldsymbol{\beta}'_i = [\beta_{i1} \dots \beta_{in}], \quad i = 1, \dots, r.$$

The task of determining the long-term plan may be interpreted as one of determining a program [**x**, **y**] *consisting of an extremely large number of variables**. It is a desire of the planners that the program should satisfy the equation system*

$$\begin{aligned} \boldsymbol{\alpha}'_i \mathbf{x} + \boldsymbol{\beta}'_i \mathbf{y} &= 0 \qquad i = 1, \dots, r, \\ f_j(\mathbf{x}, \mathbf{y}) &= b_j \qquad j = 1, \dots, s. \end{aligned} \tag{1.7}$$

1.4. Plan Coordination

Having expressed the traditional plan index system in the most general form and in symbols, it will be easier for us to refer to the different elements of the model.

The particular process by which the planners try to find the solution of the equation system described in the model of traditional planning is called p l a n c o o r d i n a t i o n***.

* Vector and matrix notations are frequently applied in the book. See B. KREKÓ [91] in Hungarian or E. BODEWIG [11] in English.

** At present, no one will be able to tell exactly how many variables and equations are contained in this equation system. Their number may be put at the order of 10^5 even by the most cautious estimate, but it may be of the order 10^6.

*** On the subject see A. BRÓDY [15], pp. 47–56.

Plan coordination is the process of the simultaneous reconciliation of the documented and auxiliary plan figures in order to implement all the plan equations, whether documented or auxiliary.

The coordination of the plan takes place at many different levels. It may take place vertically: the aggregating Departments of the NPB (e.g. the Financial, the Investment, the Manpower, etc. Departments) will reconcile their own summary figures with the so-called Specific Departments and the Ministries, each responsible for a sector of the production, turnover and consumption of the economy. In such cases the different summary quotas flow downwards, whereas the figures relating to the filling up of these quotas, to their quantification, their detailing and, together with them, suggestions to amend the original target figures go upwards.

At the same time coordination is going on also horizontally. E.g. the representatives of the producing and consuming productive branches as well as of home and foreign trade agree about the production and distribution of certain specified products.

Coordination can take many forms: written notes and counter-notes, conferences with a great number of participants for reconciling figures; discussion in a narrow circle of a business in which they are directly interested; the instantaneous change of a figure, based on a mere telephone information, etc. With a greater or lesser intensity several thousand persons take part in the coordination of a long-range plan.

If we revert now to the model of the traditional plan we can characterize the plan coordination as follows:

Everybody (institution or person) who takes part in the coordination is directly responsible for certain specified *variables* (documented and auxiliary plan figures), as well as for certain specified plan *equations* (also: for documented and auxiliary equations). Each of them "bargains" about his *own* figures, and does so in such a way as to secure the equality in his *own* equations*.

Nobody, not one participant of the plan coordination can survey the whole plan equation system. Not even those who occupy peak positions

* Several participants in the coordination have further objectives beyond the equality of their individual equation. In the terminology of mathematical programming this is expressed by saying that they have an "objective function". Thus the planners responsible for the individual sectors would aim at having their particular sector *allocated* more (investment, material, imported product, etc.) while being at the same time obliged to *yield* less (to have smaller production, export, etc. obligations).

in planning can survey the whole equation system; even *they* deal only with certain variables and certain equations. Usually with the variables and equations which they consider the most important.

Let us see a few examples: the representative of the balance of payments is the competent department of the NPB. This department will coordinate the most important export and import items with the different Branch Departments. Let us assume that in the course of this work the suggestion to export a bigger quantity of a certain type of machine to the socialist countries arises. However, those responsible for planning the foreign trade of the machine in question will protest: the demand of the socialist countries for this machine is limited. As a result of this protest, one of the auxiliary equations, the constraint of the export of this type of machine will not be exceeded and an attempt will be made, to make up for the loss, with some other export item. Should some other unrealistic suggestion be made, again another planner will protest, in the name of his own plan equation.

The plan coordination can be compared to an attempt to solve a simultaneous equation system of gigantic proportions with the method of "trial and error", a special method of reconciliation by gradual approximation.

When the plan coordination begins, in fact one cannot know for certain if there is a solution to this gigantic equation system or not; whether it has a single solution or several; and of course it is not proved whether this process of reconciliation converges toward some solution. In any case it should be borne in mind that generally the plan coordination is going on in the hope that there is a solution and that it is unique; so far it has never been suggested that several parallel plans should be drawn up.

Since precise equality cannot usually hold for all the documented and auxiliary equations, a certain hierarchy among the plan equations has developed. A certain unpronounced, undeclared but tacitly still recognized priority order has developed among the practical planners: in what interconnections an absolute equilibrium must be reached and in what sectors a potential disequilibrium can be at least tacitly tolerated; what plan figures must be planned with great precision and in which cases a higher degree of inaccuracy can be admitted.

Let us take first of all the plan equations. At the top of the hierarchy we do not find the synthetic balances but the product balances and together with them the foreign trade balances as well as from among the synthetic balances the production targets included in the gross national product balance. This order prevails especially in the middle phase elaborating the details, after the first introductory steps, but before the ultimate termination.

All the other plan equations, including the synthetic balances, have only secondary impacts; they summarize and partly check the results of the computations developed while the balances of products and the foreign trade balances were drawn up. Of course, the non-documented auxiliary plan equations exercise a relatively slighter influence since it is not revealed in the course of planning if they do not produce equality. The product balances are the most "tangible", the auxiliary plan equations are the least "tangible" – the rest of the equations occupy an intermediate position from this point of view. All this will, on the whole, establish a certain hierarchy also among the plan figures. A much smaller importance is attributed to the establishment of variables of a residual character which have only a "gap-filling" task than to the concretely determined items, even if also such residual items belong exceptionally to the documented plan figures (this is e.g. the case when planning the changes in stock). Besides we can say also in general that the planning of the non-documented auxiliary plan figures of type y is done obviously less thoroughly, less carefully than that of the documented plan figures of type x whose execution can be duly checked.

How shall we evaluate the method by which the equation system is solved which is used in the traditional planning process through plan coordination? The process actually tries to solve the immense equation system with a kind of guesswork, with repeated trials although we are well aware of the fact that equation systems with considerably fewer variables and equations cannot be solved by mere guessing.

All this criticism of the primitivity of these methods is no doubt justified; and this is why mathematical methods which bring us nearer to the solution of this equation system are of such great importance.

On the other hand, let us also recognise the advantages of this process. We, Hungarian mathematical economists who approach the problem of planning with more exact methods, input–output tables and programming models, with electronic computers, are not able to cope with an equation system of such immense proportions in the present state of computing techniques. Therefore we do not even try to undertake this job but content ourselves with mathematical models highly aggregated and based on economically simplifying assumptions. (I shall discuss these difficulties arising in the application of mathematical methods more fully in later chapters.)

In spite of the reservations made above the effect which the non-documented auxiliary part of the plan equation system exercises on the plan should not be underrated. An immense material of information and routine in the best meaning of the word has piled up in thousands of planners engaged in plan coordination. When the agent of a capitalist foreign trading firm tells the managers of his firm that not more than, say, 10 000 radio sets can be sold on a certain market at a certain price he will simply say so on the basis of his business experiences, not by applying mathematical statistics, and yet his statement will be well-founded in many cases. Our planners have also developed a similar sense and routine after many years' experience.

Moreover, the coordination of the plan will bring together the parties of opposite interests: the representatives of the producers and buyers, the allocators and claimants of investment funds, the consumers of import products and the persons responsible for buying the import items, etc. The clash of supply and demand which will take place on the market at a time when the delivery contracts are concluded, when the resources and the products are actually used takes place here at least partly in *advance*, as a sort of *prevention*, in the form of a certain bargaining. A certain search for a compromise between supply and demand is already going on in advance. In the United States "brain-storming" is regarded as a significant discovery of creation-psychology, i.e. to arrange "work discussions" with a task to generate ideas. In the course of plan coordination "brain-storming" is taking place on a mass scale; experiences are exchanged in great numbers and information reaches all the interested parties. The traditional method of planning even though it applies methods which from many points of view can be regarded primitive, can concentrate into a unity of place and time the collective experiences of thousands of skilled planners.

CHAPTER 2

THE TRADITIONAL INVESTMENT EFFICIENCY CALCULATIONS

2.1. Central Permits for the Main Investments

One method of fundamental importance in controlling the long-term development of the economy is the issue of central permits for the main investments.

The government's regulations lay down precisely for which investments central permits are required*. According to the Investment Code investments above the so-called "value limit" must be individually enumerated in the central plan. The value limit differs from one sector of industry to the next – in the case of power stations for instance it is 20 million Ft, in the chemical industry and engineering 10 million Ft, in the light industries 5 million Ft.

The permits are issued by the head of the superior authority concerned (in the case of state industry by the minister concerned), in agreement with the President of the NPB. As a rule the Minister of Finance and the Minister of Foreign Trade must also put forward their opinion before a decision is made, and if the investment affects the activities of other ministries as well, then the plans must be previously checked with them too.

The document serving as the basis for central permission is in official parlance designated as the "investment program". Since the word "program" is in this book, in accordance with the general usage of mathematical programming, used in its broader sense, the official "investment program" which serves as the basis for central permission will here be referred to as the *permit paper*.

The permit paper does not comprise the plan of the investment activities of an entire sector, but always applies only to one particular, concretely specified project, e.g. the modernization of a particular factory, the establishment of a new plant, etc. It describes the economic object of the investment, the product to be made with the new facility, lists the mate-

* A government order [195] issued in 1961 comprehensively laid down the procedure for investments and renewals. It is referred to in the economic administration as the Investment Code and will be quoted by that name in this book.

rials necessary for its operation, sets out the technology of production, the schedule for carrying out the investment, the necessary machines, etc.

The permit paper is often preceded by less detailed, preliminary proposals. Some preparatory work may indeed begin on this basis. In principle, however, only approval of the permit paper may be regarded as an actual *investment decision.* From the moment of approval, the implementation of the investment is a *state resolution,* or in other words a central instruction which the institution to whom it is addressed is obliged to carry through.

The presentation and the central approval of permit papers go on continuously, meanwhile the elaboration of a long-term plan takes place in *every five* years. Therefore in the "limit list" (in the seventh group of plan indices, treated in section 1.1) there are investment actions which are covered by a permit paper and also such which are not.

2.2. The Index g_n

One of the most important chapters of the permit paper is concerned with the calculations of economic efficiency which prove that the investment is desirable. The Investment Code sets out exactly what indices of economic efficiency must be determined in the permit paper. Indices of economic efficiency are here understood to denote those indices which compare the returns of a particular activity (in the present case an investment or production) with the expenditures. In Hungarian practice the index of economic efficiency is generally a fraction, in which the numerator contains the returns and the denominator the expenditures, or *vice versa.* The efficiency indices differ from each other in the scope of the returns and expenditures which they consider, the period to which they apply, and the figures (the prices, etc.) with which they operate.

One of the indices of economic efficiency in the paper is the so-called g_n index, which is the following*:

$$g_n = \frac{S}{\gamma P + R}, \tag{2.1}$$

* For the sake of the uniformity of the symbols in this book, the author uses his own symbols instead of those in the Investment Code.

The g_n index was first introduced on the initiative of M. TURÁNSZKY; for a substantiation of its principles see Turánszky's book [169].

where

S = the income from one year's production of the plant established through the investment. (For the sake of brevity only the method for computing the index g_n in the case of the establishment of *new* plants will here be treated)

P = the total investment cost. This is the sum of all those initial costs necessary for bringing about the new production facility, which must therefore be advanced *once* only

R = the operation costs of the plants' annual production. As against the *unique* investment costs, these are *continuous* ones which arise each year. They are the sum of all those costs which are necessary for continuous output and for the continuous maintenance of the facilities established through the investment

γ = rental on capital (expressed as a decimal fraction).

Soviet and Hungarian economic literature frequently uses the symbol Δ for the quantity here denoted by γ. This departure from the more usual symbol is because it is used for other purposes in mathematics (to denote a small increment).

Some authors in the literature of the socialist countries use the term "interest", while others use other expressions to denote the same factor, e.g. "efficiency coefficient", "lucrativeness normative", "general economic coefficient", etc.

Some time ago the government made a rent on capital actually payable by the enterprises on the production fund used by them*. The production fund includes the fixed capital: machinery, buildings and equipment as well as the working capital: stocks of raw materials, semi-finished and finished products and the uncompleted production. The rent on capital is the product of the rental and the production fund: γP. As the term "rent on capital" has by now been adopted both in the official regulations and in accountancy practice for the cost factor proportional with the production fund, it

*The concept is plainly akin to the category of "capital" in the western literature. Nevertheless we shall use often the term "production fund", in accordance with the usual terminology of economic literature in the socialist countries. The purpose of this terminology is to stress the fundamental change that has taken place in the ownership of the means of production, and the corresponding change in the social function of the production fund.

appeared most expedient to adopt it here, too. The term will, accordingly, be used throughout the book.

The economic meaning of the rental γ and the problems concerning its numerical value will be treated later, in chs. 16 and 18.

As regards calculation with formula (2.1), the following should be borne in mind:

– The income must be calculated at world market prices, in foreign currency, but using the rate of currency exchange determined by the NPB to convert to Ft. The rate of currency exchange thus expresses the quotient of Ft per foreign monetary unit, in the given calculation.

– The part of the investment costs which originally arose in foreign currency must also be converted to Ft according to the rate of currency exchange determined by the NPB.

– The investment costs include not only the fixed capital, but also the costs of bringing about the working capital necessary for operation. Moreover this formula also includes the so-called related investment costs under this heading. The explanation of this concept will take place in a later chapter.

– The rental on capital is in the efficiency calculation according to the valid regulation 20 per cent.

– The costs of operation also include depreciation.

– Those materials figuring among the materials costs of operation which are actually imported or could potentially be imported or exported, i.e. which are generally objects of international trade, must not be calculated at the valid domestic Ft price but at world market prices, in foreign currency. The world market prices must be converted to Ft using the rate of currency exchange determined by the NPB.

An investment is regarded as favourable if the value of the g_n index is over 1. This ultimately gives a picture of a special, long-term "lucrativeness" of the investment, calculated in considerable part at world market prices.

The value of the index is over 1 if it is desirable to substitute home production for import of the product concerned, if the import savings are greater than the costs, including the 20 per cent rent charged for investments.

It is a noteworthy fact that according to the official instructions the determination of the g_n index departs considerably from the valid prices. The actual money income of the new firm established through the investment (or an old firm thus expanded), will stem from the officially fixed Ft price of the product. The magnitude of the income figuring in the numerator of the index is independent of this, for it is derived directly from the world market price. If the firm processes imported materials, it pays an officially fixed Ft price for them too, which the National Price Bureau in its *price determination* calculates according to the usual rates of exchange (or some other principle, e.g. by considering the domestic production cost of a similar Hungarian-made product). On the other hand for the purposes of the g_n index the world market price of the imported material is the point of departure, and it is converted to Ft according to the rate of currency exchange of the NPB, which differs from that of the Price Bureau. The firm generally pays actually 5 per cent rental on capital, while here 20 per cent is used for calculation.

There is therefore an actual price system, with an actual rental on capital and actual rate of currency exchange which is in fact valid for the everyday activities of the firms and serves as a basis for their actual accounting. And quite independently of this, more or less divorced from it, there are computational prices, computational rental on capital, computational rates of currency exchange, which must only be used on the papers of the calculations of economic efficiency, specifically to determine the economic efficiency index*. These we shall call official computational prices, rental on capital, rates of currency exchange, or comprehensively the official computational evaluations to distinguish them from other, non-official computational evaluations, worked out by the author or other research economists to determine economic efficiency.

The Investment Code describes the determination of several further indices. Here are some, by way of example:

– Investment cost per unit product.

– Investment cost per income from production, calculated at the domestic price free of turnover tax.

– Income per worker employed, calculated at the domestic price free of turnover tax.

– Output value minus operation costs, per investment costs.

– In the case of investments aimed at cutting costs: the annual saving from cost reduction, per investment cost. In other words, the pay-off period of the investment cost in years.

*In this book the expression "shadow price" is used exclusively to denote the prices obtained as solutions of the dual problem of a linear (or non-linear) program. This is only one kind of computational evaluation. The computational evaluation is a broader concept – it embraces all the kinds of prices which are used in calculations of economic efficiency, but *not* in practical financial accounting.

The regulations prescribe that in making investment decisions serious consideration should be given to how favourable the indices of the proposal are. They do not, however, make it obligatory to reject proposals with unfavourable indices, e.g. where the g_n index is smaller than 1. Moreover the regulations do not lay down what is to be done in the case of proposals where one index supplies a favourable, the other an unfavourable picture. In practice at any rate, the g_n index has become the "primus inter pares", and it is the indications of this index that are primarily considered.

The determination of indices of the economic efficiency of investments became obligatory in 1957, whereas before it was only sporadically that some institutions, acting on their own initiative, used similar indices for their calculations. They have since become the accustomed usage and have struck roots. Thus, though they may not perhaps look back on so long a past as the use of balances, the latter being practically coeval with socialism, they must now nevertheless be included among the basic methods of traditional long-term planning. The extent to which the recommendations of these indices are actually accepted, and the difficulties involved, will be discussed later. It is, however, an undubitable fact that they have promoted the spread of the correct view that attributes importance to the economic efficiency and economic desirability of investment projects.

CHAPTER 3

INPUT–OUTPUT TABLES

3.1. Main Definitions

The methods of traditional planning described in chs. 1 and 2 require further improvement in many respects. One of the most important tasks is to assure the consistency of the plan indices. This is the main purpose of the application of *input–output tables*. (In the following: I–O tables.) The I–O tables in Hungary belong usually to the type of the open, static Leontief models. The model is well-known; a knowledge of the elementary notions concerning I–O tables is presupposed*. The main relationships are laid down here only to ensure uniformity in terminology and notation.

$$g_{kl} = \frac{v_{kl}}{v_l}, \quad \begin{matrix} k = 1, \ldots, N, \\ l = 1, \ldots, N, \end{matrix} \tag{3.1}$$

where

- N = the number of economic sectors
- v_l = *gross output* of the lth sector (Ft)
- v_{kl} = commodity produced in the kth sector and utilized in the lth sector (Ft)
- g_{kl} = *technological coefficient*; the quantity of a commodity produced in the kth sector required for the unit output of the lth sector (Ft/Ft).

$$\mathbf{v} - \mathbf{G}\mathbf{v} = \mathbf{d}, \tag{3.2}$$

where

- $\mathbf{v}$ = the N-component vector of gross outputs v_k; the vector of gross output

* For an introduction to I–O analysis see R. Dorfman *et al.* [37], chs. 9 and 10, or O. Lange [96] and in Hungarian A. Bródy [15]. For a more detailed study the reader should be primarily referred to W. Leontief [99, 100].

G = the Nth order matrix of technological coefficients g_{kl}; the inner square of the technological matrix

d = the N-component vector of final outputs d_k; the vector of final output.

$$\mathbf{v} = (\mathbf{E}-\mathbf{G})^{-1}\, \mathbf{d} = \check{\mathbf{G}}\, \mathbf{d}, \tag{3.3}$$

where

E = unit matrix of the Nth order

$\check{\mathbf{G}}$ = the inverse of matrix (**E**−**G**), hereafter called for short the inverse matrix. Its general element will be denoted $\check{g}_{kl}$*.

The economic meaning of the inverse matrix which is to play a central part in the subsequent analysis, will be illustrated here with an example. Let coal mining be the lth sector and the chemical industry the kth sector. In coal mining a number of chemical products are used: explosives, carbide for the miners' lamps, etc. The chemical products that go into the production of one unit of coal at the *mine* constitute the g_{kl} component of the technological matrix. This is the direct material input coefficient, the direct chemicals requirement of one unit – 1 Ft – gross output in coal mining. But there are indirect requirements as well**. In the production of the mining machinery, too, chemicals, e.g. plastic parts, has been used; the same applies to the production of the miners' rubber boots, etc. But this is not the whole story. In the mining machine factory rolled steel has, been used, the product of a metallurgical industry which, in turn, is also a consumer of chemicals. The indirect chemicals requirements of coal mining are thus composed of those of the machine factory, the rubber boots factory, etc., which supply the needs of coal mining; of those of the power plants, metallurgical works, etc., which supply the needs of the latter factories; and so on. Materials require-

* In the following, the notation ˇ is always to mark the magnitudes connected with the inverse of matrix (**E**−**G**), such as the product of some vector with this inverse matrix, etc.

** The attributes *direct* and *indirect* in connection with I–O tables should not be confused with the concepts of "direct" and "indirect" ("overhead") costs, used in accounting and costing. In the present work the two concepts will always be used in connection with I–O tables, direct input meaning here the input arising *within* the lth sector, indirect input that arising in other sectors as a result of activities in the lth sector.

ments can thus be conceived of as forming rings, like water does around a stone thrown into it. Direct and indirect chemicals requirements together constitute the total material input coefficient, the total chemicals requirements of coal mining. It is this total that can be determined by means of the inverse matrix. Element $\check{g}_{kl}$ of the inverse matrix indicates the sum total of direct and indirect inputs of the product of the kth sector which go into the production of one unit – of 1 Ft value – of the final output of the lth sector.

In the light of this example the economic implications of (3.3) should now be clear. We know the final output of coal required (e.g. for households, for exports, for stock-piling, etc.) and we know also the final output targets of the chemical industry, the engineering industry and the other sectors. Multiplying this vector (**d**) with inverse matrix ($\check{\mathbf{G}}$), we obtain gross output (**v**) required for all sectors of production reciprocally to meet each other's needs (considering also the multiplying effects), and to yield, in addition, the desired **d** amount of final output as well*.

3.2. Total Contents Calculations

In section 3.1 we were dealing only with the inner square of the technological matrix. This, however, does not embrace the whole range of inputs, only part of them. Let us take, for example, the I–O table prepared by the Hungarian Central Statistical Office to present input–output flows in the Hungarian national economy as a whole for the year 1959**. The inner square of the table gives the flow of home produced commodities. Further row vectors attached to the lower part of the inner square of the technological matrix reflect other inputs to production, such as e.g. import materials, wages, depreciation, etc., consumed in the production of one unit in the lth sector. These are thus special technological coefficients which reflect the demand for inputs originating from spheres *outside* the system represented by the inner square, i.e. that for external inputs. It will depend on the special character of each individual I–O table which external input types should be taken into consideration and according to what division.

*For inversion of Hungarian I–O tables see V. Nyitrai's paper [139] in [109] as well as A. Rácz and L. Ujlaki [143].

**More precisely: the so-called *B*-variant of that table. See [187].

A further notation should now be introduced:

$$\mathbf{U} = \begin{bmatrix} u_{11} & u_{12} & \cdots & u_{1N} \\ u_{21} & u_{22} & \cdots & u_{2N} \\ \cdot & \cdot & \cdots & \cdot \\ \cdot & \cdot & \cdots & \cdot \\ \cdot & \cdot & \cdots & \cdot \\ u_{K1} & u_{K2} & \cdots & u_{KN} \end{bmatrix}, \tag{3.4}$$

where **U** stands for the matrix of K rows and N columns of external input coefficients u_{il}*. The matrix $\begin{bmatrix} \mathbf{G} \\ \mathbf{U} \end{bmatrix}$, i.e. the inner square and the matrix of external input coefficients taken together, gives the technological matrix of the I–O model.

The I–O model described above belongs to the type of *open* static Leontief models. We call it open because it takes into account the external inputs and final outputs originating from and directed to spheres *outside* the system.

Multiplying the ith external input coefficient vector with the inverse matrix we get

$$\check{\mathbf{u}}_i' = \mathbf{u}_i' \check{\mathbf{G}}, \qquad i = 1, \ldots, K. \tag{3.5}$$

The $\check{\mathbf{u}}_i'$ row vector thus obtained is called the ith total contents coefficient vector belonging to the I–O table. What do the components of this vector express?

Let e.g. $\mathbf{u}_1'$ be the row vector of direct wage input coefficients and the 4th column the sector of the chemical industry. In this case u_{14} will express the amount of direct wages contained in a unit of chemical product, taking into account exclusively the wages paid out in the chemical industry itself in the course of producing the product in question. $\check{u}_{14}$, on the other hand, will contain, in addition to direct wages as above, also the wages paid out in the power industry in the course of producing the amount of power which went into the production of one unit of chemicals; those paid out in coal mining in the course of producing the amount of coal which went into the production of one unit of chemical product and of the amount of power required thereto – and so on. The total of these components constitutes the total wages content of one

* In the Hungarian terminology of I–O techniques this is — not quite aptly — termed the "lower wing" of the technological matrix, on the analogy of the term "side wing" used to denote the final output matrix.

unit of chemical product. In the same sense we shall speak of total imports content coefficients, total depreciation allowance content coefficients, etc.

Let final output d_l be given and the following operation be carried out:

$$\check{u}_{il}\, d_l = \check{k}_{il}, \qquad i = 1, \ldots, K, \qquad l = 1, \ldots, N. \tag{3.6}$$

Here total contents $\check{k}_{il}$ express the absolute amount of external input of the ith input type required to produce final output d_l in the lth sector. The measurement of $\check{k}_{il}$ may be expressed in terms of forints, dollars, number of workers, tons, etc., according to the unit of measurement fixed for the external input type in question when determining row vector $\mathbf{u}_i'$.

3.3. The Characteristics of the Breakdown by Sectors

After clarifying the terminology let us turn to the main subject of this chapter: the application of I–O tables to planning. In our national planning three kinds of input–output models are used. The difference lies primarily in that what qualifies as a *sector*, i.e. what is to be regarded a row and what a column in the inner square of the Leontief model.

The three main types which we are dealing with have the following features in this respect:

First type. The rows and columns of the inner square are the large branches of the economy (construction, transport, agriculture, etc.), but within the industry the sectors are administrative *authorities*, the addressees of planning, e.g. Ministry of Light Industry, Ministry of Building and Construction.

Second type. Rows and columns of the inner square are *branches* defined by the criteria usual in industrial statistics: e.g. textile industry, engineering, plant cultivation, etc.

Third type. The rows and columns of the inner square are *products* or groups of products: e.g. coal or cotton fabric.

Those not closely familiar with socialist planning will at first reading not appreciate how great the difference is between these three types of models. The large I–O tables of the western countries usually belong to the second type: they break down the country's economy by the criteria of industrial statistics. Also in our country the *statistical* I–O tables which give an account of a past period are drawn up by such a principle.

Why can we also find other types of tables in planning?

Let us recall what has been written in ch. 1, in the first place about the balance system of products and resources described there. The products are not allocated to *branches* but to administrative *authorities*, addressees, and the different authorities are not "pure" as to their branch affiliation. E.g. the bulk of the building activity in the country is supervised by the Ministry of Building and Construction, but also other superior authorities have smaller building enterprises; similarly the bulk of machine production is controlled by the Ministry of Metallurgy and Engineering, however, some mining machines are manufactured by smaller machine factories supervised by the Ministry controlling mining, and likewise some of the textile machines are produced by the ministry in charge of the textile industry.

If an I–O table is used only to forecast the main interconnections of the economy as a whole this problem can be dismissed. But if the table serves for actually *allocating* resources and products we must not disregard the question of *who* should be entrusted with the output of a product, who should be allotted the resources. Thus e.g. the investment allocation is managed not by an "intangible" engineering branch or building branch but by an institution, a ministry or another superior authority, with a responsible leader in charge. This is the explanation of the fact that in the traditional balance system the columns of the balance system are authorities, "addressees".

At the same time in the rows of the traditional balance system we find products and not authorities. The Ministry of Light Industry does not consume products of the Ministry of Metallurgy and Engineering in general, but special machines; not products of the Ministry of Heavy Industry in general, but coal, electric power, etc. This again is due to the fact that the balance system does not merely serve to make forecasts, but the central leadership of the economy wishes to dispose of the most important products, intends to plan centrally the utilization of the most significant items.

As we see: the traditional balance system is divided row-wise by products, column-wise by authorities. It cannot be transformed directly into a quadratic table in which both the rows and the columns are divided along identical principles. This is why in recent years not one but three types of tables have been drawn up to complement the traditional method of planning. Let us take them one by one.

3.4. The "Chessboard" Balance Broken down by Authorities

The type of balances whose inner square is divided by "addressees", authorities, is called chessboard balances in Hungarian terminology. Of this type usually tables containing 20–40 sectors are drawn up.

Such chessboard balances have been used for the annual operative planning since 1957. Since 1959 we have begun to use such balances also for long-term planning, thus e.g. when the Five Year Plan covering the period 1961–1965 was drawn up a plan balance for 1965 was made. Now, at the time when the new Five Year Plan for 1966–1970 is being drawn up a similar plan balance is being processed for 1970*.

These I–O tables include not only productive but also trading sectors: different groups of wholesale companies constitute sectors of their own. Such sectors are e.g. the stockpiling companies of the Ministry of Heavy Industry or of the Ministry of Metallurgy and Engineering, the engineering stockpilingcompanies of this latter ministry, etc. Accordingly, the inner square matrix **G** of the table does not indicate how much the lth sector *consumes* of the output of the kth sector in the plan year but how much it *purchases* from the output of the kth sector. The inner square does not reflect the productive consumption of the product but the turnover within the productive sphere. Of course, these two are usually not too far from each other; still they are mostly not identical since a purchase can take place also to increase inventories or, inversely, consumption can take place also by reducing stocks. A potential time lag, the lag between purchase and consumption, is not uniform in the different branches of the economy and it is not constant but changes in time – and this change cannot be read off directly from the table.

It follows from the foregoing that we cannot regard the g_{kl} technological coefficients formed from the chessboard balance as magnitudes determined exclusively or overwhelmingly by the technology applied but they are influenced by the actual organizational breakdown of the economy, the actual division of responsibility among the different ministries and authorities, changes in the time lags between purchase and consumption, etc.

The main significance of the drawing up of a chessboard balance does not lie so much in the mathematical operations customary with I–O tables (although they are also performed) but, however strange it may sound, the drawing up in itself exercises the greatest effect. For, this table is *not* drawn up by starting out from the statistically determined technological

*See M. Augustinovics [8] and T. Morva [129].

coefficients of an earlier period. The technique of the drawing up is quite different and is characteristic just of the conditions of a centrally planned economy.

As a start the different forecasts obtained as a result of traditional planning are used. Let us look at the diagram of the balance and let us try to remember ch. 1, in which the traditional system of plan indices was discussed. Among the documented plan figures the aggregate costs of all addressees are determined and within them material costs, wage costs, depreciation allowance and net profit. The material costs equal the sum of the components belonging to a single column vector of the inner square **G** whereas the different row vectors of matrix **U** can be formed from the other cost items and the plan figures of the net profit. The traditional system of plan indices further indicates the gross production of the different authorities, i.e. the totals of rows. With a slight transformation of the documented plan figures the vector of final output can be determined: it can be derived from the plans of home trade, foreign trade and investments. The difference between the gross and the final outputs indicates the sum of the components of the row vector to be found in the inner square.

So we have "drawn the limits" of the inner square; we have obtained the so-called border amounts: below the total material consumption, to the right the total output available for productive consumption.

From the traditional system of plan indices we cannot obtain directly data relating to the elements of the inner square **G**. The process is the following: every superior authority – or rather the specialized department of the NPB controlling the planning activity of the former – will indicate the components of its own column and its own row. First it will independently plan the distribution of its own product among the superior planning authorities as well as its own requirements as to the output of the other superior authorities; all this, however, in a way that it will remain within the pre-determined limits of the border amount, i.e. the sum of the components of the rows and of the columns in the inner square.

Thus in our first approach we obtain two figures for each place in the table: a demand and a supply figure. This duality of the data is interesting already in itself: it throws light upon potential disequilibria in as much as certain producers overestimate (or underestimate) the demand, the possibilities for selling and some consumers overestimate (or underestimate) the supply available or their own requirements.

Then begins the checking of the two figures through direct negotiations. Perhaps it does not sound far-fetched if I compare this checking to a certain extent to the activity at a commodity exchange. Both here and there the supply and demand of an immense market is concentrated in one single place. Both here and there special bidding is going on to reconcile supply and demand. But this similarity should not be exaggerated. Not to mention other differences this peculiar "exchange" of ours designed to bring about a reconciliation of the data is much more concentrated than the capitalist commodity exchanges; here every producing branch, without exception, is represented and the output of a product or a group of products – if we disregard now the competition of foreign trade – is, so to say, concentrated in the hands of one authority. Although, as I have mentioned, this concentration is not complete: some products and services are issued in parallel by several authorities.

This cross-checking goes on until in each case the two figures are replaced by one. This checking, the determining of the elements in the inner square of the chessboard balance, is jokingly called "chessplaying" at the NPB; today this work forms an organic part of the normal course of planning.

As has been seen it is a special improvement on the model of traditional planning mentioned in ch. 1. The initial equation system, the drawing up of matrix **G** is solved here too with the method of "trial and error". Also in this case each planning section is responsible for some equations: for its own column and own row. At this stage the mathematical model is only there to provide it with a logically consistent scheme: but the solution itself does not take place by using mathematical methods but the traditional method of plan coordination.

We must see this clearly: although as a result of "chessplaying" all the places in the inner square will now contain only one figure each, not all of these figures will be uniformly acceptable to us. There are instances where we can find an actual coincidence of supply and demand but behind it it may happen that there is implied some hidden potential imbalance. In such cases the faults of the planners have to be corrected by the facts. This, however, may involve losses: a shortage of materials may arise or the demands of productive consumption are covered from goods meant for exports or for the consumption of the population; or inversely: superfluous inventories may arise.

After "chessplaying", the filling-in of the inner square, has actually taken place the planners will proceed to the usual input–output analysis: they compute the technological coefficients, invert the inner square, perform the total requirement-calculations, etc. This again will later facilitate calculations of new plan variants in future stages of planning.

We have seen that here the start was not made from statistically known technological coefficients with a view to defining with their aid the matrix

G of the plan period but inversely: from the planned supply and demand data matrix **G** was derived first and the coefficients were calculated from it.

It is open to challenge how far the table of coefficients thus obtained is reliable; it is, however, beyond doubt that this procedure has helped a great deal in the preliminary disclosure of certain disproportions. It is cheaper from the macro-economic point of view if these disproportions are revealed inside the walls of the Planning Board in the course of "chessplaying" than if they were realised later, in the interfirm turnover, on the market.

3.5. Interbranch Balances

The use of statistically well-founded I–O tables, divided by the interbranch system of industrial statistics has been dragging on for quite a time in planning just because their breakdown showed a great deviation from the "addressee" aspect of traditional planning. Now, however, the planners, statisticians and mathematicians in charge of these matters have elaborated some methods which have enabled us to "communicate" between these two types of division; they let us transform the figures originally given in interbranch breakdown into breakdown by authorities and vice versa. This method requires in the first place a certain expansion, detailing of the system of plan indices. The authorities must plan not only in an overall manner but they have to break down their own forecasts by the branch system of industrial statistics. Let us take for example the output of the Ministry of Light Industry; of which we have the production of the textile industry, the production of the leather and footwear industry, engineering production, building activity, etc. Thus the plan data can be broken down both by authorities and by branches.

This makes it possible to use in planning statistical I–O tables. Now for instance when drawing up the plan for 1966–70 computations have been made to check on the forecasts for 1970. As a start for these calculations the gross output vector and the final output vector drawn up with traditional planning have been adopted. They have been transformed from the "authority pattern" into the "interbranch structure" and then a whole series of computations was made with their aid. In order to describe these calculations let us introduce the following symbols:

$\mathbf{v}$ = vector of gross output obtained from the 1970 plan drawn up by the traditional method

d = vector of final output obtained from the 1970 plan drawn up by the traditional method

$\mathbf{G}_{59}$ = technological coefficient matrix based on statistical data of 1959

$\check{\mathbf{G}}_{59}$ = $(\mathbf{E}-\mathbf{G}_{59})^{-1}$ inverse matrix for 1959

$\mathbf{G}_{65}$ = technological coefficient matrix based on the chessboard balance of 1965

$\check{\mathbf{G}}_{65}$ = $(\mathbf{E}-\mathbf{G}_{65})^{-1}$ inverse matrix for 1965.

The following calculations based on the above data have been made:

$$\bar{\mathbf{v}}_{59} = \check{\mathbf{G}}_{59}\,\mathbf{d} \tag{3.7}$$

$$\bar{\mathbf{v}}_{65} = \check{\mathbf{G}}_{65}\,\mathbf{d} \tag{3.8}$$

$$\bar{\mathbf{d}}_{59} = (\mathbf{E}-\mathbf{G}_{59})\,\mathbf{v} \tag{3.9}$$

$$\bar{\mathbf{d}}_{65} = (\mathbf{E}-\mathbf{G}_{65})\,\mathbf{v}. \tag{3.10}$$

At the end of the computation **v** was compared to $\bar{\mathbf{v}}_{59}$ and to $\bar{\mathbf{v}}_{65}$ and **d** to $\bar{\mathbf{d}}_{59}$ and to $\bar{\mathbf{d}}_{65}$.

This comparison is going on now in the initial stage of the drawing up of the new plan. The control calculation has revealed some significant differences and called attention to the potential disequilibria in the first plan balances. In cases of this kind the potential causes of such differences are analyzed one by one. E.g. actual technological changes compared to the coefficients of 1959 and 1965. Or: wrong planning of several components of the vectors **v** and **d**. All these errors must be corrected in the subsequent stages of planning*.

3.6. Balance Based on Breakdown by Products

Let me briefly mention a third type of balances. Let us recall again the description of the traditional plan index system: ch. 1 mentioned the balances of products as the second group of balances in which the rows stand for products, the columns for authorities. In the previous section we have discussed the I–O table which adopts the column-wise division of the traditional balance system; now I wish to mention the table which adopts the division by rows**.

* See for further details L. ÚJLAKI [170].

** See J. DÖME *et al.* [39].

The Department of Materials and the Scientific Section of the National Planning Board have drawn up a balance with an inside square of 230 rows and 230 columns. In this balance each row and each column represents a priority product or a priority group of products allocated within the product balance system of the NPB. This balance does not cover the whole social production, only its smaller part. It was not drawn up by "chessplaying" like the balances broken down by authorities, but was built on technological coefficients. The planners responsible for drawing up year by year these product balances in the framework of traditional planning determine a number of items (but not all items) of the balance with the aid of technological coefficients. They are called in the Hungarian practice "material standards" or "material normatives": e.g. the pig iron needed for producing one ton of steel, the amount of cloth needed for producing a man's suit, etc.

Here again I have to stress the organizing power of the model. Earlier the material standards of the product balances were hidden only in the desks of the competent planners; they were not documented and were not discussed and checked by the experts; the material standards were not available for each item in the balance, there was no uniformly adopted method for drawing up material standards. Some of them were statistically well-founded figures, others were based on careful technical estimates but some of them on less reliable rough estimates. When the I–O table is drawn up, a number of plan figures are transferred from the auxiliary category y into category x, into the category of documented plan figures. When using the I–O table broken down by products we take these coefficients out of the desks to elaborate them by uniform methods.

When the table was drawn up, all the technological coefficients were put onto punched cards. Where no coefficient was available they were computed with the aid of statistical data or technical computations, or through the combination of the two procedures. Once the technological matrix was drawn up, its Leontief inverse consisting of 230 sectors was computed.

I should further mention a very characteristic feature of this table. Like the traditional system of plan balances it fails to include the small coefficients in the matrix **G**. It replaces them with zero and instead these small material requirements are included in one total among the claims for final output. But the final output includes here also the output required by the production of articles other than the 230 priority products allocated in the NPB product balances.

At present a new, even more detailed I–O table broken down into 307 sectors is being drawn up.

3.7. Checking the Consistency of the Plan

The input–output calculations solve great simultaneous equation systems. But however big these tables should be they are not adequate to solve the *whole* system of plan equations. For this very reason the I–O technique cannot be more than an auxiliary instrument of planning, and it cannot adopt all the functions of traditional planning.

Let us take a somewhat general view of what we have done in the course of the processes described in this chapter. Let us take as an example the control calculations performed with tables of an inter-branch breakdown of the second type.

From the scope of the traditionally determined plan figures **[x, y]** we have singled out the vector of gross outputs, **v**. This is still variable at the time of planning. Yet we regarded it as if it were not variable

TABLE

The Hungarian

No.	Scope	Accounting year	Special purpose
1	National economy	1957	
2	National economy	1959	
3	National economy	1961	
4–9	National economy	1949–1964 in every year	Preparation of annual plans
10	National economy	1965	Preparation of the five year plan
11	National economy	1970	Preparation of the five year plan
12	National economy	1963	Planning of material balances
13	National economy	1960	Analysis of prices
14	National economy	1960	Analysis of prices
15	Siderurgy	1958	
16	Agriculture	1959	
17	Construction	1960	
18	Textile, clothing, leather and shoe industries	1960	
19	Textile, clothing, leather and shoe industries	1960	

but *constant*. Then we solved the following equation system: $\bar{\mathbf{d}} = (\mathbf{E}-\mathbf{G})\,\mathbf{v}$ and the $\bar{\mathbf{d}}$ thus obtained was compared with the **d** obtained through traditional planning. We did the same also in the reverse direction: we took from among the traditional plan figures the vector of final output **d**. This, although it was variable, we regarded temporarily as constant and computed $\bar{\mathbf{v}} = \check{\mathbf{G}}\,\mathbf{d}$. Afterwards we compared this $\bar{\mathbf{v}}$ with the **v** obtained in the course of traditional planning.

By neither procedure could an attempt be made to determine both **d** and **v** *simultaneously*, although in fact at the same time both are unknowns of the big plan equation system. The I–O calculation only renders aid to this simultaneous determination by helping to reveal the inconsistencies, the faults made in the course of the simultaneous determination by the traditional method.

3.1
input–output tables

Constructed by	Measurement unit	Order (N) of the inner square of the technological matrix	Has the inner square of the technological matrix been inverted?	References
CSO	Ft	38	yes	[186], [108], [143]
CSO	Ft	96	yes	[187], [110]
CSO	Ft	54	yes	[191]
NPB	Ft	about 40	yes	[129]
NPB	Ft	45	yes	[8]
NPB	Ft	19	in course	[170]
NPB	physical units	233	yes	[39]
Price Control Board	Ft	268	yes	[42], [194]
Price Control Board	Ft	1300	in course	[42]
Institute for Economics	Ft	31	yes	[157]
CSO	Ft	45	yes	[24]
Office of Construction Techniques	Ft	56	yes	[66]
Institute for the Textile Industry	Ft	192	yes	[76], [149]
Institute for the Textile Industry	physical units	192	no	[76], [149]

3.8. Other Input–Output Tables

Sections 3.3–3.7 described only the tables worked out by the National Planning Board and employed directly in planning operations. However, for the sake of completeness mention should be made also of the tables compiled by other institutions on the basis of different methods (usually of statistical data), as part of these will also be used in our own calculations.

Table 3.1 gives a survey of the economy-wide and sector I–O tables compiled in Hungary up to the present.

A few tables should be pointed out in some detail.

The model of the Price Control Board deserves particular attention. This table of unusually large dimensions does not cover the whole volume of social production. Each row and column here is a representative product intended to characterize with its individual data a wider group of products. The model, which may be regarded as the "representative sample" of the mass of products of the national economy, lends itself especially to the tracing of the effects of changes in the price structure, be they due to price changes of individual products or product groups, or to the modifications of pricing principles. The question as to whether the model can be directly employed for working out the computational prices used in investment efficiency calculations will require further study.

The I–O tables marked 15–19 each "magnify" a sector in the national economy presenting the connections between the sector in question and the rest of the national economy. They may be helpful in "refining" the computational price system, in breaking it down in a more detailed manner.

CHAPTER 4

THE "FOOTHOLDS" OF MATHEMATICAL PLANNING

The I–O tables discussed in ch. 3 lead on to the subject-matter proper of this work, the methods of *mathematical* planning. Although I–O tables will be mentioned repeatedly in the next chapter, the exposition will not center on them but on the mathematical *programming* models. I–O tables have by now become a familiar method of planning – the same cannot as yet be said of mathematical programming.

Before proceeding to deal in merit with the problems of programming, a few remarks should be made as a preliminary on the relationship between programming – or, to use a more general term, mathematical planning – and the traditional planning methods.

The *general replacement* of traditional planning by the mathematical methods of planning now or in the near future, is a mere delusion, for a number of reasons. For one thing, the application of the mathematical methods involves several difficulties. These will later be discussed, so that only the headings are listed.

All economic calculations operate with prices. The prices, however, have been adjusted to the planning and economic methods so far customary. They serve their ends, with more or less reliability as the case may be.

Economic calculations require data. The book-keeping and statistics which provide the data have been evolved according to the requirements of traditional planning and are more or less closely tailored to satisfy them.

We have few computers of relatively small power. Yet presumably the performance of the vast mass of calculations involved in the everyday work of planning would be too much for the present computer facilities even of countries which are much richer in computers.

And finally perhaps the most important factor: there are too few experts with skill in the application of mathematical methods. Organized training to this end has only recently been instituted at the Hungarian universities and the experts who have so far emerged are in fact self-taught in this sphere. The thousands of practical business managers and planners have become used to the traditional methods. They are familiar with them, and for the time being can work only with them. Some are reluctant to adopt new methods, but even those who are not imbued with this conservatism know little of them and are only now beginning to make their acquaintance. Interest in these methods has indeed shown an extraordinary growth. Very many people are attending mathematical courses, and the (as yet rather scarce) Hungarian literature on mathematical economics is widely read. All in all, however, the personnel resources for the general, mass application of mathematical methods are not yet available.

In a word, the mathematical methods are at present still living in a strange environment, in the atmosphere of the traditional methods. This involves numerous difficulties and necessitates many allowances and compromises.

At the same time it should also be pointed out that the mathematical methods of planning (at least at the level of the results so far attained in econometric research) have not only advantages but also disadvantages with respect to the traditional methods. We shall return to these in the course of a later comparison.

Under such circumstances the only realistic and reasonable aim must be to achieve some kind of cooperation between the traditional and the mathematical methods of planning. *The present role of the mathematical methods in most spheres is to check, supplement and correct plans drawn up by the traditional methods. In the not too distant future these new methods will gradually be able – in certain spheres and in the solution of certain circumscribed tasks – to undertake a replacement of the traditional methods.*

Planning by mathematical methods is as yet unable to proceed on its own, without aid. It needs "footholds", which are provided by planning carried out with the traditional methods. As regards the investigations described in this book there are several senses in which we may speak of such "footholds":

(1) In the case of each model separate decisions were made on the extent to which the *actual* prices used in everyday financial accounting should be used, or instead of them, the *official computational* prices, rental on capital, rate of currency exchange and official computational evaluations generally, as is the practice with calculations of investment efficiency carried out in the course of traditional planning. Or again, to what extent these latter should be replaced by *non-official* computational evaluations which are more in conformity with mathematical methods.

Thus in some calculations, for instance, the rental used in the g_n index, the rate of currency exchange prescribed by the NPB, etc., were adopted. There were even cases where they were adopted despite the fact that we were not convinced of the faultlessness of the computational evaluation used. They were adopted in order to compare the result with that obtained through the use of the computational evaluations we had worked out. Or else they were adopted simply because no better ones could be found and it was not intended (indeed it would have been impossible) to solve all the open questions of accounting by means of a few programs.

(2) The situation is similar in the case of the *plan figures*. It was not intended by means of these models to determine all the figures of the long-term plans. Some figures of the plans worked out by traditional methods we considered *given**. Independently of the fact that these are in actual fact not constants but may still be changed in the planning phase, our models treated them as constants. The figures adopted as quasi-constants from the traditional plan will henceforth be referred to as plan directives.

(3) The various models will of course differ according to which figures they regard as constant plan directives and which as variables. The models have, however, an important common feature from this point of view: *the plan figures for non-productive consumption and the domestic requirements arising from them, have in every case been regarded as plan directives*. The optimization task prescribed for the programming models is not the maximization of the satisfaction of social requirements. Instead, *the general optimality criterion of the models is to minimize social input required to satisfy the domestic requirements related to non-productive consumption, as laid down by the planning bodies*. How this general principle can be concretely applied, depends on the special character of the model. This determines the form in which the plan directives referring to the domestic consumption requirement are incorporated in the model, the way in which the scope and financial accounting of the input to be minimized is defined, whether the advantages attainable through foreign trade should be included among the possibilities of input savings, etc. However, the various forms and different concrete considerations always lead to the enforcement of the same general principle**.

* That was mentioned already in section 3.7, concerning the I–O tables, but it is valid *in general* for the mathematical planning methods.

** A broader treatment of the problem of the optimality criterion will be undertaken in ch. 27.

It is fully realized that this involves a considerable narrowing of the scope of research. It is held, however, that such a narrowing makes it much easier in the present stage of the use of mathematical methods, to construct the models and apply them in practice.

PART 2
SECTORAL PROGRAMMING MODELS

Introduction

The main aim of Part 2 is to explain the basic ideas of the mathematical programming of long-term sectoral planning, and the basic differences between this approach and the traditional planning process.

It has seemed best, therefore, instead of abstract disquisitions to demonstrate sectoral programming on two concrete examples – those of programming for the cotton and the man-made fibres industry. Since all mathematical models constitute coherent, self-sufficient entities, the demonstrative models will be described in their entirety, to facilitate an understanding of their internal unity. However, the two sectors are merely examples, and their detailed discussion is only undertaken for didactic reasons. Technical details will, therefore, not be dealt with here, nor will the major part of the data relate to the programming projects. (These can be found in the final reports on the individual projects.) Although I will refer here always to already *completed* sector programs only, it is worth mentioning that when these pages go to the press there are *40 sectoral programming projects* in preparation, all of them linked up with the calculations of the 1966–70 long-term plan. More recent models may differ in some particulars from the first sector programs which served as their model, but their main characteristics are the same.

The discussion is narrowed down by making a few temporary simplifying assumptions. These assumptions are gradually resolved in the subsequent parts of the book:

(1) It is assumed that all figures are precisely known. The possible uncertainties of the figures are treated in Part 3.

(2) The optimality criterion in both sectoral models is the minimization of the input. The achievement of this optimum and the financial accounting of the input take place for the time being through use of the official computational evaluations, or related means. It will be the task of Part 4 to go closer into an examination of the financial accounting of inputs. This will be the place to discuss how far it is desirable to substitute other computational evaluations for the official ones.

(3) Only those decisions are considered that arise within the sector. The fitting of these decisions into the national plan takes place by means of plan directives adopted from the traditional plan. For the time being we shall not go into how sectoral programming can be used for a critical revision of the plan directives. This will be treated in Part 5.

(4) Only structural decisions are treated. The calculations are used to plan the state of things to be attained by the end of the long-term plan period (in practice, by the *terminal year*.) No investigation is undertaken of the time distribution or time coordination of the activities taking place between the moment of the decision and the terminal year, only the consequences of the activities by the end of the plan period being considered. The questions concerning the time-aspects will be touched in Part 5.

Because of the temporary simplifying assumptions, the two sectoral models are presented in their simplest form only. In the actual calculations several other models, modified in various respects, were also used. Different calculations were carried out with the help of these models. They will, however, be discussed later, in Parts 3–5.

CHAPTER 5

THE CHOICE BETWEEN TECHNOLOGICAL ALTERNATIVES THE MODEL FOR THE COTTON INDUSTRY*

5.1. Decision Problems

One of the first tasks in formulating a mathematical model for the purposes of economic efficiency calculations, is to determine the *decision problems* which must be answered. The decision problems of the model are understood to mean those questions for whose solution alternative possibilities exist, and where calculations performed on the basis of the model must furnish the clue to choosing the most favourable alternative.

The cotton industry is the broadest sector of Hungarian light industry, and also the most significant for exports. The long-term plan elaborated by traditional methods, prescribed a considerable increase in the output of cotton fabrics both for home consumption and for exports. The present model was not intended to revise the domestic cotton requirements, nor even the export targets – the output target of the cotton fabrics balance was therefore treated as a plan directive. Instead, the investigation was focussed on the problem of what technological alternatives could be chosen to reach the prescribed level of cotton fabric output**.

The decision problems to be faced were the following:

(1) How should the output of fabrics be increased – by technically modernizing the existing weaving mills, or by building new ones?

(2) In the case of a part of the present machinery a choice may be made between operating the machine in its original form, modernizing

* The results of the research project have been published in the papers [72] and [73]. A detailed account is given in the official final report [77].

The research was done by a team commissioned by the Ministry for Light Industry and headed by the author. Its members were the mathematicians P. Wellisch and Z. Marcsányi, textile works chief engineer F. Kotányi, textile works economists Dr. S. Fülöp, Dr. J. Pécsi and Dr. L. Szabó. Work on the electronic computer was directed by T. Frey.

** Related decision problems — the choice between technological alternatives — were in the focus of the mathematical programming investigation which was carried out in the industry of electric power in France (see P. Massé [122]).

it by way of alterations or supplementary investments, or else finally dismantling it.

(3) In the case of another part of the present machinery there are only two alternatives – either to retain, or else to scrap the machine.

(4) If new machines are purchased, a choice may be made between many types. Which type should be chosen, and how many of a particular type should be purchased?

It should not be thought that the industrial administration presents the decision issues to the programming economist in a "cut and dried" form. The research worker has to select them from a multitude of problems which in a sense constitute a unity, and may be examined as parts of one common model. In the course of the present project it was necessary to conduct a series of talks with the industry's administration in order finally to circumscribe the decision problems that were to be posed.

5.2. The Scope of Programming

The scope of the investigation for the cotton industry was set out – in general terms – by the commission received from the Ministry for Light Industry.

The production of cotton fabrics takes place in three vertical phases that follow successively after one another. They are the spinning mill, the weaving mill and the finishing shop. The terms of the commission set out that only the second of these phases, that of weaving, should be considered, and the other two not. Weaving, however, should be examined not in one mill, but in all the firms belonging to the Cotton Industries Directorate of the Ministry.

The weaving mills comprise several manufacturing processes. To begin with there is the actual process of weaving, though even this is not wholly homogeneous, for the weaving looms may be classified into several categories according to the product – the grey cloth – that they weave. Some are used to make *plain* cloth, others *weft-pattern* cloth (e.g. checked shirts, handkerchiefs, etc.), while a third and smaller group produces *special* materials (satin, looped fabrics, etc.). Within these groups, moreover, cloth of various widths is also woven (e.g. plain cloth is made in widths ranging from 70 cm up to 160 cm).

The weaving mills also include the *dressing* shops which prepare the yarn obtained from the spinning mill for weaving. The dressing shop includes a number of processes which succeed each other vertically, or are performed parallel with one another. They are diagrammatically shown in figure 5.1.

In the model the four most important dressing operations indicated in figure 5.1, those of cross winding, pirning, warping and sizing, were selected for emphasis, beside the actual weaving. This does not mean that the other operations which were neglected (and are represented by dashed contours in the figure), are technologically superfluous. It is, however, the four operations that have been included, which engage the most and the costliest fixed resources – those of the others are diminutive in comparison – so that they are the ones to be primarily considered in investment decisions.

It will now be clear which production processes have been included in the investigation. Together they comprise the programming scope.

The programming scope does not necessarily coincide with the "official" organizational units of production and administration. Thus in the cotton industry the organizational units are:

(1) the weaving mill (or shop) as part of a firm
(2) the firm
(3) the sector of industry as a whole.

The scope of the present programming project does not comprise the whole sector, but only one third; it includes practically all the weaving mills, but only "practically" so for some of the less significant units are not considered.

*The criterion in determining the programming scope should not be the organizational structure, but rather the area that will constitute a more or less organic unity from the point of view of the economic planning problem to be investigated**. In the present case the aim was to compare the main trends for the development of cotton weaving, and *from this point of view* the above boundaries to the programming scope seemed the most appropriate.

* Thus the programming scope of the model for the aluminium industry was made to include the production of bauxite, alumina and aluminium, which belong under the authority of the Ministry for Heavy Industry, moreover the export and import of these products, which are handled by the Ministry for Foreign Trade. It did not, on the other hand, include some of the by-products of the aluminium industry, though these too are produced by firms belonging to the Ministry for Heavy Industry.

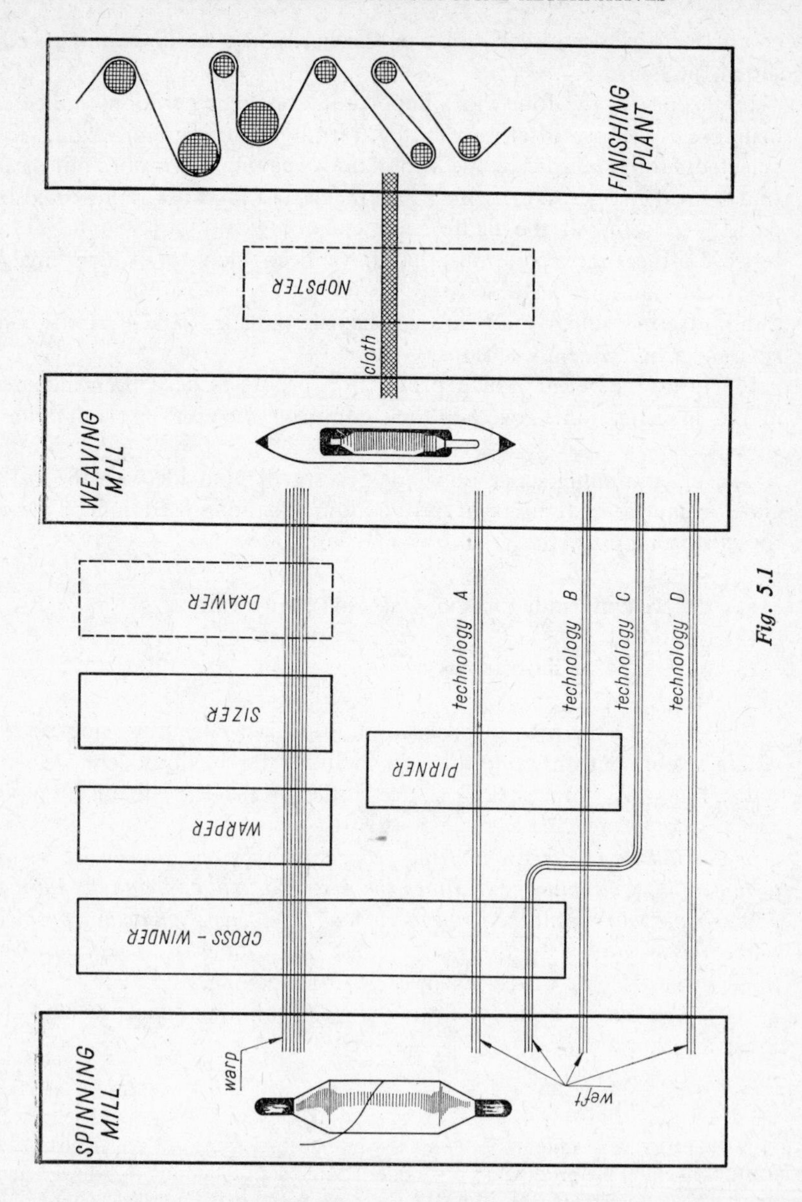
FINISHING PLANT
NOPSTER
cloth
WEAVING MILL
DRAWER
SIZER
WARPER
CROSS - WINDER
PIRNER
technology A
technology B
technology C
technology D
SPINNING MILL
warp
weft

Fig. 5.1

The circumscription of the programming scope is by no means easy. In the case of the cotton weaving industry's project, as well as in the cases of the synthetic fibre and aluminium industry, the final definition was preceded by many discussions. The determination of the programming scope establishes the "breadth" of the model, while the selection of the decision problems sets its "depth". Although the discussion of the decision problems has in this book preceded that of the programming scope, this does not imply a chronological order for the two tasks. Both have in fact to be tackled together, simultaneously. The two questions are most closely interlinked, one reason being that the dimensions of the model are ultimately subject to the limits imposed by the computing techniques available. Any broadening of the scope of programming must be paid for by a decrease in the depth of the investigation, while narrowing the programming scope will permit a more detailed examination, comprising several alternatives, of the problems arising within that scope.

The manifold work of planning requires both the broader programming models, and also those which are narrower, more concentrated, but penetrating deeper. These supplement one another.

5.3. Activities, the Variables of the Model

The term *activities* is understood collectively to comprise all the economic processes (e.g. production, investment, construction, imports, etc.) which are examined as part of the model. The object of the calculations carried out on the basis of the model is to determine which of the alternative activities should be undertaken, and at what level. The level of an activity is the term applied to its breadth and magnitude.

The activities in the model for the cotton weaving industry are operations aimed at achieving a certain composition of the machinery stock and buildings of the industry by 1965, at the end of the plan period. These operations include the continued running of the existing machines by providing for regular general repairs, the partial alteration and modernization of the existing machines, the dismantling of existing machines, the acquisition and introduction of new machines, the construction of new buildings – all during the period from 1961 to 1965. All the activities in the model comprise one such operation, or the combination of several operations.

The symbol for the level of an activity is x_{jkl}. The quantities of the form x_{jkl} are the *variables* of the calculation. The unit of measurement is 1 machine. Thus, if, for instance, $x_{jkl} = 1000$, this means that those operations must be carried out as a result of which the jklth machine group will consist of 1000 machines by 1965.

What are the specific features of a machine group? To what characteristics do the three suffices allude?

The first characteristic is the *product*. The programming scope comprises the output of seven kinds of product ($j = 1, 2, \ldots, 7$):

1. Narrow plain cloth (woven on looms less than 136 cm wide)
2. Broad plain cloth (woven on looms over 136 cm wide)
3. Weft-pattern cloth
4. Sized yarn
5. Warped yarn
6. Pirned yarn
7. Cross wound yarn.

These seven "products" actually each comprise a broad range, making up a product group consisting of the sum of many concrete articles.

The second characteristic is the *location category* ($k = 1, 2$). Location category 1 is that the machine will be located in an old building, already extant at the time of programming. Location category 2 is when the machine is to be located in a new building, subsequently to be erected. Activities of level x_{j2l} thus include building operations – the erection of the buildings necessary to locate these machines.

The program must supply an answer to whether a particular activity should be carried out in an old or a new plant, but it need not give any closer indication of the *location* of the activity. This in fact means that the determination of the figures for the various activities (the investment costs, output figures, etc.) is not based on the particular situation at one or other of the plants, but on the *average for the industry*. The program merely prescribes that 2000 out of the stock of broad looms at the old plants must be dismantled and 1600 new ones installed in their place, but it does not state at which plant the replacement of the machinery should take place.

Finally a third characteristic is that machines producing the same product and identically located, differ from one another in respect to *technology*. There are several technological variants among machines suitable for producing the jth product and located according to category k; their number n_{jkl} differs for each product and location category as well ($l = 1, \ldots, n_{jk}$). It would take too much space to enumerate all variables of the cotton industry model. It should suffice instead to list, for the sake of illustration, the machine groups which contribute to the output of product 1, a narrow plain cotton cloth. Before listing them, it must, however, be pointed out that the largest groups of the old machinery already extant in 1960 – the plain weaving looms, moreover the cross winding and pirning machines – have been subdivided into the two technical classes of "better" and "worse" machines, the latter comprising those of lower productivity.

1.1. Narrow Plain Looms Located in Old Buildings

1.1.1. Continued operation of the old, worse machines. Continued operation is understood to mean running them in the same technical condition in which they are. Their unvarying output is maintained by general repairs carried out at the necessary intervals.
1.1.2. Dismantling of the old, worse machines.
1.1.3. Continued operation of the old, better machines.
1.1.4. Dismantling of the old, better machines.
1.1.5. "Acceleration" of the old, better machines. This involves a minor technical alteration that permits a considerable rise in the rate of revolution.
1.1.6. Automation of the old, better machines by means of import investments. In this case the machine is modernized by mounting "added automata".
1.1.7. Installation of new automatic shuttle changing looms. These are the cheapest but least productive type.
1.1.8. Installation of new automatic bobbin changing looms. Medium price, medium productivity.
1.1.9. Installation of new automatic shuttle-less looms. These are the most expensive but most productive type.

1.2. Narrow Plain Looms Located in New Buildings

1.2.1. Installation of new automatic shuttle changing looms.
1.2.2. Installation of new automatic bobbin changing looms.
1.2.3. Installation of new automatic shuttle-less looms.

It will be noted that the assumption has been made and will continue to be applied, that only new machines can be installed in the new buildings. The possibility of transferring old machines from old buildings to new ones, has been ruled out.

The compilation of the list of activities to figure in the model is no easy task. Here it was again a case of *embarras de richesse*, for in actual fact a good many more activities might be considered. There are more new machinery types to be purchased, there are several other known ways of modernizing the old machines, etc. The necessary limitation of the dimensions of the model, however, led to a reduction of the list. The aim was, on the basis of discussions conducted with the experts, to incorporate the most characteristic activities in the model, that would best represent the alternative courses of technical development. Any preliminary selection of this kind requires much circumspection, all the more so since the outright *rejection* of a possible activity is no less responsible a decision than the acceptance of another. A negative decision may also involve a "loss", for if the activity which is rejected would actually have been the optimal solution, then the non-optimal activity which was accepted and is carried out, results in a loss compared to the former.

The determination of the values of the variables x_{jkl} furnishes answers to the decision problems listed in section 5.1, viz:

(1) How much new building space should be constructed and to what extent should technical modernization be undertaken in the old factories?

(2–3) What is to happen to the old machinery?

(4) What kind and how many new machines should be acquired?

The answers given to the decision problems are both quantitative and qualitative. They are qualitative in that they determine the line of activities to pursue, setting out which tasks should be carried out and which abandoned, but they are also quantitative in stating how much of each activity is to be performed.

The totality of the variables enumerated – the program $\mathbf{x}$ – effectively furnishes the composition of the machinery stock of the whole of the cotton weaving industry, moreover the size of the total building space at a particular time.

5.4. External Constraints

It is not possible to carry out any arbitrary program. There are facts which have to be taken into account. Constraints are the mathematical formulations of facts which limit the arbitrary choice of programs.

Let us consider the constraint system for the model of the cotton industry. The first group of constraints governs the *output targets* of the programming scope.

Output Target for Narrow Plain Cloth

$$\sum_{k=1}^{2} \sum_{l=1}^{n_{1k}} f_{1kl}\, x_{1kl} = v_1, \tag{5.1}$$

where

f_{1kl} = the output coefficient. This is the annual cloth output of one unit of the klth plain loom, with normal utilization of the loom's performance

v_1 = the plan directive for the cloth output of the cotton industry in 1965.

The constraint has been stated in the form of an equality. It is assumed that it is not desirable to overfulfil the output target.

The following two constraints are analogous with the one above.

Output Target for Broad Plain Cloth

$$\sum_{k=1}^{2} \sum_{l=1}^{n_{2k}} f_{2kl}\, x_{2kl} = v_2. \tag{5.2}$$

Output Target for Weft Pattern Cloth

$$\sum_{k=1}^{2} \sum_{l=1}^{n_{3k}} f_{3kl}\, x_{3kl} = v_3. \tag{5.3}$$

The second group of constraints is concerned with the limits of the *resources available* to the programming scope.

Gross Investment Fund

$$\sum_{j=1}^{7} \sum_{k=1}^{2} \sum_{l=1}^{n_{jk}} h_{jkl}^{\text{inv}}\, x_{jkl} \leqq w^{\text{inv}}, \tag{5.4}$$

where

h_{jkl}^{inv} = the resource input coefficient. This is the gross investment requirement in forint per unit machine of the jklth activity. In effect it comprises the following:

– For the machines of the present machinery stock which are to continue in operation, the general repair costs arising during the five years;
– For the new machines, the cost of acquisition and installation;
– For machines that are to be dismantled, the returns to be obtained from scrapping them. (Since these reduce the overall costs of the programmed sector, they will appear as negative costs);
– For machines to be located in new buildings: the building costs;

w^{inv} = the gross investment fund for the cotton weaving industry in forint.

The simplifying assumption involved in this constraint is as follows: It is assumed that the sum available for gross investment may be freely apportioned between general repairs, modernization and acquisition of machines, and the erection of new buildings*.

This assumption is a radical departure from the usual planning practice and the financial and organizational forms, which draw a rather sharp distinction between so-called "renewal" (usually mainly general repairs), and "investment"**.

Capitalist Foreign Exchange Quota

$$\sum_{j=1}^{7} \sum_{k=1}^{2} \sum_{l=1}^{n_{jk}} h_{jkl}^{exch} x_{jkl} \leqq w^{exch}, \tag{5.5}$$

where

h_{jkl}^{exch} = the import investment requirement in dollars from capitalist countries, per unit of the jklth activity. This is of course zero in the case of investments not requiring capitalist foreign exchange

w^{exch} = the capitalist foreign exchange quota of the cotton weaving industry, in dollars.

* The sum required for the maintenance of buildings was at the outset subtracted from the gross investment fund planned by the State. Since the building industry is a bottleneck of the national economy, the possibility of demolishing old buildings and raising new ones in their place did not even arise. Thus there was no choice to be made in this respect, so no corresponding provision had to be made in the calculations.

** Q. v. in section 1.1 and I. NEMÉNYI [134] pp. 256–272.

Since, as has been pointed out, building is a bottleneck of the national economy, the building opportunities are also considered to be limited.

Building Quota

$$\sum_{j=1}^{7} \sum_{l=1}^{n_{j2}} h_{j2l}^{\text{build}} x_{j2l} \leqq w^{\text{build}}, \tag{5.6}$$

where

h_{j2l}^{build} = the building requirement in m² of floor space per unit machine of the $j2l$th activity

w^{build} = the building quota of the cotton weaving industry, reduced to m² of floor space.

The bounds w^{inv}, w^{exch} and w^{build} were regarded as plan directives. The point of departure was the following:

The official plan* worked out by the traditional methods had earmarked definite sums for investments as a whole, as well as for imports from capitalist countries and buildings in particular. *Our own program proposal could not require more of these resources than did the official plan.*

So far specifically investment inputs have been discussed. The question arises whether it is not necessary in the cotton weaving industry to consider the utilization of materials and manpower, and some categories of the operative inputs necessary for continuous operation, as also being bounded.

If there were a grave lack of labour, it would be necessary to prescribe as a constraint that, say, the manpower requirement of the cotton weaving industry may not in 1965 be larger than a particular figure. Since, however, there is at present no shortage of labour in this field, it was not necessary to incorporate such a constraint in the model.

The input of materials was also not regarded as being bounded.

It is another question of course, that *thrift* has to be exercised in all the operative inputs. This, as we shall see, is part of the program.

The fact that none of the operative inputs need be regarded as bounded, is a consequence of the special circumstances of the cotton weaving industry's model, and cannot be generalized.

* What is called in this work the official plan, is the plan based on traditional methods which we are to revise by means of mathematical methods. In some cases it is a definitely approved and documented plan, in others but a set of plan proposals worked out by traditional methods and still pending approval.

5.5. Internal Constraints

Having considered the constraints which link the programming scope – both as a producer and as a consumer – with the "outer world", i.e. the national economy, we may now turn to those which govern the "internal affairs" of the sector to be programmed.

The next, and third group of constraints are the *material balances* which are familiar from planning practice. Their object is that the output capacity of the dressing shops should cover the total needs of the weaving mills.

Sized Yarn Balance

$$\sum_{k=1}^{2} \sum_{l=1}^{n_{4k}} f_{4kl}\, x_{4kl} = \sum_{j=1}^{3} \sum_{k=1}^{2} \sum_{l=1}^{n_{jk}} g_{jkl}^{(4)}\, x_{jkl}, \tag{5.7}$$

where

f_{4kl} = the output coefficient. This is the annual output in kg of a unit sizing frame of the *kl*th technological variant

$g_{jkl}^{(4)}$= the material input coefficient. This is the annual sized yarn requirement in kg per unit *jkl*th loom located in old buildings, provided the loom's annual output equals the output coefficient f_{jkl} of the constraints (5.1)–(5.3).

The constraint has been stated as an equality, for there is no need for any sized yarn beyond that required by the looms.

The following two balances are analogous with the above:

General Warped Yarn Balance

$$\sum_{k=1}^{2} \sum_{l=1}^{n_{5k}} f_{5kl}\, x_{5kl} = \sum_{j=1}^{3} \sum_{k=1}^{2} \sum_{l=1}^{n_{jk}} g_{jkl}^{(5)}\, x_{jkl}\,; \tag{5.8}$$

General Pirned Yarn Balance

$$\sum_{k=1}^{2} \sum_{l=1}^{n_{6k}} f_{6kl}\, x_{6kl} = \sum_{j=1}^{3} \sum_{k=1}^{2} \sum_{l=1}^{n_{jk}} g_{jkl}^{(6)}\, x_{jkl}. \tag{5.9}$$

Somewhat different from the above, is the constraint for cross wound yarn. Cross wound yarn is also required outside the cotton weaving ndustry, for the woolen and hosiery industries, etc.

Cross Wound Yarn Balance

$$\sum_{k=1}^{2} \sum_{l=1}^{n_{7k}} f_{7kl} \, x_{7kl} = \sum_{j=1}^{3} \sum_{k=1}^{2} \sum_{l=1}^{n_{jk}} g_{jkl}^{(7)} \, x_{jkl} + v_7 \,, \tag{5.10}$$

where

f_{7kl} = the annual output of the klth cross winding machine in kg
$g_{jkl}^{(7)}$ = the annual cross wound yarn requirement in kg of the jklth loom
v_7 = the external delivery obligation for cross wound yarn. This is a plan directive.

Constraints (5.7)–(5.10) provide for the *general* proportions between the dressing shops and the weaving mills. It is necessary, however, to go beyond this and also to provide for certain *special* proportions. The figures for the output of the automatic looms were determined on the assumption that they receive their yarn not just from any kind of dressing machine, but from modern machinery which supplies high quality yarn. This was laid down in the form of special constraints which prescribe that the quantity of yarn supplied by modern dressing machines should not be less than the requirements of the automatic looms. For the sake of brevity, I will not go into their detailed description here.

The next, fourth group of constraints expresses the *status quo* existing at the date of programming and inherited from the previous period. This must, of course, be considered when determining the course to be pursued.

To begin with, there are the existing buildings. The floor space requirement of those machines which we wish to locate in the old buildings cannot be larger than the space at present available.

Bounds of the Old Shop Space

$$\sum_{j=1}^{7} \sum_{l=1}^{n_{j1}} h_{j1l}^{\text{loc}} \, x_{j1l} \leqq w^{\text{loc}}, \tag{5.11}$$

where

h_{j1l}^{loc} = the floor space requirement in m^2 of unit machine of the $j1l$th activity, with respect to the old shop space
w^{loc} = the total old shop space in m^2. This is a fact figure whose magnitude was determined by special measurement.

Another given feature is the old machinery stock, with regard to which the program must decide whether the old machines should continue to be operated or – if such an activity is included in the model – modernized, or else dismantled.

As an example, we will describe the first constraints prescribing the distribution of the stock of narrow plain looms.

Distribution of the Old Stock of Narrow Plain Looms

$$x_{111} + x_{112} = H_1 , \tag{5.12}$$

$$x_{113} + x_{114} + x_{115} + x_{116} = H_2, \tag{5.13}$$

where

H_1 = the old stock of "worse" narrow plain looms
H_2 = the old stock of "better" narrow plain looms.

Constraints (5.1)–(5.13) form, together with the other constraints of a similar character, the model's system of constraints. Let us briefly summarize them:

(i) External output obligations
(ii) Input bounds
(iii) Internal proportions
(iv) Facts of the *status quo.*

Finally there is the stipulation that the values of the variables may not be negative:

$$x_{jkl} \geqq 0 , \quad l = 1, \dots, n_{jk} ; \; j = 1, \dots, 7 ; \; k = 1, 2. \tag{5.14}$$

5.6. The Objective Function

The aim of the calculations is to select the optimal program from among those programs, which satisfy the system of constraints. The economic content of our optimum criterion is (as has been pointed out in the introductory ch. 4), that *the given output, prescribed as a plan directive, must be achieved with the minimum social input.* The social input is measured in money (forints). The objective function is:

$$\begin{aligned} C(\mathbf{x}) &= \sum_{j=1}^{7} \sum_{k=1}^{2} \sum_{l=1}^{n_{jk}} C_{jkl} \, (x_{jkl}) = \\ &= \sum_{j=1}^{7} \sum_{k=1}^{2} \sum_{l=1}^{n_{jk}} c_{jkl} \, x_{jkl} \longrightarrow \min ! \end{aligned} \tag{5.15}$$

where

C_{jkl} = the cost function of the *jkl*th variable
c_{jkl} = the cost coefficient of the *jkl*th variable.

In actual fact the costs of the cotton weaving industry depend on numerous factors, e.g. the volume and the composition by articles of the output, the quality of the yarn dressing, etc. These factors, however, fall outside the scope of our investigations. On the basis of the assumptions already set forth and of others treated in the official final report, the output volume, the articles produced, and certain technological features have been regarded as *given. Attention may therefore be directed exclusively towards those costs whose magnitude depends on the level of the activities and actions determined in the program.* The costs in this group will be called costs depending on the program.

The costs in the objective function include only the costs depending on the program. These comprise the following:

(1) The purchase price of new machinery, the installation costs of the new machines, the alteration and general repair costs of the old machines.

(2) The construction costs of erecting new workshop buildings.

(3) The supplementary investment costs necessary to start production in the new buildings.

These three elements of the costs depending on the program together make up the *investment costs.*

(4) The cost of general repairs to machinery.

(5) The wage costs in the case of work where the number of the personnel depends on the type of machine (actual machine operators, fitters and the lower supervisory staff).

(6) The overhead wage costs figuring among the general costs (overheads), do not as a rule belong to the class of costs depending on the program. There is one case where an exception must be made. The overall indirect wage costs of the industry are different when a set volume is produced by the existing old mills from when new additional mills are established where new non-productive personnel must be employed. Actually, we have here a cost relation which does not lend itself for exact treatment within the framework of a linear model. The establishment of a new plant will always require a certain amount of overhead costs (e.g. the manager's salary or the door-keeper's wages, etc.). These overhead costs will be the lower per machinery unit the larger the new plant. This circumstance we had to disregard in order to preserve the

linearity of the model. We have, accordingly, charged the same amount of surplus wage cost to every machine unit set up in a new building*.

(7) The cost of the electric power needed to operate the machines.

(8) Those auxiliary and maintenance material costs whose size depends on the types of machinery.

(9) Direct material costs do not as a rule depend on the program. Consequently it was not necessary to include the rental for the working capital engaged – this again may be regarded as approximately constant for a given volume and output assortment. On the other hand the costs depending on the program were made to include the surplus waste arising with certain types of loom.

The cost components listed in points (4)–(9), together constitute the *operation costs***.

As formula (5.15) shows, it is assumed that the magnitude of the costs depending on the program is proportionate to the level of the activity, so that the objective function is *linear*. At this stage the assumption of linearity is merely pointed out, its justification will be discussed later.

In the course of the actual programming for the cotton industry, several kinds of objective function were used for parallel computing. All were identical with regard to the points treated above (the scope of the costs depending on the program and the linearity assumption), but they differed in the computational evaluations employed (prices, rental, exchange rates, etc.). One of these types of objective function is in its economic content closely related to the g_n index, the investment efficiency formula of traditional planning, and uses essentially the same official computational evaluations as that index:

$$c_{jkl} = \gamma\, p_{jkl} + r_{jkl}, \qquad l = 1, \ldots, n_{jk};\; j = 1, \ldots, 7;\; k = 1, 2, \quad (5.16)$$

* We first made a preliminary estimate of the volume in which the activities aimed at constructing a new building would enter into the optimal program, and calculated the surplus wage cost on the basis of this estimated plant size. The *estimated* plant size was then compared with that *obtained* by programming. It turned out that the estimates were approximately correct and that the simplification did not lead to any notable error.

** The general repair costs must be borne by the gross investment fund, so that from the point of view of constraint (5.4) they are regarded as investment costs. However, with respect to the time of their appearance they are obviously not *initial* investment costs, but *continuous* operation costs. This was why they had to be included among the operation costs in formulating the coefficient for the objective function.

where

p_{jkl} = the investment cost per unit of the *jkl*th activity (see points (1)–(3) of the above list)
γ = the rental on capital. The actual figure is 0.2
r_{jkl} = the operation cost per unit of the *jkl*th activity (see points (4)–(9) of the above list).

The detailed analysis of the computational evaluations used will be undertaken in Part 4.

5.7. The Mathematical Summary of the Problem

Let m denote the number of constraints and N the number of variables representing economic activities. The constraints stated in the form of inequalities are transformed into equations by means of slack variables*. In the case of a lower bound the slack variable with coefficient -1 will indicate the extent to which the bound had been surpassed. In the case of an upper bound the slack variable with coefficient $+1$ will indicate the extent of the bound's non-utilized part. Let M denote the number of slack variables. Then n, the total number of the model's variables, will be

$$n = N + M\,. \tag{5.17}$$

The following vector and matrix notation is introduced:

a_{ih} = the coefficient of the hth variable in the ith constraint
$\mathbf{A}$ = the m-row, n-column matrix of the coefficients a_{ih}
b_i = the constraint-constant on the right hand side of the ith constraint

* Thus e.g. the ith constraint had originally been given in the form

$$\sum_j \sum_k \sum_l a_{ijkl}\, x_{jkl} \leqq b_i.$$

With the introduction of slack variable x_i we obtain the following equation:

$$\sum_j \sum_k \sum_l a_{ijkl}\, x_{jkl} + x_i = b_i.$$

$\mathbf{b}$ = the m-component vector of the constraint-constants b_i
c_h = the unit cost of the hth variable
$\mathbf{c}'$ = the row vector of the costs c_k
x_h = the level of the hth variable
$\mathbf{x}$ = the program, i.e. the column vector consisting of the levels $x_1, x_2, \ldots, x_n$ as its components.

Having introduced this notation, the problem may then be formulated as follows:

Let the $\mathbf{x}^*$ vector (or optimal program) be found from among the feasible vectors, i.e. those that comply with the conditions

$$\mathbf{A}\,\mathbf{x} = \mathbf{b}, \qquad \mathbf{x} \geqq \mathbf{0}\,, \tag{5.18}$$

for which the value of the objective function $\mathbf{c}'\mathbf{x}$ is the minimum, i.e.

$$\mathbf{c}'\mathbf{x}^* = \min_{\substack{\mathbf{A}\mathbf{x}=\mathbf{b}\\ \mathbf{x}\geqq\mathbf{0}}} \mathbf{c}'\mathbf{x}\,. \tag{5.19}$$

Since both the constraint system and the objective function are linear, the result is a *linear programming problem.*

The most familiar procedure for numerically solving the general linear programming problem is the *simplex method**. In the case of the calculations for the cotton industry, a somewhat modified version of the simplex method was used**.

5.8. The Practical Results of Programming in the Cotton Industry

The following is a brief account of the practical conclusions which could be drawn from the programming of the cotton weaving industry. It shows that the programming of investments leads to proposals that can be *put to good practical use.*

* To mention only a few summary works on linear programming, see A. CHARNES *et al.* [19], S. GASS [43], G. HADLEY [47] and S. KARLIN [63]. The standard Hungarian-language work on linear programming is that of B. KREKÓ [90].

** The method used has been described in a paper by T. FREY [77]. The calculation for the cotton industry was, incidentally, the first relatively large-scale linear programming problem to be solved in Hungary with the help of an electronic computer.

In putting forward the proposals, attention was drawn to the fact that the calculations were able to determine only the *main features* for investment policies and technical development. They could not provide guidance in matters of detail.

Some comparisons will be presented between the results of the calculations and the official plan, i.e. the targets valid on 1st June 1960. Here again, a comparison of only the main features will be attempted, omitting the details.

One of the main lessons from programming was that *building must be kept at the minimum level possible. Added production must, as far as it can, be achieved without building, through the modernization and expansion of the existing mills.*

Table 5.1 shows that the calculations fully corroborated the principle that had already been stressed in several official documents both in the Soviet Union and Hungary.

TABLE 5.1

Proportion of machinery and building investments in the cotton industry

	Percentage according to the official program	Percentage according to the proposed program
Of the total *gross* investments net machinery		
investments	54.0	89.5
general repairs to machinery	19.5	9.3
building	26.5	1.2

A calculation was undertaken more specifically to compare the efficiency of exchanging machines or erecting new buildings. A program was worked out, whose idea was to retain all the old machines and to cover the part of the requirement beyond the capacity of the old machinery, exclusively with new machines located in new buildings. This would be the *pure case* of increased production without exchanging machinery. The program worked out on this assumption is a "feasible" one, i.e. it complies with all the prescribed constraints. On the other hand the total cost of this program is some 15 per cent higher than that of the optimal one, which requires far less building.

It is appreciated that the recommended decrease in building construction will cause certain difficulties. Modernization, the exchange of machinery, the reorganization and expansion of old plants, are generally troublesome jobs, and it is far more rewarding to establish a new mill which is modern from the outset. There was consequently a certain reluctance on the part of some technical executives to accept modernization.

The following considerations must, however, be borne in mind:

– We cannot carry the burden of the backwardness of the old plants with us as an eternal impediment. From time to time the old plants must be modernized and technically up-dated, while the surplus requirement *above* this may be satisfied with new machines installed in modern buildings.

– It is a familiar fact that the facilities of the building industry are now a bottleneck of the economy. It may consequently be necessary to reduce building even where it might otherwise be economical. This is obviously even more the case where the efficiency calculations of the sector itself do not indicate the desirability of building.

All these considerations led us to propose that the ratio of machine investments to building, be altered in favour of the machinery.

According to the calculations it is worth while to go a good deal further in the exchange of old machinery and automation, than was projected in the official plan. This applies particularly to dressing, where modernization proved eminently advantageous.

Let us first have a look at the dressing processes. The official plan prescribed the partial modernization of the dressing shops. The calculations led to a proposal for practically total modernization. This is shown in table 5.2.

TABLE 5.2

Dressing carried out by modern machinery in the cotton industry

	1960 Actual situation (in per cent)	1965 According to the official program (in per cent)	1965 According to the proposed program (in per cent)
Sizers	0	56.6	100.0
Warpers	0	52.8	100.0
Pirners	0	54.1	59.6
Cross winders	36.4	65.9	100.0

It was only in the case of pirning that it was not practicable to recommend full modernization, because the foreign exchange quota did not permit it. If the exchange quota were greater, the full modernization of pirning would also be included in the optimal program*.

With regard to the weaving mills, the calculations bore out above all the economic efficiency of accelerating the old looms. Every loom that can, by means of suitable alterations, be accelerated, must be speeded up.

The desirable proportions of machinery exchanges and automation are shown in table 5.3.

TABLE 5.3

Modernization of the stock of looms in the cotton industry

	1960 Actual situation	1965 According to the official program	1965 According to the proposed program
Percentage of output woven on mechanical looms	86.2	65.2	43.4
Percentage of output woven on automatic looms	13.8	34.8	56.6
Number of looms to be dismantled	–	795	4943

The decision problems included the question of what machinery types to acquire. The calculations permitted a definite stand to be taken on the following set of disputed questions:

– It is not worth while modernizing the old looms by importing "added automata".

– The installation of the most modern and most expensive shuttleless automatic looms is, in our conditions, at present not desirable.

– Of the weft pattern looms, the less productive but cheaper type should be acquired.

– Instead of modernizing the old sizers, it is better to acquire new ones.

– Of the warpers, the less productive but cheaper type should be acquired.

– For pirning, the more productive (and more expensive) type must be installed.

From what sources can the exchange of machinery and automation in excess of the official plans be financed, when it has been decided – and

* This was proved by a control calculation in which the restriction on the use of capitalist foreign exchange was waived.

incorporated in the constraints of the model – that the program's investment requirement may not be larger than the investment costs projected in the official plan?

The problem can be solved by regrouping the sources:

– The recommended program makes use of almost the whole gross investment quota. Within this, however (as table 5.1 shows), it achieves a considerable change in the ratio of machine investments and building to the former's advantage.

– The recommended program prescribes a considerable exchange of machinery. In most cases the machines to be exchanged will *no longer* have to be subjected to general repairs, while for the new machines these will *not yet* be necessary. Thus only a small part of the gross investment quota must be devoted to general repairs. According to the official program, 26.5 per cent of the total gross machinery investments would have had to be spent on general repairs, while the figure for the proposed program is only 9.4 per cent.

This too shows that it is good to prescribe a gross investment quota, since it permits rational transfers between the "renewal" and (net) "investment" funds.

– The calculations were based on the general requirement that output of the dressing shops should be in equilibrium with the requirements of the weaving mills. It is necessary beyond the satisfaction of this stipulation also to provide considerable capacity reserves in the sizing and warping shops, since each machine unit here supplies a large number of looms, so that any serious failure would upset the operation of many of them. For this reason the efficiency of the sizing and warping machines was in these calculations, from the very outset, determined so as to provide for a 16 per cent capacity reserve. Every sixth machine is always a reserve unit. Having stated this, let us examine table 5.4.

TABLE 5.4

Dressing shop capacity as a percentage of weaving mill requirements in the cotton industry

	1960 Actual situation	1965 According to the official program	1965 According to the proposed program
Sizers	99	130	100
Warpers	105	122	100
Pirners	97	132	100
Cross winders	99	115	100

It may be worth while to provide for some surplus *over* the 16 per cent safety reserve (the figure required for a 100 per cent equilibrium), which we recommended*. Moreover, part of the surplus capacity projected in the official plan may be justified by the "indivisibility" of these big machines. It is always necessary to install a whole machine, even where, say, three quarters of its capacity would do.

Yet even if all this is considered, the official plan is obviously "too safe". A decrease therefore appears justified. The elimination of this malproportion makes considerable investment funds available, which may in turn be devoted to exchanging machines and modernizing the stock of machinery.

All in all, the optimal program proposed as the outcome of the calculations results in savings of some 15 per cent compared to the official program, worked out by traditional methods.

The Technical Council of the Ministry for Light Industry discussed the concluding report of the research project. They stated that they agreed with the practical proposals put forward on the basis of the calculations, as the general course to be followed. They called upon the Industrial Development Division of the Ministry and the Cotton Industry Directorate to pay attention to the recommendations in drawing up their final plans and amending the official targets. This they duly did.

* An over-great capacity reserve cannot, however, be justified on the grounds of safe operation. It generally takes no more than a few days at the most to mend machines that have broken down or to carry out general repairs. This loss can therefore be met from material reserves.

CHAPTER 6

THE PROPORTIONS OF PRODUCTION, EXPORTS AND IMPORTS
THE MODEL OF THE MAN-MADE FIBRES INDUSTRY*

6.1. Decision Problems

The manufacture of man-made fibres is developing apace, throughout the world. Hungary, however, for a long time lagged behind in this respect and confined herself to the manufacture of viscose yarn. In recent years increasing force has been lent to efforts aimed at developing a man-made fibre base of our own. The first steps have actually been taken towards this end, but the brunt of the job still lies ahead.

Since we are here faced with the establishment of a new industry, the situation that has so far developed plays little part in determining the further steps to be taken; the scope of free choice is very wide. The decision problems with which the present investigation was concerned, were the following:

(1) Which fibres and which intermediaries (the materials used in man-made fibre manufacture) should be manufactured in Hungary, and which should be the products whose domestic requirement is to be permanently met by imports?

(2) How much shall we make of the products whose domestic manufacture is to be organized? Should they only meet home requirements or also be exported?

(3) Closely connected with the two first questions is the question whether we should make many kinds of product, basically for home requirements, or fewer kinds of product in relatively large quantities, exporting the surplus and importing the missing products? In other words, how far should our economic policies be "autarkic", or how far should we exploit the advantages to be gained from an international division of labour and from foreign trade?

* The model of the calculations was proposed in [83], and the results were presented in a final report [85]. The research project was carried out by a team commissioned by the Ministry of Heavy Industry and headed by the author. Its members were: mathematicians Th. Lipták and P. Wellisch, economists J. Földeák, M. Tardos, B. Tarlós and T. Vidos, chemical engineers L. Futó, G. Kováts and F. Verden. Calculations on the electronic computer were directed by T. Frey.

(4) What should become of the man-made fibre industry that has so far been developed? Should it continue to be operated in its present form, be technically developed, expanded, or dismantled?

(5) In organizing the manufacture of new products, which of the several available technological variants should be adopted for our technology? This is in most cases tantamount to asking: from which firm shall we purchase the equipment of the new factory?

It will be seen that the scope of problems (4) and (5) is akin to those treated in the model for the cotton industry. They are concerned with a choice between technologies, and decisions over existing facilities. The sphere of investigations has, however, now been considerably expanded, by the determination of the basic ratios of output and foreign trade. The program plans the economic structure of the production and the foreign trade of man-made fibres.

The point of departure in the case of the cotton industry was that the cotton output level to be attained was given. Both the domestic requirement and the export target were plan directives – in the model only the sum of the two appeared, as the output target. Now, in the case of the man-made fibres industry, the domestic requirement is again taken to be a plan directive. The output plan, however, cannot be regarded as given, for the very aim here is to determine the extent to which the domestic requirement should be met from production or from imports, and what to produce for export, beyond the domestic requirement.

The model for the cotton industry was used to draw up a five-year plan, while here the task was to work out a fifteen-year plan, for the period of 1961–1975. In actual fact, however, all those investment activities that had partly already taken place, or were in part to take place later in the 1961–1965 period, were considered as given. The task was interpreted only as determining what should be done in the ten-year period of 1966–1975. And here again, as with the cotton industry's model, the object was merely to examine what conditions should come about by 1975, what activities were necessary between 1966 and 1975 to bring about these conditions, while no attempt was made to examine the time distribution or phasing of these activities.

No investigation was made, moreover, of the location and territorial distribution of the new production facilities to be erected.

It is worth noting at this juncture that answers to essentially the same decision problems are also given in the programming project for the bauxite and aluminium industry, which is also concerned with the ratios of exports and imports to be attained in the period of 1966–1975, and with technological choice problems. Due to the peculiarities of the industry, some additional, special problems are also analyzed in the light of this model, e.g. the desirable qualitative indices of domestic bauxite extraction, the desirability of common investments and permanent cooperation with other countries, etc. Since, however, the main features of the bauxite-aluminium model are similar to those of the model for the artificial fibres industry, no comprehensive account of it will be given*.

6.2. The Scope of Programming

The scope of the project evidently includes man-made fibres – both viscose fibres, and also the synthetic ones**. It was a problem, however, to decide which of the intermediary substances necessary for the manufacture of fibres should be included in the scope of programming, how far to go back from the fibre towards the initial materials of oil, natural gas and coal. Due to the computing limitations imposed on the dimensions of the model, the programming scope cannot be extended too far, for this could only be done to the detriment of the model's "depth", i.e. of the details of the available choices.

The following demarcation criteria were laid down with respect to the intermediary substances:

(1) The programming scope should include those intermediaries whose main consumer is the man-made fibre industry (e.g. caprolactame, whose main consumers are the polyamide fibre plants). It should not, on the other hand, include intermediaries which may also be used for man-made fibre manufacture, but where this is not their primary sphere of utilization (e.g. in the case of benzol, or sulphuric acid).

(2) Only those intermediaries should be left out of the programming scope which may be imported without limitations, i.e. where neither technical nor natural factors render their import impossible.

Apart from the man-made fibres and certain intermediaries, the scope of programming was also made to include the manufacture of cellophane. Cellophane production takes place parallel with the manufacture of viscose yarn, in the same plant; the semi-finished product between

* For a more detailed account of the model for the bauxite and aluminium industry, see B. MARTOS *et al.* [119].

** The expression "man-made fibre" is used as a collective term, to include both the viscose and synthetic fibres.

cellulose and the finished product may be used equally to make either cellophane or viscose yarn. This close manufacturing link justifies the inclusion of cellophane production in the programming scope.

The determination of the scope of products to be investigated is (particularly in the case of the intermediaries) somewhat arbitrary. Many arguments can be advanced in favour of omitting some and including others. This arbitrariness is to some extent unavoidable. The chemical industry is one which is very closely interlinked. Once it is decided to consider not the whole of the chemical industry but only a part, this will unavoidably be *out of context* with respect to the whole. This limits the effectiveness of the computations, but could not be a reason for not carrying them out. The difficulties of demarcation are in any case palliated by two considerations:

One is that though in the computing process it is only with respect to the above products that we ask whether to make or import, or whether to make only for home use or also for exports, on the other hand the operation *costs* comprise all the preceding chemical or non-chemical processes. The following is a list of the main products which were separately considered among the costs of the productive activities of our model:

Acetone
Aluminium chloride
Ammonia gas
Benzol
Dimethyl formamide
Hexanetriol
Caustic soda
Methanol
Oleum
Paraxylol
Nitric acid
Sulphitcellulose
Ammonium sulphate
Gasoline straight-run
Sulphur
Sulphuric acid
Adipic acid
Ethylene
Hydrogen
Propylene
Coal
Electric power
Vinyl chloride
Cooling water
Demineralized water.

The other consideration is that the course of the calculations so far, does not conclude the investigation. It may be assumed that the calculations will be continued at a future date, and the opportunity will then arise to "reach back" and include further intermediary materials in the programming scope.

The programming scope was, in consequence of the decision problems already outlined, made to include the export and import of the products belonging to it, as well as their output.

It may once more be stated, as in the case of the cotton model, that the programming scope does not coincide with the organizational units of the administration. At the time of the investigation, the production treated in the model belonged to not one, but three Divisions of the Ministry of Heavy Industry. Furthermore, in the administration the direction of productive activities and of foreign trade are sharply divorced – in the present case the former belong to the Ministry of Heavy Industry, the latter to the Ministry of Foreign Trade. The unity of the problem, however, makes it necessary to circumscribe the programming scope in the above manner, irrespective of administrative categories.

6.3. The Activities

The activities of the model are classified according to three criteria, and three suffices are accordingly used to distinguish the activities.

The first characteristic of the activities is the *product* with which they are concerned. The following products are treated:

(1) Polyamide yarn* (Nylon 6)
(2) Polyester staple (Terylene)
(3) Polyacrylonitrile staple (Orlon)
(4) Polyacrylonitrile-vinylchloride copolymer staple
(5) Polypropylene yarn
(6) Polypropylene staple
(7) Rayon yarn
(8) Rayon staple
(9) Cellophane
(10) Caprolactame
(11) Phenol
(12) Ethylene glycol
(13) Dimethyl terephthalate
(14) Acrylonitrile
(15) Polypropylene.

The product is indicated by the first suffix ($j = 1, \ldots, 15$).

* Polyamide staple is not included in this model because the development of its manufacture is to take place in the period up to 1965, and its further expansion is not planned. The official attitude on this point was treated as a plan directive, and it was not intended to review its correctness with the help of this model.

Three kinds of activity are distinguished with respect to each product:

1. Production
2. Import
3. Export.

These are indicated by the second suffix ($k = 1, 2, 3$). Several technological variants were considered for some of the products. The technological variant is indicated by the third suffix ($l = 1, \ldots, n_j$). In the case of export and import activities no technological variants are involved and, accordingly, no third suffices are used.

The activity level is symbolized by x_{j1l} ($l = 1, \ldots, n_j$; $j = 1, \ldots, 15$) or by x_{jk} ($j = 1, \ldots, 15$; $k = 2, 3$). Its units are tons/year. In the case of the production variables it is 1 capacity unit, which is able to produce 1 ton of product under normal operation in 1975. In the case of the foreign trade variables, it is the import or export of 1 ton of product in 1975. The variables representing economic activities and the slack variables together form the program $\mathbf{x}$.

6.4. The Constraints

The first group of constraints is that of the balances of the man-made fibres and cellophane, i.e. of the end products.

Final Product Balances

$$\sum_{l=1}^{n_j} x_{j1l} + x_{j2} - x_{j3} = v_j\,, \qquad j = 1, \ldots, 9\,, \tag{6.1}$$

where

$v_j =$ the domestic requirement of the jth final product in tons, in 1975. This was adopted as a plan directive from the official long-term plans worked out by the traditional methods.

The next group of constraints is that of the balances of intermediary products.

Balances of Intermediaries

$$\sum_{l=1}^{n_j} x_{j1l} + x_{j2} - x_{j3} = \sum_{\substack{i=1\\ i\neq j}}^{15} \sum_{l=1}^{n_i} g_{i1l}^{(j)}\, x_{i1l} + v_j\,, \qquad j = 10, \ldots, 15\,, \tag{6.2}$$

where

$g_{i1l}^{(j)}$ = the intermediary's input coefficient. This is the quantity in tons of the jth material necessary to produce unit quantity of the ith product, manufactured by the lth technology. This is, of course, only positive in the technologically justified cases – otherwise it is zero

v_j = the external requirement – from outside the programming scope – for the jth intermediary, in tons (e.g. caprolactame is also used for the production of polyamide yarn, as well as for plastics). This is a plan directive. In the case of some intermediaries (e.g. acrylonitrile or dimethyl terephthalate), there is no external requirement ($v_j = 0$).

All the product balances – both those of the end products and also of the intermediaries – have been stated in the form of equalities. No stockpiling has been planned in these balances.

The growth of output is bounded from above by various factors. First, it was assumed that exports could not be unbounded.

Export Bounds

$$x_{j3} \leqq F_j\,, \qquad j = 1, \ldots, 15\,, \tag{6.3}$$

where

F_j = the upper limit of the exportable quantity. This was estimated after consultation with foreign trade experts.

The domestic production of some substances is bounded by raw material limitations. For instance the propylene necessary for its manufacture will only be available in limited quantities during the plan period.

Polypropylene Quota

$$\sum_{l=1}^{n_{15}} x_{15,1l} \leqq z^{\text{prop}}, \tag{6.4}$$

where

z^{prop} = the polypropylene material quota. This was adopted as a plan directive from the long-term plan worked out by traditional methods.

The investment resources are also limited.

Investment Quota

$$\sum_{j=1}^{15} \sum_{l=1}^{n_j} h_{j1l}^{\text{inv}} x_{j1l} \leqq w^{\text{inv}} . \tag{6.5}$$

Capitalist Foreign Exchange Quota

$$\sum_{j=1}^{15} \sum_{l=1}^{n_j} h_{j1l}^{\text{exch}} x_{j1l} \leqq w^{\text{exch}}, \tag{6.6}$$

where

h_{j1l}^{inv}, h_{j1l}^{exch} = the resource input coefficients. These are the investment requirement in Ft and the capitalist foreign exchange requirement in $ respectively, of unit capacity for the manufacture of the domestically produced jth product by the lth technology

w^{inv}, w^{exch} = the investment quota and capitalist foreign exchange quota respectively, for the period 1966–1975. They were adopted as plan directives from the official long-term plan proposal worked out by the traditional methods. The investment quota and capitalist foreign exchange quota of the present model are taken as being equal to the total of what the original plan proposal had earmarked for the investments of the programming scope.

Finally the last group of constraints is concerned with the existing viscose plant facilities. E.g. both the new capacities for making viscose final products (except for the viscose fibre produced by the new technology), and the old end-product making facilities use the equipment of the existing viscose factory for making the semi-manufactured product, which is modern so that its dismantlement would certainly not be desirable. This capacity for semi-manufactured product output is, however, limited.

Semi-manufactured Viscose Product Capacity

$$\sum_{j=7}^{9} \sum_{l=\text{old}} \alpha_{j1l} x_{j1l} \leqq H , \tag{6.7}$$

where

α_{j1l} = the semi-manufactured product's input coefficient. Its unit is expressed in tons of processed cellulose per ton of end-product. The denotation "old" below the summation symbol indicates that summation is carried out here only with respect to the variables which utilize the old semi-manufactured viscose product capacity

H = the existing semi-manufactured product capacity. This is a factual figure.

To limit the production carried out by means of the old capacities, other similar constraints have also been prescribed.

The main groups of constraints are thus the following:

(i) External output obligations
(ii) Internal proportions
(iii) Bounds of investments and operations inputs
(iv) Export bounds
(v) Bounds relating to old capacities.

Once more, we have obtained a linear constraint system.

6.5. The Objective Function

In this investigation too, several kinds of objective function were used for computing. For the time being, the type of objective function using the official computational evaluations (or close to them), will be treated:

$$C(\mathbf{x}) = \sum_{j=1}^{15} \sum_{l=1}^{n_j} [\gamma P_{j1l}(x_{j1l}) + R_{j1l}(x_{j1l})] + \\ + \sum_{j=1}^{15} \sum_{k=2}^{3} s_{jk} x_{jk} \longrightarrow \min! \tag{6.8}$$

where

C = the total cost of the programming scope
γ = the rental on capital
$P_{j1l}(x_{j1l})$ = the investment cost of the $j1l$th production variable, at a level of x_{j1l}
$R_{j1l}(x_{j1l})$ = the operating cost of the $j1l$th production variable, at a level of x_{j1l}

s_{jk} = the import purchase price of the jth product ($k = 2$), or its export sales price ($k = 3$). The latter is negative, for export returns decrease the total costs of the programming scope.

The cost function of the foreign exchange variable is linear, those of the production variables are non-linear. The latter question of non-linear cost functions will be treated in a later chapter.

6.6. The Practical Results of Programming in the Man-made Fibres Industry

The programming project for the man-made fibres industry yielded results of practical use and contributed to the sound elaboration of the sector's long-term plan.

During the past years it was a debated issue, whether it was at all worth while to develop this industry in Hungary. The programming showed that its development was desirable. Coverage of part of the demand by domestic production, the export of part of the domestic output supplemented by the import of other products, are far more advantageous than to depend exclusively on import. It is worth while to devote the whole of the investment sum earmarked for this sphere in the official plans, to developing the man-made fibres industry.

Previous to these calculations there was contention over which products should be singled out for manufacture, and what technology should be used to make them. It is not possible here to go into the concrete results of the programming in this respect, but in fact we were able to adopt a definite stand on the basis of our calculations. It turned out for instance, that in further development projects it should be the synthetic and not the viscose fibres that should be given priority, that it was worth while to develop the domestic production of polyester and polypropylene fibres, etc*.

The value of the objective function for the program regarded as most favourable in the course of computing, was about 12 per cent lower than for the official plan. The program we have recommended for Hun-

* Not only the model described in this chapter was used to formulate this opinion, but also other computations, e.g. a stochastic model. The description of the methods used there will follow in later chapters of the book.

garian man-made fibre manufacture and foreign trade, can save the Hungarian economy several hundred million Ft annually*.

The Ministry for Heavy Industry, which had commissioned the research project, submitted our report to its scientific advisory bodies and after discussion with the experts adopted our recommendations as the general line for the development of the man-made fibres industry.

* It has been calculated that even if only one tenth of the possible savings revealed by programming becomes effective, the entire cost of computing is recovered *in a single day*.

CHAPTER 7

COSTS AS A FUNCTION OF THE ACTIVITY LEVEL

7.1. The Subject and Arrangement of the Treatment

In the course of the first account of the models for sectors of industry presented in chs. 5 and 6 no closer investigation was made of the way in which costs vary as a function of the levels of the activities concerned. Only a brief reference was made to whether the variation of costs should be treated as a linear or a non-linear function, but no reasons were given. The subject of the present chapter is a somewhat more detailed treatment of cost functions. It is proposed to show the considerations that prompted the adoption of one or other type of cost function, and the simplifying assumptions involved in these types. This will make it necessary to survey and classify the various types of cost functions from at least a few different points of view. The present chapter, however, *does not claim to be complete* in this respect. Its treatment will be confined to as much as is necessary to elucidate the "background" to our models*.

The arrangement of the material is as follows:

Section 7.2 presents the common simplifying assumptions of all our models.

Section 7.3 classifies the cost functions used as objective functions in programming models, from a mathematical and computational point of view. The aim of the classification is to show how far the various types of objective function are "manageable" in the course of the solution of large-scale programming problems on electronic computers. It is not intended in the course of this discussion to present the details of the various computing procedures. The classification is meant only to provide general information for economist readers on which type of programming problem is easier to solve and which more difficult with the methods at present available.

Section 7.4 is a classification according to a different point of view. It considers the different activity groups, (e.g. production with the given

* On the classification of cost functions see further e.g. J. Dean [31], pp. 247–348, moreover with respect to linear and non-linear programming models, chs. 5 and 6 of the book of W. J. Baumol [9].

facilities, expansion of production, etc.) in turn according to their economic content, setting out the typical cost variations of the various activities.

Section 7.5 describes how the economies of scale were considered in the investigation of the man-made fibres industry.

Finally section 7.6 is about the numerical determination of the parameters used to calculate the economies of scale.

7.2. Common Simplifying Assumptions

The models described in chs. 5 and 6 (and also those later to be treated in Part 5, on the programming of the national economy) differ from each other in many respects in their approach to costs. They all agree fully, however, in applying four simplifying assumptions. These are the following:

(1) Our models treat the activity levels as *continuous* variables.

There are so-called *discrete programming* methods, which make it possible to handle non-continuous variables in programming models. These procedures, however, are far more awkward than the continuous ones from the computing point of view. As far as I am informed, no discrete programming model has so far been used in any *major* practical project abroad. Nor could we envisage their employment in Hungary, primarily because of our limited possibilities as regards computing techniques*. Therefore, we are (and will most probably be for some years to come) compelled to content ourselves with continuous variables. In other words, it could be assumed that the levels of the activities were perfectly divisible. Let us see how far this assumption requires a departure from the actual situation.

In the cases of output and foreign trade activities complete divisibility can only be assumed if the product involved in the activity (i.e. produced, exported or imported) is itself fully divisible. In the present instance yarn, fabric, man-made fibre and the chemicals used in the manufacture of man-made fibre, may all be said to be such products.

* This is the more regrettable as the use of models with discrete or with "mixed" (partly continuous, partly discrete) variables would enable the building in of various "logical constraints" into the model. For example, it would be possible to prescribe that activity *A* could be carried out only if activity *B* were already figuring in the program. Or: activity *C* would exclude the inclusion of activity *D* into the program; and so on. For further particulars see e.g. G.B. DANTZIG [27].

The level of investment activities could be regarded as perfectly divisible if the new capacities established as the result of these activities were themselves divisible at will. This is, of course, never the case. In practice, however, the establishment of, say, a new weaving or spinning mill may always be regarded as approximately divisible, since a single loom or spinning-machine is a relatively small and inexpensive unit, while the program is concerned with decisions on setting up several thousand units. It is true that it is impossible to install 1/3 or 7/10 of a machine. On the other hand if the optimal program happened, for instance, to prescribe the acquisition of precisely 4227.7 machines, the rounding-up of the results to 4228, or indeed to 4230, will obviously cause no difficulty.

The situation is not quite so simple in the man-made fibres industry, where very large and costly units of machinery are involved in certain processes and technological phases. If the program here says that 3.5 units are to be set up, then the ultimate results may be substantially altered according to whether the decision is in favour of three or four units. This, however, is not generally characteristic of the whole man-made fibres industry, so that according to the experts of the chemical industry the simplifying assumption of divisibility again does not lead to grave distortions. On the other hand, if we had carried out our calculations for electric power generation or the iron and steel industry, our difficulties would probably have been much greater*.

(2) Another question that is associated with the previous one, is the extent to which the variation of costs is continuous and smooth as a function of the level of activity – whether there are breaks or sudden leaps. The cost functions used in the present models are all continuous and smooth (i.e. they may be twice continuously differentiated).

(3) In our models the total cost of the program is the sum of the costs of the individual activities:

$$C(x_1, x_2, \ldots, x_n) = \sum_{i=1}^{n} C_i(x_i) . \tag{7.1}$$

* It may sound paradoxical, but here the traditional planning methods, working without exact tools, have the advantage over us that they are not bound by rigid algorithms and by the limits of the computer's storing capacity. The planner using the traditional methods will naturally plan for one foundry or two foundries, but never for one and a half. We, on our part, have to resort to cumbersome, and for the present impracticable, algorithms in order to enforce this simple principle.

There are numerous economic problems where the application of this assumption would not be justified*. In the case, however, of the sector (and later national) long-term planning problems described in this book, it is a reasonably close approximation to the actual situation to regard the total cost of the programming scope as being additive, i.e. to assume that it arises through simple summation of the *separate* costs for the various concrete economic activities, such as production, investment, exports and imports.

(4) In our models the *system of constraints* is in every case linear, as opposed to the objective function, which is in some models non-linear.

This assumption is in the case of some relations self-evident. The constraint in the model for the cotton industry bounding the distribution of the old machine stock (see (5.12)–(5.13)) is a case in point. Obviously, for instance, the requirement that the sum of the stock of sizers to be continuously operated, modernized and dismantled, should be equal to the total number of old sizers, may be adequately expressed in a linear equation, neglecting, of course, the previously mentioned simplification arising from the indivisibility of the machines.

The application of linearity is more questionable in the case of those constraints which are related to expenditures and output that change as functions of the levels of activities, e.g. the constraints bounding investment resources. In these cases linearity sometimes involves a lesser, but in some instances a fairly considerable simplification with respect to actual conditions. To avoid repetition this problem will not be discussed in detail at the present juncture, since it is from the economic point of view fully analogous with the problem of the costs and output considered in the objective function, to be treated later. All that need be said now is that the assumption of linearity was maintained even where this involves considerable simplification. It is true that programming procedures are also available for cases where the constraint system is wholly or

* Let us, for instance, consider the short-term production program of a factory. Let the components of the program be x_i $(i = 1, \ldots, n)$ – these are the output volumes of the various articles. The overall costs C of the factory are composed of two parts. One part, $\Sigma_i K_i$, depends on the magnitude of the different variables, the other part G on the other hand, depends only on the total volume of the factory's output.

$$C(x_1, x_2, \ldots, x_n) = \sum_{i=1}^{n} K_i(x_i) + G\left(\sum_{i=1}^{n} x_i\right). \tag{7.2}$$

On this type of cost function see references [78] and [79].

partially non-linear*. These, however, are difficult to handle from the computing point of view, especially in the case of large constraint systems. They were therefore not used in the present investigations. In these more problematic cases the cruder simplification involved in assuming the constraints to be linear, was as far as possible compensated by a more accurate consideration of the variation of costs.

7.3. The Classification of Cost Functions from the Mathematical and Computational Point of View

In this section (having in point (4) above already touched on the problem of the constraints), we shall concern ourselves only with the cost functions used as objective functions. Since, according to assumption (3) above, the total cost of the programming sphere is the sum of the costs of the individual activities, it will suffice to treat the cost function types of one activity in each case.

The classification from a mathematical and computing point of view is summarized in table 7.1. The following observations will be made in the sequence of the table's numbering.

1. Linear cost functions. In some of our models all activities, in others certain groups of activities have been described by means of linear cost functions. In many instances these exactly, or at least closely correspond to the facts. For example the cost of importing products purchased from the socialist countries is indeed strictly proportionate to the volume imported, since prices are fixed and there are no discounts for larger consignments.

In other cases on the other hand, the assumption of linearity involves a far more inexact reflection of the facts. The economist setting up the model must then consider two, mutually contradictory requirements. On the one hand the operations with linear models are very much simpler from the mathematical and computing points of view, than with the non-linear ones (particularly, as we shall see, with certain types of non-linear models). On the other, the unjustified use of linearity may distort the outcome of the calculations. Individual decisions have to be made in each case to determine which consideration is to prevail.

2. Convex cost functions. In this case the function of the marginal costs is an increasing one.

* See for instance the work of S. Karlin [63].

TABLE 7.1

Classification of cost function types

Nature of function	1	2		3		
Cost function	Linear	Convex		Concave		
Marginal cost function	Constant	Increasing		Decreasing		
Analogous return function	Linear	Concave		Convex		
Analogous marginal return function	Constant	Decreasing		Increasing		
Computing method	Simplex method, or similar iterative procedure yielding an exact solution	2.1	2.2	3.1	3.2	3.3
		Exact solution of the original non-linear programming problem	"Lineariza-tion" of the original non-linear prob-lem	Exact solution of the problem by determining all extreme points	Approximate solu-tion by "trial and error" methods	Transformation of the task into a discrete programming problem

The case is shown in figure 7.1. Here and also in figure 7.3, $C(x)$ denotes the cost function and $C'(x)$ the marginal cost function.

This type of cost function is in the Hungarian literature (in conformity

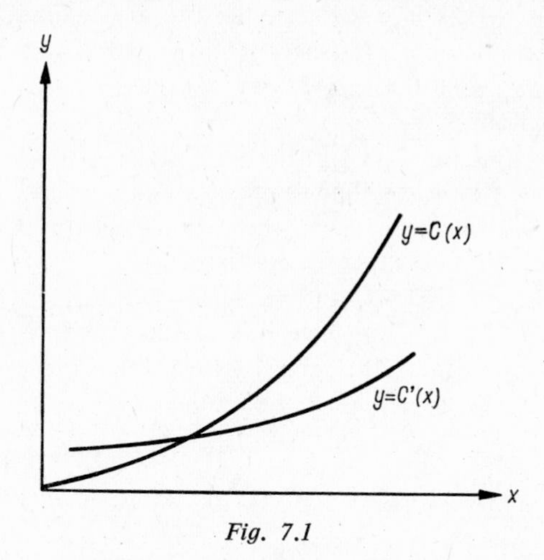

Fig. 7.1

mainly with the German literature on industrial economics) called cost progression. This type is both from the mathematical and economic points of view analogous with the case of the concave return function or decreasing marginal return function (diminishing profits)*.

The class of problems where the constraint system is linear and the objective function to be minimized is convex (or the objective function to be maximized concave), may be conveniently handled for computing purposes. There are two main ways of solving such problems.

2.1. The convex minimization problem itself is solved. There are several algorithms available for this purpose, including some that may be fairly easily handled from the computing point of view**.

* Too little would be said if we were to talk only of "convex" or "concave programming problems". It is of fundamental importance to distinguish whether the problem is one of convex *minimization* (this is type 2) or convex *maximization* (type 3). The two problems are each other's opposites both from the economic and also the mathematical and computing points of view. For precisely this reason care is always taken in this book to stress whether the problem is one of concave or convex *minimization* or *maximization*.

** See for example H. W. KUHN and A. W. TUCKER [92]; K. J. ARROW *et al.* [5], moreover the book of M. P. KÜNZI and W. KRELLE [94] for a summary survey.

2.2. The problem may be "linearized" by the device of prescribing a linear programming problem whose exact solution may be accepted as an approximation of the original non-linear problem*. The mode of transformation makes it possible to let the approximation be as close as desired. Since, however, this involves a growth in the number of variables, the manageable dimensions for computing of the derived linear problem set a limit.

(a) The cost function $C_j(x_j)$ of the jth activity is approached by linear functions for a number of line-segments. One method is to mark out a set number m_j of abscissae on the x_j axis, where $0 < X_j^{(1)} < X_j^{(2)} < \ldots < X_j^{(m_j)}$ and to substitute the corresponding linear functions for each of the chords joining $(0, X_j^{(1)}), (X_j^{(1)}, X_j^{(2)}), \ldots, (X_j^{(m_j-1)}, X_j^{(m_j)})$ for the function $C_j(x_j)$ (figure 7.2). The last scaling point is placed so that there should be no practical possibility for the level to extend beyond it. The formula of the approximate function is:

$$\tilde{C}_j(x_j) = \begin{cases} c_j^{(1)} x_j, & \text{if} \quad 0 \leqq x_j \leqq X_j^{(1)} \\ c_j^{(2)} (x_j - X_j^{(1)}) + c_j^{(1)} X_j^{(1)}, & \text{if} \quad X_j^{(1)} \leqq x_j \leqq X_j^{(2)} \\ \cdots\cdots\cdots\cdots\cdots\cdots & \\ c_j^{(m_j)} (x_j - X_j^{(m_j-1)}) + c_j^{(1)} X_j^{(1)} + & \\ + c_j^{(2)}(X_j^{(2)} - X_j^{(1)}) + \ldots + c_j^{(m_j-1)} (X_j^{(m_j-1)} - X_j^{(m_j-2)}), & \\ \quad \text{if} \quad X_j^{(m_j-1)} \leqq x_j \leqq X_j^{(m_j)}, & \end{cases} \tag{7.3}$$

where the slope of the linear line segments is

$$c_j^{(1)} = \frac{C_j(X_j^{(1)})}{X_j^{(1)}}, \qquad c_j^{(2)} = \frac{C_j(X_j^{(2)}) - C_j(X_j^{(1)})}{X_j^{(2)} - X_j^{(1)}}, \ldots,$$

$$c_j^{(m_j)} = \frac{C_j(X_j^{(m_j)}) - C_j(X_j^{(m_j-1)})}{X_j^{(m_j)} - X_j^{(m_j-1)}}.$$

It is obvious then, that $\tilde{C}_j(x_j) \geqq C_j(x_j)$, moreover that by marking out more points $\tilde{C}_j(x_j) - C_j(x_j)$ can be made as small as is desired.

(b) In place of the activity variable x_j, a number m_j of non-negative variables $x_j^{(1)}, x_j^{(2)}, \ldots, x_j^{(m_j)}$ is postulated, and x_j in the original linear system of inequalities is replaced by $(x_j^{(1)} + x_j^{(2)} + \ldots + x_j^{(m_j)})$, moreover the supplementary linear constraints

$$x_j^{(1)} \leqq X_j^{(1)}, \; x_j^{(2)} \leqq X_j^{(2)} - X_j^{(1)}, \ldots, \; x_j^{(m_j)} \leqq X_j^{(m_j)} - X_j^{(m_j-1)} \tag{7.4}$$

* See A. Charnes and C. E. Lemke [18]. A description of the procedure may be found e.g. in the book of A. Vázsonyi [173].

are introduced. In the augmented system of linear inequalities thus obtained, let the objective function coefficient $c_j^{(k)}$ correspond to the variable $x_j^{(k)}$, and solve the linear programming problem with the aim

$$\sum_{j=1}^{n}\sum_{k=1}^{m_j} c_j^{(k)} x_j^{(k)} \rightarrow \min! \tag{7.5}$$

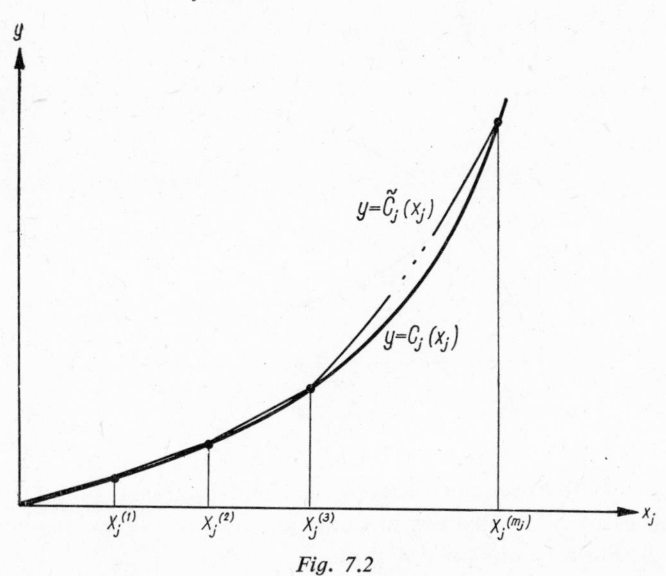

Fig. 7.2

Since the objective function of the programming problem prescribes the minimization of costs, the optimal program will be certain always first to exhaust the cheaper possibility, and only to avail itself of a more expensive one if the cheaper ones are no longer sufficient to fulfil the constraint conditions. Making use of this feature of the objective function we obtain automatic compliance with the requirement that in the optimal program $x_j^{(2)}$ can only be positive once $x_j^{(1)} = X_j^{(1)}$. Similarly $x_j^{(3)}$ may only have a positive value in the program if $x_j^{(1)} + x_j^{(2)} = X_j^{(2)}$, etc.

In our calculations so far, we have preferred method 2.2, the linearization of the convex cost function, to method 2.1, the direct solution of the convex minimization problem. In future, however, it may come to the application of method 2.1 – from the point of view of computing techniques this is entirely possible*.

* Although literature has an ample number of "elegant" solutions to offer to problem 2.1, these will hardly be attractive to the economist because – at least

3. Concave cost functions. In this case the marginal cost function is a decreasing one. The curve is shown in figure 7.3.

This type of cost variation, also called cost degression, is

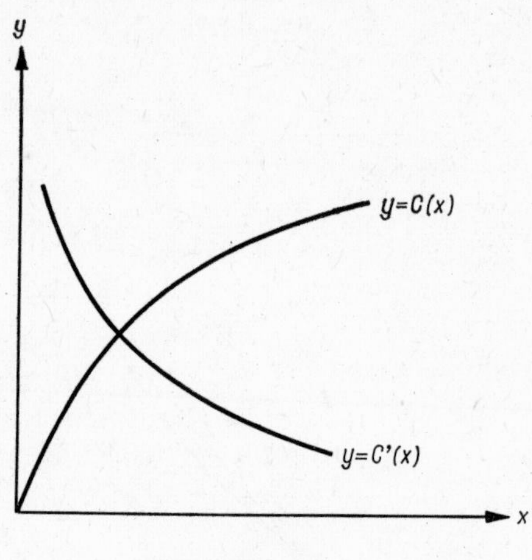

Fig. 7.3

analogous both from the mathematical and economic points of view with the case of the convex return function, i.e. of an increasing marginal return function (profit progression).

In contrast to the "good" type 2 non-linear cost function discussed above, this type is "bad" for mathematical and computing purposes. The class of programming problems where the objective function is of type 3 (a concave function to be minimized or a convex function to be maximized) can *not* be solved by a relatively simply applicable algorithm such as the simplex method, leading to an exact optimum in a finite number of steps.

The following solutions are available:

3.1. In theory it is possible to determine the extremal points of the set of feasible programs and to calculate that extremum for which the value of the objective function is smallest. This program is then the solution

---

as far as long-term planning is concerned – it is cost degression rather than cost progression that constitutes a really "exciting" problem. Alas, literature will not offer the same easily manageable algorithms for the former as it has for the latter.

of the problem. An algorithm worked out by H. Uzawa ([5] pp. 23–31 and 179–188) may be used with some modifications, to determine the extremal points. It is also possible to use the *successive method* worked out by Th. Lipták ([83], Mathematical Appendix) in the first phase of the man-made fibres investigation.

These methods could not be applied in practice in the course of our work, since the storage requirements of both would have exceeded the store capacity of the computers available in Hungary.

3.2. We shall be content to achieve an *approximate* solution of the concave minimizing programming problem. In this case one would tend at first sight to say that a similar solution is available for concave cost functions as for the convex cost functions above. The continuous function would then be approached by linear line-segments introducing independent activities for each line-segment, bounding their levels by suitable constraints, and thus reducing the problem to a linear programming problem.

Unfortunately things are not all that simple, for our objective function impels us to minimize costs. Thus, if the scheme outlined above were followed in programming, an absurd situation might arise where the optimal program would, for instance, include the construction of the part of a new plant producing over 5000 tons – this being the cheapest part – while the construction of the more expensive part producing under 5000 tons would not be planned in the program*, whereas the relative savings over the 5000 ton capacity mark arise precisely because the establishment of the first 5000 ton facility has already involved costs which do not grow at all, or else only to a disproportionately small extent, if the capacity is further increased. In other words, it is not possible in this case to set up partial variables that may be handled as mutually independent activities, and thus the problem cannot be reduced to the solution of a linear programming problem.

In programming the man-made fibres industry we had to make do with an approximate method which, though not sufficiently reassuring from the mathematical point of view, according to the checks carried out nevertheless led to acceptable results in the given concrete instance*. The results thus obtained for programming the man-made fibres industry

* In the reverse case, that of the convex cost function, it has been seen that no such danger arises. The objective of minimizing costs impels the program first to utilize the first and cheapest phase, and only once this has been exhausted, to proceed to the second and subsequent ones.

** The approximation method is described in Appendix A.

have only been treated as a first, tentative stage and it is intended to undertake further research in this respect.

The present survey does, of course, not pretend to completeness. It is, e.g., possible to conceive of a programming problem where the objective function is neither convex nor concave. This will be the case when the cost function of some economic activities is convex and that of others concave.

3.3. The literature describes schemes in which the solution of non-linear programming problems with *continuous* variables is approached by transformation into a discrete programming problem. Due to the computing difficulties of discrete programming mentioned above, we have so far made no attempt at applying this expedient.

In the ensuing sections we shall see how important this third type of cost variation – the case of diminishing marginal costs or economies of scale – is, from the economic point of view. It is one of the great shortcomings to date of mathematical programming research, that no algorithm has yet been worked out for a solution (or a reliable, good approximate solution) of the problem by a method that is easy to handle for computing purposes. This fault is, of course, not fortuitous but due to the basic difficulties arising from the mathematical nature of the problem. It must, however, be stressed that this is one of those urgent problems in which the economists now engaged in applying mathematical models expect help from the research mathematicians.

7.4. The Characteristic Development of Costs for Various Types of Activity

Section 7.3 presented a brief survey of the various problem types from the point of view of the model's mathematical nature, and thus its amenability to computing. Now the question will be approached from the angle of its economic content. Let us consider the various types of activity in turn, and see how the costs vary as functions of the activity level. The classification will also be accompanied by brief references to the way in which these costs were actually treated in the sector models of chs. 5 and 6.

1. Production activities in the case of production on a given stock of fixed capital. (E.g. the output of fabric on the machines of the old stock of looms; the output of viscose yarn on the existing manufacturing facilities, etc.) In this case the type of cost function is similar to that of short-term costs, even if we are concerned with long-term planning. (Of course only from the point of view of dependence on the level of the activity, and not as regards the concrete composition of the costs.)

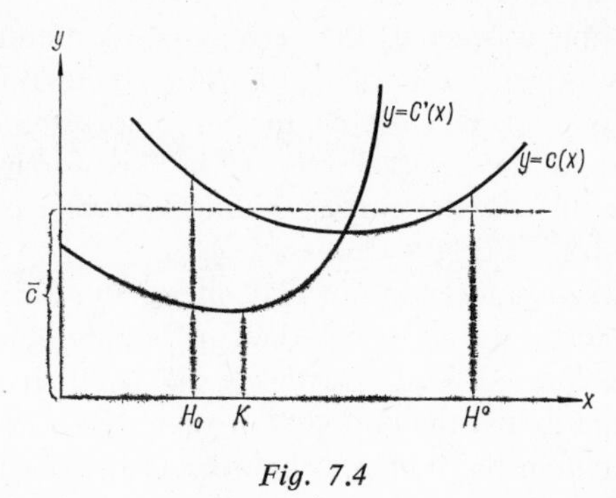

Fig. 7.4

This similarity is evident, since this too is a case of production on a given set of facilities, a given stock of fixed capital, while net investment costs or capacity expansion costs in the narrower sense do not arise.

The typical case is the U-shaped marginal and average cost function which is familiar from economic theory (see figure 7.4). In the figure $c(x)$ is the function of the unit cost and $C'(x)$ that of the marginal cost.

A rise in the level of the activity does not involve the increase of all costs; there are some relatively constant, or at least more gradually increasing costs, e.g. the salaries of the leading personnel, the costs of service shops, laboratories, etc. This is the reason for the diminishing average costs at the beginning of the curve. Above a certain limit, however, output can only be augmented through progressive costs, e.g. the employment of a night shift with payment of night rates and lighting costs, overtime work, the use of especially high quality material to boost productivity, etc.

In Hungary relatively few numerical investigations have been carried out to determine short-term cost functions*. At any rate the Hungarian investigations to date have confirmed the validity of using U-shaped short-term average cost function. It has, however, also been shown that in the middle semi-circle of the U, i.e. in the region most important

* The first investigation was conducted in the textile industry by Th. Lipták and the author (see [78] and, in English, [79]).

More recently A. Máriás has been doing similar work in the engineering industry [120], and A. Deák in cellulose manufacture [32].

for practical purposes, the average cost undergoes relatively little change. This corresponds roughly to the interval $[H_0, H^0]$ of figure 7.4.

Two practical expedients were adopted in our programming models.

1.1. An upper limit was set to the activity at the point where the cost progression grew sharper (H^0 of figure 7.4). Up to this point a linear cost function was applied. Cost coefficient $\bar{c}$ corresponded roughly to the average cost of the interval $[H_0, H^0]$. This, for instance, was the procedure followed with the corresponding variables of the model for the cotton industry.

The mathematical model did not explicitly state, but the users of the model tacitly assumed the limitation that we would not accept the model as optimal if the level of activity with the old facilities were very small ($x < H_0$). The fact is that the unit cost of such low-level activity is actually much higher than the unit cost figuring in the linear cost function. (This would lead us to the "upper left arm" of the U.) If the programming was to produce such a result, we would rather omit this activity from the model and work out the program over again. In practice this contingency did not arise and the levels of these activities were within the interval $[H_0, H^0]$.

1.2. The level of the activity was bounded at the point where the random cost assumes its minimal value (point K of figure 7.4). A *concave* cost function was applied in the interval $[0, K]$. This was the course taken in the man-made fibres model. As in the course of these investigations we wanted to concentrate on the phenomenon of cost degression, we have disregarded this phase of the expansion of production where cost progression is already asserting itself.

2. The expansion of production by expanding given, old fixed capital stocks and existing facilities. (E.g. the installation of new looms in old weaving mills, the expansion of an old alumina factory, etc.)

In these cases we have rising marginal costs and a convex cost function. We start with relatively favourably utilizable resources, e.g. an old factory building, or the part of the old machinery stock that can still be usefully operated, etc. These advantageous resources are, however, limited in extent and have therefore, as the volume of production is expanded, to be combined with other, less favourable resources, leading to ever more unfavourable resource combinations.

In the manufacture of alumina, for instance, a certain rise in output can be achieved by relieving the bottle-necks of the old plant. This is the cheapest expedient. The next step is the expansion of the plant by relatively little building, filling the hitherto vacant floor space, rearranging the machines and purchasing certain new ones. This is a more expensive operation. The next possibility is a more radical expansion of the factory, combined with a thorough technical modernization of the equipment. This is still more expensive. Finally, when this possibility has also been exhausted, we may build a new factory. This is the most costly course of all.

To handle this type of cost variation in our models of industrial sectors, the procedure described as case 2.2 in section 7.3 was applied. The activity was decomposed into part-activities, these were separately bounded, and described by linear cost functions. The division into part-activities was in these cases evident from the technical point of view, too.

3. The establishment of new plants. Here we are mainly concerned with the familiar phenomenon generally referred to as the "economies of scale", i.e. the advantages of large-scale operation and mass production. The growth in the size of plant is accompanied by relative savings. This phenomenon is particularly marked in the chemical industry, to which man-made fibres belong, so the latter will serve as an example.

Relative savings appear in the *investment* costs of a larger plant. For instance:

– The main instruments of chemical production are the various tanks and pipelines. Their price rises not in proportion to their capacity, but to only a smaller extent. Nor need the dimensions of the buildings to accommodate them be increased proportionately.

– The design costs of a larger plant are not proportionately larger than the similar costs of a smaller one. Indeed, a considerable part of the design costs is independent of the size of plant to be established.

– Certain building costs (e.g. the cost of preparation) do not rise proportionately with the size of the building job.

– In purchasing machinery, a price discount may be obtained if larger quantities are bought. Moreover, more favourable credit conditions can be negotiated.

Relative savings also arise in the *operating* costs of larger plants. For example:

– Larger output – and thus the servicing of larger tanks and piping – does not require a proportionate increase in the numbers of personnel. The clerical and auxiliary staffs also do not increase proportionately with the size of the plant. Economies of scale with respect to wage costs are particularly marked in the chemical industry.

– The capacities of certain auxiliary plants and laboratories need not be increased in proportion with the capacity of the basic productive plant.
– The costs of storage and sales do not rise proportionately with the volume.

This then is a case of diminishing marginal costs and hence a concave cost function. It has been shown in section 7.3 that concave minimizing programming problems are extremely difficult to solve. In the case of the man-made fibres investigations these difficulties were nevertheless faced, because failure to consider the relative savings due to mass production would have involved a bad distortion of the practical results of the calculations.

4. Foreign trading activities. Advantages and savings may also appear in the case of import transactions if the activity is expanded. The seller may grant a discount for the purchase of larger consignments. Conversely, in selling larger export consignments we may ourselves be forced to give a price discount. In the case of a cost minimizing model we then have diminishing marginal costs, i.e. a concave cost function for imports. Since export returns figure as negative costs in cost minimizing models, an export price that diminishes as a function of the activity-level will lead to rising marginal costs and thus to a convex cost function.

This relation was neglected in the case of our models, and simple linear cost functions were used, for two reasons. Firstly, as has been pointed out, in trade between socialist countries it is not customary to grant discounts as functions of the size of a consignment. Secondly, we have no adequate basis for numerically calculating the price discounts we may expect in foreign trade with the capitalist countries.

7.5. The Consideration of the Advantages of Mass Production in the Man-made Fibres Industry

On the basis of the above it is now possible to put into concrete form the objective function which was only described in general terms in the account of the man-made fibres model (6.8). The following cost function was used with the production variables*:

$$C_j(x_j) = P_j\left(\frac{x_j}{X_{0j}}\right)^{\pi_j} + Q_j\left(\frac{x_j}{X_{0j}}\right)^{\Psi_j} + r_j x_j\,, \tag{7.6}$$

* Departing from the notation of ch. 6 we shall here, for the sake of simplicity, use only one index in reference to the serial number of the variable.

where

X_{0j} = the predetermined, postulated plant size for the jth productive activity. It was for this constant plant size that the designing engineers calculated the investment and operation costs

P_j = the rent on capital and maintenance costs* for the postulated plant size X_{0j}

Q_i = the annual operation wages cost for the postulated plant size X_{0j}

π_j, ψ_j = degression exponents. Their value is between 0 and 1

r_j = other operation costs per unit product, other than wages costs. Their main factor is material costs. These are approximately proportionate to the activity level, the assumption of linearity is therefore not too gross a simplification in this respect.

The above cost function is a concave power function. Project engineers in the American and West German petrochemical industries use this formula, which we also took from literature on the economic problems of the chemical industry**. The numerical value of the degression exponents was also determined according to the literature. For end products the degression exponent of the investment costs and that of the wages costs is in most cases about 0.6–0.7, while for the production of intermediaries the exponent of the wages costs is very much smaller, around 0.2, i.e. the degression is far more powerful.

The detailed data can be found in table 7.2.

The type of function (7.6) proved advantageous from the practical point of view, in that it was akin to the approach of the designing engineers participating in the research work, who furnished the technical data. The designing engineer does not, as a rule, work out cost functions, but determines the figures for a fixed plant size. Function (7.6) makes it possible to deduce the cost function from the figures of a plant of fixed size.

* The maintenance costs represent the inputs which are necessary for simply reproducing the fixed capital on unchanged level. The detailed explanation will be given later.

** See the works of J. M. Berk and J. E. Haselbarth [10], W. Isard *et al.* [58], H. Kölbel and J. Schulze [89], S. M. Peters [141], and R. Williams [178]. Statistical investigations abroad, conducted in other sectors of industry, have also led to cost functions of types similar to function (7.6). For examples of the cost investigations conducted in thermal power stations, dairies, etc. see J. Dean, [31], pp. 300–301.

TABLE 7.2

The exponents of degression in the man-made fibres industry

Name of product	Degression exponent of investment costs			Degression exponent of wages costs		
	Reference	Data in literature on subject	Exponent used in calculation	Reference	Data in literature on subject	Exponent used in calculation
Orlon staple	—	—	0.67	[60]	0.6	0.6
Terylene staple	—	—	0.67	[60]	0.6	0.6
Nylon 6 yarn	[89]	0.67	0.67	—	—	0.6
Other final products	—	—	0.67	—	—	0.6
Caprolactame	[89]	0.77	0.77	—	—	0.22
Phenol	—	—	0.6	—	—	0.22
Ethylene glycol	[60]	0.625				
	[10], [89]	0.78	0.7	—	—	0.22
Dimethyl-therephtalate	[60]	0.67	0.67	[60]	0.218	0.22
Acrylonitrile	[60]	0.7	0.65*	—	—	0.22
Polypropylene	[10], [89]	0.9**	0.9	—	—	0.22

* The source refers to another kind of technology than that assumed in connection with the corresponding activity in our model. The lower degression exponent is motivated by the difference in technology.

** The source refers to the production of polyethylene which from the point of view of cost degression is analogous with that of polypropylene.

It has been pointed out above that our programming models do not reflect the advantages of mass production. For instance the diminishing character of the marginal investment costs is not expressed in the constraint (6.5) imposed on the investment resources. This, however, causes no great error. The reason why the utilization of certain resources was bounded by appropriate constraints, was the desire to make sure that the program should under no circumstances require *more* of them than is permissible. Neglect of the economies of scale at this juncture merely means that we have made somewhat "over-sure", and that the program will in fact require rather *less* resources (investments, construction, foreign currency, etc.) than the amount indicated in the constraint on the model. The economies of scale are thus not forgotten, for as we have seen they are expressed in the objective function.

In section 7.3 it has been pointed out that we had to make do with an approximate procedure in place of an exact solution of the concave minimizing problem. To check our method, the following calculation was carried out:

The objective function was "linearized". The designing engineers who participated in the investigations determined the "normal plant size" for the various production activities, drawing on their routine, foreign experiences, etc. Let this be called $\bar{x}_j$. Next, using the original, non-linear cost function, we computed the cost per unit capacity for the assumed "normal plant size". Let this be called the "normal unit cost" and denoted by $\bar{c}_j$, so that

$$\bar{c}_j = \frac{C_j(\bar{x}_j)}{\bar{x}_j}. \tag{7.7}$$

This "normal unit cost" was now substituted as the coefficient in the objective function of the linear programming model*.

Next we determined the optimum program for the problem which had thus been "linearized". Let this be denoted by $\mathbf{x}^*_{\text{lin}}$ (as opposed to the program $\mathbf{x}^*_{\text{non-lin}}$, being the relatively most favourable objective function value obtained through the approximate procedure for non-linear programming).

In the next step we compared the objective function values belonging to $\mathbf{x}^*_{\text{lin}}$ and $\mathbf{x}^*_{\text{non-lin}}$, now calculating both for the original, non-linear cost function. It turned out that the cost of $\mathbf{x}^*_{\text{lin}}$ was about 3 per cent higher than that of $\mathbf{x}^*_{\text{non-lin}}$. *The result of the mathematically more exact procedure based on an economically cruder simplifying assumption is further off the actual economic optimum, than that which is mathematically non-exact and approximate, but based on economically more precise assumptions***.

One of the characteristic features of the program $\mathbf{x}^*_{\text{lin}}$ obtained from the linear model, is that it is more scattered than the program $\mathbf{x}^*_{\text{non-lin}}$ calculated from the non-linear objective function. For instance both prescribe the production of nylon 6 yarn for domestic consumption and for export. According to the program obtained from the non-linear

* It may be argued, whether this is the most suitable way of "linearization" or not. In the course of the control calculations the point of departure was that this would have been what we should have had to do if we had from the outset intended to carry out linear programming. In determining the technical and cost figures we had per force to rely on the estimates of the designing engineers taking part in the work. These engineers, however, at least in Hungarian practice to date, do not determine cost functions, but estimate costs for a single plant size – one that they consider the normal size. We shall later return to this latter point.

** For details see the Final Report [85].

model it is to be made by one kind of technology, while according to the program from the linear model a part should be made by technology "*A*", a part by technology "*B*". Or to take another example: according to $\mathbf{x}^*_{\text{non-lin}}$ the old viscose capacity is to be wholly concentrated on the manufacture of cellophane, while $\mathbf{x}^*_{\text{lin}}$ divides the semi-manufactured product capacity between the manufacture of cellophane and viscose silk. The two examples clearly show that the concave cost function is a far more powerful incentive towards the concentration of production.

Let us examine the problem of the concentration of production more closely.

A comparison was made of the following programs for the man-made fibres industry:

(1) A "fully autarkic" program. All the products for which a domestic requirement arises are, according to the constraint system of the model, produced at home. Foreign trade is excluded.

(2) The official program drawn up by non-mathematical methods.

(3) The most favourable program obtained on an electronic computer.

(4) A program that is "extroverted" in the extreme, in that the original export constraint in the model was lifted with respect to one of the products. This would thus not be a feasible program according to the original model.

Of the above programs only (3) was obtained by programming on an electronic computer, (2) was given, and programs (1) and (4) were constructed by us to provide a "pure" demonstration of particular economic policy trends. The results of the calculations are shown in table 7.3.

TABLE 7.3

Effect of the concentration of production in the man-made fibres industry

	1	2	3	4
Type of program	"Autarkic"	"Official"	"Most favourable"	"Extro-verted"
Kinds of product made	13	10	8	2
Exports, thousands of tons	0	38.3	59.3	663.5
Value of objective function (million Ft per year)	7740	7272	6425	5255

The table emphatically shows the significance of concentration. The fewer the kinds of product on whose production we concentrate our resources, the more apparent the advantages of mass production become.

Attempts at autarky render production very expensive. Far-reaching efforts should therefore be made to exploit the advantages arising from the international division of labour.

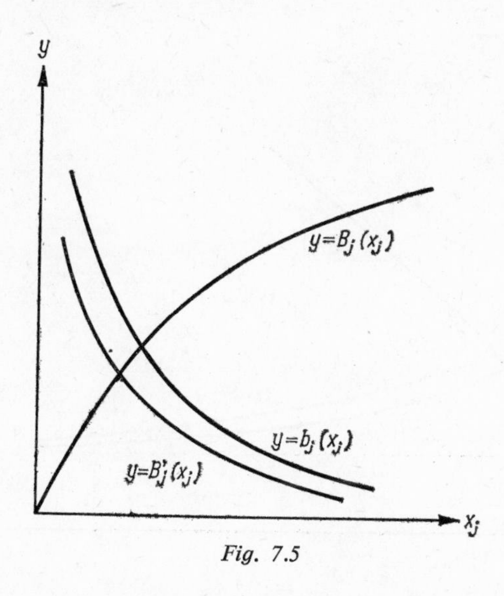

Fig. 7.5

The investigation of the application of concave cost functions has not been finally concluded. It has been decided in these further calculations to use a cost function differing from the type of (7.6).

To show the problems involved, let us take the investment costs from function (7.6) and write them in a simpler form:

$$B_j(x_j) = P_j \left(\frac{x_j}{X_{oj}}\right)^{\pi_j} = p_j\, x_j^{\pi_j}\,. \tag{7.8}$$

The functions of the corresponding unit costs and marginal costs are:

$$b_j(x_j) = \frac{B_j(x_j)}{x_j} = \frac{p_j\, x_j^{\pi_j}}{x_j} = p_j\, x_j^{\frac{1}{1-\pi_j}}\,, \tag{7.9}$$

$$B_j'(x_j) = \pi_j\, p_j\, x_j^{\frac{1}{1-\pi_j}}\,. \tag{7.10}$$

All three functions are presented in figure 7.5.

As the plant size is increased, both the unit investment cost and marginal investment cost tend to 0, though the marginal cost is always below the unit cost. The same is the case with the unit and marginal

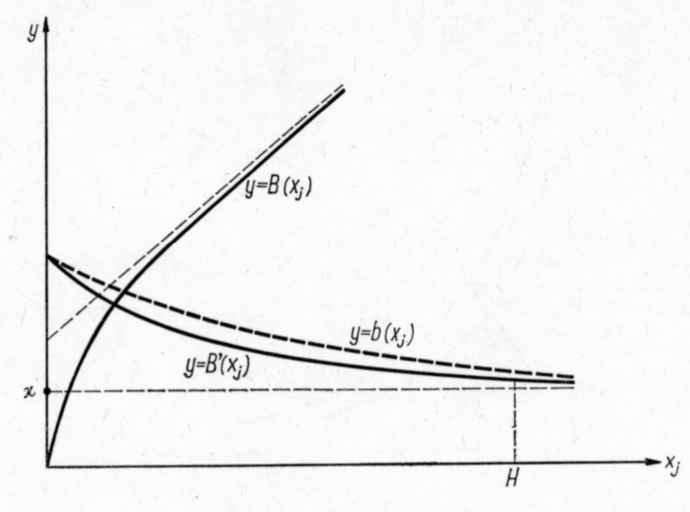

Fig. 7.6

wages costs – they too, tend to 0. Only the material costs do not "disappear" as the plant size is increased.

This, however, is not a sufficiently realistic characterization of the actual trend of costs. The truth is rather that above a certain plant size no more relative savings accrue, either in the investment or the wages costs. It will therefore be better to use the following type of cost function for both the investment and wages costs:

$$B_j(x_j) = \mu_j + \varkappa_j x_j - \frac{\mu_j \xi_j}{x_j + \xi_j}. \tag{7.11}$$

The unit cost and marginal cost functions of this hyperbolic cost function are:

$$b_j(x_j) = \frac{B_j(x_j)}{x_j} = \frac{\mu_j}{x_j} + \varkappa_j - \frac{\mu_j \xi_j}{x_j^2 + \xi_j x_j}, \tag{7.12}$$

$$B_j'(x_j) = \varkappa_j + \frac{\mu_j \xi_j}{(x_j + \xi_j)^2}. \tag{7.13}$$

From expressions (7.12) and (7.13) it is clear that as x_j is increased, both the unit cost and marginal cost tend asymptotically to $\varkappa_j$ (see figure 7.6). If the constants are suitably chosen, then over a certain plant size, practically speaking over the normal "maximal" plant size, the unit cost and the marginal cost will both be very close to $\varkappa_j$. In the figure this plant size is marked H.

This type of function properly reflects the actual curve of the savings attainable through mass production. Over a certain limit these economies are practically negligible and the cost function becomes almost linear. Figure 7.6 clearly shows that beyond the plant size H, the function $B_j(x_j)$ more and more closely approaches the dashed straight line which is the asymptote of the hyperbola.

A numerical determination of the function requires the knowledge of at least three points, if possible within the interval $[0, H]$. As a rule it is also possible in practice directly to give an upper estimate of $\varkappa_j$, i.e. of the unit cost that will show no practical decrease beyond H. This of course is, theoretically, not an accurate estimate of $\varkappa_j$ for the unit cost only tends towards $\varkappa_j$, actually attaining it in infinity. The difference is, however, negligibly small and the magnitude of $\varkappa_j$ can in any case not be determined precisely in designing engineering practice.

7.6. Determination of the Parameters of the Function

Another line of research pursued in connection with the application of concave cost functions has been to find a sounder basis for determining the numerical values of the parameters.

Mention has been made of the fact that in the case of the investigation of the man-made fibres industry, the degression exponents π_j and ψ_j of expression (7.6) were taken from literary sources. It is indeed one advantage of this type of function that once these exponents are known, the cost figures need only be worked out for a single plant size X_{0j}.

The sources based their figures partly on statistical findings and partly on technical and economic calculations.

The first difficulty arose at the outset, in that it was only for a part of the products comprised in the model that directly corresponding figures could be found in the literature. For the rest, we had ourselves to make estimates based on analogies, derived from the figures available for other, similar products*. The simple adoption of foreign figures is,

* See table 7.2.

moreover, not a reassuring procedure. The ratios of prices, wages and costs are different in the countries where our sources were compiled to those in Hungary. Consequently it may be presumed that the degression exponents there are not entirely appropriate in our circumstances*.

Moreover, since it is intended to use functions of the type of (7.11) in the future in place of (7.6), we shall no longer be in a position simply to adopt the figures in the sources quoted, for they only furnish the exponents of functions of the type of (7.6).

What method then is to be used to determine the figures? Let us continue with the example of the chemical industry. In the United States there are some firms that have in the course of time themselves built over a hundred plants to make the same product. Under such circumstances it is possible to determine cost functions on the basis of factual figures. The Hungarian chemical industry on the other hand is too small for the parameters of the cost function to be calculated from the necessary number of facts. The course to be pursued is therefore to have the designing engineers plan a particular investment for various plant sizes, and the figures thus obtained – relating to particular, fixed capacities – can be processed by the usual statistical methods to determine the parameters of the function. This should not be regarded as merely an enforced solution which we are obliged to adopt for lack of the necessary number of factual figures. The procedure also has a number of advantages, for the engineers' estimates can more consistently conform to the principle of *ceteris paribus*. Thus the engineers can really calculate cost figures that postulate absolutely identical circumstances, identical technologies, identical product-mixes, an identical level of personnel skill, etc. They are in fact perfectly compatible, differing on one point only: they relate to different plant sizes.

The first steps in this direction have already been taken. A calculation of this type was, for instance, prepared in the investigation of the bauxite and aluminium industry, relating to various kinds of investment activity. Further extension of these investigations requires, however, a large apparatus and can therefore be successful only if the official organs provide for investment proposals to be worked out simultaneously in several variants and for various plant sizes.

* Information has recently also become available on the cost functions compiled by the designing engineers of the Soviet chemical industry. See e.g. V. C. KOROTKHEVICH [88]. The Soviet price structure is more like the Hungarian, but even this cannot make up for the lack of figures compiled according to the concrete situation in this country.

CHAPTER 8

FIRST COMPARISON WITH THE TRADITIONAL METHODS

The two preceding chapters described the structure of the models of two sectors of industry. There are still many open questions to which we shall return later, but it will nevertheless be useful at this stage to make a first comparison between the traditional and the mathematical methods of planning.

Those objective functions which have been set down in chs. 5 and 6, are closely related to the most important index of the economic efficiency of investments used in traditional planning – the so-called g_n index. We shall therefore for the time being assume that with respect to the *optimality criterion* there is no difference between the programming procedure and the traditional calculations of economic efficiency. There are, however, other differences; let us now consider these.

8.1. Broader Opportunities for Choices

The first substantial difference is that *mathematical programming offers the decision-making body broader and more organized opportunities for making choices.*

According to the present practice, no alternative proposals are worked out when the permit application is submitted. The choice is essentially limited to a "yes or no" answer, to approving or rejecting the application which is submitted*.

This phenomenon is so general, that it is not even worth while to quote an example**. The official schemata and forms themselves, on the basis of which the permit applications are prepared, do not even provide space for listing several alternatives. This is the accepted, normal system for the planning and approval of investments.

* This is not essentially affected even if there is argument over matters of detail at the program sessions.

** See the paper of L. Lukács [107] on this subject.

In an earlier stage of the preparation of investment proposals, well before the submission of the permit application over which the investment decision is taken, various alternatives are, it is true, generally mooted. Indeed some of the preliminary investigations are intended precisely to compare several variants. These alternatives, however, generally "fall by the way", before they ever reach the really authoritative sessions where approval is actually granted. At the critical point, the proposal which is submitted mostly appears without any competitors.

This preliminary sifting may, of course, be justified, provided that convincing calculations prove that the alternatives which are abandoned are *certainly worse* than the one proposal for acceptance. It would indeed be a pity to burden the decision-making body with studying alternatives which are certainly not worth while to be put into practice.

In the great majority of cases, however, this is not the position. Only one proposal is put to the decision-making body, though the preliminary surveys have shown precisely that other variants for solving the same task also deserve serious consideration.

For instance in the cotton industry approval was granted to building a new weaving mill. At the session *no* alternative proposal was submitted on whether the rise in output volume to be achieved through the new mill could not be attained by modernizing the old weaving mills. Yet as has been shown, it was ultimately this version that proved the more favourable.

The step-by-step sifting of alternatives, selection in *temporally consecutive* stages, is no substitute for the *simultaneous* comparison of several alternatives.

It should objectively be stated, that the mere wish to achieve the simultaneous comparison of several alternatives, would in itself not require mathematical programming. This can be done without it. *One of the important features of mathematical programming, however, is that it provides an organized form, a framework, and at the same time an incentive, for the simultaneous comparison and joint examination of a large number of alternatives.* The choice between alternatives is part of the essence of programming; without this it would simply lose its meaning.

Of course – as has been pointed out – there is need for previous selection even in the case of mathematical programming, if only because the number of possibilities is always tremendous, and the dimensions of the model are limited, for one thing, by the computing facilities. But after the preliminary sifting, the mathematical programming model sets up several alternatives simultaneously, beside one another, even immediately before the decision is made.

The problem of choosing has so far throughout been treated as that of a qualitative choice: "Should this be done, or that?" Should we build, or modernize an old plant? Should automatic shuttle changer looms be acquired? Should polyamide or polyester fibres be made? And so forth.

In actual fact quantitative problems also arise. How large a factory, with what capacity should be built? How many new machines should be acquired?

Generally the question is not simply that one activity is carried out and the other not – as a rule several are carried out together, and they may be combined in various proportions. The question for instance is not of *either* exchanging the machinery *or* building, but of *both* machinery exchanges *and* building. But in what ratio? The question is not one of exchanging either the weaving looms or the preparatory machinery, but rather both – only what is to be the proportion?

The various activities can thus be combined in many ways. It does not require familiarity with the rules of the calculus of combinations to see that the number of possible combinations of the various investment activities that can be carried out in a sector of industry, is incredibly large.

In those rare cases where, in the course of the usual examinations of economic efficiency, several alternatives are compared, an attempt is made to consider *a few* combinations. Thus for example a working party of the cotton fabric industry worked out a few variants in connection with the investment problems which we also examined, and carried out calculations of economic efficiency for their cases. The results are shown in table 8.1.

The compilation of the variants involved very much work. Nevertheless this is only a fraction of the possible combinations of investment activities. Why, for instance, could not the entire machine stock of the Goldberger Works be exchanged for only automatic shuttle changing or for only automatic bobbin changing machines? Why could added automata not be applied in the Hungarian Cotton Industry plant? Why could not a part only of the machinery at Sopron be exchanged, as the Goldberger variants planned?

We have thus arrived at the actual limit of the capacity of the traditional calculation method. *Without a suitable mathematical procedure, it is an impossible task to select the best out of all the possible combinations in the case of decision problems which arise in choosing between a relatively large number of alternatives.* With mathematical programming on the other hand, this is fully possible.

Another practical advantage of mathematical programming should also be mentioned at this juncture: it is possible as a matter of course to

TABLE 8.1

Investment variants in the cotton fabric industry

Serial number	Name of firm	Type of machinery	Building requirement	Order according to index of economic efficiency
1.	Békéscsaba Weaving Mill (planned new plant)	Automatic shuttle changing looms	New building	9
2.	Goldberger Textile Works	Part of the looms are automatic shuttle changers, the rest are accelerated mechanical ones	Old building	5
3.	Goldberger Textile Works	Part of the looms are automatic shuttle changers, the rest have added automata	Old building	10
4.	Goldberger Textile Works	Part of the looms are automatic bobbin, changers, the rest are accelerated mechanical ones	Old building	8
5.	Goldberger Textile Works	Part of the looms are automatic bobbin changers, the rest have added automata	Old building	11
6.	Hungarian Cotton Industry Spinning and Weaving Mill	Automatic shuttle changing looms	Old building	1
7.	Hungarian Cotton Industry Spinning and Weaving Mill	Automatic bobbin changing looms	Old building	3
8.	Sopron Cotton Industry	Automatic shuttle changing looms	Old building	7
9.	Sopron Cotton Industry	Added automata looms	Old building	6
10.	Sopron Cotton Industry	Used mechanical looms dismantled from other mills	Expansion of old building	2
11.	Szombathely Cotton Industry	Automatic shuttle changing looms	Expansion of old building	4

operate the principle of "equal chances", i.e. to see that the many alternatives are compared *according to identical assumptions.* In the course of the calculations, for instance, the technical and cost characteristics of all the alternatives were calculated with identical wage rates, identical power tariffs, etc. This is of course again a principle whose enforcement does not require mathematical programming; it could in fact also be operated in the course of the usual calculations. In practice, however, the alternative proposals (where they are prepared at all) are usually drawn up independently of one another, on the basis of different assumptions and different initial data. On the other hand the incorporation of the various alternatives in a single model, more or less forces the programmer to ensure compatibility and to calculate according to uniform principles. It is characteristic, for instance, that although in the course of years numerous surveys have been compiled on the development of the Hungarian synthetic fibres industry, including some thorough and detailed works, nevertheless at the time of our investigation the mutually compatible technical and cost data of all the production alternatives of the model, compiled according to identical principles, were not ready and available. They had to be collected from a large number of sources by our own research group.

8.2 Choice Based on Simple Ranking

Let us return to the example of the investment variants prepared for the cotton fabrics industry and set out in table 8.1. The variants were ranked according to the index of economic efficiency. This choice based on simple ranking is not exceptional; the simultaneous calculation of economic efficiency for several variants itself suggests the idea of ranking them according to the index and choosing the ones at the head of the list in making a decision. This type of choice, however, is limited by the following factors:

(1) The variants, or some of them, are actually not independent of each other. In some cases a particular favourable variant can only be adopted if other, less favourable ones are adopted with it.

(2) There are external factors which limit the unrestrained adoption of the variants at the head of the list.

The question may also be analysed in a more general form. Given a linear programming model, e.g. the one for the cotton industry, where both the constraint system and the objective function are linear. The question is: according to what criterion is it certainly *not* worth while to include an activity among the variables of the model? When can it be discarded straight away, even before programming?

In this case all the constraints are set down in such a form that the coefficients denoting output should have positive signs, and those denoting expenditure should have negative signs.

The objective function of the model prescribes the minimization of costs. Under these circumstances the jth activity dominates activity h, if one of the following two domination criteria is valid:

Domination Criterion 1

$$c_j = c_h , \tag{8.1}$$

$$a_{ij} \geqq a_{ih}, \quad i = 1, 2, \ldots, m , \tag{8.2}$$

and for at least one i

$$a_{ij} > a_{ih} , \tag{8.3}$$

or

Domination Criterion 2

$$a_{ij} \geqq a_{ih}, \quad i = 1, 2, \ldots, m , \tag{8.4}$$

$$c_j < c_h . \tag{8.5}$$

The economic content of the two criteria is the following*:

Criterion 1. Activities j and h are equally favourable from the point of view of the objective function. From the point of view of at least one constraint, j is definitely more favourable having greater output or smaller expenditure, while as regards the other constraints it is not less favourable. Thus, for example, it may have a smaller requirement of floor area, while being otherwise no worse than another similar activity**.

Criterion 2. Activity j is, as regards the constraints, no worse than h.

* It is not intended here to discuss all the cases of domination. The criteria in expressions (8.1)–(8.5) are merely examples, to explain the other relations discussed here.

** It may occur, even though only exceptionally, that the problem has several equally optimal programs. In this case application of Criterion 1 might permit the previous sifting out of activities which would be included in at least some of the optimal programs, even though not in all.

From the point of view of the objective function it is definitely more favourable.

If it is noted before programming that activity j dominates h, then the latter can be left out of the model. It has no chance at all of being included in the optimal program, since j necessarily displaces it.

It has been seen that the criteria of domination are fairly strict*. In comparing two activities, the objective function and all the constraints must be considered together. It should be noted that it is fairly rare for either of the two criteria to be satisfied in practice. Far more frequently one activity has advantages and disadvantages, compared to the other, e.g. in the case of two machines for similar purposes, one is cheaper than the other but it is more expensive to operate, etc.

Now the choice based on ranking *in itself* would mean that only the relation (8.5) is regarded as important, and that alternative preferred, where the index of economic efficiency is higher. The rest are rejected. Yet it is not at all certain that this alternative really does dominate the rest since the constraints are valid not only in the programming model but also in real life.

It is often heard in economic life that some activity or other would appear, according to the index of economic efficiency, to be very economical, but that unfortunately no investment resources are available for it. Or else that it would be economical to purchase a particular piece of import machinery, but that unfortunately there is no foreign currency for it. Or again, that it would be economical to expand the capacity of certain processes, but that unfortunately the utilizing plants require other materials, necessitating the expansion of less economical capacities.

These complaints indicate a misunderstanding of the concept of what is "economical". No activity is economical in itself, *independently* of outer circumstances and of the other activities conducted in the national economy. *An activity is economical, if it is relatively the most favourable one amid the given circumstances.* The complaints quoted above, the clauses introduced by the word "unfortunately", often indicate precisely those realistic facts from which no one who seeks this relative optimum may become divorced.

* In constructing the man-made fibres model, use of the above domination criterion led to the previous rejection of some alternatives.

8.3. The Balance Method and the Requirement of Economic Efficiency

In order to answer these points let us return to the coordination of the plan, the checking of balances and plan indices, described in ch. 1. The question arises after surveying the programming models, of the extent to which coordination of the plans may be regarded as an iterative process, aimed at solving a programming problem through trial and error.

There is some truth in this. In this "model" the balances play the part of constraints, while the economic index g_n acts as objective function. What is sought in the course of coordination is a feasible solution, satisfying the constraints, which is at the same time also relatively favourable from the point of view of the g_n indices.

It must, however, also be pointed out that this description is not accurate or full.

The "objective function", the optimality criterion expressed in the index of economic efficiency, is more or less lost. To this extent there is undoubtedly some truth in the complaints previously quoted, which protest against the neglect of the recommendations (though these are, as we have seen, only partly justified), of the calculations of economic efficiency. The very approximation in the course of plan coordination to a single feasible and possible plan which is set up in the balance system and satisfies the "tacit" constraint system* requires so great an effort, that no energy is left for selecting the optimal one from among what is really a large number of feasible programs.

Let us take an example. When our first proposals for the long-term plan period were worked out, the Ministry of Light Industry prepared an investment plan in which it recommended the realization of 131 projects. The g_n indices of all the projects were calculated and the proposals were accordingly ranked. Finally, when the plan was checked, 29 proposals were deleted while the rest were included in the approved plan. Those which were left out included many proposals where the g_n indices were over 1 and appeared favourable. In most of these cases the reason for deletion was that the necessary investment resources were not available. On the other hand the plan ultimately included several proposals whose index of economic efficiency was under 1. The reason given was that these projects are also necessary, as a rule, in order to secure the equilibrium of the corresponding product balance of the economy. The

* In terminology of ch. 1: the documented and auxiliary plan equations.

figures are shown in table 8.2. There is no real correlation between the indications of the g_n index and inclusion in, or sifting from the plan. The correlation coefficient between inclusion in the plan and the g_n index is 0.022 in the case of the figures of table 8.2.

TABLE 8.2

The selection of investment proposals in the light industry

g_n index	Number in original proposal	Deleted in the course of plan finalization	Ratio of deleted proposals as percentage of original total
Over 1.5	18	4	22.2
1.5–1.2	28	6	21.4
1.2–1	31	6	19.4
1–0.8	34	8	23.5
Under 0.8	20	5	25.0
Total	131	29	22.1

At the same time it may unfortunately not be said that loss of the obctive function is the price paid for having full compliance with the ysem of constraints (the balance system). It is practically impossible, ss t was pointed out in ch. 1, to establish the solution of so vast a system f equations, the set of plan equations by trial and error.

aIt is precisely here that mathematical programming offers great opporonities. It provides the technical means for implementing the aim that derlies the traditional method of planning, namely simultaneously to nhieve both the equilibrium and the optimal nature of the plan*.

nThe essence of mathematical programming is that it *formulates the most acceptable compromise between the "realistic facts" and the "considerations of economic efficiency" not in a round-about way, by trial tnd error, but by going straight to the point.* It organically links the balance method, through the system of constraints, and the requirements of economic efficiency, through the objective function. These were htherto separated, leading separate existences. Moreover it gives "equal

* The paper of J. M. MONTIAS [128] contains noteworthy remarks on the relation between the requirements of equilibrium and optimization, and the use to this end of mathematical methods in a socialist planned economy.

rights" to the aim of optimization, which so far was willy-nilly forced to take a second place as a result of the great efforts to achieve equilibrium in the plan. The requirement of economic efficiency indeed becomes the main criterion of choice in the programming model.

8.4. The Connection between the Sector Programming Model and the Traditional Plan Index System

As has been shown when surveying the "prototypes" of sector programming models, many of the plan variables and plan equations of the traditional plan index system described in ch. 1 will appear also in the programming model. Let us take, for example, the programming project for the man-made fibres industry.

(1) Some individual product balances of the traditional index system appear in the model. All the types of man-made fibres to be found in the model and also most of the intermediary chemicals belong to the so-called priority products allocated in the product balances of the National Planning Board. These balances are fully included in the model, with all their items. Let us take e.g. the terylene balance. The traditional plan sets out the level of the production, the level of exports, the level of imports and the level of home consumption of the textile industry. The first three of these traditional plan figures are included as variables also in the model, whereas the last is a constant figuring on the right side of the constraint.

(2) The model includes among the constraints certain quotas available from materials produced outside the synthetic fibre industry such as e.g. the fund of propylene materials. A product balance is being drawn up also for this product in the framework of traditional planning. Here, however, the whole balance will not appear in the model of mathematical programming but only a single item of it: the propylene quantity allocated to the synthetic fibre industry. This is one of the unknowns of the traditional plan equation system, one of its documented plan figures: now, however, it figures as a constant in the programming model*.

(3) In the programming model we regard the investment resources as limited; the same resources which the traditional balance system distributes through the relevant resource balances. Here the case is similar to that of the propylene quota: one of the unknowns, variables in the

* This idea will have special significance in the description of programming on a national level.

plan equations system, appears in the program model as a constant bound.

So far I have spoken about such variables and constraints of the programming model as are connected with the documented variables and equations of the traditional plan equation system. But as ch. 1 has stressed: the traditional plan equation system contains a whole series of non-documented, auxiliary equations as well, drawn up only as complementary computations, or existing only in the minds of certain planners. In our programming model also equations of this type arise: e.g. upper constraints on exports, capacity limits, etc. The programming model "promotes" these equations: it gives them equal rights with the docuy mented equations. This means they have to be documented also more accurately and strict provisions have to be made that they be actuall- complied with.

The approval of the so-called priority investment actions* is taken independently of the documented balance equations in the traditional plan index system, it is organically not connected with them. Now they also form an organic part of the model: they appear in some of the domestic production variables which imply certain investment actions taking place in the period 1966–1974.

The foregoing might be summarized as follows:

The programming model enables us to fit organically together the different elements of the traditional index system. It will decide simultaneously about a whole number of variables of the traditional plan, it will solve simultaneously a whole number of equations: variables whose coordinated values are approximated by the particular iteration process of traditional plan coordination.

All this provides a possibility of improving the internal consistency of the original plan worked out on the basis of traditional methods, realizing at the same time considerable savings as against the official plan. It has been shown that savings up to 12–15 per cent had been attained both in the calculations for the cotton industry and in those for the man-made fibres industry. But what is probably even more important is the "pedagogical" role of mathematical programming, the light it throws on the connections between the plan targets and the internal logics of the plan structure and the stimulus to rationality and reasonable choice it gives to the planner.

* See the seventh group of documented plan indices in ch. 1.

8.5. The Computing-technical Limitations

We must not hesitate to point out objectively the weak points of the present-day programming models. An individual sectoral programming model deals usually with but a few dozen plan variables and plan equations. Traditional planning, although it does not provide the exact solution to a single equation, takes account of a much greater number of relationships. Should we eliminate from the traditional plan equation system (1.7), for example, the variables and equations relating to the man-made fibres industry, much more could be obtained than that which figures in our programming model.

I will not enlarge here on all the difficulties of mathematical programming (the problems of data compilation will be dealt with in a later chapter), but this is the point where a few words must be said about the computing problems. The largest linear programming problem which can be solved without difficulty* on the computer with the comparatively greatest capacity now in operation in Hungary, is one containing not more than 100 constraints.

Very much larger computers are known to operate abroad. The Hungarian electronic computer facilities are also certain to be augmented with more powerful equipment. There will, however, always be realistic limitations to computing, which set bounds to the size of our models.

In drawing up a model it is always a tempting thought to broaden the scope of investigation and attempt to answer more problems. If this temptation is not resisted, it will result in specious paper reports. Those, however, who wish really to compute, *must establish a sober compromise on the one hand between fullness, detail and accuracy, and on the other, the actual computing facilities.*

The necessary computing limitations of the dimensions of our models lead to two important conclusions. First, the comprehensive and more general programming carried out at the upper level must be linked with the more concrete and detailed programming related to a particular field, carried out at the lower level. In the present case, calculations for the sector of industry, must be combined with those for the *plants.* In the cotton industry for instance, a plant programming scheme of this type was carried out for experimental purposes in the Goldberger Works, one of the largest Hungarian textile mills. The possibilities for linking programming at the higher and lower levels will be discussed in detail later.

* Without resorting to slower and more cumbersome auxiliary stores (e.g. film stores) and decomposition methods.

The second conclusion is that the practical recommendations based on mathematical programming must not be "exalted" and over-estimated. The detailed figures of the final results of programming must not be taken for unequivocal instructions and mechanistically applied.

Programming with the use of mathematical methods does not imply the conclusion of the work of planning, but introduces a new phase. It does not replace the work of industrial administration, but is an auxiliary aid to it. Programming furnishes a framework which must be filled in – the details of execution must be planned, and in doing so *the results of programming must necessarily be corrected according to the relations, the conditions of the firms and the technical and economic considerations which the programming scheme could not – in order to keep the mathematical model practicable – itself consider*. This can, of course, be no excuse for letting subjective prejudices and arbitrary considerations lead to a departure from the optimal program determined by mathematical methods. The program should only be corrected in so far as objective circumstances and facts not considered in the model render this necessary.

For all these reasons the practical recommendation worked out by programming is a contribution to the "strategic plan" for investment and technical development, and is not intended to determine the operative details of the "tactical plan". The latter must, if no supplementary detail programming models are available, be elaborated by the traditional planning methods.

PART 3

THE TREATMENT OF UNCERTAIN DATA

Introduction

Throughout this book we have so far assumed that all data were certain and exactly known. We shall now abandon this hypothesis and proceed to examine the treatment of uncertain data.

Speaking generally, the main properties of certain data are that

(a) they are based on an adequately representative and reliably processed statistical survey covering some earlier period of time; and that

(b) they may be assumed to remain constant or, at least, fairly constant over time.

These properties will be satisfied by the statistically registered technical indicators, expressed in physical units (e.g. performance data of machines, capacity data, material input coefficients, etc.), of certain types of adequately tested technical equipment already in operation for some length of time.

Purchase and selling prices fixed contractually and secured by adequate penalties by the seller or buyer abroad, may, although on the basis of different criteria, be also considered as certain.

Only a small part of the data involved in investment efficiency calculation will answer these strict criteria. All other data must then be considered as uncertain.

The factors of uncertainty connected with investment efficiency calculation, with structural decisions can be classified from several view-points. Without pretending to completeness and theoretical generalization, I propose to deal here with three main categories of uncertainty:

(1) Some *real* inputs and real outputs of an activity may be uncertain. Thus there may be uncertainty about the prospective technical performance of a new machine, about the construction period of an investment project, etc. The term "real" indicates here that the problem does not consist in how to convert the value of this real input or real output into forints. What we have to deal with in this category is primarily the uncertainty of information of a technical character. However, the uncertainty of prospective import and export prices, to be quoted in

foreign currency, may also be counted under this heading. They, too, constitute real inputs and real outputs whose uncertainty can be separated from the problem of the rate of exchange at which their dollar or rouble prices should be converted into domestic currency.

A related problem is that constituted by the uncertainty of certain constraint constants of activities or activity combinations, e.g. our knowledge of the market constraints of exports lacks considerably in exactitude.

In all such cases we have to deal with uncertainties due to the lack of an exact knowledge of some objectively existing and real (present or future) given thing, of some *extrinsically given* magnitude independent of ourselves. Let us call these summarily the uncertainties due to the lack of information. It is mainly this type of uncertainty that will be discussed in the next third part of this book.

(2) It may be problematical how to express some real magnitude, be it extrinsically given or intrinsically determinable by economic administration, in terms of forint. For example, we may know the electric power consumption of a new machine in kWh on the basis of statistical observation but it may be problematical how to fix the unit price of electric power.

This type of uncertainty is due partly to the theoretical shortcomings of financial calculations and partly to the practical difficulties of computing.

The uncertainties connected with the computational evaluations will be discussed in full detail in Part 4 of the book.

(3) The sector models discussed so far covered individual spheres of activity which were taken out of their economy-wide context. What connected the scope of programming with the other sectors of the national economy were primarily the plan directives (output obligations, resource quotas, etc.). But at the time when partial decisions are being examined the plan directives must still be considered to some extent uncertain. Programming takes place in the planning phase and it may be due exactly to the result of the programming calculations that the original plan directives are subjected to alterations. Here we have to deal with magnitudes which are in contrast with the performance of a machine of given technology or the dollar price of some imported commodity not extrinsically given but *intrinsically determinable*. They are uncertain only as long as their magnitude is not determined by the top organs of economic administration.

The problem of the targets awaiting the decision of a higher authority will be dealt with in Part 5 of the book.

CHAPTER 9

THE DIFFICULTIES OF DETERMINING TECHNICAL AND COST DATA

9.1. The Mechanism of Data Supply

In the writings of economists and of those engaged in activity analysis in capitalist countries, references are frequently made to the difficulties due to the fact that a major part of the relevant data are treated as a business secret by private firms.

Our own investigations did not meet with this difficulty, a fact that has greatly eased our work. It may be stated in general that the socialist planned economy, with its broad, organized, highly centralized and uniform supply of data, favours also from this point of view the application of mathematical methods. There are, however, special difficulties which are mainly due to the novelty of the application of these methods under our conditions. The present section is to deal primarily with these difficulties.

Part of the data used in the programming models are estimates regarding the future, characteristics of technologies hitherto unknown in Hungary, etc. Such data will be inevitably uncertain. However, our models also required data which characterize actual facts *in present-day Hungary* and which were still not available in a perfectly certain form.

At present, the structure of data supply is generally adapted to the information requirements of operative management. (Although not entirely: complaints are frequently being voiced because of the inadequate harmony between operative management, and the work of traditional planning which forms part of it on the one hand, and the structure of data supply on the other.) But it can hardly meet the information requirements of the mathematical models. As a matter of fact, the mathematical methods will frequently require a data grouping and data structure entirely different from that regularly supplied by the data-supplying mechanism actually in operation. This will lead to a number of grave difficulties. A few only should be mentioned here.

The system of regular data supply records the data according to organizational units (e.g. ministries, industrial directorates, enterprises, plants, etc.). However, the scopes of our programming models will not necessarily be coincident with the official organizational units. (For a discussion of the subject see sections 5.2 and 6.2.) Thus, for instance, a special survey had to be carried out to determine the cotton industry's scope of operation to enable us to include these data in constraint 14 of the model.

There is another viewpoint from which the recording of data according to organizational units will cause difficulties. The choice between technological variants constitutes a prominent feature of our models. Thus, for example, the automatic machines already in operation in Hungarian mills figured among the alternatives of the cotton industry model. The data available did, however, not show directly the auxiliary material and electric power consumption of bobbin-changing automatic looms in a mill, because the plant data normally supplied would record only the auxiliary material and electric power consumption for the mill as a whole, where old mechanical and new automatic looms are working side by side. In such cases, too, separate and special surveys had to be carried out in order to determine the required technical and cost data.

In other cases again our sectoral model explicitly required average data of the industrial sector under investigation. Thus, in the cotton industry model we wanted to employ sector averages for the tariffs of steam and electricity, as our model did not take a stand on the question of the territorial allocation, according to enterprise, of the activities. These charges, too, had to be calculated separately, for the sector averages were not available.

Similar experiences were gained in other industrial sectors as well. *The methods of planning and of economic efficiency calculation are now making sudden and rapid progress, owing to the application of mathematical methods. Accountancy and statistical data processing must, therefore, be developed so as to meet the increased and special requirements of these types of calculation.*

Besides, this is the normal course of progress; it is usually the requirements of planning and economic calculation that set the tasks to accountancy and data supply.

Those engaged at present in mathematical programming of long-run plans must face these difficulties and procure the required figures by means of surveys and data assembling activity. But with the spread of mathematical programming, the demand will also become more urgent for securing the data required in programming – or at least a major part of them – by means of an *organized mechanism of supply.*

At present, the difficulties of data collecting still compel us to make allowances. Often they compel us to adopt the mechanism, classification and data system of traditional planning and accountancy even in cases where theoretical considerations would call for other methods of calculation. But we must do so in order to be at least able to "fill up" with data the framework of the model.

9.2. Random and Tendentious Errors in Estimation

In the foregoing it has been shown in detail that the lack of exact information will tend to make the estimation of some technical and cost data uncertain.

Whenever the data were handled *objectively and without prejudice* by those carrying out the estimation, the errors in the latter will be of a random character and due exclusively to imperfect information.

The case is entirely different when those carrying out the estimation have a personal interest in the realization (or non-realization) of the investment project in question. In such a case the estimation is often *prejudiced.*

To take an analogy from ballistics: in the first case, the dispersion of the points of impact is due to accidental errors in aiming; in the second case the fault is with the aiming device and it is the gun that pulls in one direction or the other.

Do there occur tendentious errors of estimation in the traditional calculations of investment efficiency?

As pointed out before, the official decisions on investments are based on a document in which all characteristic production, technical and cost data pertaining to the project in question are presented. This document I proposed to call the *permit papers.* It will be important to ascertain the extent to which the data submitted in the permit papers are in fact realized.

Unfortunately, it will be rather difficult to gain an insight into the facts. For years it had been the accepted practice to discuss thoroughly the individual estimates in the permit papers *before* taking a decision, but nobody would trouble to control *ulteriorly* the realization of the estimates.

Since 1960, the Hungarian Investments Bank is carrying out regularly so-called ulterior rentability surveys, in the course of which the realization of the estimates of permit papers are carefully controlled item by item*. Let us call the ratio of the actual and the planned figures the realization coefficient.

* In the compilation of the data which follow, I had the valuable assistance of Mrs. J. DEÁK (Hungarian Investments Bank). See also [33].

Details of the ulterior rentability surveys carried out in 1960 and in the first half of 1961 are summed up in table 9.1*.

Before proceeding to evaluate the data in the table, a few words on their reliability.

The reports of the bank, though they can hardly be considered as absolutely accurate, are certainly suitable to indicate the trends, based as they are on individual surveys of the investments. All data which appeared unsatisfactory from any point of view have been omitted. Moreover, when checking, we found that had the omitted data also been taken into consideration, the trends which will be analyzed in the sequel (overspending, etc.) would have become even more conspicuous.

The set of data whose characteristics have been established varies between 42 and 90. (Every survey did not contain data on all the relationships under investigation.) This is not too great a number. The investments under survey were selected at random.

Since it is only for 12–18 months now that investigations of this type are being carried out, no analysis of the dynamics of the phenomena was possible**.

It was our endeavour always to compare, within the limits of possibility, the estimates of the permit papers with the factual data. In the case of a number of investments we had, however, only a document of later date, the so-called "*plan-targets*" at our disposal. This, being drawn up at a later stage of planning, contains more accurate cost estimates than the permit paper. Table 9.1 presents, therefore, a somewhat more favourable picture of the situation than it actually is***.

* Drawing up investment projects is under actual conditions a matter of routine. The same agencies (investment departments, designing offices) and the same persons (officials in and heads of investment departments, engineers and economists in designing offices) are regularly engaged in the preparation of documents of this character.

As long as the given concrete forms of material and moral incentives as well as the given organizational forms of investment planning, approbation and control remain unchanged, the typical results and errors concomitant with the given methods are bound to "reproduce themselves" *en masse*. It seems, therefore, warranted to consider the realization coefficient of the estimates *a random variable*.

** The changes which have since occurred in the price level (adjustment of prices as per 1st January, 1959) have been balanced by the usual index adjustments.

*** In the 1960 survey material of the Hungarian Investments Bank, the permit papers of 8 investment projects were available together with the plan target estimates. In the case of the permit papers overspending averaged 54.2 per cent, in that of the plan targets 8.9 per cent.

TABLE 9.1

Permit paper estimates and their realization

	Number of data processed	Average realization coefficient of estimates	Standard deviation	Standard deviation in per cent of the mean	Confidence interval with 95 per cent probability*
(1) Total investment costs	90	122.2	36.2	29.6	114.6—129.8
(2) Construction costs	58	126.7	48.9	38.6	113.9—139.5
(3) Machinery investment costs	42	105.3	39.0	37.0	93.2—117.4
(4) Other investment costs	62	163.5	121.3	74.2	132.7—194.3
(5) Realization period**	79	149.4	65.7	44.0	134.7—164.1
(6) Production	90	103.9	18.2	17.5	100.1—107.7
(7) Specific investment costs	81	122.2	37.2	30.5	114.0—130.4

* The concept of the confidence interval as illustrated in row (1) should be interpreted to mean that the interval between 114.6 per cent and 129.8 per cent may be assumed with a probability of 95 per cent to contain the expected value of the realization coefficient of all investment costs.

** The periods during which investment work was suspended at central orders have been deducted when calculating realization periods.

The least reliable are the data which refer to estimated and actual production. By lack of suitable preliminary figures, the "plan index" is often fixed only ulteriorly. This row of data must therefore be taken with reservation.

Let us now survey the conclusions to be drawn from the table.

Actual total investment costs are frequently higher than the estimates. The average (arithmetical mean) of overspending is quite considerable, reaching as it does the value of 22.2 per cent.

Individual realization percentages show quite considerable variation around the mean of overspending; the standard deviation amounts to 29.6 per cent of the mean. *The standard deviation measures the random errors contained in the estimates.*

The extent to which the investment will, when all is said and done, draw on or overdraw the estimated amount depends, among others,

---

The data available for comparison are extremely scarce. Such as are available indicate the well-known fact that the plan targets are more mature and better founded documents than the permit papers. It is, however, on the basis of the latter that investment *decisions* are made.

on a number of incidental, chance factors. Such factors are the high or low quality of designing; the organized or disorganized character of the investment; the degree to which the cooperating firms are meeting or falling short of their obligations; the timely or delayed arrival of import shipments; and others. All these factors will greatly vary from investment to investment.

On the other hand, *the 22.2 per cent mean of the overspending reflects the tendentious distortions, biases in the estimates.*

We have examined whether this trend asserts itself more strongly in the case of greater investment projects than in that of the smaller ones. It was, however, not possible to establish a correlation between the size (total cost) of the investment and the proportion of overspending.

The three principal cost groups differ as to the uncertainty of investment cost estimates. Machine prices are generally exactly known, be it domestic or foreign makes; the relative data can be easily controlled already at the stage when the permit is granted. Construction cost estimates are considerably less reliable, with an average overspending of 26.7 per cent, and the estimates of so-called "other" costs are least so. The latter are generally known to be the least "tangible".

The data relating to the realization period show marked protractions in carrying out the investment projects. In the majority of cases the estimates could have been realized if certain organizational requirements (up-to-date construction methods, deliveries of machinery according to a suitable schedule, etc.) had been met. However, in relation to the *actual* realization periods which are at present general, the estimates are low.

As already pointed out, the figures relating to production tend to touch up reality. Yet it seems realistic enough to assume that effective capacities are generally not lower, and often even higher, than the planned ones.

To sum up, it may be stated that *there is a marked tendency to "underestimate" costs, especially construction costs and those coming under the "other" heading, as well as the period of realization**. It is the "chauvinism" of the investing firms or sectors that comes here into play. The investing party – in order to secure the granting of a permit – will endeavour to make investment costs appear lower in the preliminary calculations than the actual requirements**. It will be assumed that the permit

* See also L. LUKÁCS [107].

** In connection with the investment rentability calculations, someone told the following witty anecdote: "A passer-by asks the boys shooting at a wooden fence: 'How is it possible that you always hit the exact centre of the circle?' – The boys answered: 'By shooting first and drawing the circle afterwards'."

TABLE 9.2

Realization coefficients and their frequency distribution

Interval of the realization coefficients (in per cent)	Frequency (Number of investments surveyed)	Relative frequency (in per cent)	Probability according to the fitted log-normal distribution (in per cent)
60	0	0	1.1
60– 80	6	6.7	8.3
80–100	19	21.1	20.1
100–120	23	25.6	23.7
120–140	19	21.1	20.1
140–160	9	10.0	12.7
160–180	7	7.8	7.1
180–200	3	3.3	3.7
200–220	2	2.2	1.7
220–240	1	1.1	0.8
240–260	1	1.1	0.4
260	0	0	0.3
Total	90	100.0	100.0

once granted, overspending and the protraction of the realization period would not matter too much; the investment project once launched would hardly be stopped later on; and the amount of overspending would ultimately be paid out. Nor does the system of material incentives connected with the investments counteract these tendencies, as the fact of overspending does not involve any sanctions*.

The phenomena are generally known. It is not within the scope of this work to trace in detail the motives and factors behind these tendencies. This would require a thoroughgoing analysis of all material and moral incentives connected with the investments as well as of the organ-

---

This is what frequently happens to the estimates. First comes the "shooting" — it is decided that this or that alternative will turn out favourable. Then the circle is drawn — the estimates are manipulated in a way that the calculation should produce the required result.

* The motives behind the cautious planning for capacities are not quite clear. The phenomenon can probably be explained on the basis of the fact that planned capacities are in advance accounted for, "put into the plan", as resources in the product balance; falling short of planned capacities is therefore judged more severely.

izational problems of planning, execution and control, etc. Here it should suffice to point out that the data of the permit papers contain typical errors and tendentious distortions, a fact borne out by table 9.1.

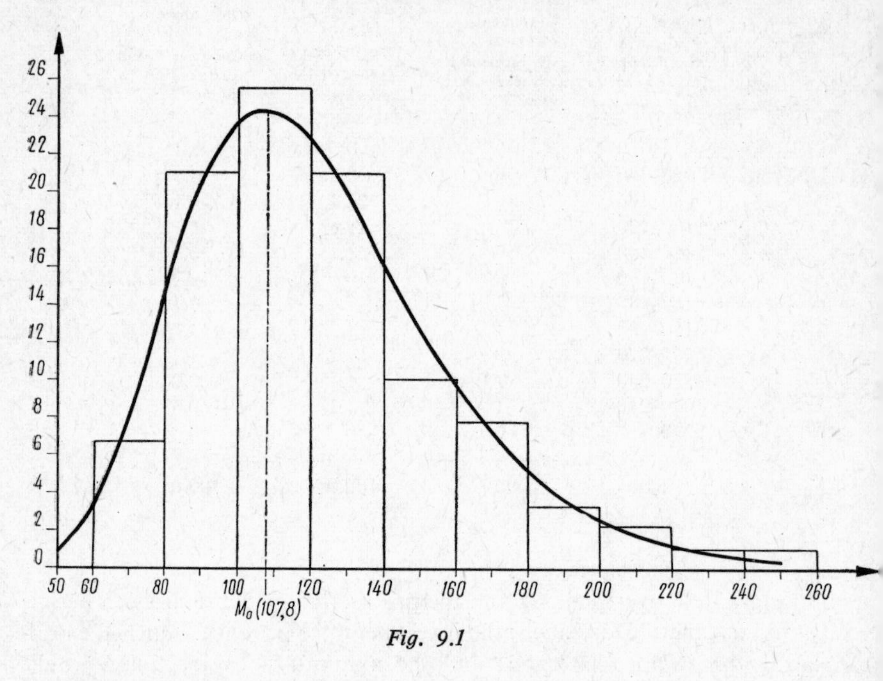

Fig. 9.1

On the basis of the total investment cost data presented in table 9.1, a further calculation has also been carried out. Let us denote the ratio of actual and planned total investment costs with **Q**.

This realization coefficient **Q** was found to be a random variable which lends itself to satisfactory characterization by what is called the log-normal distribution. This is shown in table 9.2 and in figure 9.1.

The third column in the table shows the relative frequencies established empirically on the basis of the Hungarian Investments Bank surveys, e.g. in 10 per cent of all cases surveyed by the bank, the realization coefficient was within the range of 140–160 per cent. The fourth column shows the probabilities calculated on the basis of the fitted log-normal distribution, e.g. there is a 20.1 per cent probability for the realization coefficient to fall within the range of 120–140 per cent. The histogram in the figure shows the relative frequencies established on the basis of the bank's data, while the continuous curve represents the fitted probability density function. The figure also shows the empirical values to be close to the corresponding values of the fitted function*. A test carried out in this connection also proved that the empirically established relative frequencies did not considerably differ from the continuous density function.

Some characteristics of the random variable are interesting from the economic point of view.

The *most frequent* value, the mode (M_0 in the figure) is 107.8 per cent. It is thus higher, but not much higher, than the cost estimates. However, the mean of the realization coefficients lies considerably higher at 122.2 per cent.

The distribution is asymmetrical. The slope of the curve is rather mild at the right of the mode – the maximum value of the density function – while at its left it is considerably steeper. In economic terms this can, in my opinion, be interpreted as follows:

As pointed out before, it is not in the interest of those submitting the permit papers to set the estimates of investment costs too high. Errors in this direction will, nevertheless, occur; these, however, are not tendentious. Those drawing up the plans will not *voluntarily* commit an error of this type, and the dispersion of the data in this direction is, therefore, not significant. This fact finds its expression in the steep slope of the left side of the curve in figure 9.1.

It is the wish of those submitting the project that the permit should be granted. This fact constitutes a factor operating in the direction of "underestimating". However, not all projects go an *equal way* in this direction. On the one hand, not all planners are conscious of their responsibilities in the same degree, and, on the other hand, not all projects are worth the trouble of "face-lifting". If, for example, a favourable decision had already been taken beforehand concerning the granting of the permit, then it will not be worth while to underestimate the costs – the fate of the project will not be endangered even by a less advantageous economic index. But whenever the fate of the project seems doubtful, it will be worth while to "buttress" it by somewhat optimistic figures.

* On log-normal distribution see A. RÉNYI [148], pp. 209–210, or H. CRAMÉR [23], p. 220.

The density function of log-normally distributed random variable $\mathbf{Q}$ is

$$g(y) = \frac{1}{\sqrt{2\pi}\,\sigma y} \exp \frac{-(\ln y - m)^2}{2\sigma^2}, \quad y > 0. \tag{9.1}$$

In our present case, the parameters of the fitted function are:
m = the expected value of the natural logarithm of the data = 4.76
σ = the standard deviation of the natural logarithm of the data = 0.29.

As a consequence of the great variety of factors, the degree of underestimation tends to show a wide dispersion. This is brought to expression in the mild slope of the right side of the curve shown in figure 9.1.

The probability of overspending as against estimated costs amounts to 60.9 per cent.

Let Q_{80} denote the realization coefficient of which the following is known: that there is an 80 per cent probability that the value of actual realization coefficient Q will be below this Q_{80} value. In the theory of probability this latter value is called the 80 per cent *quantile** of random variable Q.

In the present case $_{80} = 148.4$ per cent. In other words: it may be expected with an 80 per cent probability that overspending as against cost estimates will not exceed 48.4 per cent, and the probability of exceeding even this value is only of 20 per cent.

The observation of a larger set of data would render our knowledge about the probability distribution of errors in the estimates more accurate. As the scope of the relevant data widens, the analysis must be accordingly extended. The *dynamics* of the tendencies under observation must also be drawn into the orbit of the investigations which must come to cover the characteristic differences between the individual domains and industrial sectors, and other aspects too.

9.3. Promoting Unbiased Work

How can the tendentious biases described in the foregoing be counteracted in the course of the rentability calculations?

The most important thing is to eliminate the factors tending to induce the biases, to modify in a suitable manner the systems both of material and moral incentives and of supervision. There are real possibilities for carrying out such modifications; it is, however, not within our present scope to discuss the concrete ways and means.

As those submitting the permit papers are known to be actually biased in the majority of cases, it will be expedient to have their estimates supervised by persons unprejudiced *by virtue of their position.* Supervision should, whenever possible, be carried out by specialists who are not prompted to partiality either by their official position or by any personal interest.

* On the concept of the quantile see A. Rényi [148], pp. 285–287; H. Cramér [23], p. 181.

In this sense, too, our programming investigations have resulted in a control of the original plans. The economists responsible for directing the investigations were *by virtue of their position* not interested to "make out a case" for one or the other viewpoint.

In our investigations top executives of industrial sectors and enterprises, who could be expected to be more or less partial, also participated, if only in an advisory capacity. The very nature of the investment programming model was, however, favourable to more objective estimation. In the cotton industry program we sought to work out the optimal composition of the machine fleet required to meet given output obligations stipulated in a *given production plan*. The executives of industries and enterprises who participated in our work were warned of the possible consequences of errors in the estimates. If they underestimated the efficiency of the automatic machines and modern equipment, the calculations would not show the acquisition of the latter profitable, although it was in the interest of the persons concerned to render their respective industries more up-to-date. If, on the other hand, they overestimated the prospective efficiency of such machinery, the calculations would show a lower number of machines to be required to meet the obligations contained in the given production plan, and envisage a lower investment amount than actually needed. The production plan may then prove overtight, a circumstance they would hardly welcome as the responsible managers of the domain concerned. It was thus in the proper interest of the specialists participating in our work to give neither too low nor too high but reasonably accurate estimates.

Apart now from the example of the cotton industry, the "Janus face" with which industrial executives would react to the production plan on the one hand and the investments plan on the other, is a generally known phenomenon. When dealing with the *investments* plan, they usually strive to convince the higher organs of administration of the prospective high efficiency of new and modern machinery. The overoptimistic estimation of the technical efficiency of such equipment is a frequent occurrence (although the contrary can also be met with). When discussing the *production* plan, on the other hand, they tend to estimate prospective capacities rather cautiously and pessimistically. Besides, this double-faced attitude is also made possible by the fact that decisions concerning investment rentability and planning for production targets are carried out at different levels.

The model types described in the present work afford a possibility for reducing the effect of this duality. *As a matter of fact, the model includes both the production and the investment plans.* The constraints which prescribe the output obligations and the objective function which indicates the economic results contain *identical* data of technical efficiency. One cannot, therefore, be at the same time too optimistic in one direction and too pessimistic in the other; the very nature of the model will help the intrinsic harmony and consistency of the decisions.

The objectivity of the estimation can be increased also by relying, whenever possible, on *collective* rather than individual *estimates*. In this respect we have gained favourable experiences in the course of the industrial sector investigations. The engineers and economists who took part in the investigations carried out their work of estimation collectively, correcting one anothers recommendations on the basis of their individual experiences. The estimates of the research team were then submitted to a broader committee of experts which, after thorough discussion, partly corrected them. All this went a long way towards rendering the estimates more reliable and objective.

So far we have been speaking of the methods of increasing objectivity. We should, at the same time, be aware of the fact that this may not always be possible. The distortive factors, although eliminable, may *for the moment* be still at work. Nor will it always be possible to have the estimates worked out by unbiased specialists; and so on. As a consequence, top economic administration will often be compelled to base their decisions on data prepared in the normal course of investment planning, although these may be expected to be biased. What can be done in a case like this?

The purpose could, in my opinion, be served by *a type of control calculation which "discounts", as it were, the error presumably contained in the permit papers*. For example, one could suppose that the realization coefficients of the estimates of costs, realization period and planned capacity will correspond to the average calculated up till now. Accordingly, if one considered, by lack of a more suitable index, the 22.2 per cent calculated in the foregoing as the average rate of overspending, one could add a round 22 per cent to the originally submitted cost estimates. After correcting the rest of the data in the same way, the efficiency of the investment project could be revised. We shall revert to this type of control calculation in greater detail later on.

The comparative calculation described in the foregoing is aimed at finding out what would happen if estimated costs were exceeded. Would this definitely render the investment project inefficient? The sober-minded consideration of this possibility is not inconsistent with the demand that the investment directives issued after granting the permit should approximate to realistic and realizable but *not unduly pessimistic* estimates. To impose on the investor the higher safety values employed in the control calculations would constitute an unjustifiable slackness. The directives must be more strict and challenging than that.

When carrying out the control calculations it should be borne in mind that the numerical inferences drawn from earlier data – such as the conclusions concerning the mean or the probability distribution of errors in the estimates – are valid only as long as the *conditions do not change* under which the data concerned had been established. As soon as any changes occur in the system of the material and moral incentives, the management of investments, etc. – and a number of changes would indeed be desirable – the numerical inferences will lose their validity.

CHAPTER 10

SENSITIVITY ANALYSIS. PARAMETRIC PROGRAMMING

10.1 Serial Calculations

If we could be absolutely certain about all assumptions and all data involved in our model, it would be sufficient to carry out a single programming project the results of which could be unequivocally considered the optimal program. No long-term calculations will, however, afford such certainty in actual practice. It will therefore be usually expedient to carry out entire programming series instead of a single project.

We must examine numerically what the consequences would be if we replaced the original assumptions by others as our starting points. What would be the consequences of our numerical data not reflecting the exact reality? How "sensitively" would the optimal program react to this – would it be modified as a consequence?

The calculations meant to provide an answer to these questions will be called in the following s e n s i t i v i t y a n a l y s i s*. These calculations will thus show *how modifications in the preliminary assumptions and original data will affect the optimal program.*

The result of the calculation series and of sensitivity analyses will be not a single "optimal" program but several ones, each of which may be called so with respect to its own preliminary assumptions and data. These will thus in each case be *relative* optima only, whose collective study and comparative analysis will help to reach a rational decision. Accordingly, the notion of an "optimum" must not be overrated from the economic point of view when dealing with programming projects.

One type of sensitivity analysis is concerned with the study of the programs obtained as a result of changing the f r a m e w o r k of the model. By the latter I mean here the types of constraint, objective function, etc. employed – in other words, all that can be denoted by mathematical symbols without the use of numbers. A case in point is the comparison of results obtained by using a concave cost function on the one

* On sensitivity analysis see E. L. ARNOFF and S. S. SENGUPTA [2], vol. 1.

hand and a linear one on the other in the programming project for the man-made fibres industry (see section 7.5).

Another type of sensitivity analysis concerns itself with the study of the effects of changing the *numerical* values which we substitute for the symbols, i.e. the characteristics of the model, in a model of given framework*. For example, in the course of programming for the cotton industry we examined how changes in the price of the machines will affect the optimal program.

The most simple type of sensitivity analysis, and an extremely useful one at the same time, is the comparison of the results of calculations carried out simultaneously. This is what we practically always do when studying the effects of changes in the model framework but the same can be done when investigating the effects of changes in the numerical characteristics figuring in the model. In such cases, the comparison is carried out with discrete values of the magnitude in question fixed in advance.

In certain cases it will be possible to employ for the purpose of sensitivity analyses of this type a special method called parametric programming.

10.2. Parametric Programming

Let us take an example. We have to carry out a programming project of which we know all the characteristics except the coefficients figuring in the objective function. As a matter of fact, even the data necessary for the numerical determination of these coefficients would be available, we only do not know the rental on capital which would be justified from the economic point of view. We want to determine the coefficient c_j figuring in the objective function, on the basis of the formula:

$$c_j = \gamma p_j + r_j, \qquad (10.1)$$

where

γ = the rental on capital
p_j = investment cost per one unit of the jth activity
r_j = operation cost per one unit of the jth activity.

* In the case of a model of given framework, the set of numerical values which determine the optimal program, will here be referred to as characteristics of the programming model. For example, in the case of a linear programming project similar to that described in ch. 2, these characteristics are the numerical values of the elements of matrix **A** and of the components of vectors **b** and **c**′.

The method we will employ is to set ourselves a whole range of programming problems instead of a single one. Let the rental be 5 per cent in the first problem, 6 per cent in the second one, 7 per cent in the third one, and so on. These problems resemble one another, they are, as it were, closely related. What the members of this problem "family" have in common is that in each of them the framework of the model is identical, and so are the numerical characteristics, except the rental which affects the magnitude of the coefficient in the objective function. The problems differ from one another in the different numerical values which we substitute for the symbol γ.

It would be conceivable to solve the individual problems in this problem range individually, independently from one another. One could work out the problem first on the basis of a 6 per cent rental, put aside the result, work it out at a 7 per cent rental, then at an 8 per cent rental, and so forth. To each problem there belongs an optimal program. There are, however, methods which will enable us to work out the whole problem range by means of a single *calculation series*. These methods are called parametric programming. In our example it is the rental on capital that constitutes the parameter. The following part of this chapter will not treat the problem of a vector parameter, but will be confined to the case where the parameter is a single real number.

What we mean by parametric programming can be described in the most general terms as follows.

The characteristics of the programming problem are, at least partly, not constant values but variables – functions of what is called the parameter. (In our former example vector $\mathbf{c}'$, the whole of the coefficients in the objective function, is a function of the parameter.) It follows that the *optimal program* itself – which is determined by the characteristics of the problem – is a *function of the parameter*. Let λ denote the parameter in general and $\mathbf{x}^*$ the optimal program:

$$\mathbf{x}^* = \mathbf{x}^*(\lambda)\,. \tag{10.2}$$

Let us now determine $\mathbf{x}^*(\lambda)$, i.e. the optimal program as a function of the parameter.

Here parameter λ is a real number. The problem can be further generalized if we allow the parameter to be a vector. For example, the magnitude of the coefficient in the objective function will depend on λ_1, the rental on capital; λ_2, the rouble rate of exchange; λ_3, the dollar rate of exchange; λ_4, the rate of increase in the level of wages. In this case the parameter will be $\lambda = [\lambda_1, \ldots, \lambda_4]$.

In order to understand the *economic meaning* of the parameter as interpreted in the following, we should see clearly that changes in the parameter do not, usually, express actual changes over time in the economic magnitude in question. The real and actual value of the parameter we do *not know and for this reason* we vary it – "let it run" through different values – while trying to ascertain the changes this brings about in the functionally related objective function. In this case we thus *wish to draw economic inferences from the functional relationships existing between the different parameters and the optimal program.*

In its entirely general form described above, the problem of parametric programming is a considerably wide one. In actual practice we must usually bring in rather substantial restrictions in order to attain a soluble problem.

The most important restriction: the characteristics of the problem should be *linear* functions of the parameter.

Secondly: it is important to consider which characteristics of the problem will depend on the parameter, e.g. the characteristics of the objective function alone, or the constraints alone, or the coefficients in the constraints alone, or all these together. So far, algorithms suitable for use on computers have only been developed for special cases. Some of the latter will be discussed in section 10.3 below.

The problem is facilitated by the fact that in actual practice we are usually not interested in all the possible values that the parameter in question may take. Nobody will wish to know how the optimal program would turn out in the case of a 1000 per cent rental on capital. It will always be possible, on the basis of economic considerations, to fix a lower and an upper limit for the parameter which it will not be worth the trouble to go beyond in the course of the analysis. Let these limits be denoted by the symbols λ_0 and λ^0. As a consequence, the problem of parametric programming reduces itself to determining the function

$$\mathbf{x}^* = \mathbf{x}^*(\lambda), \qquad \lambda_0 \leqq \lambda \leqq \lambda^0. \tag{10.3}$$

In such a case the problem may be nothing more than e.g. to determine all optimal programs which will be attained if we let the rental "run through" the range between 3 per cent and 30 per cent.

There is a further factor to facilitate the problem. *In the majority of cases, not all the changes in the parameter will bring about a fundamental change in the optimal program.* Let us examine this question in some detail.

We will call the set of the indices of variables with a positive value in the optimal program, the s t r u c t u r e of the program. Two different programs may have an identical structure. For example, in both programs we have the same variables with a positive value; thus, among others, variable 1, but while in the first program $x_1 = 1000$, in the second program $x_1 = 2000$. *The programs with an identical structure mark out an identical direction of activity but differ from one another in the extent of the activity in the given direction.*

Now, one of the following two cases will be frequently met with in parametric programming:

(a) To several subsequent values – a whole range – of the parameter there belongs the *same* optimal program.

(b) To several subsequent values – a whole range – of the parameter there belongs an optimal program of the *same structure*, although the value of the individual variables within the same structure will vary.

In the first case we may speak of a quantitative identity interval, in the second case of a qualitative identity interval of the parameter.

Economic analysis requires a knowledge of the *bounds* of the identity intervals. In this connection too, we will introduce the appropriate terms:

The bounds of the quantitative identity intervals we will call the parameter's quantitative characteristic values, the bounds of the qualitative identity intervals the parameter's qualitative characteristic values.

10.3. Some Practical Examples

To illustrate the methods of sensitivity analysis, we shall give below some examples from the practice of our programming calculations.

A typical case of parametric programming: the coefficients figuring in the objective function are partly or wholly dependent on the parameter which is a real number. This is the case, for example, where the cost factors taken into account in the objective function are dependent on the rental on capital or on the rate of exchange.

We made a number of similar computations in our sectoral investigations; we shall return to them in Part 4, treating the problems of the rental on capital and those of the exchange rate. This is comparatively the simplest case as far as the calculation problem is concerned. In such cases, provided that the model is similar to that described in this book, we will obtain more or less wide quantitative identity intervals*.

* In the cases where we are dealing with a linear programming problem which we intend to solve by means of the simplex method, and the coefficient in the objective function is a linear function of the parameter, the method described by S. Gass [43] (ch. 8), may be employed.

Another typical problem of parametric programming is the analysis of the effects on the optimal program of changes in the characteristics of an activity.

Let us start from the following assumptions: The jth variable *does not* figure in the optimal program. The characteristics of the jth activity are the following: coefficient c_j figuring in the objective function, and $\mathbf{a}_j$, the jth column vector of the matrix of the coefficients figuring in the constraints (thus e.g. in the programming project for the cotton industry, the activity's annual product, gross investment requirement, capitalist foreign exchange requirement, space requirement, material requirement, etc.).

Let us furthermore assume that both coefficient c_j and column vector $\mathbf{a}_j$ are functions of some parameter λ. (In the case of the column vector, it may probably be part of the components only that will depend on the parameter.)

In this case *it will be comparatively simple to establish the characteristic value of parameter λ which will bring the* j*th variable within the scope of the optimal program.*

I am giving below a brief description of a sensitivity analysis of this type carried out within the framework of the cotton industry calculations.

From among the new automatic looms it was the cheapest but least productive shuttle-changing type that figured in the optimal program, driving out the more expensive but also more productive bobbin-changing type. When the results became known, doubts were raised as to whether we had taken into account realistically the differences in productivity between the two types.

To check the results we carried out the following control calculation.

We retained the data with which we had originally characterized the shuttle-changing loom, i.e. a performance of 210 r.p.m. with an efficiency of 87 per cent. The characteristics of the bobbin-changing loom (the 118th activity in the model), on the other hand, we considered as the functions of a parameter: the loom's revolutions per minute. For the sake of simplicity, we defined parameter λ as follows:

$$\lambda = \frac{\text{r.p.m. of the bobbin-changing loom}}{\text{r.p.m. of the shuttle-changing loom}}$$

with the given efficiency coefficient of 87 per cent. On parameter λ will depend the following characteristics of the loom:

$$a_{1,118}(\lambda) = a''_{1,118}\,\lambda\,, \tag{10.4}$$

where $a''_{1,118}$ is the annual product of the loom at 210 r.p.m.

$$a_{7,118}(\lambda) = a''_{7,118}\,\lambda\,, \tag{10.5}$$

where $a''_{7,118}$ denotes the loom's annual sized warp requirement at 210 r.p.m. The coefficients $a''_{i,118}$ in the rest of constraints of a product-balance character should be interpreted in a similar manner.

Accordingly, in the case of the bobbin-changing loom, the column vector of all coefficients figuring in the constraints will be

$$\mathbf{a}_{118} = \mathbf{a}'_{118} + \mathbf{a}''_{118}\,\lambda\,, \tag{10.6}$$

where $\mathbf{a}'_{118}$ is the column vector composed of the part of coefficients $a_{i,118}$ which is independent of the parameter, and $\mathbf{a}''_{118}$ the column vector composed of the part of coefficients $a''_{i,118}$ which depends on the parameter.

The coefficient in the objective function will be

$$c_{118} = c'_{118} + c''_{118}\,\lambda\,, \tag{10.7}$$

where c'_{118} is the part of unit cost independent of the parameter, and c''_{118} the part of unit cost depending on the parameter; the former consists basically of investment costs, the latter of operation costs. Some elements of the latter are, strictly speaking, not exactly proportional to the r.p.m. (e.g. power costs will grow progressively with increasing r.p.m.) but the assumption of linearity does not constitute here an inadmissible inaccuracy.

The question now is, what critical r.p.m. must the bobbin-changing loom regularly attain in order to drive out the shuttle-changing loom from the optimal program? By what percentage must it exceed the latter, i.e. what is the characteristic value* of parameter λ?

The results** of the calculations are presented in table 10.1. For the sake of comparison we also present in the table the r.p.m. estimates of the Cotton Industry Directorate.

A similar characteristic value can also be established when column vector $\mathbf{a}_j$ is not dependent on the parameter and a functional relationship

* For the calculation method employed see [77].

** When evaluating the results it should be borne in mind that the question here is not whether with the bobbin-changing loom 230 r.p.m. can be attained at all. The key issue here – as throughout our calculations for the cotton industry – is whether in the Hungarian cotton industry as a whole this performance can be as an average regularly attained.

TABLE 10.1

Critical r.p.m. of the bobbin-changing loom

	R.p.m., bobbin-changing loom at 87 per cent efficiency	R.p.m., bobbin-changing loom as a percentage of r. p. m., shuttle-changing loom
The bobbin-changing loom comes within the optimal program if	230	108.5
Estimates of Cotton Industry Directorate:		
for 2nd year of running-in	213	106.1
for 3rd year of running-in	233	107.1

exists only between the latter and coefficient c_j in the objective function. In this case it will be extremely simple to determine numerically the characteristic value*.

A calculation of this type has been carried out e.g. in the framework of the programming project for the cotton industry. There, we worked out for some Hungarian-made textile machines the highest cost of production and, on the basis of the latter, the highest price which would still allow them to figure in the optimal program.

Or again, in the project for the man-made fibres industry, when we sought to find out the lowest export price which would still warrant the setting up of an excess capacity to produce more of a product than its home requirement.

Finally, another example, we established the optimal program on the basis of given numerical characteristics. It will then be *possible to define for each individual characteristic the interval within which its numerical value can change without modifying the optimal program* (provided that the numerical value of all other characteristics of the problem remains unchanged)**. To use a term borrowed from technical language these will be the *tolerance limits* of the characteristic in question.

For example, we have worked out the optimal program in the knowledge that annual operation costs of an activity were Ft 20 000. After programming it turned out that the optimal program will be the same whatever the costs between Ft 19 400 and Ft 20 800.

* See [77]. Besides, this problem can also be interpreted as a special case of that described in paragraph 1, where vector $\mathbf{c}'$ was a function of the parameter.

** For a discussion of the method – as applied to linear programming – see M. COURTILLOT [22].

It will be easy to see that from the mathematical point of view the determination of tolerance limits comes within the scope of parametric programming. The only limitation here is that we analyze the effects of changes in a single datum only, and seek to determine the limits of *one* identity interval only, one which extends below and above the original value of the parameter in question.

10.4. The "Neighbourhood" of the Optimum

In the course of our calculations we endeavoured not only to work out the optimal program but also to explore the "neighbourhood" of the optimum, i.e. the sub-optimal program with an objective function value only slightly less favourable than that of the optimal program. A knowledge of these will prove most useful. As a matter of fact, when making a decision, some points of view may arise which were not previously taken into account in the model's system of constraints and objective function, but which must nevertheless not be disregarded. It is for this reason that in the course of the project's practical realization one will have to take into consideration also the programs which are not much less favourable than the optimal program as far as the objective function is concerned, and more advantageous than the optimal program as regards the points of view which were not taken into account in the model.

Thus, in the man-made fibres industry it would be advantageous to develop propylene production as a vertical combination, producing the basic polypropylene material as well as both propylene rayon and fibre. The organizational advantages of this solution must be obvious. Our mathematical model, however, treating as it did the production of basic polypropylene, propylene rayon and propylene fibre as separate activities, did not show the advantages of combination and joint production. As a consequence, the program with the most favourable objective function value covers only the production of polypropylene and of propylene rayon, without that of the propylene fibre. On the other hand, there were programs in the "neighbourhood" of optimum, with an only slightly less favourable objective function value, which contained the production of all three products. In a case like this, top management will be faced with the problem of deciding whether it would not be worth while to meet the comparatively slight surplus cost indicated by the objective function, for the sake of joint production, or, in more general terms, for the sake of an advantage which, although not expressed by the objective function, can still realistically be expected.

10.5. The Significance of Sensitivity Analysis

Summing up what has been said above, it may be stated that one of the most important results of sensitivity analysis consists in it enabling us to establish the *common elements and stable points* of programs which are optimal from different points of view. Which are the activities which will figure in the optimal, or near-optimal, program, even in the case of different preliminary assumptions and data, different numerical characteristics? Which again are those activities which will not figure in any optimal program? The answer to these questions will facilitate beforehand the decisions with which top management is faced; it will be relatively safe to decide for the former and against the latter activities. There will, of course, still remain an open question: that of the "unstable" activities, of those which figure in the optimal program in the one case and do not figure there in the other. But in such a case too, sensitivity analysis provides a basis for further investigations by establishing the factors to which the optimal program will be sensitive – the assumptions or data on which the favourable or unfavourable estimation of an activity will depend.

The traditional investment efficiency calculations carried out by more primitive methods have the weakness of being much too "self-reliant". They frequently conceal their simplifying assumptions and uncertainties; they produce the illusion that top management could safely rely on them when making a decision. "Whenever the value of an indicator is above 1, it is all right; whenever it is below 1, it is wrong" – judgements like this may easily be misleading.

Sensitivity analysis will have a somewhat chilling effect on this self-reliance. It will at once become clear that optimal decisions depend on a great number of factors, with uncertain and debatable ones among them. I am, however, convinced that hesitation at the sight of the results of sensitivity analysis is a healthy phenomenon, as it will prompt to more profound investigations and many-sided analysis*.

* In my book, considerably more types of sensitivity analysis and parallel programming are described than required for normal use. The reason is that in our own investigations we had to face the double task of solving the practical problems set by higher economic administration and working out a programming methodology on the basis of scientific research.

CHAPTER 11

"PESSIMISTIC" AND "OPTIMISTIC" RANKING

11.1. The Problem of Decisions with Uncertain Consequences

In the course of discussing the treatment of uncertain data in chs. 9–10, we have so far been dealing with such questions as e.g. the sources of the uncertainty about some data, the foundations of estimates, the carrying out of sensitivity investigations, etc. All these showed that some of the data in long-term calculations were *uncertain.* For this reason, the question logically poses itself and this will be the subject-matter of chs. 11–14:

How can rational decisions be reached, once the consequences of a decision are partly uncertain?

This question constitutes the central problem of what is called *decision theory*. It is one that has engaged the attention not only of economists, but especially of mathematicians and mathematical statisticians for the past twenty years. The most important – one may say, epoch-making – work in the field is that of J. Neumann, an outstanding mathematician of Hungarian origin and O. Morgenstern*.

The questions posed by decision theory, its mathematical formulations, are thought-evoking. The possibilities of its application are, however, limited by the character of our investigations, which is quite different from that of the previously mentioned works. The authors engaged in decision theory would seek the criteria of rational decision-making on the basis of rather abstract formulae, conforming to rather general postulates. In a certain sense, this is the merit of their works, enabling as it does the utilization of some of their results – illustrated possibly by examples taken from card games or property insurance – in the solution of practical problems of the socialist planned economy. We must, however, not expect their works to provide recipes for the solution of such problems.

* See [136]. This work was followed by several others of considerable importance. See A. Wald [176], H. Chernoff [20], L. J. Savage [153], J. Milnor [127]. For a comprehensive survey of the development of decision theory see K. J. Arrow [3] and R. D. Luce and H. Raiffa [106].

It should, moreover, be pointed out that the methods and propositions of decision theory are still the subject of much controversy even among its adherents. What we have to do with is rather a thought-evoking beginning than a fully developed theory.

The models described in the following touch on the problems of decision theory. The field is, however, narrowed down to investigations *into some decision problems concerning investments in a socialist planned economy.* Without aspiring at particular scientific standards, our exposition is rather concerned with the practical aspects of the problems involved. What follows below cannot be considered a satisfactory solution of the problem – it is merely a first attempt, aimed at giving an impetus to start the debate on the related questions in this country.

For a better demonstration of the problem, let us begin with a practical example taken from the programming project of the man-made fibres industry. Before proceeding, it will, however, be necessary to say a few words about the *mathematical form of the estimations.*

11.2. The "From-to" Form of Estimation

It is a normal procedure in economic life to characterize uncertain data by two values instead of a single one – by the *lower* and *upper limits* which the data in question will certainly not exceed or for which there is only a very small probability to be exceeded. To use the accepted term: the data are presented in the "from-to" form. The application of this form will prove expedient also in investment efficiency calculations.

The estimates concerning the technical, cost and foreign trade data were worked out in "from-to" form by the experts participating in the project for the man-made fibres industry.

Let Z denote the datum in question, which may be a price, a cost factor, etc. We ignore its exact value; all we know is that it will be within two limits:

$$Z_0 \leqq Z \leqq Z^0. \tag{11.1}$$

Let $\bar{Z}$ denote the middle point of the datum interval between the two limits, or, more exactly, the arithmetical mean of the limits Z_0 and Z^0.

$$\bar{Z} = \frac{Z_0 + Z^0}{2}. \tag{11.2}$$

The uncertainty of the data can be characterized by the ratio of the difference between the limits and the mean, and the mean itself. This ratio we will denote by U:

$$U = \frac{Z^0 - \bar{Z}}{\bar{Z}} = \frac{\bar{Z} - Z_0}{\bar{Z}}. \tag{11.3}$$

This we shall call the g r a d e o f u n c e r t a i n t y. For practical purposes it can be expressed in percentages. As will be shown later: the determination of the grade of uncertainty is usually not sufficient for the characterization of the uncertainty of the data. But provisionally we have to be contented with it.

To give the estimated data in "from-to" form will be expedient whenever *the choice is between alternatives whose characteristic data differ not only in numerical magnitude but also in the grade of uncertainty.*

For example, in the course of programming for the man-made fibres industry we were faced with the alternative of continuing to expand the production of cellulose-based viscose fibre or launching the production of various types of synthetic fibre. We have here at least four grades of uncertainty about the alternative activities, viz.:

(a) The production of viscose fibre in this country goes back several decades and we have an exact knowledge of the technical and cost characteristics involved.

(b) "Nylon 6" fibre has been produced for some two years in a minor plant of a few hundred tons capacity. Our knowledge of the process is less profound than in the case of viscose production, but some experiences have already been gained and some statistical observations made.

(c) There exist man-made fibres and technological processes in the production and application of which we have so far no experience in Hungary, but about which we possess extensive information based on study tours abroad, inquiries, literature data, offers of suppliers, etc. Though obviously less reliable than the direct experiences mentioned under (b), these sources provide none the less some basis for calculations.

(d) Finally, there are types of man-made fibre which have only recently appeared abroad, such as polypropylene, about whose technical and cost data only little is known. Yet it would be a mistake to neglect them in the course of calculation as according to the scanty information available they have many advantageous technical and economic properties.

As can be seen, the grade of uncertainty increases as we proceed from category (a) to category (d).

We are not requiring anything impossible from the construction engineer or the industrial or foreign-trade expert when we ask them to give their estimates in "from-to" form. It was much more unnatural when in the practice of traditional investment efficiency calculation engineers were required to supply single constant figures even for the data about which he was uncertain himself. *The "from-to" form is not unnatural – in our planning practice it is the natural form of estimation.*

Clearly, these indices (the span of the interval and the grade of uncertainty) cannot be considered as the entirely exact characteristics of the data concerned. And yet, putting the uncertainty at 20 per cent only to find afterwards that reality differed by 23 per cent from the mean value of our estimate, will constitute a less grave error than to rely *exclusively* on the mean value, in accordance with the actual practice of traditional investment efficiency calculations. As a general rule, it may be stated that even a not entirely exact indication of the above described criteria of characterizing the grade of uncertainty will provide a better approach to reality than could ever be achieved if the uncertain character of the estimates were entirely neglected.

11.3. Ranking in the Man-made Fibres Industry

I will now describe one of the calculations carried out in the framework of the project for the man-made fibres industry. In the course of these calculations no programming took place, the productive activities were *ranked* only, according to some definite efficiency index.

To carry out this ranking, the scale of each productive activity was first fixed, with plant sizes determined in accordance with the following principles:

– For the activities directly competing with one another, equal plant sizes were fixed as far as possible.

– The fixed plant sizes were compatible with the technical, material-supply and capacity constraints of the model's system of constraints.

– Wherever observance of the former principle made it possible, plant sizes were fixed to allow for production for exports over and above domestic requirements.

All intermediary materials required in the production of man-made fibres which were supplied by the activities figuring in the model were accounted for at import prices. In doing so we were led by the principle that profits accruing from the intermediary materials employed should show in the material *producing* instead of the material *consuming* activity.

The index on which our ranking was based constitutes a special computational rate of profits, Γ_j:

$$\Gamma_j = \frac{C_j(x_{0j})}{s_j^{(i)} v_j + s_j^{(e)} (x_{0j} - v_j)}, \tag{11.4}$$

where

x_{0j} = the plant size fixed for the jth activity
$C_j(x_{0j})$ = the annual computational costs in Ft, in the case of an x_0 plant size. This was determined on the basis of cost function (7.6) in the model of the man-made fibres industry
$s_j^{(i)}$ = the product's import unit price converted into Ft
$s_j^{(e)}$ = the product's export unit price converted into Ft
v_j = domestic demand for the product. This figures on the right side of the model's corresponding constraints.

TABLE 11.1

Ranking according to mean

Ordinal No.	Production activity	Computational profit percentage
1	Polypropylene yarn	44.4
2	Cellophane in new plant	31.8
3	Nylon 6 yarn, technology "B"	30.6
4	Phenol	29.0
5	Polyacrylonitrile-vinylchloride copolymer staple	28.6
6	Ethylene glycol	27.1
7	Rayon yarn	25.0
8	Nylon 6 yarn, technology "A"	24.9
9	Polypropylene	21.9
10	Orlon staple	13.3
11	Terylene staple	11.9
12	Caprolactame, benzol based	7.3
13	Dimethylterephthalate	5.1
14	Polypropylene staple	4.8
15	Cellophane in old plant	−3.7
16	Acrylonitrile	−15.8
17	Rayon staple in new plant	−17.2
18	Caprolactame, phenol based	−27.4
19	Rayon staple in old plant	−43.1

Thus, in the denominator of formula (11.4), the amount of the product required to meet domestic demand, i.e. to replace imports, has been accounted for at import prices, and the additional quantity meant for export, at export prices.

There are three different methods to determine the profit rate:

(i) C_j, $s_j^{(i)}$ and $s_j^{(e)}$ were determined on the basis of the mean of data given in "from-to" form.

(ii) The calculations were based on the pessimistic values of the data given in "from-to" form. For all data which express cost and input, this means the upper limit. On the other hand, for all data which express returns (i.e. for returns accruing from secondary products in the numerator as well as for import savings and export returns in the denominator) pessimistic value means the lower limit. The pessimistic rate of profits will thus express the profit rate attained in the least favourable course of events.

(iii) The calculations were based on the optimistic values of the data given in "from-to" form. This is the logical opposite of the interpretation given in (ii).

TABLE 11.2

Ranking according to "pessimistic value"

Ordinal No.	Productive activity	Computational profit percentage
1	Cellophane in new plant	23.7
2	Polypropylene yarn	21.3
3	Rayon yarn	14.7
4	Nylon 6 yarn, technology "B"	13.4
5	Ethylene glycol	12.7
6	Nylon 6 yarn, technology "A"	12.3
7	Cellophane in old plant	−9.1
8	Phenol	−9.6
9	Polypropylene	−28.6
10	Polyacrylonitrile-vinylchloride copolymer staple	−29.2
11	Rayon staple in new plant	−31.5
12	Dimethylterephthalate	−36.6
13	Caprolactame, benzol based	−39.9
14	Acrylonitrile	−42.8
15	Orlon staple	−45.4
16	Terylene staple	−46.7
17	Rayon staple in old plant	−51.4
18	Polypropylene staple	−56.6
19	Caprolactame, phenol based	−87.2

We have thus three different rankings which are presented in tables 11.1, 11.2 and 11.3.

11.4. First Selection

What information can be obtained from these three rankings? A few inferences will be quite obvious.

(1) Some alternatives involve a loss even in the optimistic case (see the last two rows in table 11.3). This is a weighty argument for their definite dismissal.

(2) Some alternatives are even in the pessimistic case more advantageous than others in the optimistic case. Accordingly, the alternatives in the first six rows of table 11.2 may be preferred to those in the last four rows of table 11.3. In this respect, the former *dominate* over the latter.

(3) It will be especially worth while to ascertain whether there is no domination relationship between the directly competing alternatives.

TABLE 11.3

Ranking according to "optimistic value"

Ordinal No.	Production activity	Computational profit percentage
1	Polypropylene yarn	64.0
2	Polyacrylonitrile-vinylchloride copolymer staple	56.5
3	Phenol	53.9
4	Polypropylene staple	47.1
5	Polypropylene	46.4
6	Terylene staple	46.4
7	Nylon 6 yarn, technology "B"	45.4
8	Orlon staple	42.1
9	Ethylene glycol	39.4
10	Cellophane in new plant	39.3
11	Caprolactame, benzol based	38.6
12	Nylon 6 yarn, technology "A"	35.8
13	Dimethylterephthalate	35.2
14	Rayon yarn	34.6
15	Caprolactame, phenol based	12.3
16	Acrylonitrile	7.3
17	Cellophane in old plant	1.6
18	Rayon staple in new plant	−3.5
19	Rayon staple in old plant	−35.2

It can be observed that in all orders of precedence, cellophane production in a new plant precedes the rest of the viscose alternatives which – according to the model's system of constraints – may claim the same restricted old semi-product capacity. Similarly, technology "B" of nylon 6 yarn production precedes in each case technology "A" of the same production. As a consequence, two out of the six alternatives considered as advantageous in the second paragraph above may be left out of consideration.

As can be seen, "pessimistic" and "optimistic" ranking has already provided some useful information. It helps us to dismiss some alternatives which are either definitely disadvantageous or else dominated by other variants. After this selection the problem of choice will be, if not outright eliminated, at least considerably narrowed down.

11.5. The Safety Ranking of Alternatives

Let us, at the present stage, not take a stand for any of the three rankings, i.e. those according to optimistic, mean and pessimistic values. Instead, let us examine the question in a more general way. We define profit rate (11.4) as a function of s a f e t y l e v e l ϑ as follows:

$$\Gamma_j(\vartheta) = \bar{\Gamma}_j - (\Gamma_j^0 - \Gamma_{0j})(\vartheta - 0.5) =$$

$$= \bar{\Gamma}_j \left[1 - \frac{\Gamma_j^0 - \Gamma_{0j}}{\bar{\Gamma}_j}(\vartheta - 0.5)\right], \qquad 0 \leqq \vartheta \leqq 1, \qquad (11.5)$$

where

$\bar{\Gamma}_j$ = the profit rate according to mean value
Γ_j^0 = the optimistic profit rate
Γ_{0j} = the pessimistic profit rate.

If $\vartheta > 0.5$, the profit rate according to mean value should be *decreased* by the expression $(\Gamma_j^0 - \Gamma_{0j})(\vartheta - 0.5)$ which plays in this case the role of a kind of u n c e r t a i n t y p e n a l t y. If $\vartheta < 0.5$, the profit rate according to mean value should be *increased* by the same expression whose role will then be that of an u n c e r t a i n t y b o n u s. Finally, if $\vartheta = 0.5$, the profit rate according to mean value should be neither increased nor decreased.

Let us now consider safety level ϑ a variable, a parameter, and run it through the interval between 0 and 1. In this case the order of precedence

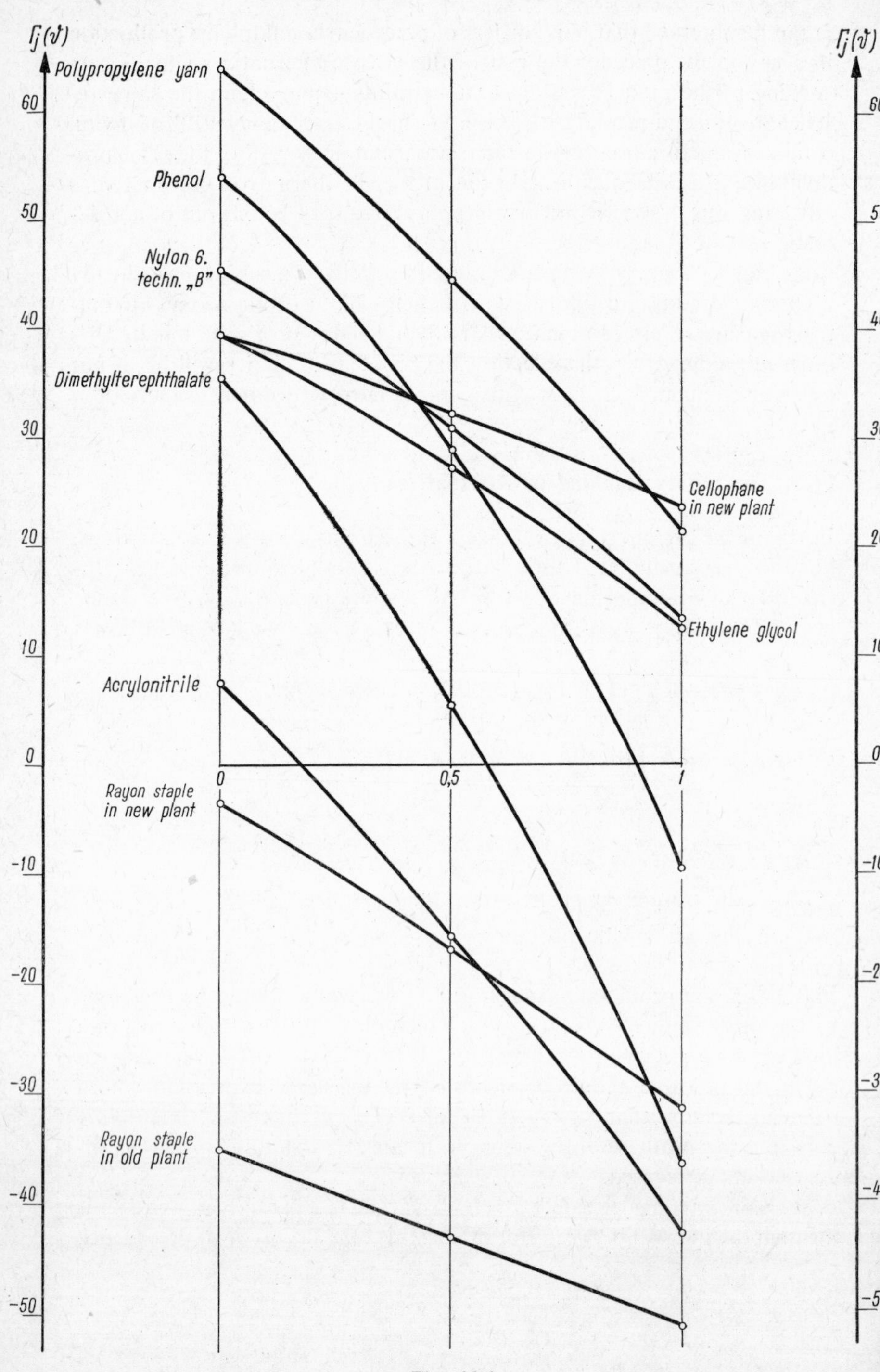
$\Gamma_j(\vartheta)$
Polypropylene yarn
Phenol
Nylon 6. techn. „B"
Dimethylterephthalate
Acrylonitrile
Rayon staple in new plant
Rayon staple in old plant
Cellophane in new plant
Ethylene glycol
60
50
40
30
20
10
0
-10
-20
-30
-40
-50
0
0,5
1

Fig. 11.1

of the 19 alternatives according to the computational profit rate will be a function of parameter ϑ. The procedure, which we call the s a f e t y r a n k i n g of alternatives, is presented in figure 11.1.

In the figure, computational profit rates are measured on the axis of ordinates, safety levels on the axis of abscissas. The rate of profit for each alternative is represented by a separate curve*. The curves of the individual activities follow each other on the left side according to the optimistic, in the middle according to the mean-value, on the right side according to the pessimistic order of preference.

Let us, for the time being, consider only the practical aspects of the question. What informations will be conveyed by safety ranking, by figure 11.1, to top management, which can be utilized before taking a more definite stand on the question of a desirable and suitable safety level?

The figure suggests the obvious thought that it would be useless to choose any of the alternatives whose curve does not lie comparatively *high* in the figure in any of the safety levels. If it would be realistic to spend the whole investment fund on a single alternative, only two of them could be taken into consideration: the production of polypropylene yarn (in the case of $0 \leqq \vartheta \leqq 0.94$), or that of cellophane in a new plant (in the case of $0.94 \leqq \vartheta \leqq 1$). As in actual practice it would, for various reasons, hardly be realistic to concentrate all investment activity on a single alternative, we may include into the alternatives coming under consideration those which are among the two or three most advantageous ones at any of the safety levels.

In this way, a further selection has been carried out and the problem of choice further narrowed down.

When all is said and done, the rankings given and the selections described above show in the case of the man-made fibres industry the advantageous character of four activities. These are: the production of nylon 6 yarn under technology "B", that of polypropylene yarn and of ethylene glycol, and the manufacture of cellophane in a new plant. These are among the first six both in the ranking according to mean value and thàt according to pessimistic value; nor is the optimistic profit rate below 39 per cent in the case of either. As a consequence, these alternatives can be recommended even in the case of due weighing of the uncertainties.

* To avoid overcrowding in the figure, only parts of the curves are shown.

11.6. The Deficiencies of the Procedure

In our practical example, the inferences described in sections 11.4 and 11.5 were aimed at separating the "good enough" alternatives from the "certainly bad" ones, and from those than which "certainly better" ones exist. This is useful but not sufficient. On the basis of what has been said up to this point, no sufficiently unequivocal proposals can be submitted to higher economic administration and this for several reasons.

Firstly, because what we carried out was mere ranking, whereas, as shown in ch. 8, any well-founded decision should rest on programming.

Furthermore, because the general criteria of decisions with uncertain consequences have, in fact, as yet not been cleared*. No answer was so far given to questions such as: What are the properly defined economic contents of the terms "uncertainty penalty", "safety level", etc.? What safety level should reasonably be required? The main purpose of the present chapter was to make us, by means of the simple technique of ranking, "enter into the spirit" as it were, of the related problems before proceeding to the discussion of the more profound questions of decision criteria in subsequent chapters.

Finally, the "from-to" form itself will leave a certain feeling of want, mainly for the following reasons:

(1) Whenever the specialists carrying out the estimation are asked whether it may be claimed with 100 per cent certainty that the estimated data will in reality not exceed the "from-to" limits, their answer is rarely in the affirmative. They will usually point out that although the chances for this to occur are very slight, the possibility must not be ruled out altogether.

(2) It is most unlikely that unfortunate circumstances should coincide in a way as to bring about the most unfavourable trends in the formation of *all* factors affecting profits, i.e. the realization of the "pessimistic"

* Those acquainted with the literature on decision theory will have seen that the safety ranking of alternatives was essentially a special case of applying the so-called *Hurwicz criterion* (L. HURWICZ [56]).

As long as $\vartheta = 1$, we have applied the *maximin criterion.* In this special case this was equivalent with the application of the *maximin regret* criterion. It will be remembered that in other cases the two criteria will lead to different decisions.

As long as $\vartheta = 0.5$, we have relied on the *Laplace criterion.*

As long as $\vartheta = 0$, our decision was based on the *maximax criterion.*

For a popular survey of decision criteria see W. J. BAUMOL [9], pp. 371–375. More detailed analyses of the individual decision criteria as well as of the postulates that form their bases, are given by J. MILNOR [127] and R. D. LUCE and H. RAIFFA [106].

limit value of the computational profit rate. Part of the materials affecting profits may advance in price but this may be, partly or wholly, balanced by a more than averagely favourable trend in other price and cost factors. Investment requirements may exceed the mean value but labour force requirements may fall short of it, and so on. Deviations in both directions from the mean may more or less cancel out one another. It is therefore most likely that the profit rate emerging under the impact of a multitude of factors will be nearer to the mean than either to the pessimistic or to the optimistic limit.

(3) The rankings discussed above have dealt with the various alternatives independently from one another. Yet they are interrelated in a multiple manner, among others also from the point of view of their movements within the "from-to" interval. Should e.g. the world-market price of caprolactame rise above the estimated mean value, this will react on eight alternatives in our model, viz. on the production, export and import of nylon 6 staple as well as on the production, export and import of caprolactame. It would, therefore, be unrealistic to calculate the profit rate of nylon 6 staple production on the basis of the assumption that the price of caprolactame will reach the upper limit and that of nylon 6 staple the lower one. Yet this is exactly what we did when calculating the pessimistic profit rate.

To eliminate these deficiencies, we will resort to methods of probability calculation. This leads us to the subject-matter of the next chapter.

CHAPTER 12

SAFETY PROGRAMMING

CO-AUTHOR:

TH. LIPTÁK

12.1. Survey of the Exposition

In the next three chapters, all or part of the data employed in efficiency calculation will be regarded as *random variables*, and probabilistic methods will be used in support of the decisions.

The exposition will proceed as follows:

In section 12.2 the reasons will be given which warrant the use of probabilistic methods. In section 12.3 we will describe the methods of transforming uncertain data into random variables. The special type of parametric programming called "safety programming" will be described in section 12.4 and its economic interpretation given in section 12.5.

Chapter 13 will deal with the problem of safety and risktaking.

With the principles and methods of computation theoretically surveyed in chs. 12 and 13 we will in ch. 14 present their practical application as illustrated by the programming model of the man-made fibres industry.

12.2. The Justifications for Applying Probabilistic Methods

Historically, the theory of probability has evolved as a mathematical doctrine to explain and analyze random mass phenomena. Is it then warranted to use the probabilistic methods for the purpose of economic calculations based on uncertain data? How can we, indeed, characterize the investment costs of a new Hungarian polypropylene rayon plant as a random variable, having had no previous opportunity to observe statistically the investment costs of a whole range of such plants, but being just engaged in constructing the first one?

It would seem obvious to argue that this was not warranted because each individual economic decision constitutes a non-recurrent event without a parallel*. It is, nevertheless, our opinion that the application of

* In the literature on the subject this view is represented in its most extreme form by G. L. S. SHACKLE [155]. His views are, however, contested by a number of authors, e.g. by G. MERK [126], R. S. WECKSTEIN [177], etc. We, for our part,

the probabilistic methods is warranted also in economic calculations based on uncertain data.

First of all, it should be pointed out that – as will be seen in the sequel – we will employ only some elementary notions of the theory of probability, such as probability itself, expected value, standard deviation and correlation coefficient, which are used in the normal theory of probability for the "rough" description, measuring and averaging of some deeply hidden properties of a stochastic character. In the case of decision under uncertainty, their role will become similarly descriptive. Accordingly, when speaking of the application of probabilistic methods, we are doing so simply for lack of a more suitable expression.

We will speak, for example, of the "expected value" and the "standard deviation" of a random variable represented by an estimated cost datum given in "from-to" form. In the case of random mass phenomena, both values have an experimentally controllable meaning: e.g. in the course the independent recurrences of a given random event, the average of the observed values, will – in accordance with the law of large numbers – tend towards the expected value, and the same law will assert itself also in the case of standard deviation. At the same time, the formal-descriptive role of the two concepts is the following: the expected value constitutes the weighted arithmetic mean of the possible values, with the probabilities as weights, and the standard deviation is the weighted quadratic mean of the possible deviations from the expected value, also with the probabilities as weights.

We believe that both concepts of "expected value" and "standard deviation" can be applied to the case of decision under uncertainty, if taken in their above described second – "averaging" – meaning. The expected value "locates", as it were, the uncertain datum, while the standard deviation "measures" the lack of information manifesting itself in the fact of uncertainty.

Nor are we dealing here exclusively with this descriptive role. It would be an error to overemphasize the contrasts between the phenomena under investigation and the classical type of random "mass phenomena". Let us stick to the former example, that of the new Hungarian polypropylene rayon plant. The establishment of a plant like this is in *its totality* a

---

agree with the latter authors and have also drawn on their arguments, notwithstanding the fact that our reasoning differs from theirs on some points. A survey of the debate on the subject is not within our present scope – all we intend is to make clear our own positive point of view.

For a survey of the debate see K. J. ARROW's above-mentioned work [3].

non-recurrent event. At the same time, this event is, in fact, the sum of a number of elements, of sub-events which, in turn, are no longer non-recurrent occurrences but units of a mass composed of similar events. For example, the activities carried out in the framework of setting up the polypropylene rayon plant mentioned above, were similar to:

(1) the construction of a number of polypropylene rayon plants set up abroad;

(2) all other plant constructions carried out in the Hungarian man-made fibres industry;

(3) all plant constructions carried out in the Hungarian chemical industry;

(4) all plant constructions carried out in Hungary, etc.

It can be seen that the mass of events broadens as we proceed from (1) towards (4) – at the same time, however, the relationship, the analogy between the individual event under examination (the new polypropylene rayon plant) and the broader mass of events becomes less and less close. Now, the experts, when giving their estimates concerning the individual event under examination, will actually draw on the informations yielded by the mass of analogous events, basing their conclusions thereon.

As a matter of fact, the possibility of drawing inferences from a mass of analogous events exists in all cases of estimating the characteristics of an economic event. Under the conditions of a socialist planned economy there are particularly great possibilities to utilize this type of indirect information. The decisions are taken here not by entrepreneurs isolated from one another but – as a consequence of the centralized character of the administration – by institutions to which numerous investment projects are regularly and continually submitted. Nor is it exclusively the National Planning Board with its decisive role in all major investment projects, that we have in mind; on a lower level, the officials in charge of investment matters in the economic ministries and in the investment departments of the individual industrial directorates are also in a position to survey, continually and extensively, a great number of investment projects. Under the circumstances, it would hardly be warranted to consider the investment decisions as some single, non-recurrent events – the number of direct and indirect information is too great for that.

As a consequence, the type of event under investigation cannot be characterized simply as a "non-recurrent event", nor as a "mass phenomenon", but rather as a combination of the two. And this fact in itself warrants already the use of such concepts of the theory of probability as the expected value, standard deviation, etc. in describing and characterizing this type of event. The estimates concerning the economic event under investigation will be the less uncertain:

(1) the greater the number of the analogous events on which the inferences are based;

(2) the more unique these inferences;

(3) the closer the analogy with these events.

Thus, for example, the estimates concerning investment costs of a new polypropylene yarn plant will be the less uncertain the greater the number of polypropylene yarn plants with known data and the smaller the standard deviation of these data. As for point (3), our estimates will be better founded if we start from the data of polypropylene yarn plants than if we were to base our inferences on the data of nylon 6 yarn plants. Of course, in actual practice, the inferences which can be drawn from direct informations and those which can be drawn from indirect ones are usually combined.

Standard deviation is the index number to measure the degree of lack of the complete information required for absolutely sure estimation. The more stable the empirical foundation of the estimate, and the more numerous, unique and direct the information available, the smaller the standard deviation which will characterize the estimated datum.

Let us illustrate this relationship by an example: the cybernetic experiments in the course of which electronic computers are taught to play some games. As long as the computer knows the general rules only, it will lose many plays. Should it, however, be programmed to "learn", i.e. to store in its memory the lessons drawn from previous plays in order to utilize in subsequent plays the analogies afforded by them, its play will grow increasingly successful. Here we have to do with a direct relationship – and with one at that which can be numerically measured, experimentally observed and suitably characterized by an index number – between the quantity and quality of the "experiences", the inferences drawn from analogous cases and stored in the memory of the computer, on the one hand, and its success in the game, on the other. The case of the specialists setting up the estimates is a similar one; with them, too, the success of the estimation will depend on the quantity and quality of the information "stored" in their memory (both of the information with direct bearing on the subject of the estimate and of those relating to the analogous phenomena from which inferences can be drawn). Standard deviation constitutes an easily manageable concept to express this relationship.

Accordingly, it is not the degree of some subjective feeling that is measured by standard deviation, such as, for example, the degree of surprise felt over the possible occurrence of the event, etc. It actually reflects an objective relationship (the quantity and quality of the available informations) but in lack of a suitable measuring instrument it does so in a rough form only, on the basis of individual or collective estimation.

We are well aware of the intricate character of the question raised here about the justifications for employing the probabilistic methods, an issue whose aspects are not only mathematical but epistemological, sociological and economic as well. This is a problem that requires further study*. Here again, we can observe that characteristic course of scientific development where the practical needs manifest themselves first and it is thereupon that science sets out to find the most suitable method of meeting them. Partial uncertainty of the data on which economic decisions are based is an inevitable occurrence in actual practice. It is therefore a *must* to find the most suitable method of treating uncertain data. For the present moment, there seems to exist no tool better suited for the purpose than the application of the probabilistic methods**.

12.3. Uncertainty and Probability

In many cases – thus e.g. in that of the project for the man-made fibres industry – the estimations of the experts were given in "from-to" form. They started from the following assumptions:

(1) Those preparing the estimates assumed that it was not impossible to exceed the "from-to" interval, although the chances for this to happen had to be considered as slight.

(2) Those preparing the estimates assumed that the occurrence of the average value or of one near to the average was more probable than that of the "from-to" limits or of values near to these limits.

(3) Those preparing the estimates were unbiased and not interested in any distortion of their estimates. It could therefore be taken for granted that deviations from the average in both directions were equally likely to occur.

* A truly pure application of the probabilistic methods may only be possible if the theories of the latter dealing with mass phenomena on the one hand and decisions under uncertainty on the other, could be united into a single mathematical doctrine. Although experiences with this end in view have already been carried out, no satisfactory solution of the problem could so far be reached.

** Nor do we – as must be clear to the reader – consider this to constitute the *only* possible solution.

Should we wish to represent uncertain data of this type by a random variable, it will be, on the basis of the above three properties, expedient to choose a probability distribution where the expected value falls into

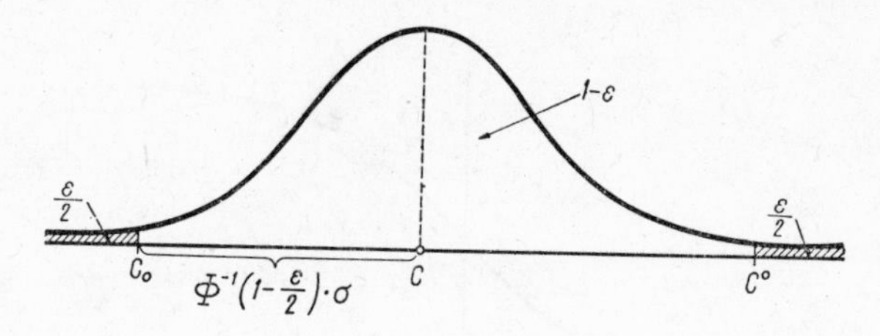

Fig. 12.1

the midpoint of the "from-to" interval and is both symmetrical and "smooth" around this point; moreover, where the value of probability outside the "from-to" interval is only slight, equalling, let us say, a definite small positive ε value, e.g. $\varepsilon = 0.02$. The type of the distribution being, within the limits of these requirements, of no particular importance, it can be stipulated that, subject to these conditions, the distribution of the variable should be normal: expected value C and standard deviation σ, characterizing the corresponding normal distribution, should be determined uniquely by "from-to" limits C_0 and C^0 and the value of ε:

$$C = \frac{C_0 + C^0}{2}, \qquad \sigma = \frac{C^0 - C_0}{2\Phi^{-1}\,(1 - \frac{1}{2}\varepsilon)}, \tag{12.1}$$

where

Φ^{-1} = the inverse function of the normal distribution function defined by formula

$$\Phi(x) = \frac{1}{\sqrt{2\pi}} \int_{-\infty}^{x} \exp\left(-\tfrac{1}{2}u^2\right) du \tag{12.2}$$

(see figures 12.2 and 12.3). By means of formula (12.1) we have thus transformed estimates of "from-to" types with properties according to (1)–(3), into normally distributed random variables.

In a similar manner, it will be possible to transform a set composed of more or less closely related estimates into a multi-dimensional normal distribution. This requires only the additional assumption that the individual data groups are independent of other groups, or that the individual data are either independent from each other or else their mutual relationship can be described by a given correlation coefficient of positive or negative value. These assumptions together with the expected values and standard deviations are known to determine uniquely the parameters

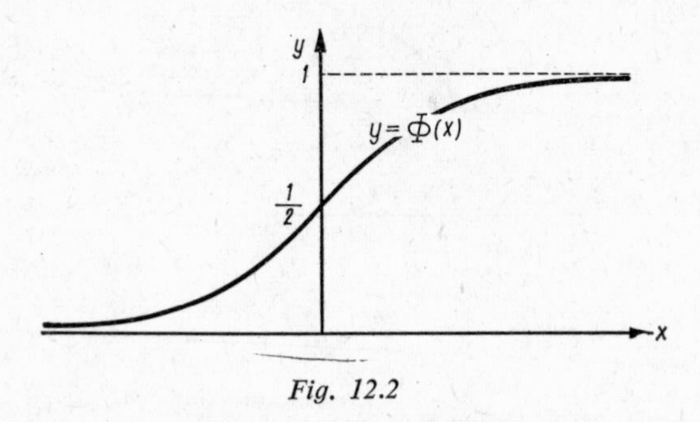

Fig. 12.2

of the corresponding multi-dimensional normal distribution*. It is exactly these properties that lend an importance to normal distribution from the point of view of our problem – its "regularity" of distribution and its character of being determined by expected values, standard deviations and correlation coefficients.

In the programming project for the man-made fibres industry, where probabilistic methods were first employed, uncertain data were represented by normally distributed random variables. This, however, does not constitute the only possible solution and in other cases it may be expedient to work with other types of distribution.

Thus e.g. when employing normal distribution, it was one of our starting assumptions that the estimates were unprejudiced. However, the situation is different if we have no reason to suppose that those preparing the estimates are unbiased. In section 9.2 we have dealt in detail with the phenomenon of tendentious distortions in the investment efficiency calculations attached to the permit papers, with estimates frequently based on investment costs lower than realistic, in order to secure approval to the project. It was shown there that the realization coefficient of the estimates can be easily characterized by an asymmetrical – log-normal – distribution.

This case differs essentially from that described above as far as point (3) is concerned: if the data used in our programming model were taken from the calculations attached to the permit papers, then the lack of objectivity and the distortions in the latter would justify the expectation of

* See e.g. H. Cramér [23], pp. 310–317.

an asymmetrical, e.g. log-normal, distribution around the expected value instead of a symmetrical, normal one. It could then be assumed that the expected value of these random variables will deviate from the

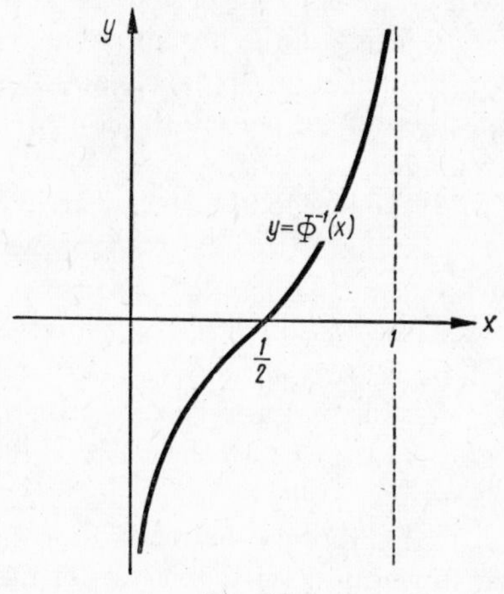

Fig. 12.3

preliminary estimates in the permit papers in the same proportion as was, according to observations, the case with actual realization on an average; e.g. the figures given in section 9.2 show this deviation to average 22 per cent.

It must be emphasized that the transformation of data taken from the permit papers into random variables in this manner would rest on *substantially different foundations* than the transformation of unbiased expert estimates given in "from-to" form as described in formulae (12.1)–(12.2). In contradistinction to the transformation discussed above, the probability distribution employed here is based on the statistical observation of a mass phenomenon (the actual realization of the preliminary data figuring in the permit papers). But what we observed here is not the *object* of the estimates, e.g. the investment costs of dozens of new polypropylene rayon plants; it is their "*subject*" – the reliability of the persons, collective groups or institutions preparing the estimates.

The logic of this reasoning may be illustrated by the following comparison.

Carrying out a series of experiments let us first weigh various objects on an inaccurate balance and then control the weights on a precision one. In this way it will be possible to work out the probability distribution of deviations between the results of inaccurate and precise weighing. Now we will no longer accept the results yielded by the inaccurate balance but will transform them into a random variable under the assumption that actual weight will deviate from that indicated by the inaccurate balance in the same probability distribution as in the case of previous weighings.

In our case, the data figuring in the permit papers represent the results obtained by means of the inaccurate balance, and the data produced by ulterior efficiency investigations represent the control figures obtained by means of the precise balance.

No calculation of this type has actually been carried out in our practice so far. Up to now, the estimates for our projects were always specially prepared for the purpose and we employed various methods to secure their unbiased character (see section 9.3). It is, however, conceivable that in other future calculations we will have to resort to data contained in investment permit papers. In this case it may occur that the data will be transformed into random variables on the basis of the train of thought described above.

It should be clear that although the method of the uncertain data→random variable transformation introduces an element of arbitrariness into the calculations, this is of a secondary character only, consisting as it does in the choice of the "weights" which figure in "averaging".

12.4. The Model of Safety Programming

Let us now turn to our programming model. For simplicity's sake we shall disregard the fact that some of the coefficients and constraint-constants figuring in the system of constraints may also be uncertain, and will treat them as constants*. The uncertain data figuring in the objective function, on the other hand, we shall transform into random variables, in accordance with what has been said in sections 12.2 and 12.3.

The decision problem now takes the following form:

From among programs $\mathbf{x}$ which satisfy the conditions

$$\mathbf{Ax} = \mathbf{b},$$

$$\mathbf{x} \geqq \mathbf{0}, \tag{12.3}$$

* In the actual practice of the programming project for the man-made fibres industry this means that if there were among these data given in "from-to" form, they were taken into account at their average value. Some of these data were subjected to sensitivity analysis.

the one or those must be determined where the value of the stochastic objective function

$$\mathsf{C} = \mathsf{C}(\mathbf{x}) \qquad (12.4)$$

is a minimum. Owing to the fact that the value of costs in (12.4) is for all values of program **x** at the same time also a random variable, a *direct* solution of this decision problem will be conceivable only if we define which programs may be optimal and with what probability.

Although this type of solution would afford some help in making a decision, we have preferred to use another method, if for no other reason than the extraordinary amount of calculation involved in this one.

Let $C_P(\mathbf{x})$ denote the P-quantile of the stochastic cost-function under (12.4), i.e. the value – dependent on **x** – at which the probability of the event

$$\mathsf{C}(\mathbf{x}) \leqq C_P(\mathbf{x}) \qquad (12.5)$$

equals P*.

A case deserving special attention is the one where the distribution of $\mathsf{C}(\mathbf{x})$ is normal for all **x**. If $C(\mathbf{x})$ denotes its expected value and $\sigma_C(\mathbf{x})$ its standard deviation, we obtain from (12.6)

$$C_P(\mathbf{x}) = C(\mathbf{x}) + \theta_P\, \sigma_C(\mathbf{x}), \qquad (12.7)$$

where the value of coefficient θ_P is identical for all **x** and depends on the magnitude of P only**.

* If $F(\gamma; \mathbf{x})$ denotes the distribution function of $\mathsf{C}(\mathbf{x})$, i.e. the probability of event $\mathsf{C}(\mathbf{x}) \leqq \gamma$ as a function of γ, then the following formula for $C_P(\mathbf{x})$ can be obtained from (12.5):

$$C_P(\mathbf{x}) = F_I^{-1}(P; \mathbf{x})\,. \qquad (12.6)$$

F_I^{-1} denotes here the (generalized) inverse of bivariable function $F(\gamma; \mathbf{x})$ with respect to its first variable.

** The formula for θ_p is as follows:

$$\theta_P = \Phi^{-1}(P)\,. \qquad (12.8)$$

See formula (12.2) and figures 12.2–12.3. For the sake of illustration, we give below the θ_P values which correspond to some of the magnitudes of P.

P%	θ_P
50	0
70	0.52
80	0.84
90	1.28
95	1.64
99	2.33
99.99	3.71

We will now carry out the following parametric programming: for all values that parameter P may take between 0 and 1 we will determine the program $\mathbf{x}_P^*$ which is feasible according to (12.3) and where (12.6) is at a minimum. In other words: for all values of P between 0 and 1, we will *determine the program where the cost value with probability P of not being exceeded by actual cost, is the lowest.* We will call the value of P the safety level; θ_P the safety factor; objective function $C_P(\mathbf{x})$ the safety value with level P; and the resulting parametric programming

$$\left.\begin{array}{l} \mathbf{Ax} = \mathbf{b} \\ \mathbf{x} \geqq \mathbf{0} \\ C_P(\mathbf{x}) \to \min! \end{array}\right\} \quad 0 \leqq P \leqq 1, \qquad (12.9)$$

safety programming*.

In case of a normal distribution, programming with safety level $P = {}^1/_2$ simply reduces to a problem of minimization with respect to $C(\mathbf{x})$, the expected value of stochastic cost function $\mathsf{C}(\mathbf{x})$, as on the basis of (12.8) $\theta_{1/2} = 0$, $C_{1/2}(\mathbf{x}) = C(\mathbf{x})$**. With P increasing, θ_P increases continuously and, as a consequence, the role of $\sigma_C(\mathbf{x})$ – which represents the uncertainty of the data – becomes increasingly prominent.

12.5. The Economic Interpretation of Safety Programming

For the sake of an easier elucidation of the problems involved, we will base our further comments on the simpler case where we have to deal with normally distributed random variables.

We will consider safety level P a parameter whose value is determined by higher economic administration on the basis of general considerations

* A similar reduction of the stochastic objective function, although for the case of a stochastic system of constraints, can also be found in S. KATAOKA's paper [64], which appeared in the first 1963 number of *Econometrica* at a time when the present work was already in course of translation, and several years after the first publication of our programming model in Hungarian language. However, in the paper referred to, the problem is not interpreted as one of parametric programming with respect to the safety level, and only a short reference is being made to the economic interpretation of the method, without going into any detail.

** This is valid for all distributions which are symmetrical in the neighbourhood of their expected value, because here ½-quantile (median) and expected value are identical.

of economic policy. Let us e.g. put the safety level at 0.8; then $C_{0.8}(\mathbf{x})$ will give the total cost for which there is an 80 per cent probability of not being exceeded by actual cost $\mathsf{C}(\mathbf{x})$ of program $\mathbf{x}$. The probability that actual cost will exceed safety value $C_{0.8}(\mathbf{x})$ is then 20 per cent only.

It is, however, not absolutely necessary to give function $C_P(\mathbf{x})$ a direct probabilistic interpretation; even without this, the function will express certain economic relationships.

We propose to call safety strategy the attitude of the decision-making organs to the uncertainty involved in investment decisions. Through the selection of safety level P, economic administration can bring to expression a definite safety strategy. Let us distinguish from this point of view four different types of strategy.

(1) If $P = 0.5$, then $\theta_P = 0$. In this case we are basing the objective function exclusively on the expected value, disregarding entirely the standard deviation. This expresses an indifference on the part of economic administration to the risk which the uncertainty of the estimates involves. Let us call this attitude the strategy of risk-indifference*.

(2) If $P > 0.5$, than $\theta_P > 0$. Let us call the expression $\theta_P \sigma_C(\mathbf{x})$ which is added to the expected value in the case when θ_P is positive, the uncertainty penalty. This we will consider a special computational surplus cost imposed on the program $\mathbf{x}$. This penalty will be the higher (i) the greater the value of $\sigma_C(\mathbf{x})$, i.e. the more uncertain the program, and (ii) the greater the value of θ_P, i.e. the higher the safety level demanded by economic administration.

The uncertainty penalty expresses the fact that economic administration has an *aversion* to the risk which the uncertainty of the estimates involves. In the view of economic administration, the danger that actual cost may exceed expected cost is *not* counterbalanced by the chance that it may fall short of it, although the probability of the latter case equals that of the former. The potential loss as against the expected value is valued higher than the potential gain as against the expected value. Let us call this attitude the strategy of limited safety.

(3) If P tends to 100 per cent, the value of θ_P will also increase rapidly; within the safety value the weight of the expected value will relatively shrink and that of the standard deviation grow. It follows from the assumption of normal distribution that P can be 100 per cent only if θ_P

* We will not make use here of the distinction between uncertainty and risk, introduced by F. H. KNIGHT, see [67]. In our interpretation of the concept, risk is the consequence of uncertainty.

is "infinitely large"*. Of course, in actual practice even the demand for a safety level of 99.99 per cent may be called the strategy of maximum safety.

(4) If, on the other hand, $P < 0.5$, then $\theta_P < 0$. In this case, the positive expression $|\theta_P|\sigma_C(\mathbf{x})$ must be subtracted from the expected value, i.e. it can now be considered not an uncertainty penalty but an uncertainty bonus. It expresses the fact that economic administration has a preference for, instead of an aversion to, the risk involved in the uncertainty of the estimates. Here, the potential gain as against the expected value is valued higher than the potential loss as against the expected value. This attitude may be called the strategy of hazard**.

Those acquainted with decision theory will be able to identify the safety strategies with the corresponding known decision criteria. Without going into the details of the identification, we will only mention that***:

(i) In the case of $P = 0.5$ we employ what is called the Laplace criterion.

(ii) No decision criterion analogous with the case of $0.5 < P < 1$, i.e. with the application of the strategy of limited safety, has so far been discussed to any extent in literature. Yet it was exactly this criterion that we recommended to higher economic administration for the purpose of practical calculations. The point is substantiated in the next chapter of this book.

* From this point of view it might be more realistic to use a *truncated* normal distribution instead of a normal distribution, to represent the uncertainty of the estimation. It is characteristic of a truncated normal distribution that a lower and an upper limit is given which will not be exceeded in any case by the random variable, but the probability for the values in the neighbourhood of these limits to occur is slight and less than for those around the expected value.

In actual practice, although it is not impossible that the variable should exceed the "from-to" interval of the estimation, there is a realistic lower and upper limit for which the certainty of not being exceeded by the variable is 100 per cent, e.g. the cost of production cannot be less than 0.

However, the use of the untruncated normal distribution is more convenient and – although not quite unobjectionable from the theoretical point of view – quite adequate for practical purposes.

** The role of the uncertainty bonus, or the analogous concept of the uncertainty penalty, in the expectations connected with prices, has been discussed by a number of authors. See e.g. J. R. Hicks [52] and O. Lange [95]. To quote Hicks: "If we are to allow for uncertainty of expectations, . . . we must not take the most probable price as the representative expected price, but the most probable price ± an allowance for the uncertainty of the expectation, that is to say, an allowance for risk."

*** For references to the literature on decision theory see ch. 11.

(3) In the case of $P = 1$ we employ Wald's *maximin* criterion. If we are working with random variables of normal distribution and, for this reason, P only approaches unity, this means that our decision criterion will also only approach the maximin criterion.

(4) In the case of $P = 0$ we would employ what is called the *maximax* criterion. Although this is usually mentioned in literature for the sake of completeness, its use is not recommended by any author.

The parameter role of the safety level in safety programming is similar to that played by the "optimism-pessimism index" of Hurwicz's decision criterion. The differences between the two are mainly due to the fact that in our case the parameter is used in the objective function of a stochastic programming model, in a manner which lends itself for interpretation both from the economic point of view and from that of the calculus of probabilities.

A brief review of the "safety ranking" described in ch. 11 will be worth while here. The parallel is obvious. What was called "optimistic ranking" there, logically corresponds to what we call here the "strategy of hazard"; the "ranking according to mean value" to the "strategy of risk-indifference"; the "pessimistic ranking" to the "strategy of maximum safety".

Between the two methods described in chs. 11 and 12, respectively, there are several differences. There is no point in mentioning here such differences as derive from the fact that while we carried out simple ranking there, it is programming that we are speaking of here; while there we aimed at the maximization of the rate of profit, here at the minimization of costs; and so on. The essential difference from the point of view of the present analysis is that *while there we operated exclusively with the limits of the "from-to" intervals, here we transformed the "from-to" data into random variables.*

We must not, however, overestimate this difference.

Let us assume for a moment that we considered the uncertain data given in "from-to" form as described in ch. 11, a random variable with *uniform* distribution. The probability that the actually occurring value exceeds the limits is then 0, within the "from-to" interval, on the other hand, the probability is equal for all values.

With this supplementary assumption the method described in ch. 11 has become completely analogous with that in ch. 12; it can now be directly interpreted also from the point of view of probability. The main difference consists in the *different weighting* of the expected value and of the standard deviation which represents uncertainty, in the safety value, the index constituting the basis of valuation.

Besides, the assumption of normal distribution is more realistic from the point of view of the probabilistic interpretation. It is obviously not true that the probability of exceeding the "from-to" limits is 0, nor that the occurrence of the mean value and of the two limits is equally probable, etc.

CHAPTER 13

SAFETY AND RISKTAKING

13.1. A Diagrammatic Representation of Safety Strategy

Let us assume that we are carrying out safety programming with a cost function where the uncertain data are represented by normally distributed random variables. In this procedure, safety level P is meant to express the safety strategy of higher economic administration. Once economic administration has taken a stand for a definite value of P, it has also taken a stand on the question, how many and to what extent uncertain forints it would consider equivalent to 1 certain forint*.

The safety strategy can be illustrated by a set of suitable indifference lines (see figure 13.1).

A line belonging to some fixed $C_P(\mathbf{x})$ safety value in figure 13.1 shows that the same level of safety can be obtained by means of different combinations of the expected value and the standard deviation. A greater standard deviation, i.e. a greater uncertainty of the program, must be counterbalanced by a lower expected value, or inversely, to make it acceptable as equivalent for the organs of economic administration.

The slope of the line will be determined by safety factor Θ_P. The greater the safety level, the steeper the slope of the line, as in this case we will be ready to accept even a great increase in expected value for the sake of a small decrease in standard deviation.

It goes without saying that this is not the only conceivable form of the safety-preference function. One of the principal advantages of employing this type of function lies in its simple form and in the ease of its economic interpretation; its contents can be easily made clear to the executives with whom the final decisions in investment matters will rest.

We have so far left open the question of the safety level P, i.e. of the safety strategy which it would be most expedient to choose under the

* In fact, the safety strategies find their expression not only in the choice of safety level P but – as was shown in section 12.5, when comparing the uses of uniform and normal distribution – also in that of the probability distribution representing the element of uncertainty. For simplified exposition's sake, this will be disregarded in the following; the distribution of the random variables in the model will be considered as given and assumed to be normal.

conditions actually prevailing in this country. This question can be approached in two different ways. One approach is empirical: we tried to

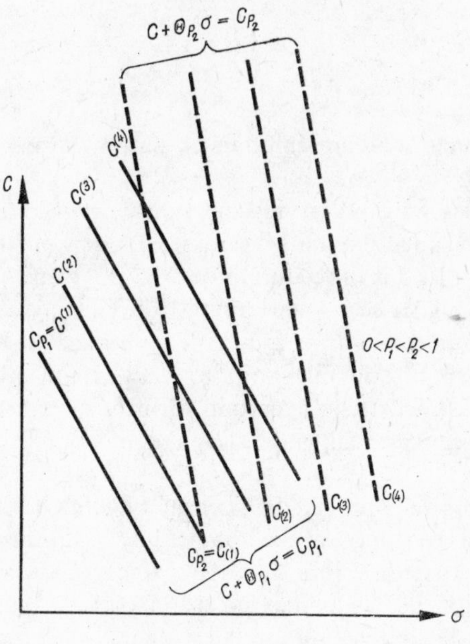

Fig. 13.1

find out the opinions of the executives themselves on the question. The results of the inquiry are summed up in section 13.2. The other approach is based on theoretical considerations; this is surveyed in section 13.3.

13.2. Executives Interviewed

In order to obtain the characteristic opinions, we have interviewed a series of economic and industrial executives. Direct questions concerning the safety level would have made little sense, as those interviewed could have no knowledge of our notions about programming according to safety value. We have, therefore, chosen an indirect mode of approach. We constructed a simple example, worded in a manner as to enable inferences concerning the safety level to be drawn from the answers.

The problem submitted to those interviewed was the following:

"Let us suppose that two alternatives for the realization of an investment project offer themselves. The costs of production and operation are the same for both, but investment costs differ. The characteristic of alternative (1) is that investment costs are exactly known, they can be termed *certain.* The characteristic of alternative (2) is that investment costs are *uncertain,* and all we know are their lower and upper limits. Or, more exactly, we know the mean value and the fact that the maximum possible deviation from this mean is of ± 20 per cent.

Let us furthermore assume that we are faced with a choice problem of this type in five different cases. The investment costs of alternative (1) are identical in all five cases but those of alternative (2) are different in each of them. The five problems of choice are summed up in table 13.1.

TABLE 13.1

Problems of choice between certain and uncertain alternatives

Case	Investment costs of alternative (1)	Investment costs of alternative (2)	
		mean	"from-to"
(A)	100	98.5	79–118
(B)	100	94.5	76–113
(C)	100	90.0	72–108
(D)	100	86.5	69–104
(E)	100	83.5	67–100

Clearly, in problem (E) preference must be given to alternative (2) whose cost will be 100 million forints at the worst, i.e. the same as that of alternative (2), but might be even less. But in the case of (A), (B), (C) and (D), which alternative will be the more advantageous one?

It can be seen that as we proceed from problem (A) towards problem (E), the mean of investment cost in alternative (2) decreases continually. The question now is, which is the case where the smaller mean and the considerably lower limit of alternative (2) compensates for the danger that investment costs may (but not necessarily will!) exceed 100 million forints, the certain amount of costs involved in alternative (1)?"

This question was put to a total of twenty persons, including both senior and junior executives, from chiefs of section and officials in the ministries and the National Planning Board to company directors and managers, all of whom would regularly be faced with investment decisions. They belonged to various departments (the National Planning Board and the Ministries of Finance, Foreign Trade, Heavy Industry and Light Industry).

The selection of those interviewed was a deliberately random one. For two or three weeks we would collect answers from persons whom we were meeting at committee sessions, in scientific associations, in the course of fact-finding, etc. All answers were given orally. We would pass in review the problems from (A) to (E) and ask for an opinion.

The answers obtained were fairly uniform. Table 13.2 presents the results of the inquiry. All we had to do was to show in tabular form, which was the problem of choice where the person interviewed has abandoned alternative (1) for alternative (2) or, at least, began to hesitate, feeling the two alternatives to be more or less equally advantageous. If he e.g. no longer insisted on alternative (1) in case (B), it was obvious – and this followed from the construction of the question – that he would not revert to it when coming to case (C) or (D).

TABLE 13.2

Results of interviews concerning decisions with uncertain consequences

Case where alternative (1) was no longer insisted on	Number of those answering to this effect	
	Persons	%
(A)	0	0
(B)	9	45
(C)	9	45
(D)	0	0
(E)	2	10

What is the meaning of these results from the point of view of the safety level? This question is answered in table 13.3. The table shows the percentage of safety level corresponding to answers which would consider case (A) or (B) etc. as the one where alternatives (1) and (2) are equally advantageous.

An example will show the train of thought on which the inferences concerning the safety level can be based.

Investment costs of alternative (2) were considered as a normally distributed random variable with a standard deviation which is 6.7 per cent of the mean. This would approximately correspond, neglecting a 1 pro mille probability, to a 20 per cent degree of uncertainty.

TABLE 13.3

Inferences concerning the safety level

Case where alternatives (1) and (2) are considered to be equally advantageous	Safety level to which this corresponds (%)
(A)	60
(B)	80
(C)	95
(D)	99

Let us take, for example, case (C). Should the person interviewed answer to our question that his choice was *not* alternative (2) but alternative (1), this means that he, on his part, would add to the 90 million forint mean value of alternative (2) an "uncertainty penalty" *higher* than 10 million forints. This follows from the fact that he considered alternative (2) less advantageous than alternative (1) with its 100 million forint cost.

Should, on the other hand, the person interviewed consider both alternatives (1) and (2) equally advantageous in case (C), this means that he, on his part, would inflict on alternative (2) an "uncertainty penalty" of 10 million forints – a penalty that would make the 100 million forints of alternative (1) equal the 90 + 10 million forints of alternative (2).

Now, in the case of a normally distributed random variable with mean 90 and with a standard deviation which is 6.7 per cent of the mean, it will be at a safety level of approximately 95 per cent that the upper safety value (upper quantile) is 100.

This is why we may consider the answer "equally advantageous" in case (C) as a demand for a 95 per cent safety level.

For the rest of the cases inferences regarding the required safety level can be drawn in the same way.

The question now arises whether those interviewed were not influenced by the practical experience that actual investment costs generally tend to exceed the estimates and only rarely fall short of them.

The possibility can, of course, not be excluded that some of the answers were subconsciously influenced by this experience. In any case, we have strongly emphasized in the course of these oral interviews that we were dealing here with a theoretical case where the strictly unbiased character of the estimates given in "from-to" form was a postulate and the chances for deviations from the estimates in both directions were fully equal. All answers were thus given in a knowledge of this assumption.

It is most interesting that in case (A) all those interviewed still insisted on alternative (1). This means that none of them would have agreed to a safety level of 60 per cent or lower.

As can be seen, even in case (A) the mean value of alternative (2) is lower than that of alternative (1). Those interpreted were, none the less, definitely in favour of the certain alternative. For them, a potential loss of 18 million forints was not compensated by a potential gain of 21 million. This indicates a certain *hesitation to take a risk, in other words, a preference for safety as against uncertainty.*

In the last analysis, this can be interpreted as *a refusal, on the part of those interviewed, of the strategy of risk-indifference with its neglect of the viewpoints of safety.* As mentioned before, calculating on the basis of the mean corresponded to a safety level of 50 per cent, while none of those interpreted would consider a 60 per cent safety level as adequate.

Let us now investigate the opposite extreme. There were not more than two to decide for alternative (2) only in case (E), insisting in all other cases on alternative (1). These were practically for a strategy of maximum safety. They pointed out in the course of the interview that in their opinion it was not admissible to take a risk of even 1 million forints as long as there existed a certain alternative where this risk was not involved, not even if the potential loss seemed to be compensated by a potential gain of 32 million. In their view, the decisive requirement was that of 100 per cent safety.

However, the overwhelming majority of those interviewed – 90 per cent of the total – did not share these ultra-cautious views, i.e. were not in favour of a strategy of maximum safety. 90 per cent of those interviewed abandoned alternative (1) in case (B) already, or in case (C) at the latest. This goes to show that the majority essentially adopted a strategy of limited safety. The opinions varied between the safety-level limits of 80–95 per cent.

Naturally, we must not draw too far-reaching inferences from these interviews. On the one hand, the number of those interviewed was rather limited. Nor can it be taken for granted that they would *act* in actual practice as they professed to do in the course of an *oral* interview which may even have surprised them with its novel character. But the high degree of uniformity in the answers is most remarkable and adds to the authenticity of the interviews.

13.3. The Justifications for Risk-aversion

The personal opinions of those responsible for investment decisions in a planned economy are certainly not without interest. However, the main question is whether there exists some objective relationship which determines the reasonable magnitude of safety level or whether it is exclusively on the temperament, the reckless or cautious nature of economic administration that this magnitude will depend.

In my view, such objective relationships do in fact exist, only, at least in the present stage of scientific research, they lend themselves to qualitative perception rather than to quantitative assessment.

Let us first start from the following:

Our programming is carried out on the national level. In this course we are aiming exclusively at the minimization of the expected value of the cost function, disregarding entirely the uncertainty of the activities, that is to say, the standard deviation representing this uncertainty. The safety level is thus 0.5; $\Theta_P = 0$. In the national economy, many hundred – even many thousand – investment projects are realized over a period of some length. If our estimates were in each case unbiased, i.e. if they can be represented by a symmetrical distribution around the expected value, then the positive and negative deviations from the expected value will compensate each other as a consequence of the great number of the cases involved. On the national level the expected value will thus assert itself in the long run.

In a capitalist economy, the individual entrepreneur would be hardly comforted by the knowledge that a failure of his investment project will be compensated by the success of that of another entrepreneur. In a socialist economy, on the other hand, with the means of production in social ownership, it is obviously the total effect on the national economy that matters. In this sense, the socialist economy is "insurer" and "insurant" at the same time, providing as it does for the equalization of risks.

At this point of our reasoning it could be claimed that all risk-aversion is unjustified. There are, however, other factors which have so far not been taken into account.

We are dealing here with a *planned* economy where all relationships of major importance – such as the material, labour-force, financial, foreign-trade and other balances – are planned in advance (see ch. 1). Any departure from the plan will tend to upset these balances. Let us take, for example, the case when an investment project in the man-made fibres industry is completed later than scheduled, with both investment and operation costs exceeding the estimates. At the same time, an investment project in the cotton industry is completed ahead of schedule, with both investment and operation costs lower than estimated. Let us assume that as calculated on the basis of our computational cost function, the discounted amount of overstepping in the first case will exactly equal the discounted amount of saving in the second. Does this mean that the deviations have in fact completely cancelled out?

As a consequence of the protracted execution of an investment in the man-made fibres industry, the capacity of a series of firms specialized in the contruction and installation of chemical plants will have taken longer than expected. It will thus be only belatedly that they are able to proceed to the construction of further chemical plants. Nor will it be possible to shift to the chemical industry the team of workers and specialists released ahead of schedule from the construction and installation of a cotton industrial project because they will not be up to the task. If they were nevertheless shifted to the chemical industry, this would involve difficulties as well as additional cost.

One of the consequences of the man-made fibres plant's going into operation late will be the tardy appearance of a new product on the markets abroad. This may lead to the loss of some markets. Another possible consequence is the following. The Hungarian textile industry may already have counted on the synthetic fibres produced by the new plant. Now, with the Hungarian product not available, it becomes unexpectedly necessary to import them. This may force us into contracting under less favourable conditions than might have been the case if we had had sufficient time to prepare the ground. (The alternative of not importing the synthetic fibres in question will again lead to unused capacities in the textile industry.) The fact that the cotton mill goes into operation earlier will not compensate for the loss as there may be demand for its products only on other markets than those lost, or there may be no foreign demand at all.

It is also possible that local employment depended on the man-made fibres plant and the idle manpower cannot be shifted to a region where another plant happened to be completed ahead of schedule.

These few illustrations will suffice to show that any divergence from the plans will inevitably lead to difficulties: re-grouping, temporary measures involving extra cost, idle capacities, losses. The more uncertain an alternative the greater the danger of its leading to divergences from the plan. Such divergences will, in turn, lead to real economic losses as illustrated by the examples above.

Even divergences from the plan in the positive sense may cause certain temporary difficulties. (A plant may be completed ahead of schedule but the capacities needed for processing its products may not yet be ready to go into operation.) It is, however, clear that the greater trouble will be caused by the divergences in the negative sense.

The magnitude of the effect of divergences from the plans caused by uncertainty, will be influenced by three main factors.

(a) *The elasticity of planning methods and the ability to adapt quickly to unforeseen situations.* The rigidity of the planning methods employed in Hungary has already been subject to much criticism. Although some progress in this respect has been achieved over recent years, there still remains much to be done to render the methods of planning more elastic. Be that as it may, economic planning and economic administration will at a given period of time have an established "average" ability for self-adaptation, which should be taken into account as a given fact.

(b) *The sensitivity and importance of the point of the national economy where a divergence from the plan occurs.* The plan balances and estimates are closely interrelated. Disturbances will, therefore, have secondary effects which may, however, be very different as to their degree of intensity. The tardy completion of a toy factory will obviously cause less trouble than a power plant not going into operation and the resulting absence of electric power in several domains.

(c) *The supply of stocks and reserves in the national economy.* The stocks and reserves will be able to absorb or, at least, to mitigate the secondary effects of lags and losses, and to *localize* the disturbances. In view of the manifold effects of the uncertainties in investments, all types of stocks and reserves will be needed: goods and materials, foreign exchange, accessories of fixed capital, etc. The grave difficulties caused in Hungarian economic life by the lack and the unsuitable composition of stocks and reserves are generally known*. In this respect, too, some improvement could be noticed in recent years, but in several domains the composition of stocks and reserves is still unsatisfactory.

All this allows us to establish the following principles.

1. Risk-aversion is objectively justified; a safety level higher than 0.5 should be aimed at.

2. The greater the ability for elastic selfadaptation that can be expected on the part of economic administration and the more complete the available supply of stocks and reserves, the lower will be the warranted degree of risk-aversion.

* For a discussion of this phenomenon and its causes, see J. Kornai [70] and [71].

3. An equal degree of risk-aversion will not be warranted in all sectors of the national economy; it should be stronger where a potential loss is likely to have graver secondary effects.

And yet, letting oneself be induced to maximum caution by these facts would be a mistake. Not even the simultaneous failure of a large number of investment projects is likely to cause any *grave* troubles, and this for the very reasons that the favourable and unfavourable divergences from the expected value will tend to cancel out to some extent; that economic administration will be able to adapt itself more or less quickly to unforeseen difficulties; and that some stocks and reserves will actually be in ready supply. It is an advantage of the centrally directed planned economy that it enables economic administration to intervene radically in such cases and to prevent, by suitable modifications of the plans, the spontaneous secondary effects of an unforeseen disturbance to assert themselves.

It is for these reasons that the risks involved in individual investment decisions must not be overestimated. What is required in a socialist planned economy is initiative and an enterprising spirit; it would be a grave mistake to let extreme caution prevail in investment decisions and to shrink from any novel venture which necessarily involves certain risks. The following principle can be established:

4. Risk-aversion should not be too high; the safety level should definitely be below 1.*

Principles 1 and 4 imply that it will be expedient to recommend the application of a strategy of limited safety, and the definite dismissal of the strategies of hazard, risk-indifference and maximum safety.

All this does not mean that a stand has already been taken on the question of the exact value of the safety level. On the basis of the above train of thoughts it appears reasonable that the safety level should not be too near either to 0.5 or to 1. Accordingly, the following principle can be established:

* In actual practice, this means a dismissal of the strategy of maximum safety and of the maximin decision criterion. Besides, the pessimistic character of this criterion was criticized by several authors. See e.g. K. J. ARROW [3], H. CHERNOFF [20], and L. J. SAVAGE [153].

5. *In the case of safety programming, the safety level should be between the limits of 0.6 and 0.9; it should be lower for the comparatively less important sectors and higher for those of decisive importance*.*

As can be seen, this reasoning has led us to similar results as those obtained in the course of our interviews with economic and industrial executives.

* The man-made fibres industry, e.g. belongs to the less important sectors as its products are being processed by a single industry, its role in the country's exports is of minor importance only, and the number of those employed in it is relatively low.

CHAPTER 14

STOCHASTIC CALCULATIONS IN PRACTICE

14.1. Supplementary Assumptions

The stochastic calculations carried out within the framework of the research project for the man-made fibres industry were based on the safety programming model described* in ch. 12. In addition to those discussed earlier, in the course of these calculations the following supplementary assumptions were made:

(1) All data used to define the objective function and established by experts in "from–to" form were considered as normally distributed random variables. The probability that the variable would not exceed the "from-to" limits was put at 98 per cent. This means that for the present case the value of ε figuring in formula (12.1) is 0.02.

(2) A positive or negative correlation was assumed to exist between the following sequences of world-market prices employed in the calculations**:

(a) There is a perfectly close relationship between the export and import price of an individual product. Accordingly, the correlation between the objective-function coefficients of export and import activities relating to the same product is -1.

(b) There may be a (positive or negative) correlation also between the objective-function coefficients of foreign trading activities relating to different products.

(c) There is a correlation between the coefficients of the linear terms (composed mainly of material costs) in the cost function of certain productive activities, owing to the correlation existing between the prices of import materials.

(d) There is a correlation between the objective-function coefficients of some foreign trading activities and the coefficients of the linear terms

* The numerical part of the stochastic calculations of the project for the man-made fibres industry was carried out by P. Wellisch who also participated in developing the safety programming model and in its application to the concrete case.

** The correlation estimates are given in section B.2 of the Appendix.

in the cost function of some productive activities, owing to the correlation that exists between export and import prices on the one hand and the prices of import materials used in production on the other hand.

(3) All random variables not mentioned under (2) were assumed to be uncorrelated, i.e. mutually independent*.

The data which determine the value of the objective function of program are partly constants, partly normally distributed random variables. The value of the objective function is itself a normally distributed random variable, being a linear function of such variables.

On the basis of the general assumptions set forth in ch. 12 in connection with the application of the methods of the probability theory as well as on that of the supplementary assumptions listed above, it will now be possible to construct the objective function of safety programming, which will replace the original objective function (7.6) of the model of the man-made fibres industry.

$$C_P(\mathbf{x}) = C(\mathbf{x}) + \theta_P \, \sigma_C(\mathbf{x}) \,. \tag{14.1}$$

Safety value $C_P(\mathbf{x})$ is composed of two parts. The first part is *expected value* $C(\mathbf{x})$. This is identical with the non-stochastic concave cost function described in formula (7.6).

The second part is a product where *standard deviation* $\sigma_C(\mathbf{x})$ is one of the factors. This could be established on the basis of the above supplementary assumptions; to go into the details of its determination will not be necessary**. Another factor is *safety factor* θ_P which constitutes the parameter of programming.

14.2. The Problem Narrowed Down

It was not possible for us to undertake to find a *solution* of the problem of parametric safety programming. As pointed out in ch. 7, even in the case of stochastic concave programming we had to content ourselves with an approximation instead of an exact solution of the problem. The

* In the case of normally distributed random variables, zero correlation implies stochastic independence.

** The formulae for the expected value and the standard deviation figuring in the stochastic objective function of the research project for the man-made fibres industry are given in section B.3 of the Appendix.

stochastic objective function of form (14.1) is an even more complicated tool of calculation than the original non-stochastic function (7.6).

As an approximation to the solution of our stochastic programming problem we have, accordingly, narrowed down our calculation to the following:

Ten feasible programs were fixed in advance. Of all feasible programs, we sought to find the optimal among these ten only, with various values of safety level P. It is true that in this way we cannot be sure to find also the solution of the original safety programming problem. However, as the feasible programs fixed in advance were partly based on definite economic considerations, and constructed in such a way as to represent certain characteristic concepts of economic policy, the calculations carried out will allow some important inferences to be drawn.

The following programs have been compared, some of which were mentioned in section 6.5 already:

(1) The program with the most favourable expected value from among those obtained by means of the electronic computer.

(2)–(5) Programs with "fairly favourable" expected values. These, too, were obtained by means of the computer when – in the course of seeking for an optimum on the basis of the approximation method – we explored, as it were, the "neighbourhood" of that optimum.

(6) The official program defined by the traditional method.

(7) Autarkic program. Domestic demand is fully met out of domestic production; no export.

(8) Autarky with some export. This is a slightly modified version of program (7), prescribing as it does the export of two types of product only.

(9) Pure import. The opposite of program (6); all domestic demand is met from imports; no production.

(10) Extremely extroverted program. Here two products only are produced, but one of them in huge quantities the major part of which is exported. All other products are imported. In the terms of the model's original system of constraints as described in section 3.3, this program is not feasible; the export constraint of the product produced in huge quantities has been released. The program obtained in this way, although it cannot be termed realistic, is remarkable as a basis of comparison and a mental experiment.

In contradistinction to programs (1)–(5) obtained by means of the electronic computer, and to program (6) which was given, programs (7)–(10) were constructed by ourselves.

14.3. The Most Important Calculations

First of all, we determined the expected values and standard deviations of all programs; then we proceeded to ranking the programs according to the increasing order of the expected values. This is shown in table 14.1.

TABLE 14.1

Ranking of programs according to expected value in the man-made fibres industry

No. of program	Characterization of program	Expected value (million Ft)	Standard deviation (million Ft)	Is it dominated by another program?
10	Extremely extroverted	5940.9*	495.8	no
1	With the most favourable mean, provided that raw material exports are not unrestricted	6425.2	247.3	no
2	Fairly favourable mean	6428.9	251.5	yes
3	Fairly favourable mean	6449.9	227.3	no
4	Fairly favourable mean	6504.3	237.0	yes
5	Fairly favourable mean	6567.0	238.1	yes
6	Official	7272.1	179.8	no
8	"Autarky", with some export	7386.7	91.5	no
7	"Autarky"	7770.4	84.4	no
9	Pure import	8438.5	283.4	yes

* To find the mean of the objective function of program (10), we took the costs of 7 plants of normal size instead of those of a single giant plant (see the considerations in section 7.6 concerning the original cost function (7.6) of the man-made fibres industry model).

From the first ranking already some conclusions can be drawn. Having to choose between two programs, we are faced with a dilemma if the first one is more favourable as regards expected value and the second one is so as regards standard deviation. Our choice will be obviously easier if the first program is more favourable than the second one as regards both expected value and standard deviation. In this case the second program is *dominated* by the first one, at least as far as expected value and standard deviation are concerned. Out of the ten programs we found four to be dominated by other programs. It is remarkable that the program envisaging imports only should be among these – it is the least favourable as regards expected value, standing at the same time on the last place but one as regards standard deviation.

In the course of the subsequent analysis, the extremely extroverted export program will also be disregarded. Our stochastic model does not adequately reflect the fact that beyond a certain limit export possibilities, too, tend to become increasingly uncertain. As a matter of fact, the export price estimate ought to have been given in a way which allows for a widening of the "from-to" interval as a function of the volume of exports. Or, alternately, export constraints which are themselves random variables ought to have been built into the model, to indicate the uncertain character of the limits of export possibilities. This, however, would have meant a fundamental change in constructing our model, a change which it was not possible to undertake at the time.

The following calculations were thus based on five programs. First of all, we have worked out the safety values of these programs with different safety levels. The results are presented in table 14.2.

The ranking presented in table 14.2 was supplemented by another calculation, that of parametric safety programming. The safety level was

TABLE 14.2

Safety values of programs in the man-made fibres industry

No. of program	1	3	6	8	7
Characterization of the program	With the most favourable expected value	With a fairly favourable expected value	Official	"Autarky" with some export	"Autarky"
Safety level: 69.1%					
Safety factor: 0.5					
Safety value, million Ft	6548.9	6563.5	7362.0	7432.5	7812.6
Order of precedence	1	2	3	4	5
Safety level: 84.1%					
Safety factor: 1					
Safety value, million Ft	6672.5	6677.2	7451.9	7478.2	7854.8
Order of precedence	1	2	3	4	5
Safety level: 97.7%					
Safety factor: 2					
Safety value, million Ft	6919.8	6904.5	7631.6	7569.7	7939.2
Order of precedence	2	1	4	3	5
Safety level: $1-10^{-4}$%					
Safety factor: 5					
Safety value, million Ft	7661.8	7586.4	8170.9	7844.3	8192.4
Order of precedence	2	1	4	3	5

treated as a parameter and was let run through the interval between 50 per cent and $100–10^{-12}$ per cent. We have noted which programs are optimal with the various P values. What we were dealing with is, of course, only relative optimality: we wanted to find out which programs are optimal, not of all programs but only of the nine feasible programs considered here*. It turned out that in this interval two further programs were dominated by other programs, in addition to the four programs so dominated according to table 14.1. There are thus only three programs that can be termed optimal within one or another of the now observed intervals of P.

The results of the parametric programming calculation are represented in figure 14.1. On the horizontal axis are measured the values of Θ_P safety factor belonging to the P safety levels. The straight lines of different ilopes represent the objective function values of the individual programs, s.e. the safety values, the P quantiles of costs. The breaking points of the lower envelope, marked by a heavy line in the figure, are the critical points of the safety level. Such a breaking point can be observed e.g. at the value of $\Theta_P = 1.23$ which corresponds to a safety level of 89 per cent. Below this point, program (1) is optimal, above it program (3).

From the point of view of the practical problems of the man-made fibres industry, the ranking presented in table 14.2 and the parametric programming represented in figure 14.1 admit of the following conclusions:

(1) Program (1), the one with the most favourable mean as calculated on the basis of the realistic (export-constraint) model, is also the most favourable one as regards safety value, provided that the safety level is lower than 89 per cent.

(2) In the safety-level interval between 89 per cent and $100–10^{-12}$ per cent, program (3) is the most favourable one, a program which is also based on the realistic (export-constraint) model and calculated by means of the computer, with a mean but slightly higher than that of the former one. The slightly higher mean of program (3) as against program (1) is counterbalanced by the slightly smaller standard deviation in the case of program (3) in this safety-level interval.

Both programs include the following activities:

polyacrylonitrile-vinylchloride copolymer fibre production and export
terylene production and export
nylon 6 yarn production, technology "B", and export

* From this calculation, the extremely extroverted program (10) was omitted.

polypropylene yarn production and export
cellophane production in new plant and export
ethylene glycol production
polypropylene production.

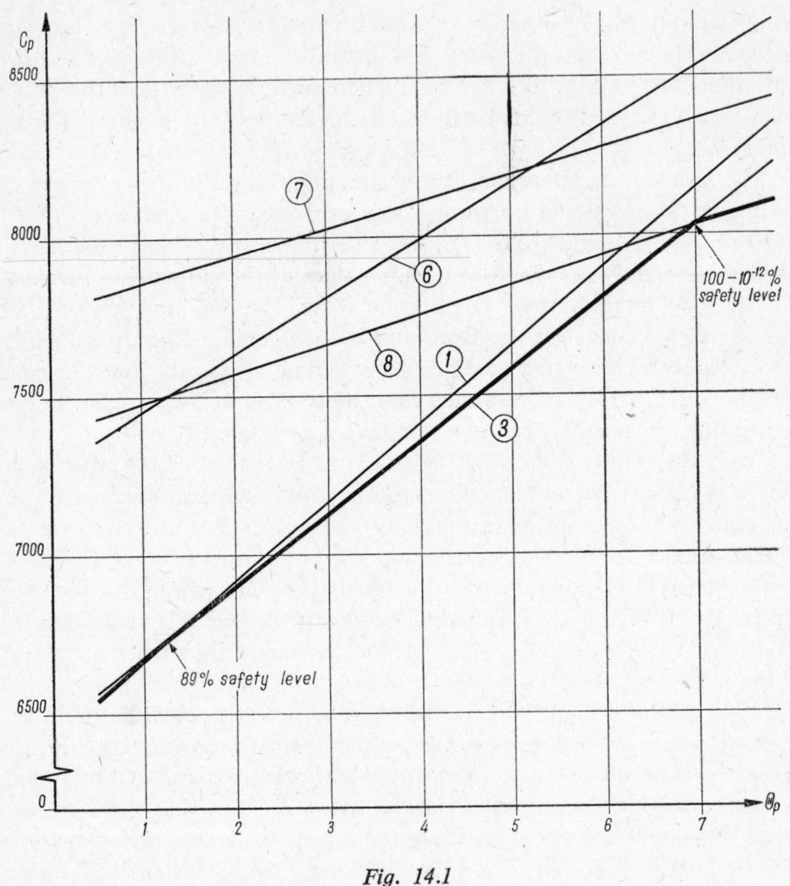

Fig. 14.1

Between the two programs, the following divergences exist:

Program (1) prescribes, in addition to the activities listed above, also the production of phenol and the export of polypropylene.

Program (2) prescribes, also in addition to the activities listed above, the production of polypropylene fibre, as well as a lower volume of terylene production and export than in program (1).

(3) Should a degree of safety higher than $100-10^{-12}$ per cent be required (which is approximately equivalent with the application of a strategy of maximum safety), we must choose an essentially autarkic program which admits of a minimum of external trade only. In our opinion, however, it would hardly be appropriate to base the development of a new industry on an economic policy aimed at eliminating all risks. The choice of this program is, accordingly, not recommended.

(4) At any safety level, it was possible to find a program which is more advantageous than the official one.

14.4. The Effects of the Concentration of Activities

In our stochastic programming model there is a multiple relationship between the concentration or the diversification, the scattering of the activities on the one hand and the safety value of the program on the other. This can be represented in a more generalized form, as shown by the schematical example given in the Appendix C. Here I shall confine myself to describing and commenting upon the concrete experiences gained in the course of the project for the man-made fibres industry.

(1) One of the components of safety value is the expected value of costs (see function (7.6)). The expected value of the cost of productive activities was represented by a concave cost function meant to express the relative advantages concomitant with large-scale production and the increase in plant size. *The requirement to reduce the expected value of costs will, therefore, act towards a concentration of productive activities.* This was shown in detail in section 7.5.

(2) Another component of safety value is the standard deviation, multiplied by the safety factor. *The requirement to reduce standard deviation will act towards a scattering of the activities.*

As a matter of fact, it is a certain equalization of risks that tends to assert itself increasingly in such cases*. To take an example from the field of horse-racing: risks can be reduced by backing not a single horse with a high bet but a great number of horses with low bets, provided that the chances of the horses are independent of one another. Were we, for example, to set up a single terylene plant with a capacity in excess of domestic requirements, and the price of terylene were to decrease to a

* The effects of the concentration and division of investments on the safety of the consequences of decision are dealt with (in connection with portfolio selection) by H. MARKOWITZ [118], pp. 102–115.

higher degree than expected, heavy losses could be incurred. When a terylene plant and a polypropylene plant whose markets are independent of each other, are simultaneously set up, there will be a chance that possible losses incurred in the production of terylene would be offset by the profit yielded by polypropylene production or conversely.

This relationship is clearly represented in table 14.3 where the 9 programs are ranked in the ascending order of the standard deviation. Program (9), which does not contain any productive activity, has been omitted here.

TABLE 14.3

Programs ranked according to standard deviation in the man-made fibres industry

No. of program	Characterization	Number of products envisaged	Standard deviation (million Ft)
7	Autarky	13	84.4
8	Autarky with some export	13	91.5
6	Official	10	179.8
3	"Fairly favourable"	9	227.3
4	"Fairly favourable"	6	237.0
5	"Fairly favourable"	7	238.1
1	Most favourable	8	247.3
2	"Fairly favourable"	8	251.5
10	Extremely extroverted	2	495.8

Nor will the safety of the program depend exclusively on the degree of concentration. It will also be affected by the safety of the individual activities contained in the program as well as by the degree of correlation existing between them. In any case, the table above also shows the unfavourable effects of the concentration of production on safety.

(3) The correlation between the cost characteristics of the activities also exerts an influence on safety and on concentration.

Let us take, for example, the production of and the external trade in two types "M" and "N" of rayon. There is a positive correlation between the world-market prices of rayon types "M" and "N". Accordingly, between the export price of rayon type "M" and the import price of rayon type "N" the correlation is negative. Under the circumstances, it may be worth while to produce the one and to import the other, and this out of the following consideration. Should the world-market price of the former rise export returns, too, would increase. This could counterbalance the increase in cost that is likely to occur in connection with the import of the other type which is being produced in the country. To take the inverse case: the loss incurred as a consequence of a fall in the price of the domestically produced and exported fibre may be wholly or partly offset by the circumstance that a fall is likely to occur also in the price of the other type of fibre, making for import savings.

The example demonstrates the risk-decreasing effect of a negative correlation. The next example is to show the risk-increasing effect of a positive correlation.

It was pointed out in connection with (2) above that by carrying out simultaneously two non-correlated and independent productive activities, e.g. by setting up a terylene fibre and a polypropylene material plant, potential profits and losses may be balanced. It is obvious that no such equalization can be expected in the case when two plants producing nylon 6 yarn are established, with world-market prices of their products rising and falling simultaneously.

From the point of view of economic policy this admits of the conclusion that *it should be our endeavour to include in the scope of our programming project activities between which there is the lowest possible degree of positive, or the highest possible degree of negative correlation.*

A methodological lesson that can be drawn is that the correlation between costs and returns of the activities must be studied most carefully and taken into account in the course of the calculations.

The type of stochastic objective function employed in the programming project for the man-made fibres industry has the advantage that it lends itself to the simultaneous reflection of the three relationships described above, viz. the cost-decreasing effect of concentration, the safety-increasing effect of scattering diversification and the effects of correlation.

14.5. A Methodological Remark

Let us, finally, add a remark of methodological character to the survey of the stochastic calculations. Good care must be taken to apply equal standards and to proceed objectively when assessing the degree of uncertainty involved in the various data. The *proportions* of the degree of uncertainty of the various data should genuinely reflect the relative differences in uncertainty.

Our basic assumption that there was a 98 per cent probability that the characteristics of events which are to occur in the future would remain within the limits of the estimated "from-to" interval, is clearly an uncontrollable one. The correct figure might be 90 per cent. But how far would this affect the final results of the calculations? To make this clear, let us return to the figure presenting the safety-value functions. A modification of our basic assumptions in the sense indicated above would render the straight lines steeper*. Accordingly, the points of intersection would shift and critical safety values decrease, e.g. the critical safety value of programs (1) and (3) would shift from 89 to 81 per cent. On the other hand, the programs whose safety-value lines are intersecting would remain the same; the same programs would be more favourable at a lower and the same at a higher safety level. Nor would this – with a given safety level – change the order of precedence of the safety value of the programs. Accordingly, the relation between the dominating and dominated programs would not change either. In short: the comparison of the programs would lead to the same consequences as far as economic policy is concerned. It is only the interpretation based on the theory of probability, the *numerical* inferences regarding the safety level, that would be modified, and these are, after all, of minor importance.

* Let the standard deviation of a datum given in any "from-to" form be σ in the case when the probability of the actual value to remain between the "from-to" limits is 98 per cent, and σ' when this probability is 90 per cent. From formula (12.1) it follows that $\sigma' = v\sigma$, where

$$v = \frac{\Phi^{-1}(0.99)}{\Phi^{-1}(0.95)} = \frac{2.326}{1.645} = 1.41.$$

The shift to 90 per cent had thus the same effect as if we had multiplied the standard deviation of all data by the same constant factor. However, the standard deviation of the objective function value is a first-degree homogeneous function of the standard deviation of the coefficients, see Appendix B, formula (B.4). As a consequence, the standard deviation of the objective function value belonging to any program will be multiplied by the same factor: $\sigma_C' = v\sigma_C$. In conformity with formula (12.7), the new quantile of the objective function value will be:

$$C_P(\mathbf{x}) = C(\mathbf{x}) + \Theta_P\, \sigma_C'(\mathbf{x}) = C(\mathbf{x}) + \Theta_P v \sigma_C(\mathbf{x})\,.$$

CHAPTER 15

SECOND COMPARISON WITH THE TRADITIONAL METHODS

The official instructions concerning the investment efficiency calculations contain no provision for the case when some of the data involved are uncertain and there are no practical means to ascertain their value with greater precision. But although the instructions are lacking, there is an established practice of dealing with the problem and it is this practice that we will briefly survey in the following.

In this connection we will have to distinguish between the efficiency calculations as they stand on paper, and the problems as they are being thought over, discussed and actually dealt with by those making the decisions.

In the written text of the efficiency calculations there is nothing to point to the uncertainty of any data – on the contrary, they would convey the impression of containing perfectly exact figures only. For example, in the usual calculations we will find figures like this: the world market price is 297 dollar/ton – even if the price were actually to fluctuate between 280 and 310 dollars at the given time, not to speak of the fact that even the average price may be shifting upwards or downwards later on*.

In sections 14.3 and 14.4 above, the reliability of the data contained in permit papers – the basic documents of decisions – were extensively discussed. It was shown that over a period of some length a tendency to negative bias manifested itself.

What now is the real attitude of those making the decisions to the uncertainty of the data?

First of all: far from being a discovery of theoretical economists, the uncertainty of data in investment estimates is a fact well-known to exe-

* An official dealing with investment projects in one of the industrial ministries has told me that whenever he encounters data given in "from-to" form in a calculation, he will return it for revision. He will insist on further investigations into the matter until the uncertain data can be replaced by exact figures. As a result, those carrying out the calculations will strive to *conceal* the uncertainties involved in the calculation.

cutives in the various domains of economic life. This is actually one of the reasons of their distrust of efficiency calculations. The distrust is only increased by the frequent occurrence of tendentious distortions. (An official responsible for all investment projects under one of the industrial ministries declared that whenever an estimate is submitted to him, he would always add 20 per cent before investigating the efficiency of the investment.)

The executives who make the decisions will often be heard to declare that calculation and life are two different things, that calculations must not be fetishized, etc.

The men of practice will endeavour to size up the risks involved in an investment, fully aware of the fact that the magnitude of these risks is not unimportant from the point of view of the national economy. They will, however, be able to do so only on the basis of qualitative considerations, one may even say, led by their instinct, for the lack of suitable quantitative methods.

The fact that the traditional efficiency calculations have up to now avoided and neglected the problem of the uncertainty of data has brought much discredit to these calculations (as a matter of fact, to all types of economic calculation). This is what encourages some executives to disregard the recommendations of efficiency calculations even in the cases where they are realistic and provide good orientation.

Nor is all this surprising: decision under uncertain conditions is one of the most difficult problems of economic theory and one which has not been satisfactorily solved to the present day. Neither the procedure described in chs. 14–20, nor any similar method can solve the problem completely. They will certainly not work wonders. We must acquiesce in the fact that nothing can be said with certainty where the basic data are uncertain. No mathematics will ever be able to change uncertainty into certainty as if by magic. Nor will mathematics enable us to neglect the most important task which consists in decreasing risk and uncertainty by a better prediction of future economic processes. The application of our methods may nevertheless prove useful, and this from the following viewpoints.

They afford an opportunity for reasonable *selection*. There will be some activities which will not be brought under the optimal program by any of the parameter values, nor by any realistic preliminary assumption. This negative information will also provide an important basis for decision: it will not be worth while to choose these activities.

The methods will enable us to select from a set of possible activities *some that may be termed "sufficiently favourable" and "acceptable"*.

When a variety of parametric programming and sensitivity analysis has been carried out, a number of activities will emerge which figured in various optimal programs and were among the first in ranking according to various viewpoints. This will be a weighty argument for giving them preference.

Decisions are facilitated by the fact that it will not be necessary to take a stand beforehand on the magnitude of certain critical parameters, e.g. in the case of safety programming on that of the safety level. It is an important advantage of parametric programming that it proves that to quite wide intervals of the parameter there belongs, a quantitatively but at least qualitatively, identical program.

The proposed methods will *contribute to a more objective treatment of estimated, uncertain data.* In the course of the traditional calculations, estimated data are frequently the subject of much manipulation; calculations are based now on more favourable values, now on less favourable ones, according to what they are intended to prove. The methods described in the foregoing treat the estimated data according to a uniform principle within the individual calculations, e.g. all are treated pessimistically, or all are taken at their mean value, etc.

By applying the proposed methods, *the concrete decision problem will be reduced to a more general problem of decision.* Let us take, for example, the stochastic model of the man-made fibres industry. Here the concrete problem consists in deciding which of the model's economic activities should be utilized. The more general decision problem is: how great a risk should be taken? For the economic administration, the sensitivity analysis carried out in the course of programming lifts the possibilities of choice to a higher level.

PART 4

COMPUTATIONAL EVALUATIONS

Introduction

In Part 2 of the work when sectoral models were first described it was assumed that the objective function was based on the *official* computational valuations. We will now abandon this simplification and attempt to replace the official computational evaluations with our *own ones* in the calculations.

The sectoral programming models represent individual sectors of the national economy as a whole. In the course of the calculations we shall endeavour to fit the partial models and with them the sectoral programs into the economy as a whole in its optimum state of equilibrium. To this end two principal methods offer themselves: the suitable determination of the constraints (output obligations, resource constraints, material quotas) connecting the sectoral model with the rest of the national economy, on the one hand, and of the prices employed in the objective function, on the other.

Now, will it be possible to give full effect to these endeavours? To my best knowledge, this has not been done by anyone as yet. Investigations carried out to this end will be described in some detail in Part 5. Meanwhile, within the framework of isolated sectoral programming projects, we are setting ourselves a considerably more modest task. Let us survey our position. For one thing, we have at our disposal the traditional balance system – one of which no one will claim that it ensured optimum allocation of products and resources – to furnish the plan directives serving as model constraints. Furthermore, we have the actual price system, of which no one will claim either that it exerted an optimum influence on the decisions of lower-grade economic units and institutions.

Under the circumstances, our endeavours in the course of the programming projects were confined to *employing in the objective function such computational evaluations of our own as would give a better direction to the sectoral program than was the case with the application of the actual prices and the official computational evaluations traditionally used in investment efficiency calculations.*

In connection with the computational evaluations employed we depend mainly on intuition. We are not able to *prove* that they are really better than the actual prices and the official computational evaluations; even less can we prove that they are really *appropriate*, that they will ensure the harmonious fitting of the partial sectoral decision into the general optimum.

The chapters which follow will show, if nothing else, the *difficulties of rational calculation*. Even this may prove useful, as many people are convinced of the ease and simplicity of the procedure. Moreover, I believe that practical efforts towards establishing rational methods of calculation – even though they will not always lead to satisfactory results – may help to clear the theoretical issues. In the course of calculation and planning, in contact with living practice, theoretical problems may become clear the clarification of which would not have been possible in a purely speculative way.

CHAPTER 16

THE GENERAL ACCOUNTING PRINCIPLES OF THE COMPUTATIONAL PRICE SYSTEM

16.1. The Role of the Accounting Principles

The chapters that follow will describe accounting principles. The latter are *not* proven formulae obtained by way of deduction from an economy-wide optimization model. Our sole purpose in establishing them here is to make it clear how we *proceeded*, what principles we employed in the course of the calculations. Even this constitutes an advance over the traditional planning methods where the accounting principles employed are often not openly declared.

When establishing our accounting principles the following criteria were set up:

– An accounting principle should not come into conflict with the logical considerations self-evident for those engaged in planning.

– An accounting principle should be more advantageous and more reasonable than the practice of traditional planning and of the actual price system. It should admit of the guess (even if it cannot be proved) that it constitutes a better approach to the general optimum.

– The accounting principles should be employed in a logical manner, so as to render the models consistent from this point of view.

I do not want to give the impression as if the accounting principles described had already been established when the first sectoral programming projects were embarked upon. They were being developed in the course of progress; some of them were first set up in a rather improvised form only, with the theoretical clarification following later on; others were even modified in the course of the calculations.

For the time being, I would suggest these accounting principles – for the want of better ones – to those intending to engage in similar calculations. It is certain, however, that in the case of a wider application of sectoral programming the accounting principles themselves will also undergo further development.

16.2. The General Formula of the Computational Price

In order to *avoid* the actual and valid domestic price system, the following two principal methods will be resorted to:

Accounting principle 16.1. Domestic inputs will be reduced in general to two primary domestic inputs, i.e. labour input and production fund utilization.

Accounting principle 16.2. Import inputs will be accounted for at foreign-trade prices, reckoned in foreign currency, which will be converted into forints by means of computational exchange rates. Moreover, some of the domestic inputs will also be treated as if occurring in foreign currency and will, accordingly, be converted into forints on the basis of the foreign-trade price.

I propose to call the foreign-trade price the price at which the purchases of the Hungarian foreign trading agencies are effected on markets abroad (import price) and at which Hungarian goods are sold on foreign markets (export price)*. For transactions taking place on socialist markets, the foreign-trade prices will be reckoned in roubles, while transactions on capitalist markets will be reckoned in dollars.

The method based on accounting principle 16.1 will henceforth be called accounting for domestic input, that based on accounting principle 16.2 accounting for foreign-trade input. Our computational price system rests on the combination of the two accounting principles.

The type of the computational price of the ith product may be summed up in the following formula:

$$\begin{aligned} s_i = {} & \Omega(q_i^{\text{dir}} + q_i^{\text{indir}}) + \\ & + \gamma(p_i^{\text{dir}} + p_i^{\text{indir}}) + \\ & + D_{\text{Rbl}}(r_{i,\text{Rbl}}^{\text{dir}} + r_{i,\text{Rbl}}^{\text{indir}}) + \\ & + D_{\$}(r_{i,\$}^{\text{dir}} + r_{i,\$}^{\text{indir}}) + \\ & + \gamma(D_{\text{Rbl}}\, p_{i,\text{Rbl}}^{\text{dir}} + D_{\$}\, p_{i,\$}^{\text{dir}}). \end{aligned} \tag{16.1}$$

* Foreign-trade prices will be reckoned ex border. Later on we will revert in detail to the problem of their determination.

The upper suffices "dir" and "indir" occur several times in the formula. The suffix "dir" refers to inputs occurring in the course of the production of the *i*th product at the works themselves where the product in question is produced. The suffix "indir", on the other hand, refers to products which, although contributing ultimately to the production of the *i*th product, do not occur at the works producing the *i*th product but at some other plant or, possibly, in some other sector of production. This concept of indirect input was discussed in the chapter dealing with I–O tables.

Let us now proceed to the interpretation of the symbols contained in the formula:

s_i = the computational unit price of the *i*th product, in Ft

q_i^{dir}, q_i^{indir} = the direct and indirect actual wage cost per unit of the *i*th product, in Ft

p_i^{dir}, p_i^{indir} = the direct and indirect production-fund requirements of domestic origin per unit of the *i*th product, in Ft

$p_{i,\text{Rbl}}^{\text{dir}}$, $p_{i,\$}^{\text{dir}}$ = the direct import production-fund requirements per unit of the *i*th product, in Rbl and $

$r_{i,\text{Rbl}}^{\text{dir}}$, $r_{i,\text{Rbl}}^{\text{indir}}$ = the cost of direct and indirect import materials purchased in socialist markets and utilized per unit of the *i*th product, in Rbl

$r_{i,\$}^{\text{dir}}$, $r_{i,\$}^{\text{indir}}$ = the cost of direct and indirect import materials purchased in capitalist markets and utilized per unit of the *i*th product, in $

Ω = the computational wage factor

γ = the computational rental on capital

D_{Rbl}, $D_\$$ = the computational rouble and dollar exchange rates.

As can be seen, the symbol of several factors contains the suffix "*i*", indicating the fact that these are the characteristics of the *i*th product. The factors Ω, γ, D_{Rbl}, $D_\$$, on the other hand, do not contain this suffix "*i*" because these represent computational valuations uniformly valid for all products.

The items in formula (16.1) may be grouped in several ways. One method would be to put in the first and second row the items accounted for as domestic inputs in accordance with accounting principle 16.1 and in the third, fourth and fifth row those accounted for as foreign-trade inputs in accordance with accounting principle 16.2. The latter should be reckoned in roubles or dollars and converted into forints on the basis of the computational exchange rates.

Another method: those figuring in the first, third and fourth row are continuous inputs. Those appearing in the second and fifth row are non-recurrent inputs: utilizations of the production funds. Multiplying the value of the production funds by γ we obtain the computational rent on capital. This may be considered as if it were occurring continuously, i.e. as if it were paid in by the producing firm actually on each product, and can therefore be added to the continuous inputs in the first, third and fourth row.

The first row contains the actual wage costs. Let these be multiplied by computational wage factor Ω (greater than unity). The result will represent the computational wage costs. The difference between computational and actual wage costs, i.e. $(\Omega-1)\ (q_i^{dir} + q_i^{indir})$ may be considered as representing the computational pay-roll tax*.

This leads at the same time to an accounting principle:

Accounting principle 16.3. When accounting for domestic inputs, labour input is measured by computational wage costs, production-fund utilization by computational rent on capital.

To sum up it may be stated that computational price s_i is composed of three main parts: total computational wage contents, total computational rent on capital and total computational import contents**.

Our task will now be to give a thorough explanation and to make concrete both price formula (16.1) and accounting principles 16.1–16.3. This is a rather intricate task which calls for an approach from several sides. The present chapter is first to deal with a few more general problems of a comprehensive character; further details will be elaborated in independent chapters.

* I propose to call computational pay-roll tax *all* costs accounted for in addition to actually paid wages and in proportion to wage costs.

In present-day actual practice in this country, there are two items which present themselves over and above actual wages and in proportion with the latter, viz. the 10 per cent social insurance rate and the 15 per cent pay-roll tax. Thus, in actual practice $\Omega = 1.25$.

** The reader who has followed up the price debates of recent years in this country will be able to recognize the close relationship between formula (16.1) and the so-called "multi-channel" type of prices. For a discussion of the subject see T. Nagy and Zs. Esze [131].

16.3. The Sphere of Application of Foreign-trade Prices

The first problem which must be answered right away is: When should we apply principle 16.1, that of accounting for as domestic input, and when principle 16.2, that of accounting for as foreign-trade input?

Part of the boundary between the two main accounting methods is natural, part of it artificial and more or less arbitrary. The division is a natural one in the following cases:

– The inputs deriving from actual imports must be *definitely* accounted for as foreign-trade inputs, irrespective of whether they constitute operational inputs (in practice, import materials) or direct investment inputs (in practice, import machinery).

– The inputs in connection with which no foreign-trade transaction can conceivably arise, must be *definitely* accounted for as domestic inputs. Thus e.g. non-transportable chemicals liable to explode, or bricks, etc., cannot be accounted for as imports.

At the same time it will be necessary to apply other accounting principles which appear less plausible.

Accounting principle 16.4. All indirect production-fund requirements will be accounted for as domestic inputs.

This accounting principle is clearly inaccurate as a considerable part of the production funds, especially as far as machinery is concerned, is of import origin. In actual practice, however, it would be rather difficult, though not impracticable, to trace all indirect machinery requirements, i.e. to ascertain which of the machines originate from imports. Here, we have not tried to do so. Accordingly, in formula (16.1), when determining *direct* production-fund requirements, we have made a distinction between p_i^{dir} (accounted for in Ft) and $p_{i,\text{Rbl}}^{\text{dir}}$ as well as $p_{i,\$}^{\text{dir}}$ (accounted for in Rbl and \$, respectively). In fact, it is possible to draw these limits, at least as far as calculations referring to products manufactured in new plants are concerned. Indirect production-fund requirements, on the other hand, are represented in the formula by the single symbol p_i^{indir} only, reckoned in Ft.

Accounting principle 16.5. The products where the quantity destined for domestic utilization is partly derived from domestic production but in major part from imports, can be accounted for at import prices.

Accounting principle 16.6. The products deriving from domestic production but exported regularly and in sizeable proportion, can be accounted for at export prices.

Accounting principle 16.7. The products deriving from domestic production which, though not entering in any considerable quantity into external trade, could none the less be imported or exported (i.e. potential import or export products), can be accounted for at import or export prices, respectively.

The above three principles are more or less arbitrary. Accounting principles 16.5 and 16.6 are more defensible, principle 16.7 is less so. All three are stated here not in the compulsory but in the concessive sense: these principles *can* be employed in the calculations. The possibility of their application was considered separately in the case of each product. We usually resorted to the application of principle 16.7 only if this proved more practicable than accounting for as domestic input in accordance with principle 16.1. As a matter of fact, the latter is considerably more difficult and complicated to apply – nor is it more satisfactory as regards economic justification.

The application of the above three principles can be justified to some extent on the basis of the opportunity cost principle. In the case of a domestically produced material we renounce the possibility of import, thus saving the import cost. The import cost constitutes the opportunity cost of domestic production. Similarly: if the entire quantity produced is utilized domestically, we renounce the possibility of export, thus losing the export revenue. The export revenue constitutes the opportunity cost of domestic utilization.

In an economy of a more closed and autarkic character this approach would hardly be justified. In the Hungarian economy, however, external trade plays a most important part. In 1962, the volume of imports corresponded to 30 per cent of total national income. The country lacks a great number of the basic raw materials and this reason alone would be sufficient to compel us to engage in external trade – not to speak of the other advantages deriving from international trade and the international division of labour. It is these facts that lend justification to the views which consider even the products remaining outside the scope of external trade the potential subjects of the latter.

The procedure is also in accordance with the principles of the official methods of investment efficiency calculation which prescribe the application of foreign-trade prices not only for actually imported and exported materials but also for the potentially importable and exportable ones*.

* See Hungarian Investments Code [195].

This train of thought, however, goes only part of the way to substantiate accounting principles 16.5–16.7. Let us first consider a simple case. Product A is partly imported, partly domestically produced. Domestic production as calculated on the basis of principle 16.1 proves more costly than import cost converted into forints on the basis of the computational rate of exchange. What should be the computational price of product A under these circumstances, the "domestic price" according to principle 16.1 or that derived from the import price? The question cannot be answered by only considering exclusively product A. It may not be worth while to enlarge the domestic production of product A because resources could be put to a more efficient use by enlarging the production of product B or product C. In this case the additional requirements of product A will be covered by imports – it will then be reasonable that those utilizing the products should pay a price corresponding to its import price. The case is an entirely different one if it is profitable to enlarge the production of A notwithstanding the fact that its domestic production is more costly than import. It may namely be expedient to enlarge its production if this meant less additional cost than that involved in substituting domestic production for the import of product B or product C. Should this be the case then the price of product A must conform to domestic input.

This highly simplified example serves to illustrate the following more general conception.

No country can in its price system conform mechanically to foreign-trade prices and lose touch with the domestic situation, not even in the case of a computational price system used only on paper in efficiency calculations. It is only from the plan (or, rather, the optimum program) for the national economy as a whole that it will become clear to what extent should an individual product be produced domestically or imported or exported. The decision will be affected by a great variety of production and foreign-trade constraints. The decision as to whether the price of a product should conform to the export or import price or to domestic input, will depend on the joint effect of these constraints*. As at the present moment no such simultaneous planning and price calculations are available on a national level, we are compelled to resort to working hypotheses such as accounting principles 16.4–16.7. Their application

* This could be brought to light by the "shadow price system", the ensemble of the computational evaluations of an economy-wide programming model. We shall revert to this question later on.

constitutes, however, only an emergency solution and they can be discarded as soon as working hypotheses on a more solid foundation are attained.

16.4. The Treatment of the Dynamics of Inputs

The computational price system described up to now and to be described in the following deals with the dynamics of inputs in a most superficial manner. In the classification according to time, the inputs are classed in but two categories: continuous operational inputs (in the terminology of English-language literature: flow-input) and non-recurrent ones of an investment character (stock-input). Continuous inputs are represented by computational wages, non-recurrent inputs by the rent on capital charges reckoned on production-fund utilization.

Should we deal exclusively with direct inputs, a more precise treatment of input dynamics would cause no difficulty. Thus, e.g. in the course of the programming project for the cotton industry, in some control calculations the time sequence of direct costs depending on the program was laid down for an accounting period of 30 years and subsequently their discounted total was minimized. In the case of indirect costs, on the other hand, a similar procedure is practically unrealizable for their dynamics cannot be forecast for a lengthy period under actual conditions. We had to choose between two alternatives: either to work on the basis of actual prices, a method which enables a more accurate consideration of the time sequence of inputs, e.g. calculating on a discounted cost basis; or to insist on working out computational prices and, with that, on calculating the indirect inputs, in which case an accurate reflection of the dynamics must be renounced. In view of the fact that in our investigations, and, accordingly, in this book, the emphasis was not on the problems of temporal choice nor on planning for the distribution of actions over time but on programming for an *appropriate economic structure*, the choice fell on the former solution, on the use of computational prices with a simplified dynamic treatment*.

* As pointed out before, in certain supplementary and control calculations compound interest formulae were used. A brief survey of the latter is given in Appendix D.

The term computational r a t e o f i n t e r e s t is employed throughout this book only to cover the rate of interest figuring in the compound interest formulae. This is denoted i.

Appendix D touches on the question whether it will be appropriate to identify the computational rate of interest and the rental on capital, i.e. to make $i = \gamma$.

Let us assume that our calculations were carried out in 1963 and that the planning year for which the programming project was carried out and whose workable input and output structure we are about to determine was 1970. Part of the production fund requirements taken into consideration in the course of calculation is connected with inputs previous to 1963. Thus, e.g. one of the model's variables represents the continued operation of a plant which existed already in 1963, and the production-fund requirements of this operation include also the value of the old plant's buildings and machinery. The other part of the production-fund requirements taken into consideration in the course of the calculations is connected with the inputs occurring later than 1963 ("future" inputs as related to the time of the calculation). Thus, e.g. one of the model's variables represents the operation of a new plant to be set up between 1966 and 1969. Here production-fund requirements are identical with investment costs. Price formula (16.1) does not make any distinction between the two: both are represented by coefficients p_i and both become multiplied by the same factor of capital charges. As a matter of fact, in 1970 – the year for which we were ultimately planning – both inputs occurring before 1963 and those of the period 1966–1969 will constitute *past* inputs and this justifies their common treatment.

The common treatment does, of course, not mean more than that the computational rent on capital which must be "paid" on them symbolically was for both calculated on the basis of the same rental γ. At the same time, it will usually be possible to work out concretely and separately the p_i coefficients which determine the value of the production funds of old plants on the one hand and the anticipated investment costs of new plants on the other.

Forecasting future changes in continuous inputs is an extremely difficult task. The changes in the future will partly occur as a consequence of a changing technology. To some extent this fact finds an expression in our model in the choice which the program is making between various productive activities employing old and new technologies. Beyond this, there are only two relationships where expected changes in operational inputs could be taken into consideration.

Accounting principle 16.8. Wage inputs are accounted for at the expected wage level of the plan year.

The estimates required thereto were derived from the national economic plan set up by means of the traditional methods.

Accounting principle 16.9. Foreign-trade prices were, within the limits of possibility, accounted for at the level expected for the plan year.

The above were pointed out here only as a part of the survey of the problems of dynamics and will be reverted to in detail in a later separate chapter.

Speaking of dynamics, I should like to speak here briefly also of the allowance for depreciation. In the literature on industrial management the view is extensively held that all depreciation allowance was of an inevitably arbitrary character*. We on our part mainly endeavoured to keep our views on the subject in harmony with the rest of our accounting principles. We formulated the following two principles:

Accounting principle 16.10. Wherever possible we have, instead of an allowance for depreciation, taken into account the input which ensures the maintenance of the unchanged technical level of the given fixed capital, including overhauls and replacements carried out when deemed technically necessary. This we proposed to call maintenance input.

Accounting principle 16.11. The maintenance input was accounted for as domestic input (reduced to primary domestic inputs) in accordance with principle 16.1.

We will deal with principle 16.11 and with the question of reducing to primary inputs later on when discussing the utilization of I–O tables. Here we should like to point out only that it was not possible to employ principles 16.10 and 16.11 in a fully consistent manner. In the course of programming for the cotton industry we succeeded in working out suitable estimates for maintenance costs but in the course of the programming project for the man-made fibres industry we were not able to do so. Instead, for lack of more adequate data, the renewal quota of the depreciation allowance was used in the calculations.

In connection with accounting principle 16.10 the question may arise, why is it the inputs ensuring an *unchanged* technical level that we are taking into account here? Does this mean that we are ignoring the fact that fixed capital will become obsolete? This is by no means the case; however, the phenomenon is treated here in a manner different from the usual calculations of amortization. Our models usually contain several technological alternatives, with technically more or less developed variants

* See e.g. F. LUTZ and V. LUTZ [111], p. 70.

competing with one another. It is the unlimited character of this competition that is ensured by taking into account for each technological alternative the inputs necessary for maintaining an unchanged level. The obsolescence of the earlier technique finds its expression in the fact that it will be replaced in the optimal program by the variable representing the new technology.

The author is fully aware of the fact that the highly simplified treatment of the dynamics of inputs and outputs in the system of computational evaluations described in this book as well as in the entire structure of the models employed, constitutes the weakest point in our work of research. But this is the most we were able to achieve for the time being. Neither the generally known difficulties that the problem entails nor the fact that it constitutes one of the weakest points in traditional, non-mathematical planning as well, will serve as an excuse for this weakness – they may, however, go some way towards explaining it. While throughout our investigations we endeavoured to rely on the results of traditional planning, here we found hardly anything to go by. It will be left to further research to engage in a more profound study of dynamic relationships and to work out the methods suitable for practical application in the mathematical construction of dynamic programs.

16.5. The Further Course of the Exposition

Having examined price formula (16.1) in two cross-cuts (from the point of view of discrimination between domestic and foreign-trade inputs as well as from that of dynamics) let us now pass in review its component parts.

Chapter 17 is to deal with wage-cost coefficients q_i and with production-fund requirement coefficients p_i.

Chapter 18 is to discuss the problems pertaining to computational wage factor Ω and to computational rental γ.

In ch. 19 import material costs r_i will be dealt with.

Chapter 20 will have for its subject the computational foreign exchange rates D_{Rbl} and $D_{\$}$.

Finally, in ch. 21 we will sum up the relationship between the actual and computational price systems.

CHAPTER 17

DETERMINATION OF TOTAL PRODUCTION-FUND REQUIREMENTS AND OF TOTAL WAGE CONTENTS

17.1. An Outline of the Problem

The computational price system which will be worked out here is to reflect two primary domestic inputs, namely those of production-fund and of labour-force utilization. The relevant accounting principles have been made clear in ch. 16. We shall now proceed to the examination of the methods and techniques which lend themselves for the *numerical* determination of total production-fund and wage requirements.

We want to determine the total production-fund requirements and total wage contents of the jth productive activity of the programming model:

$$P_j^{\text{tot}}(x_j) = P_j^{\text{dir}}(x_j) + P_j^{\text{indir}}(x_j), \qquad j = 1, \ldots, n, \tag{17.1}$$

$$Q_j^{\text{tot}}(x_j) = Q_j^{\text{dir}}(x_j) + Q_j^{\text{indir}}(x_j), \qquad j = 1, \ldots, n, \tag{17.2}$$

where

$P_j^{\text{tot}}, Q_j^{\text{tot}}$ = total production-fund requirements and total wage contents

$P_j^{\text{dir}}, Q_j^{\text{dir}}$ = direct production-fund requirements and direct wage contents

$P_j^{\text{indir}}, Q_j^{\text{indir}}$ = indirect production-fund requirements and indirect wage contents.

The determination of P_j^{dir} and Q_j^{dir} has already been dealt with in ch. 7, so it will not be necessary to revert to this problem. The determination of P_j^{indir} and Q_j^{indir}, on the other hand, will require thorough investigation. First of all, it must be pointed out that in order to simplify a problem which is rather intricate anyhow, we shall resort to the assumption of linearity, as opposed to the case of direct requirements which have been represented in some calculations by non-linear functions.

$$P_j^{\text{indir}}(x_j) = p_j^{\text{indir}}\, x_j\,, \tag{17.3}$$

$$Q_j^{\text{indir}}(x_j) = q_j^{\text{indir}}\, x_j\,. \tag{17.4}$$

The task thus narrows down to the numerical determination of the coefficients p_j^{indir} and q_j^{indir}. The purpose will be served by several techniques, partly combined with one another, namely

the use of I–O tables

the traditional methods of indirect requirements calculations.

17.2 The Use of Input–Output Tables

First, the calculation of productive-fund requirements will be described – the case of total wage content is analogous.

To be in a position to carry out the computations it is necessary to know the direct production-fund requirements of the individual sectors of the national economy in the breakdown of the I–O table to be used. Let p_l ($l = 1,\ldots, N$) denote the direct production fund coefficient, i.e. the production fund required for producing the unit (1 Ft) product of the lth sector of the national economy. To estimate these coefficients we have two sources to draw on:

(a) Statistical records are being kept on the value of the production funds (in the case of fixed funds both on gross and on net value) in the breakdown of the I–O table*. Unfortunately, there are many shortcomings in the valuation of the fixed funds.

(b) The production fund coefficients characteristic of the individual sectors have been worked out also on the basis of factual data referring to investments completed in the past two or three years and on that of plan data figuring in the permit papers of investment projects actually in course or about to be launched**. The basis of this method is certainly not a complete survey of data; the investments of a few recently past and immediately following years can hardly be considered as necessarily characteristic of the sector's *average*. Yet this problem was lessened to a considerable extent by the comparatively large number of the investments taken into consideration. The advantage of the coefficients obtained in this way over those derived from statistical records as described under (a) lies in the fact that they are based on cost data of living invest-

* Data on the production funds were published by the Central Statistical Office together with the 1959 I–O table of national economy and in a breakdown identical with that of the latter (see [187]).

** These calculations were first proposed by the author of this study with the aim of making use of them in sector programming. The investigations, based on an extensive survey of data, were carried out by Mrs. J. Deák [34] on behalf of the Investments Office of the National Planning Board.

ments as against the other method's often unrealistic, "dead" accountancy data on the valuation of fixed funds.

Let us now introduce the following notation:

$$\mathbf{p}' = [p_1, p_2, \ldots, p_N], \tag{17.5}$$

the row vector of N components of the production fund coefficients, in the breakdown of the national I–O table.

$$\check{\mathbf{G}} = (\mathbf{E} - \mathbf{G})^{-1}, \tag{17.6}$$

the inverse matrix. In (17.6) **G** stands for the inner square of the technological matrix of the national I–O table.

$$\bar{\mathbf{g}}_j = \begin{bmatrix} \bar{g}_{1j} \\ \bar{g}_{2j} \\ \cdot \\ \cdot \\ \cdot \\ \bar{g}_{Nj} \end{bmatrix}, \tag{17.7}$$

the column vector of N components of $\bar{g}_{ij}$ material input coefficients required for the unit output of the jth productive activity of the programming model*.

The following operation must be carried out**:

$$p_j^{\text{indir}} = \mathbf{p}' \check{\mathbf{G}} \bar{\mathbf{g}}_j . \tag{17.8}$$

The contents of formula (17.8) will be made clear by means of an illustrative example. The jth productive activity will be the opening up

* In the system of notations employed in this book, the symbol g is used to denote all material input coefficients both in the I–O tables and in the programming models. In general, this will not give rise to any misunderstanding as we are dealing *either* with I–O tables *or* with programming models. It is only here that the two occur together. The material-input coefficient of the jth activity of the programming model is therefore distinguished here by a superimposed line from the technical coefficients of the I–O table.

** The determination of indirect investments by means of the I–O table was first proposed in Hungarian economic literature by A. Bródy in [14]. The first numerical calculations on the national level were carried out by Gy. Cukor and Z. Román [26]. The methods of utilization in long-term programming models were worked out by the present author in cooperation with B. Martos [84].

and operation of a new colliery. The unit product will be coal to the value of Ft 100. The production of coal to the value of Ft 100 will require inputs of electric power to the value of Ft 4.95, iron and steel products to that of Ft 4.92, heavy chemicals to that of Ft 1.15, etc. ($\bar{\mathbf{g}}_j$).

The production of these direct material requirements will, in turn require secondary inputs. Adding the indirect requirements, the production of coal to the value of Ft 100 will require the input of electric power to the value of Ft 6.40, iron and steel products to that of Ft 9.17, heavy chemicals to that of Ft 1.46, etc. ($\check{\mathbf{G}}\,\bar{\mathbf{g}}_j$).

Now, in order to secure these amounts of electric power, iron and steel products, heavy chemicals, etc., the appropriate production funds must be made available. The product of total material requirements with vector $\mathbf{p}'$ will therefore give the total production fund required for the production of coal to the value of Ft 100.

The procedure implicitly involves some simplifying assumptions beyond those already discussed in connection with the use of I–O tables.

(1) Some inaccuracy will be due to the fact that $\mathbf{p}'\,\check{\mathbf{G}}$ indicates the *average* production fund requirements of the individual sectors, while the material requirements of the activity dealt with in the programming model are not averages but refer to a definite range of products in an individual sector.

(2) When carrying out the multiplication $\check{\mathbf{G}}\,\bar{\mathbf{g}}_j$, i.e. when computing the total material requirements of the jth activity, we are at the same time determining also the "indirect self-consumption requirements" of that sector. This means the following:

Let aluminium production be the jth activity. In the production of the chemicals, machinery ,electric power, instruments, etc., required for producing aluminium, some aluminium will, among other things, be also used. This aluminium requirement induced by the direct material requirements $\bar{\mathbf{g}}_j$ of the jth activity, I propose to call the "indirect self-consumption requirements" of that activity.

If p_j^{indir} is being determined according to formula (17.8), then it will also include the production fund requirements of indirect self-consumption. Let us now remember that the demand for aluminium in the national economy is a quantity determined by the system of constraints of the programming model. The relevant data are usually taken over from the plan prepared by traditional methods, which prescribes *total* demand for aluminium (including that due to indirect self-consumption).

The indirect material fund requirements due to indirect self-consumption constitute thus an unnecessary burden on the cost function of the jth productive activity, in our example on that of aluminium production.

The error is, however, only a minor one, as the proportion of this type of indirect self-consumption is in most sectors rather insignificant.

From what has been said it follows that indirect production fund requirements as calculated on the basis of the economy-wide I–O table must be considered only as approximate.

The determination of total wage content is entirely analogous and will thus require no detailed explanation. The difference consists in that in formula (17.8) the place of vector $\mathbf{p}'$ will be taken by vector $\mathbf{q}'$. The latter defines the direct wage contents characteristic of the individual sectors of the national economy, in the breakdown of the I–O table employed. The difficulties involved in the determination of direct wage coefficients q_l ($l = 1, \ldots, N$) are nothing like as great as in the case of the direct production fund coefficients; precise records of the relevant data are being kept even in the breakdown of the I–O table.

No mention has been made so far of depreciation. In the Central Statistical Office computations have been carried out where the row vector of depreciation allowances was introduced in the inner square as a special type of sector. The corresponding column vector was constructed of inputs of the activities aimed at the replacement and overhaul of the means of production. As a strongly simplifying assumption, the input structure of overhaul and replacement activities was taken as identical with that of gross investments*. Basing the computations on matrix $\mathbf{G}$ extended in this manner, p_j^{indir} and q_j^{indir} come to include also the production fund requirements and wage contents of the activities needed for replacing and overhauling the fixed assets (or, rather, the relative rough estimates).

17.3. Simplifying Assumptions Concerning Input–Output Tables

Section 17.2 described the application of input–output tables for the construction of computational prices. Later, in connection with foreign trade problems, the application of I–O tables will be treated again.

The model of I–O tables is based on well-known simplifying assumptions. Without aspiring to completeness, I wish to point out two – interrelated – assumptions.

* See e.g. P. HAVAS [50], and A. RÁCZ – MRS. L. ÚJLAKI [144].

(1) *Constant returns to scale* – If all inputs used up by the lth sector are increased at a rate λ, gross output of the lth sector will increase at the same rate λ. This means, at the same time, that in the cost functions based on the I–O table marginal and average cost will coincide.

(2) *Nonsubstitutability* – The product of the lth sector can be produced by a definite (the sector's characteristic average) technology only, with a definite type of fixed input structure.

These assumptions, which permit the application of the extremely simple linear I–O model, constitute a considerable simplification as compared to reality*. Let us consider some relationships in this connection.

One problem is constituted by the fact that inputs to production are often not in proportion with the size of production; decreasing as well as increasing marginal cost functions will frequently occur. This can be attributed to the effect of numerous circumstances, as shown in detail in ch. 7. In spite of our knowledge of these facts we shall, for the time being, have to desist from taking them into consideration in this connection. Should we decline to neglect them, then we ought to construct a large-scale, non-linear programming model, one in which the system of constraints was non-linear. This, however, cannot be undertaken now. And yet, the error concomitant with neglecting these relationships will be mitigated by the following factors:

– In the large aggregates into which I–O tables are divided, the effects of the factors acting in the direction of decreasing and in that of increasing marginal costs will partly cancel each other, e.g. one of the sector's products is being produced at increasing marginal costs: in overtime, in night-shifts, or with special methods. In increasing the output of another product, on the other hand, the advantages of large-scale production will assert themselves. The expansion of the aggregate *as a whole* will thus often take place at approximately constant marginal costs.

– In the short run, marginal and average costs of production will often differ. In the long run, however, there is a tendency of marginal and average costs to coincide, provided that investments are rational and aimed at establishing capacities which ensure production at minimum unit cost**.

On the basis of these considerations I am of the opinion that I–O tables which reflect *average* inputs and presume constant marginal costs

* The problems of the abstractions and simplifications on which I–O analysis is based, are extensively dealt with by A. Bródy [15].

** See A. C. Pigou [142], ch. 11 and Mathematical Appendix, furthermore J. Viner [174].

can, under the given conditions, be used as provisional and auxiliary tools in working out computational prices in long-term planning.

This does, of course, not mean that we are taking up a definitive position in the debate over the question, which price system would better serve the rational allocation of resources: the one based on average cost or the one based on marginal cost. The debate "average versus marginal" goes back to several decades and has now been resumed in a number of socialist countries with Hungary among them. In the present work, the author has repeatedly come out in favour of computational prices and computational evaluations which reflect marginal inputs and the marginal efficiency of the factors of production, thus e.g. when discussing the computational rate of capital charges and of wages, the national economic programming model, or the shadow prices. However, in actual *practice* – in the investment efficiency calculations and in the sectoral programming models worked out so far – we have been forced to abandon for the time being the theoretically clear principles to a certain degree. The calculations must be carried on in some way, until these principles can be enforced mainly by means of the national economic programming models. The application of I–O tables (although they express average inputs) constitutes a step forward from using simply the actual price system in our efficiency calculations.

The difficulties of aggregation appear to constitute another great problem. The calculations carried out by means of I–O tables are obviously less precise than those performed on the basis of an (otherwise adequate) price system which reflects the differences between the various inputs in more minute detail. The large aggregates of the I–O table tend to efface these differences.

To remedy shortcomings of this character various methods are being employed. On the one hand, I–O tables of more detailed construction have been or will be prepared, which cover each a whole industrial sector and are suitable for long-term computations. On the other hand, the calculations in which inputs are taken into account in greater detail and those based on the aggregates of I–O tables can be combined.

The application of I–O tables based on actual prices in terms of Ft is connected with another problem. We have to discuss whether the actual prices would influence the computational prices generated by I–O tables.

Our starting point is that we have a matrix of the Nth order $\mathbf{G}_{nat}$, the inner square of the technological matrix, defined not in terms of value but in those of natural or technological units of measurement, e.g. iron ore in tons and electric power in kWh. The dimensions of the element at the point of intersection of the iron-ore column and the current row will, accordingly, be given in kWh(t).

Attached to this we have external input matrix $\mathbf{U}_{nat}$, composed of K rows and N columns. This is analogous to matrix $\mathbf{U}$ described above, with the difference that when computing the coefficients $u_{nat,\, il}$, the denominator of the fraction is given in terms of natural measurement units, e.g. in the row of imports from capitalist countries dimensions are given in dollar/t, dollar/kWh, etc. In the wage row they are given in Ft/t, Ft/kWh, etc.

Let us make the following assumption:

Assumption of uniform output prices. All products have only one unit price, irrespective of the direction of output.

The price e.g. of one kWh will, accordingly, be the same irrespective of whether it is supplied to agriculture or to the engineering industry. On this assumption the price system can be characterized by the diagonal matrix

$$\mathbf{S} = \begin{bmatrix} S_1 & & & & \\ & S_2 & & & \\ & & \cdot & & \\ & & & \cdot & \\ & & & & \cdot \\ & & & & & S_N \end{bmatrix}, \qquad (17.9)$$

which I propose to call the matrix of the basic price system.

The application of this assumption will naturally weaken the accuracy of the total contents calculation. Up to the present we had no opportunity to investigate more closely the consequences of the errors due to this simplifying assumption*.

Between the technological matrix measured in natural units of measurement and in Ft, and the final output vector the following relationships can be established:

$$\mathbf{G} = \mathbf{S}\,\mathbf{G}_{nat}\,\mathbf{S}^{-1}, \qquad (17.10)$$

$$\mathbf{d} = \mathbf{S}\,\mathbf{d}_{nat}. \qquad (17.11)$$

* A related problem is discussed by A. Bródy [15].

Proposition 17.1. To a given final output $d_{nat,\, l}$ measured in natural units, there belong given total contents $\check{k}_{il}$. The same $\check{k}_{il}$ can be determined by means of an I–O table measured in Ft, independently of* **S**, *the basic price system of the table (on the assumption of uniform output prices).*

In other words: the price which we take as the starting point will not affect the results of the total contents calculation, provided that each sector sells its product at the same price on every market. This means a certain neutrality of the computational price system, its independence of the basic prices.

Proof. Let $\check{\mathbf{u}}'_{nat,\,i}$ denote the ith total contents coefficient vector belonging to the natural-unit I–O table.

$$\begin{aligned} \check{\mathbf{u}}'_{nat,\,i} &= \mathbf{u}'_{nat,\,i}\,(\mathbf{E}-\mathbf{G}_{nat})^{-1}, \\ \mathbf{u}'_i &= \mathbf{u}'_{nat,\,i}\,\mathbf{S}^{-1}, \\ \mathbf{G} &= \mathbf{S}\,\mathbf{G}_{nat}\,\mathbf{S}^{-1}. \end{aligned} \tag{17.12}$$

On the basis of definitions (17.10) and (17.12) it is now easy to see that

$$\begin{aligned} \check{\mathbf{u}}'_i &= \mathbf{u}'_{nat,\,i}\,\mathbf{S}^{-1}(\mathbf{E}-\mathbf{S}\,\mathbf{G}_{nat}\,\mathbf{S}^{-1})^{-1} = \\ &= \mathbf{u}'_{nat,\,i}\,\mathbf{S}^{-1}\mathbf{S}\,(\mathbf{E}-\mathbf{G}_{nat})^{-1}\,\mathbf{S}^{-1} = \\ &= \mathbf{u}'_{nat,\,i}\,(\mathbf{E}-\mathbf{G}_{nat})^{-1}\,\mathbf{S}^{-1} = \check{\mathbf{u}}'_{nat,\,i}\,\mathbf{S}^{-1}. \end{aligned} \tag{17.13}$$

As a consequence

$$\check{u}_{il}\, d_l = \frac{\check{u}_{nat,\,il}}{S_l}\, S_l\, d_{nat,\,l} = \check{u}_{nat,\,il}\, d_{nat,\,l}\,. \tag{17.14}$$

As will be seen later on, it is only the total contents calculations that are made use of in our computations. From this point of view proposition 17.1 – based on independence of the basic price system – is reassuring.

It must, of course, be pointed out that in practice there can be no question of complete independence, for the reason that the assumption of uniform output prices will hold only approximately. Firstly, the "product" of each individual sector is in fact an aggregate product group

* The proposition is essentially contained in S. GANCZER [42]. My exposition states S. Ganczer's proposition more accurately by laying emphasis on the fact that it is valid on the assumption of uniform output prices only.

made up of a large number of specific products. Even if the output price of a specific product were uniform for all output directions, the average price of the product group could still differ from sector to sector because of differences in the actual composition of the products required by the individual sectors. Thus, for instance, the organochemical products required by the textile industry are not identical with those required by the pharmaceutical industry. Secondly, in the case of a number of products the purchase tax contained in the output price may be based on different rates for the different sectors of input*. However, as on the national level the share of the various output directions is not particularly variable within the individual sectors (i.e. the ratios of the components of row vector $\mathbf{v}'_k$ are fairly stable), and the composition of the products within the individual sectors is not liable to much change either, the assumption of uniform output prices (for a strongly aggregated national I–O table) would appear acceptable as an approximation.

17.4. Partial "Tracing Back"

Proceeding now to the survey of the techniques employed in traditional planning, we shall deal separately with production fund requirements on the one hand and wage contents on the other, as the computation of the two differs slightly in method.

In planning based on traditional methods an interesting procedure has been adopted which does not cover the indirect production fund requirements of *all* sectors in the national economy but is suitably narrowed down in scope. The chemical industry should serve as an example; some of the results obtained in calculations carried out there have been drawn upon in the course of our investigations in the synthetic fibre industry.

The following is the essence of the procedure:

Chemical products are traced back to their respective basic material – coal, crude oil, natural gas, etc., as the case may be – while the technological processes which take place from the production of the basic material up to that of the product in question, as well as the investments needed to create the productive capacities necessary for carrying out

* The relationship between I–O tables measured in natural units and those measured in Ft, as well as the related questions of uniformity of output prices have been extensively investigated by the research team which set up the I–O tables of the clothing industries. See J. KORNAI *et al.* [76].

each individual process, are being established*. As we are moving backward from the product under investigation down to its basic material, the procedure is called "tracing back".

The procedure is characterized by two important preliminary assumptions (even if the fact is not explicitly stated by those employing it), namely:

(1) The technological process proceeds strictly *in one direction* from the basic material up to the product under investigation. I.e. it will not happen that the output of a later stage in processing is used as input to an earlier stage. In the computations based on this procedure there was either no such recurrence or it has been neglected.

(2) The joint products so highly characteristic of the production of chemicals are being separated. Investment costs are separated, "allotted" to the individual joint products in accordance with the cost accounting methods prevailing in industrial practice.

This simple procedure is in fact very similar to that carried out by means of the I–O table as described in section 17.2. To make the similarity quite clear, we shall put the procedure of "tracing back" into mathematical terms.

Let m denote the number of materials which go directly or indirectly into the production of the jth product and which are taken into account in the course of "tracing back". Let us arrange them in technological order, with the basic material, e.g. crude oil, topping the line.

Let us now construct the technological matrix of the mth order $\mathbf{G}$ from the material input coefficients of the products. The matrix will be triangular and all components under the principal diagonal will be zero. The latter follows from assumption (1) above, that of the absence of "feedbacks".

The investment coefficients of all m product types are known. These coefficients make up row vector $\mathbf{p}'$.

Also known is column vector $\overline{\mathbf{g}}_j$, made up of the material input coefficients of the jth product, in the breakdown of matrix $\mathbf{G}$.

By means of the "tracing back" technique the following operations have been carried out:

(1) The product $\check{\mathbf{G}}\overline{\mathbf{g}}_j$ – the *total* material input coefficient of the product of the jth activity – has been determined.

* What these calculations are taking into account are not production fund requirements in general but the investments needed to create *new* production funds; accordingly, it will be to these that we shall confine ourselves in the subsequent analysis.

(2) The product $\mathbf{p}' \check{\mathbf{G}} \bar{\mathbf{g}}_j$ – the indirect investment requirement of that product – was determined. The analogy with formula (11.7) is obvious.

An advantage of the procedure consists in the fact that the indirect requirements arising *within* the sector under investigation (in our example, within the chemical industry) are taken into consideration with considerably greater accuracy than in the case of the economy-wide I–O table. It was this favourable aspect that prompted us to draw on some results of these computations. Another advantage lies in its simplicity; it can be carried out even by means of rudimentary tools. The latter fact is essentially due to the triangular character of matrix **G**.

On the other hand, it is a disadvantage that the procedure does not lend itself for the determination of the production fund requirement of the *national economy as a whole* but only of parts of it, in contrast with the method based on the I–O table.

17.5. The Traditional Method of "Real Cost Calculation"

The calculation of what is called "net real costs" forms part of the regular practice of the Hungarian economy. According to the terminology employed up to now, this corresponds to the sum of total wage contents and total depreciation allowance contents. Real costs of several thousand commodities are being worked out annually by the organs of industrial management, primarily with the purpose of exercising a control over the profitability of exports. Though the technique of these computations may slightly vary from sector to sector, the essential features are throughout identical.

The procedure adopted by the Ministry of Heavy Industry will serve as an example. The starting point of the calculations is the determination of real costs of *coal.* Coal mining in Hungary is organized into 12 trusts, with each trust representing a more or less distinct coal field and, with that, a more or less distinct coal type. The cost of coal is determined by trust, on the basis of the actual outlays of the preceding year. Within this, direct wage contents, direct depreciation allowance contents and direct cost of home-produced materials are calculated, the latter in a breakdown of 29 types of material*.

* In addition to real costs of home-produced inputs those of import materials (in the terminology of this book: total import contents) are also worked out. This I will pass over here, because the calculation is essentially analogous to that of the real costs of home-produced inputs.

The next step consists of correcting the material costs, with respect to all 29 material types, by multiplying the material input coefficients, expressed in natural units, not by the actual prices, but by the net real costs worked out in the course of the preceding year's real cost calculations.

The new real cost of coal will thus be the sum of direct wage contents, direct depreciation allowance contents and the net real cost of the 29 types of home-produced materials.

The net real cost of electric power is computed in a similar manner, with the difference that coal input – which constitutes the principal factor – is already taken into account on the basis of the real cost of coal as worked out in the preceding step of the calculations.

In the case of *further products* – such as chemicals – the procedure is again similar, but here the new net real costs of both coal and electric power are already available. For all other products the calculations are carried out simultaneously, but in each case already in the knowledge of the new real costs of coal and electric power. The rest of the material input coefficients are multiplied by net real costs as determined in the course of the real-cost calculations of the previous year.

Let us now put this procedure into mathematical form, with the following provisional simplifications:

(1) No special treatment will be given to coal and electric power.

(2) The invariability of the technological matrix (including the coefficients of direct wage contents and depreciation allowance contents) over time will be taken as granted.

We have an I–O table of m sectors, each of which represents a commodity produced under the direction of the Ministry of Heavy Industry. Within the heavy-industrial domain the table is broken down in much greater detail than e.g. the one set up by the Central Statistical Office.

The calculation is of an iterative character: one step is being made in each new real-cost calculation (practically: in each year). The upper index of the symbols denotes the number of the iteration step.

In the first step of the iteration the following data are known:

$\mathbf{G}$ = the inner square of the technological matrix, a matrix of the mth order

$\tilde{\mathbf{u}}'^{(0)}$ = the vector containing the initial estimates of the sum of total wage contents and total depreciation allowance contents (in the following: net real cost), the row vector of m components of the initial net real cost coefficients

$\mathbf{u}'$ = the vector of m components of direct wage content + direct depreciation allowance content coefficients.

The net real cost vector as determined in the first step:

$$\check{\mathbf{u}}'^{(1)} = \mathbf{u}'^{(0)}\,\mathbf{G} + \check{\mathbf{u}}'. \qquad (17.15)$$

In the second step, net real costs as determined in the first step are already made use of:

$$\check{\mathbf{u}}'^{(2)} = \hat{\mathbf{u}}'^{(1)}\,\mathbf{G} + \mathbf{u}' = \check{\mathbf{u}}'^{(0)}\,\mathbf{G}^2 + \mathbf{u}'\,\mathbf{G} + \mathbf{u}'. \qquad (17.16)$$

In the tth step:

$$\check{\mathbf{u}}'^{(t)} = \check{\mathbf{u}}'^{(t-1)}\,\mathbf{G} + \mathbf{u}' = \mathbf{u}'^{(0)}\mathbf{G}^t + \mathbf{u}'\,\mathbf{G}^{t-1} + \ldots + \mathbf{u}'\,\mathbf{G} + \mathbf{u}'. \quad (17.17)$$

In view of the fact that in the case of Leontief's matrix $\mathbf{G}^t \rightarrow 0$ as $t \rightarrow \infty$, it can now be stated that

$$\check{\mathbf{u}}'^{(t)} \rightarrow \mathbf{u}'\,(\mathbf{E} - \mathbf{G})^{-1} \quad \text{as} \quad t \rightarrow \infty\,.$$

As can be seen the procedure here described has resulted in (1) the inversion of matrix $(\mathbf{E} - \mathbf{G})$ through power series expansion, and (2) the multiplication of this inverse matrix with vector $\mathbf{u}'$ (that of direct wage content + direct depreciation allowance content coefficients), leading to the construction of the vector of net real costs.

It is a well-known fact that this method of inversion is rather lengthy. Real cost calculation in this country has a past of six to seven years, so only six to seven steps could be made so far.

Nor do formulae (17.15)–(17.17) quite exactly cover the procedure of actual real cost calculation, and this for the following reasons:

Convergence is accelerated by the special treatment given to coal and electric power.

The initial estimate of $\check{\mathbf{u}}'^{(0)}$ is not an arbitrary one, but one is at pains to give an adequate estimate. For this purpose, wage contents and depreciation allowance contents are separated from the rest of cost factors by means of "tracing back" through several phases of production. Adequate initial estimates also help to accelerate the convergence.

Matrix $\mathbf{G}$ and vector $\mathbf{u}'$ on which the calculations are based are in reality taken not as constant but as variable over time. This makes for greater accuracy in the calculations, as the technical coefficients are always "up-to-date", reflecting always the latest factual data. On the other hand, this is the reason why no convergence of the procedure can be guaranteed.

Drawing now a comparison between the calculations based on the national I–O table and the traditional real cost calculations, we will find that both procedures have their characteristic advantages as well as drawbacks. An advantage of the traditional method, and this refers also to the procedure described in section 17.4, consists in the more detailed breakdown, in the more concrete observation and listing of inputs. We must not forget that in the economy-wide I–O table it is only 18 sectors that fall within the scope of the Ministry of Heavy Industry, whereas the matrix **G** which figures in formulae (17.15) – (17.17) has, in the case of the Ministry of Heavy Industry, 400–500 sectors. For example, the single coal sector of the economy-wide table is here divided into 12 sectors, etc.

As a further advantage, the traditional method follows from year to year the changes of the technological coefficients over time. The major I–O tables, being usually constructed not yearly but at longer intervals, are working over several years with unchanged coefficients.

Inconsistency in tracing indirect inputs is a basic drawback of the traditional method. In fact, the whole calculation covers only the domain of the Ministry of Heavy Industry; the commodities produced under the direction of other ministries are taken into account either at the actual producers' prices or on the basis of real cost data worked out by the other ministries in the course of real cost calculations performed at an earlier date. Moreover, the fact that – as has been shown – only a few steps of iteration have so far been made, also works for inconsistency. I–O analysis, on the other hand, by performing the "regular" inversion of the matrix (**E** – **G**), deals with indirect inputs in a consistent way.

This will make it clear why neither of the two methods has been employed here exclusively but the utilization of the results of both has been aimed at.

17.6. The Official Methodology of Investment Efficiency Calculations

The procedure described in section 17.4 has been adopted by some designing offices. The real cost calculations described in section 17.5 are carried out by the industrial ministries, for the purposes *not* of long-term planning and investment efficiency calculations but exclusively of export profitability calculations. The treatment given these questions in the official investment efficiency methodology of traditional planning – especially in connection with calculating* the index g_n mentioned in ch. 2 – must therefore be dealt with separately.

It is a positive feature of the official methodology that it makes the evaluation of indirect production-fund requirements obligatory. This is what the official instructions call "joint investments". The cost of joint investments is determined by multiplying the cost of home-produced materials by 2.5, a factor uniform for the national economy as a whole. Even if we do not regard the individual products but only the sectors, with their output composed of a whole group of products, it will be clear that the production-fund requirements of the individual sectors show a high degree of dispersion. For instance, according to the I–O table of the Central Statistical Office for 1959, total production-fund requirements per Ft 1 product value varied between Ft 0.60 and Ft 22.50. The procedure described in section 17.2, although not more than an approximation itself, gives a considerably more correct estimation of indirect production-fund requirements.

There are already plans to change the official instructions and to make use in future of the indirect production-fund coefficients obtained by means of I–O tables.

According to the official methodology, rental should be charged both on direct and indirect production-fund requirements. Notwithstanding this fact it prescribes the calculation of home-produced material inputs at actual producers' prices which already contain a considerable amount of net revenue. As a consequence, part of the net revenue will be accounted for twice, which in turn unduly raises the cost of investments.

* See the Investments Code [195].

CHAPTER 18

ATTEMPTS AT THE DETERMINATION OF THE COMPUTATIONAL RENTAL ON CAPITAL AND OF THE COMPUTATIONAL WAGE FACTOR

18.1. Objective of the Analysis

In this chapter we deal with γ, the computational rental on capital, and with Ω, the computational wage factor*. Our analysis has several objectives.

The first objective is a certain theoretical clarification. We try to answer such questions as the following: what is the role of γ and Ω in the computational price system? To what extent does the magnitude of γ and of Ω depend upon production and to what extent upon distribution? Are they stable magnitudes or changeable in time, and if they are changing, what are the characteristic trends of the change?

The conceptual clarification, the theoretical analysis is interwoven with our attempts at the quantification of γ and Ω. This is unimaginable without certain abstractions, simplifying assumptions. It would of course be desirable if we could carry out the calculations and empirical observations resulting in the quantitative magnitude of γ and Ω with as few assumptions and assumptions meaning as little simplification as possible. Unfortunately, this is not possible. The direct observation of reality, as we will see later, does not provide us with the magnitude of γ and Ω.

In such conditions a particular "retrospective" analytical technique is necessary. By this we mean the following:

One of the possible ways of analysis is generally to set out from a model, from a given system of assumptions and premises and to seek their con-

* A considerable part of what is described here, is based on research, carried out together with mathematician P. Wellisch, of which we gave an account in [86] in Hungarian and in [87] in Russian. Especially sections 18.2–18.4 and 18.7–18.10 have made use of the material of our common research.

Appendix E to this book was written by P. Wellisch, and supplies the mathematical proofs of the propositions of this chapter. The description of the statistical investigation carried out in connection with the quantification of the rental on capital is to be found in Appendix F (P. Wellisch is co-author of Appendix F).

clusions. But one is sometimes forced, as we are now, to follow the reverse course. A certain guess is given, and we seek the assumptions under which this guess is true. Although we give the accounting principles concerning γ and Ω at the end of the chapter, after the analysis, we would not like to give the impression that we have deduced these from the theoretical analyses, the statistical investigations. In fact, we have proceeded the opposite way. In our calculations we began to apply – for the lack of a better solution – insufficiently well founded accounting principles which contained a priori guesses. *In the course of* our work, to check ourselves, we carried out the analyses here described. Hence, our method has been characteristically "retrospective" analysis – we sought the premises, the model for pre-established conclusions. We wanted to establish in this way to what extent the surmised accounting principles were acceptable and if these might be replaced by better ones.

Let us hereafter call the assumption, or combination of assumptions, the model from which one or the other accounting principle logically follows, a w o r k i n g h y p o t h e s i s. As one of the objectives of our investigation we wanted to clarify what working hypothesis belongs to which accounting principle. In this connection, the investigation may bring results as that *A* accounting principle is justified if we accept working hypothesis *Z*. Or, accounting principle *B* is justified if we accept working hypotheses *X*, *Y* and *Z*, and so on.

The working hypotheses have to be evaluated too. Each working hypothesis contains certain abstractions, omissions of inessentials, inexactitudes – and with these a certain extent of arbitrariness. From this point of view, many degrees are possible. For the sake of simplicity, we have placed our working hypotheses into not more than three classes. We have called those working hypotheses a c c e p t a b l e which agree well with experience; their application is obviously justified; they may be, though not necessarily, verified statistically. These we may apply without any great doubt.

We have called those working hypotheses u n a c c e p t a b l e which are obviously and in essential contexts contrary to the observed facts.

The intermediary class are the p r o v i s i o n a l working hypotheses. It is not obvious that their application is justified; they have not been verified statistically – we may not apply them with "a clear conscience". Their application may only be justified until we may replace them with an acceptable working hypothesis. We have stipulated however, that the provisional working hypotheses should not be absurd, they should not be contrary in essence to any obvious experience or observation, i.e. they cannot be unacceptable.

After this little methodological detour, let us now describe our procedure:

In the sections 18.2–18.4, we describe a production function, and clarify a few definitions. By this, we, so to say, prepare the "apparatus" of further analyses.

Sections 18.5–18.11 describe six experiments aimed on the quantitative determination of γ and Ω. We use here the word "experiment" in a very broad sense; one attempt means a mathematical-statistical calculation based on economic data, another endeavours to draw conclusions from the empirical observation of the present economic and planning practice, a third is "a speculative experiment", it follows some train of thought which promises theoretical conclusions in order to arrive finally at the quantitative magnitude of γ and Ω.

Unfortunately, the results of all these attempts, experiments, have not been very reassuring. We have not succeeded in quantifying γ and Ω, building *exclusively* on *acceptable* working hypotheses. We have been compelled to apply *provisional* working hypotheses. But we believe that attempts leading to blind alleys, experiments which have not brought any quantitative results, may be instructive too.

Section 18.12 describes the accounting principles applied in the practical calculations and restates the working hypotheses with which they are connected. Section 18.13 draws a few general conclusions. Finally, section 18.14 deals with the sensitivity analyses in respect of the rental on capital.

18.2. The Aggregate Production Function of the National Economy

We wish to use the computational prices, according to price formula (16.1), for part-decisions, so for instance for branch programming comprising some narrower sphere of the national economy. By applying the formula consistently, we trace every part-decision back to a general problem of choice: how to combine labour and the production fund? (Foreign trade is disregarded here.) In the individual sections of our further analyses however, since we are seeking the appropriate combination of labour and of the production fund on a national scale, we discuss this problem only in its aggregate form. The changing over to aggregate magnitudes leads to many difficult hidden problems itself, but we cannot undertake the examination of these*.

Since there are two primary domestic inputs in the formula (16.1), we shall use in our theoretical analyses too an aggregate production function with two variables**. For the time being, we shall apply static functions applying to one point of time; later, in sections 18.8–18.10 we shall pass to dynamic functions.

The general form of our production function is the following:

$$Y = Y(K, L)\,, \tag{18.1}$$

where

Y = the national income at a certain point of time. In practice, of course, we do not consider the national income at a point of time but of a period, for instance a year

K = the production fund, namely, the volume of the production fund actually used at the given point of time***

L = the labour force, namely, the number actually employed at the given point of time.

We describe the statistical delimitation of the conceptual sphere of production fund in the Appendix F together with the Hungarian data pertaining to K. Let us just mention here that we use the expression "production fund" in a somewhat wider sense than is generally usual, it comprises all that which the literature of socialist planning calls the fixed, working, and turnover funds.

As we can see, we are dealing here with a strongly aggregated function****. We neglect the fact that K is composed of machines and buildings of various purposes, lengths of life, qualities, and technical levels. We similarly neglect the fact that L represents workers of varying in efficiency, trade and education.

* Further chapters of this book, dealing with the so-called "two-level planning" deal with the related problem how the decisions of the part units, the sectors may be connected with the central distribution of resources.

** Aggregate production functions have a great literature. Our analyses are based primarily on R. M. Solow [160], [161] and on H. Uzawa [171].

*** The affinity of the K factor to what is known in the western literature as the "capital" category of the production functions, is obvious. See the first footnote in section 2.2.

**** Our function having only *two* variables means that we neglect many factors which influence national income. So, for instance, even in the case of a strongly aggregated function it would be preferable to take the effect of national resources into consideration, just because for the formation of computational prices it is useful to know the computational rent connected with natural resources. But we have had no opportunity to carry out this analysis.

We assume that the magnitude of both K and L can be measured uniquely. This is a rather bold assumption as the difficulties involved in measuring the volume of the production fund are generally known. (The problem of measuring the labour force is clearly less complicated.)

The deeper we penetrate the input–output streams of the economy, the less essential the strongly aggregate collective terms become. A later chapter of this book will describe an economic model in which the production fund (its total), investment quota (its total), etc. will no longer figure as concepts, but the program will directly arrange how many and what machines, building activities, should be allocated when and where. But at present we cannot do without the aggregated categories. Incidentally, traditional planning uses aggregate magnitudes as well, when it is planning accumulation, investment, etc., comprehensively.

Throughout our treatment of the subject we operate with production functions with two variables, $Y = Y(K, L)$. We specify this function gradually, step by step, by stipulating some of its properties. To make reference easier, we shall number these properties. For the first steps of the analysis it is sufficient to stipulate the following properties:

Property 1 of the production function. There exists Y_K, the marginal efficiency of the production fund *and Y_L, the* marginal productivity of the labour force. *These two differential functions are continuous and positive.*

$$Y_K = \frac{\partial Y}{\partial K} > 0, \quad Y_L = \frac{\partial Y}{\partial L} > 0. \tag{18.2}$$

What does this property mean for the economist?

First of all, we have to interpret the functions Y_K and Y_L. The Y_K function expresses, how much the national income increases if L is left unchanged and K is increased by one unit. (More precisely, we should say it is increased by an infinitely small quantity.) This is then the partial derivative of the (18.1) production function with respect to K.

Similarly, Y_L expresses how much the national income increases if K is left unchanged and L is increased by one unit. This is the partial derivative of the production function with respect to L.

The assumption of the existence and continuity of the functions Y_K and Y_L present no problem for the economist, since in the case of such a strong aggregation we may assume that the production fund and the labour force may be combined in any ratio without leaps and ruptures, and that by combining increments of the production fund and of the labour force a surplus of national income may be achieved without leaps and ruptures.

The assumption that the differential functions Y_K and Y_L are positive, means that the production function is a strictly monotonically increasing

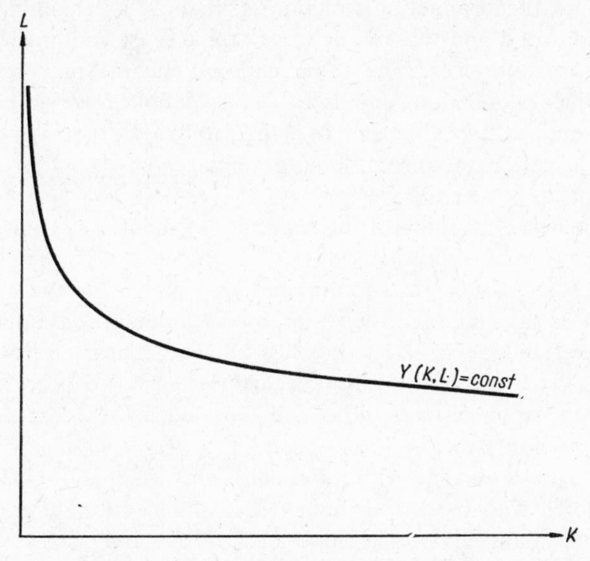

Fig. 18.1

function of both K and L. This means that if we leave the labour force unchanged, we always find such an investment opportunity (if need be, through the appropriate re-grouping of the labour force) through which the last increment of the production fund will still assist the increase of national income. The same applies to the other factor, if we leave the volume of the production fund unchanged, we always find such an employment opportunity through which the additional one person still contributes to the increase of the national income.

Property 2 of the production function. With a fixed value of the production $[Y(K, L) = Y_0 = \text{const}]$ the marginal rate of substitution Y_K/Y_L *will be a decreasing function of K and an increasing function of L.*

The second property of the production function is shown by figure 18.1. The curve in the figure is the isoquant curve of the Y_0 national income. It defines with what $[K, L]$ combinations the same unchanged Y_0 national income may be achieved. According to the second property the isoquant curve is convex from below.

From the economic point of view, the primary meaning of the second property of the production function is, that we are assuming that the production fund and the labour force are, at least within certain limits, mutually substitutable. The same national income may be produced with a larger production fund and a smaller labour force and conversely. This assumes at the same time that the production fund is "malleable", i.e. that it can be adapted to more capital-intensive as well as to less capital-intensive technologies.

The economic meaning of the *convexity* of the isoquantum curve may be summed up as follows:

We depart from a $[K, L]$ combination suitable for the achievement of Y_0, let us say $[K_0, L_0]$. Then – proceeding along the isoquant curve – we reduce L by one unit. The loss has to be compensated by some additional K. Let us mark this addition $\Delta_1 K$. Then we reduce L by another unit. The loss must again be compensated by the increase of K: let the addition be $\Delta_2 K$. The second property now means that $\Delta_2 K$ is larger than $\Delta_1 K$. The withdrawal of each further unit of L has to be compensated with increasing K increments. This is quite realistic from the technical and economic point of view (as long as we investigate the questions in terms of static theory). To compensate for the labour which has been subtracted, an increasingly developed technique, more expensive machines, automation, etc., has to be applied.

To give a few examples of sufficient conditions for the second property to be effective: if L is fixed and K increased, Y_K will decrease and Y_L will increase. On the other hand, if K is fixed and L increased, Y_L will decrease and Y_K will increase. I.e. if we leave the labour force unchanged and go on increasing the production fund, then the additional units of the production fund still assist the increase of the national income (in accordance with the first property!), but the national income increment achievable through them becomes smaller and smaller. On the other hand, labour becomes increasingly scarce and its marginal productivity increases accordingly. Similarly, if the production fund is left unchanged, then the additional labour force achieves a decreasing national income increment. In this case it is the production fund which becomes increasingly scarce.

In accordance with what has been said, the assumption of the first and second properties of the production function qualify for *acceptable* hypotheses.

18.3. The Definition and Feasibility of the Rational Computational Rental on Capital and Wage Rate

The following further assumptions have to be made:

$\bar{K}$ and $\bar{L}$ are determined by economic policy as the upper limits of the production fund and labour force at our disposal. The magnitude of the former is determined partly by the production fund thus far accumulated in the national economy, partly by the volume of the investments available for its increase, which is largely dependent upon economic policy. The labour force at the disposal of the economy is also determined on the one hand by demographic, sociological, etc. factors, but on the other, by the economic policy concerning the scale of employment. We do not discuss here how the magnitude of $\bar{K}$ and $\bar{L}$ is determined; to what extent by objective circumstances and to what extent by decisions of economic policy. Since economic policy has undoubtedly a certain influence and freedom in the determination of their magnitude, we may safely say that the *final* upper limits of these figures are fixed by economic policy.

If the planners want a maximum national income, they have to make use of the production fund and labour force at their disposal. This is self-evident from what we said in the previous paragraph about the monotonically growing character of the production function. It does not pay to leave either the production fund or the labour force unused, since each additional unit still may increase the national income.

This is a very simple p r i m a r y programming problem; we seek the optimum $[K^*, L^*]$ a l l o c a t i o n program, which satisfies the following conditions:

$$\begin{aligned} K &\leqq \bar{K} \\ L &\leqq \bar{L} \\ Y(K, L) &\rightarrow \max! \end{aligned} \tag{18.3}$$

It is clear that the solution of the programming problem is:

$$\begin{aligned} K^* &= \bar{K} \\ L^* &= \bar{L}\,. \end{aligned} \tag{18.4}$$

Let us mark the value of the objective function of the optimum program Y^*:

$$Y^* = Y(K^*, L^*)\,. \tag{18.5}$$

We illustrate the primary programming problem in figure 18.2. The curves visible in the figure are the isoquant curves of national income. The individual curves determine with what $[K, L]$ combinations, with

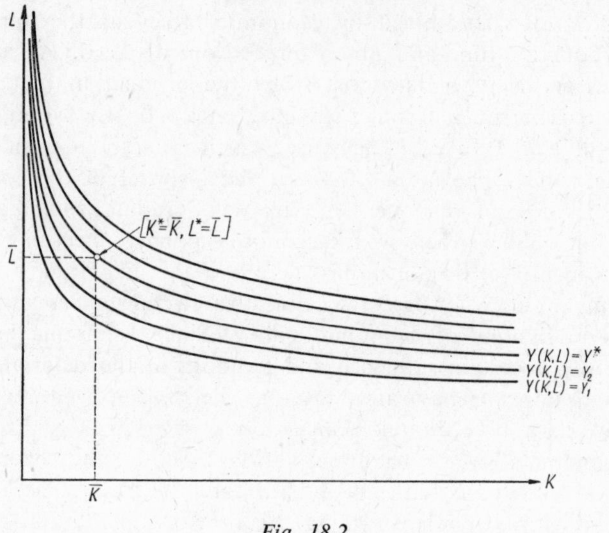

Fig. 18.2

what allocation programs the same fixed quantity of the national income, for instance Y_1, or Y_2, may be achieved. It can be seen from the figure that we achieve the maximum Y^* national income where the isoquant curve touches the oblong limiting the available production fund and labour force.

In our further treatment of the subject we shall assume that in order to achieve the objectives of economic policy, both the full utilization of the production fund and full employment are assured. As we may see, in our model it is not full employment that is the *objective*, but maximum national income, at the given accumulation share. Full employment is a means to this end. As long as we talk only of a homogenous "labour force", it is obvious that the maximum national income can only be achieved with full employment. If we subdivide the labour force (according to trade, regional distribution, etc.), it may turn out that to achieve maximum national income it would not be possible to make use of every person able to work. The reason is that the labour force cannot be regrouped at will, and the missing groups of manpower hamper the full employment of other groups. The longer the period for which we plan, the more likely the disappearance of such disproportions becomes, and the more justified the principle becomes, in practice too, that it is full employment that leads to the maximum national income.

In so far as the full utilization of the production fund is concerned, the relation (18.4) does not represent the technically maximum utilization of the available production fund, but its *normal* utilization at the given technical and organizational circumstances and labour conditions (the usual number of shifts). In the Appendix F we shall discuss the question of what may be considered normal utilization in the circumstances given in Hungary.

We had to begin with the description of the (18.3)–(18.5) primary programming problem and the simple relations connected with it in order to proceed now to the definition of the rational computational rental on capital and of the rational computational wage rate*. We may consider γ rental on capital as the "price" or evaluation of one unit of the production fund, and the ω wage rate the "price" or evaluation of one unit of the labour force. The two computational prices are needed in a secondary allocation programming problem. Let us assume, for the sake of an illustration, that the secondary problem has to be solved by a section of the National Planning Board; by that section which plans technical development, which has to choose among technologies, and which has to make an economical use of the production fund and the labour force. The section gets three items of data from its superiors: the Y^* maximum national income, as a compulsory stipulation; the γ computational rental on capital; and the ω computational wage rate: and is then instructed to solve the following programming problem:

Determine the optimum K^{**}, L^{**} allocation program which satisfies the following conditions:

$$Y(K, L) = Y^* \tag{18.6}$$

$$C(K, L) = \gamma K + \omega L \longrightarrow \text{min!}$$

In this secondary programming problem the $C(K, L)$ *computational cost function of the national economy* figures as the objective function to be minimized.

* A later section of this chapter will describe the relationship of the ω computational wage rate to the Ω computational wage factor and to *actual* wages respectively.

We present the secondary problem in figure 18.3. The parallel straight lines to be seen in the figure are the isocost-lines with a $C(K, L) =$ = const. formula of the $C(K, L)$ computational cost function of the

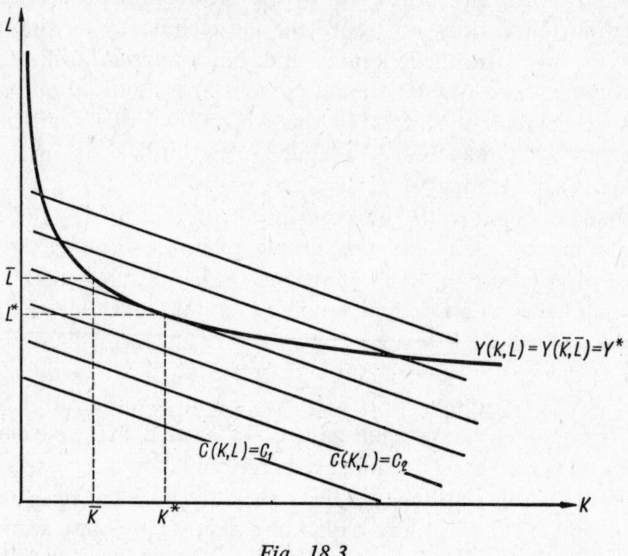

Fig. 18.3

national economy. As may be seen in the figure, the cost function has its constrained minimum where one of the isocost-lines meets the isoquant curve.

It is obvious that the optimum program obtained in the secondary problem depends upon the value of γ and ω. Now, the γ rental of capital charges and the ω wage rate may be called rational if the optimum allocation program received as the solution of the primary and of the secondary problem are identical (see figure 18.4):

$$K^{**} = K^* = \bar{K}$$

$$L^{**} = L^* = \bar{L}. \tag{18.7}$$

As may be seen, the above-mentioned section of the National Planning Board has not received quotas for either the production fund or for the labour force: we may cause it, through the choice of γ and ω to call for neither more nor less of K and of L than is available. *The purpose of the two computational evaluations is precisely to substitute for the direct prescrip-*

tion of quotas for the allocation of resources. The planner who has to minimize the costs, may be influenced through the determination of the cost factors, of the price of inputs. In our case, the planner who mini-

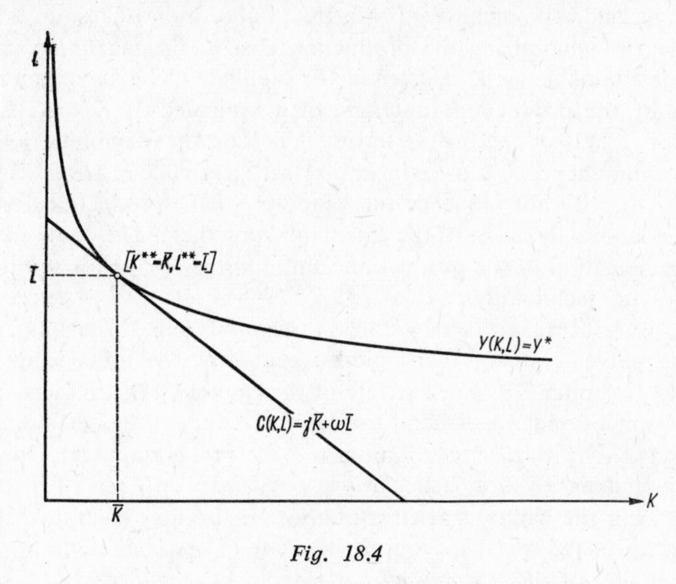

Fig. 18.4

mizes the $C(K, L)$ computational cost functions of the national economy, may be influenced through the determination of the "price" of the production fund, γ, and of the "price" of the labour force, ω. The *rational* computational rental on capital and the *rational* computational wage rate create an equilibrium between the available and the utilized production fund and labour force – without direct prescriptions; in other words, between the "supply" and the "demand" of the production fund and the labour force. And this sole position of equilibrium is the sole $[K, L]$ allocation which assures the maximum national income.

The definition may now be summarized.

Definition. The computational rental on capital, γ, and the computational wage rate, ω, are rational if the solution of the programming problem

$$Y(K, L) = Y^*$$

$$C(K, L) = \gamma K + \omega L \rightarrow \min!$$

is the optimum allocation program:

$$K^{**} = \bar{K}, \;\; L^{**} = \bar{L}\,.$$

The computational evaluations γ and ω are therefore parameters which serve to guide the planners to a rational allocation of resources in the problem of minimizing the production cost of the maximum national income attainable with the given factor supplies (which maximum is itself given by the production function when evaluated at $K = \bar{K}$, $L = \bar{L}$).

As is to be seen, according to our definition the magnitudes of γ and ω do not influence $\bar{K}$ and $\bar{L}$, the limits of the available resources. In other words, they do not influence the "supply" of the production fund and of the labour force, only the "demand" for them. They only influence the combination of the production fund and the labour force, the selection of the technology.

In this respect the role of γ differs *essentially* from, for instance, a role of the interest rate of the capitalist economy, the influencing of the supply of capital. The interest rate of the capital market influences both the supply of and the demand for capital. Although the view is gaining ground among western economists too, based on empirical experience, that its influence is not particularly strong, and is only one of the factors influencing the capital market. But however this may be in the capitalist economy, in the socialist economy the rate of accumulation and with it the "supply" of the production fund, should *not* be guided by the rental on capital. The extent of accumulation should be determined directly, taking into consideration many other aspects and requirements.

The *actual* wage influences in the socialist economy too the supply of labour, the number of persons who ask to be employed. However, we are not investigating now the actual wage but the computational wage which may differ, and generally does differ, from the actual wage.

According to our definition, the rational computational rental and wage rate are not objectively determined magnitudes, but, besides objective factors, they are considerably influenced by economic policy as well, when the latter finally determines the limits of $\bar{K}$ and $\bar{L}$, the available production funds and labour force. In this case, *the computational evaluations, γ and ω, communicate the decision of a higher body to those who have to make a decision on a lower level.* The decision of the higher body is the determination of the extent of accumulation and employment. The decision of the lower body refers to the combination of production fund and labour force, the selection of technology, for instance in the sectoral programming calculations. The computational evaluations, γ, ω, communicate the decision of the higher body, to the latter.

As may be seen from the definition of the rational γ and ω, we do not investigate to what extent each factor of production contributes to the national income. I consider the question in itself absurd. Both K and L are indispensable for the production of Y; they are necessarily *together*. Besides, today's K, the production fund that can be utilized today, could not exist without yesterday's L, the dead labour stored up in K. The discussion of this question is of course very essential from the point of view of political economy. But we investigate in this analysis exclusively what computational evaluation we should impute to K and L, so that on its basis the planner who minimizes the costs should combine them effectively, that is, we ask *what is the rational magnitude of the computational rental on capital and of wages which orientate decision-makers towards efficient actions.*

We may now lay down our first proposition*:

Proposition 18.1. If the production function has properties 1 and 2, then rational rental on capital and rational wage rate can be obtained.

Of course, we have laid down here only the feasibility of their existence, and not that the rational rental on capital and the rational wage rate may be observed in reality and are actually effective. So does it not follow from the proposition 18.1 that there may exist only a single rational γ and ω.

18.4. On the Ratio of the Rental on Capital and the Wage Rate

Proposition 18.2. If the production function has properties 1 and 2, then the ratio of the rational computational rental on capital to the rational computational wage rate equals the ratio of the marginal efficiency of the production fund to the marginal productivity of the labour force (in the position of the optimum allocation program, i.e. where the limits of the production fund and of the labour force become exhausted).

$$\frac{\gamma}{\omega} = \frac{Y_K}{Y_L} = \frac{\dfrac{\partial Y}{\partial K}}{\dfrac{\partial Y}{\partial L}} \Bigg|_{K = \bar{K},\ L = \bar{L}.} \tag{18.8}$$

* The mathematical proofs of the propositions of this chapter are to be found in Appendix E.

The first important conclusion to be drawn from this proposition is that as long as we seek exclusively the most favourable combination of the production fund and of the labour force, and do not pay attention to other factors, the value of γ and ω is a matter of indifference. *Only the ratio of γ and ω* has importance. As long as we have exclusively two limited resources which we draw into our calculations through the computational evaluations, their value may be freely assumed. But as soon as we have determined the value of either of the two, through the relation (18.8) the value of the other becomes determined too.

Reviewing the two propositions which we have made so far, we find that we have only needed *acceptable* working hypotheses in order to be able to lay them down.

What has been said so far, sets the task for the experiments at the quantification of γ and ω: the differential function Y_K and Y_L should be determined or at least the magnitude of Y_K and of Y_L in the case of $K = \bar{K}$, $L = \bar{L}$. In other words, the marginal efficiency of the production fund and the marginal productivity of the labour force should be determined at the point of the complete utilization of the available quantities of both resources.

Let us pass to the description of these experiments.

18.5. First Experiment: Observation of the "Capital Market"

Can any conclusion be drawn, as to the magnitude of γ, from the demand for investment quotas necessary for the increase of the production fund?

Let us establish – provisionally – the following working hypotheses:

(a) There is a pre-determined $\bar{K}$ production fund, which consists partly of the production fund already in operation and partly of the production fund which may be created from now on, i.e. the investment quotas. This fixed magnitude is the "supply of capital".

(b) The state does not give the production fund freely to the enterprises, but demands the *actual* payment of rent on capital. So this is not a computational but a real charge. To the actual wages the actual payroll tax, which is proportionate to the wages, has to be added here.

(c) The enterprises are interested in maximizing both their present and future profits.

(d) The enterprises know their future incomes and expenses exactly.

(e) The actual wage level is fixed, and does not depend upon the demand for the production fund.

(f) The value of γ is determined by the state as follows:

It asks an offer from every enterprise which requests a production fund: let us denote the offer of the ith enterprise by γ_i. These are ranked in a decreasing order, and then the production funds are distributed by proceeding along this list. The γ_i offer which was the lowest still allocated a production fund will become the general γ applicable throughout.

(g) The rent on capital based on the γ so obtained will figure, in accordance with the price formula (16.1) in every actual price.

It can already be seen that if each of the conditions (a)–(g) are effective, the γ resulting from them would adjust itself to the marginal efficiency of the available production fund. The proportion of the actually paid rental on capital to the actual wage rate would be rational:

$$\frac{\gamma}{w} = \frac{Y_K}{Y_L} \Bigg| \; K = \bar{K}, \; L = \bar{L} \, . \tag{18.9}$$

where

w = the actual per capita average wage rate (incl. actual pay-roll tax).

Let us consider the interest of the enterprise which offers a γ_i higher than γ. It is in a position to offer more because the production fund that it has requested has a higher return than the rent on capital that has finally been adopted: $Y_K > \gamma$. But to the enterprise that offers less than the adopted γ, the requested (but to it not allocated) production fund would bring a lower return: $Y_K < \gamma$. Accordingly, it is the offer of the "marginal claimant", i.e. γ that expresses the marginal efficiency of the production fund in the position $K = \bar{K}$, $L = \bar{L}$.

We dispense with the more detailed and more exact description of the "capital market model" – the more so as in what follows we wish to emphasize that the model itself is faulty, the working hypothesis is unacceptable.

In the practice of the Hungarian economy we tried to discover even the faintest traces of the "capital market", and we investigated whether these enabled us to draw from them conclusions regarding the γ_i offers of the enterprise, viz. the marginal efficiency of the production fund. In this connection, three phenomena are worth observing:

(1) As could be seen from ch. 2 of this book, an efficiency calculation has to be made before every investment, including the calculation of the so-called g_n index. The g_n index of the ith investment proposal is given by the following formula:

$$g_{ni} = \frac{S_i}{0.2\,P_i + R_i}, \tag{18.10}$$

where

S_i = the income from the project
P_i = the cost of the investment
R_i = the cost of operation.

It is to be expected that the value of the g_n index will be more than unity. Let us therefore consider 1 the "normative value" of this index, and accordingly write down, instead of the original (18.10) g_n index, the following formula:

$$\frac{S_i}{\gamma_i P_i + R_i} = 1. \tag{18.11}$$

So here we now introduce as an unknown, in the place of the 0.2 rental on capital figuring as the official computational one, the γ_i characteristic of the ith investment proposal. From (18.11)

$$\gamma_i = \frac{S_i - R_i}{P_i}. \tag{18.12}$$

The γ_i magnitude may be considered here the internal rental on capital of the ith investment proposal. It is nothing else than the computational profit falling to a unit of the cost of investment, a kind of computational "rate of profit". The movers of the investment proposal "offer" this "demand" rental on capital. When they hand in their g_n index, they in fact state that they would not register a loss measured by the official computational evaluations, even if they had to pay rent on capital in accordance with the γ_i factor.

Table 18.1 shows the branch averages of the g_n indices of the investments approved in 1963–64. According to this table, in the majority of branches, the value of the g_n index is above 1; the "internal" γ_i rental on capital of a great number of investment proposals is more than 0.2.

But from this we may draw no conclusion whatsoever as to the actual justified magnitude of the rental on capital and to the marginal efficiency of the investment quotas. With the present mechanism the movers of the investment proposals may set forth as high "internal" γ_i as they like – this has essentially no consequence. They need not in fact pay the γ_i which they indicated. Until quite recently the production fund, the

TABLE 18.1

*Branch averages of the g_n indices**

Branch	The number of items of investment	Cost of investment, million Ft	Average of the g_n index
Coal mining, fuel-cake production	11	2292	0.85
Oil industry	4	665	1.99
Metallurgy	6	1650	1.06
Aluminium industry	4	2120	0.77
Machine tool industry	4	172	1.47
Telecommunication industry	3	351	1.50
Precision engineering	1	96	1.22
Electrical industry	1	85	1.70
Power industry	3	1402	1.18
Mass production	2	255	1.07
Foundries	3	356	1.38
Sundry machine industry	5	649	1.29
Electric energy industry	2	1579	1.78
Building material industry	11	763	1.43
Chemical industry	12	9182	0.97
Paper industry	9	1705	0.98
Furniture industry	8	271	1.24
Printing industry	5	195	2.64
Leather- and shoe industry	7	269	1.39
Cotton industry	22	1770	1.08
Wool industry	9	132	1.49
Hosiery industry	8	250	1.07
Fibre industry	6	140	1.37
Food industry	8	765	1.03

* SOURCE: Data of the Investment Bureau of the National Planning Board.

investment quota was allocated free of charge. The buyer may safely offer a high price because he knows that in the end he is going to get the goods free. It is obvious, that no conclusions whatsoever can be drawn from the "tenders" of such a "market"*.

* In ch. 9 of this book, data exposed the extent to which investment proposals distort and "embellish" the returns and expenses that may be expected, and with these the "internal" rental on capital as well.

(2) There was one part of the investment quotas that the enterprises did not get free, but as a repayable credit at 3 per cent interest (this is the so-called credit for the reduction of production costs). Its volume is generally small; it amounts to less than 1 per cent of the investments effected by the state. Even so the available quotas have not been exhausted. The utilization of these quotas is shown in table 18.2.

TABLE 18.2

*Utilization of the investment credit quota for which interest was charged**

Year	Utilization of quota (p.c.)
1959	94.6
1960	81.6
1961	88.0
1962	98.3

* SOURCE: [113].

Just as we could draw no conclusions earlier from the offers over 20 per cent as to the marginal efficiency of the production fund, the refraining from the payment of the 3 per cent interest is no proof to such a low marginal efficiency of the production fund. Why should the enterprise draw on an interest bearing credit as long as it can receive an investment quota free of charge?

(3) It has recently been officially decreed that the enterprises are obliged to pay 5 per cent rent on the production fund which they actually use. This is a very important measure: after Yugoslavia, Hungary was the first to introduce it. But its effect cannot yet be measured. It has not yet affected the actual prices; there has been no price adjustment since its introduction. It has not made any great difference to the share of the enterprises in the profits either; their obligation to surrender part of the profits has been reduced in accordance with the magnitude of the charges. (Additionally, the interest of the enterprises in their profit is not especially strong at the present moment.) Therefore, we are unable to say anything at present of the effect of the rent on capital on the demand for production funds.

In any event, the introduction of the actually payable rent on capital indicates that in the future the effects of "mechanisms of the capital market" will become somewhat strengthened. This promises to be a healthy development. It is conceivable that this will also offer some bases for the establishment of the magnitude of the rational rental on capital.

But too much should not be expected from the actually payable rent on capital either. It is well-known how little "perfect" competition is, especially on the capital market, in the capitalist economy too. The interest rate does not depend at all upon the real marginal yield of the investments alone, but upon many other factors as well: the expectations of the entrepreneurs, the business cycle, the government's financial policy, the stability of the currency, etc.

In the socialist planned economy, the distribution of the production funds, of the investment quotas, can in no event be basically entrusted to some sort of "mechanism of the capital market". This may play an auxiliary controlling role, but cannot regulate the distribution of the bulk of the production funds. Let us think, to mention but one context, of the *long-term* material and moral stake of the management and the collective of the enterprises, the acceptance of the risk connected with investments, and of all those difficult socio-economic problems which would arise if the investment decisions were decentralized to an increased extent. For all these reasons, it cannot be expected that the conditions described at the beginning of this section should materialize. Therefore, this working hypothesis is not acceptable.

To summarize: *we have so far been unable to obtain any worthwhile bases for the establishment of the magnitude of the rational rental on capital and wage rate from the reactions (requests, efficiency calculations, rent on capital offer) of the units requesting investments. Should we in future obtain some information from these reactions, it would still not be possible to base the determination of rational computational evaluations on these.*

18.6. Second Experiment: Conclusion from Plan-variants

Let us assume that the National Planning Board, in working out the long-range plans with traditional methods, prepares the plan in *several* variants. For instance:

First variant: Plan with production fund K_1 and labour force L_1. The national income of the last plan year is Y_1.

Second variant: Plan with production fund K_2 and labour force L_1: $K_2 > K_1$. The national income with this plan variant is Y_2.

Third variant: Plan with production fund K_1 and labour force L_2. This is somewhat more than the labour force prescribed by the first variant: $L_2 > L_1$. The national income with this plan variant is Y_3.

Let us assume that the National Planning Board works out the plan variants considering all other circumstances to be unchanged. In addition, it intends the first variant to include already the relatively most favourable actions; consequently, in the second variant, the excess production fund may only be included at a lower efficiency than the efficiency of the existing production fund:

$$\frac{Y_2 - Y_1}{K_2 - K_1} < \frac{Y_1}{K_1}. \tag{18.13}$$

With the third variant, the position is analogous.

Were such variants available, we should be able to gain the following information:

$$\begin{aligned} \frac{Y_2 - Y_1}{K_2 - K_1} &\approx Y_K, \\ \frac{Y_3 - Y_1}{L_2 - L_1} &\approx Y_L, \end{aligned} \tag{18.14}$$

viz. we would obtain approximating estimations of the marginal productivity of the labour force and of the marginal efficiency of the production found, "around" the limits of the available production fund and labour force.

But no such plan variants have been prepared in Hungary so far, in the first fifteen years of planning. While the individual long-range plans were being worked out, the plan variants born in various phases of planning *followed* each other, and did not apply the "ceteris paribus" principle. On the contrary, they were prepared exactly to apply differing fundamental data, e.g. differing requirements of economic policy, etc. Therefore, from the variants following each other we cannot learn how much the national income changes if only one factor is changed and everything else is left unchanged – and they therefore cannot be used for the approximating estimation of partial derivatives either.

On account of the difficulties described in chs. 1 and 8 it cannot be realistically expected that in future simultaneous plan variants will be worked out in traditional planning.

To summarize: *No bases for the estimation of the rational computational rental on capital and wage rate can be expected from traditional long-range planning which has never before set up, nor can be experted in the future to prepare simultaneous plan variants.*

18.7. Third Experiment: Conclusion from the Distribution of National Income

We shall now describe a "speculative attempt": Can conclusions as to the magnitude of the rational γ and ω be drawn from the data of the *distribution* of national income?

The utilization of national income has two kinds of objectives: accumulation and consumption. Let us mark the accumulation share of the national income with α. Accordingly, the accumulation is αY, and the consumption $(1 - \alpha) Y$.

Let us introduce, for the further treatment of the subject, the concept of the standard distribution of the national income. Let us denote the accumulation share at the standard distribution by α^{Δ}.

Definition. In the case of the standard distribution of national income, accumulation is to consumption as the product of the multiplication of the marginal efficiency of the production fund and of the production fund itself is to the product of the multiplication of the marginal productivity of labour and of the labour force (calculating both partial derivatives at the full utilization of the factors of production).

$$\frac{\alpha^{\Delta}}{1 - \alpha^{\Delta}} = \frac{Y_K K}{Y_L L} \bigg| \; K = \bar{K}, \; L = \bar{L} \, . \tag{18.15}$$

Let us assume for a moment that some internal necessity compels the economy to apply the standard distribution of national income. In this case, it would be easy to determine the ratio of the rational computational rental on capital and wage rate.

Proposition 18.3. If the production function has properties 1 and 2, and the standard distribution of the national income is valid, then the rational computational rent on capital is to the rational computational wage rate as the accumulation share is to the consumption share.

$$\frac{\gamma \bar{K}}{\omega \bar{L}} = \frac{\alpha^{\Delta}}{1 - \alpha^{\Delta}} \, , \tag{18.16}$$

from which

$$\frac{\gamma}{\omega} = \frac{\bar{L}}{\bar{K}} \frac{\alpha^{\Delta}}{1 - \alpha^{\Delta}} \, . \tag{18.17}$$

In this case it would suffice to know α, $\bar{K}$ and $\bar{L}$ to determine the ratio γ/ω, which is so important for us. But we have to make clear: *we do not know of any internal necessity which would compel the application of the standard distribution of the national income in the socialist economy.* The actual accumulation share may be larger or smaller than or equal to the $\alpha^{\triangle}$ of the standard distribution.

We may also make clear that the share according to the standard distribution cannot be considered a desirable ratio, some sort of norm, either. Considerations of economic policy may make either $\alpha > \alpha^{\triangle}$ or $\alpha < \alpha^{\triangle}$ equally justified.

Nevertheless, in our further analysis, and in the elaboration of the accounting principles, we shall apply the assumption of the standard distribution of national income as a *provisional* working hypothesis. The justification of the assumption is not obvious at all (although it is not absurd either).

Does the application of this working hypothesis not mean that we accept Clark's theory on the distribution of income according to marginal productivity*?

Let us acknowledge first of all some conceptual analogy. Clark's distribution of income according to marginal productivity agrees with the standard distribution as defined by us, if, with reference to capitalist conditions, we make the following additional assumptions: the capitalists accumulate all their income, and the workers consume all their income. Or what is obviously equivalent: the consumption of the capitalists equals the income saved and accumulated by the workers.

After this conceptual analogy let us see what the difference consists of.

First: the adherents of the theory of distribution of income according to marginal productivity assert that the theory – at least under capitalistic conditions – is a real picture of the actual distribution of income. But this is an error. It is true that when working out their production and investment policy the enterprises consider the profit that can be expected from the increase of employment and from new investments; to this extent "capital" and "labour" compete with each other for employment. This tends to bring about a correspondence between the proportion of interest to wages and the proportion of the marginal productivity of capital to that of labour. But this tendency is limited by many other factors, such as the power of monopolies and oligopolies, the

* See e.g. [38] by P. H. Douglas, one of the creators of the Cobb–Douglas function, an adherent of Clark's theory.

intervention of the state in both the capital market and in the trend of wages, taxation, the role of the trade unions, the political and economic struggle of the working class, etc. The combined effect of all these factors may divert the actual distribution of national income from the standard distribution to a very considerable extent. For these reasons, today many non-Marxist economists concur in the rejection of the theory of the distribution of income according to marginal productivity*.

Passing to socialism, we do *not* assert that the standard distribution really reflects the actual distribution of national income. This is only *one of the possible* distributions; and if we still assume that it applies, this is only done by way of a provisional working hypothesis.

The second essential difference is that many adherents of Clark's theory assert that the distribution of income according to marginal productivity is expressly *desirable*, because this assures the correct combination of the factors of production. Here the theory goes over to the moral defence of the capitalist distribution of income.

But we do *not* deal with the question of the desirable proportions of the actual distribution of income. We maintain that this would go far beyond our topic of economics and planning; its scientific investigation would lead to the domain of political and economic sociology and even to moral questions. In our investigations, the standard distribution arises only in the context of the attempt at determining the *computational* evaluation of the production fund and of the labour force. We do not investigate what the *actual* wages of the workers should be but only what computational wage rate *should be imputed* to the labour force in economic calculations.

To sum up, *from the data of the distribution of national income, no conclusions can be drawn as to the rational computational rental on capital and wage rate, except if we make additional assumptions; so for instance if we apply, by way of a provisional hypothesis, the assumption of the standard distribution.*

* By way of illustration, let us quote the following lines by J. R. Hicks [53]: "... how do we know that the factors do get their marginal products? Are we to take it that the whole theory of monopolistic competition is only valid in the short run?"

18.8. Fourth Experiment: Conclusion Drawn from the Growth Rate of the National Economy. Description of the Model

In the first three experiments we tried to draw conclusions from static investigations. In our following analyses we shall try to draw conclusions as to the magnitude of the rental on capital from the *growth in time* of the national income, the production fund and the labour force.

Economic literature suggests the idea that the magnitude of the rental on capital adjusts to the growth rate of the national economy*. We have investigated the connections ourselves through a "speculative attempt". For the purpose of the investigation we set up a simple, aggregate growth model.

To obtain the model, we first of all specified the production function further: from the class of the functions characterized by properties 1 and 2 we lifted out a narrower subclass. The production function used for the growth model is as follows**:

$$Y(t) = A e^{\mu t} K(t)^{\beta} L(t)^{\eta}\,, \tag{18.18}$$

* It is shown primarily by John von Neumann's famous growth model (see [135]), and by the "turnpike-theorem" by Dorfman, Samuelson and Solow intending to develop this model further that – in certain defined conditions – the interest rate coincides with the rate of growth of the national economy (see [37]). A number of authors have developed the "turnpike-theorem" further, so e.g. L. McKenzie [123] and R. Radner [146].

The proposition which was to become known under the name of the "neo-classical theorem" or "golden rule", had been derived by means of models essentially entirely different from von Neumann's model both as regards the underlying economic assumptions and the mathematical apparatus employed. The proposition was worked out in the years 1960–1962 in different forms and independently from one another by the following six authors: M. Allais, J. Des-roussaux, E. S. Phelps, Joan Robinson, T. Swan and C. C. von Weizsäcker. The proposition states essentially that under definite conditions per capita consumption will reach a maximum when the rate of increase in national income and the rate of profits are the same.

The question, as to the assumptions of the simple model of growth described in sections 18.8 and 18.9 conform to and how far they differ from those of the models mentioned above, will not be dealt with here.

Incidentally, our disquisition does not investigate the interest rate associated with the conversion of the price systems applying at different points of time, but the rent on capital to be charged for the production fund at a given point of time. There is, however, a close relation between these two magnitudes. This is briefly discussed in Appendix D.

** From here on, for the rest of the chapter, it will be assumed that $K = \bar{K}$ and $L = \bar{L}$. Accordingly, we will use throughout the notation K and L in the formulae.

where

t = time as a continuous variable
A = the constant coefficient of the production function. This has no independent economic meaning; through the suitable choice of the units of measure it may even be 1
e = the basis of the natural logarithm
μ = the quality parameter of the technical level
β = the elasticity of the national income with respect to the production fund. This shows by how many per cent the national income grows if the production fund is increased by 1 per cent and the labour force is left unchanged
η = the elasticity of the national income with respect to the labour force. This shows at what percentage rate the national income grows if the labour force is increased by 1 per cent and the production fund is left unchanged.

What are the essential new qualities of the function?

Property 3 of the production function. The national income is a homogeneous function of K and L of the $(\beta + \eta)$ *degree.*

This quality means that:

$$Y(mK, mL) = m^{\beta+\eta}\, Y(K, L)\,. \tag{18.19}$$

This means that if both the production fund and the labour force are multiplie by the same m factor, the national income is multiplied by $m^{\beta+}$. In this connection, there are three possibilities:

(a) The sum of the elasticities is 1.

$$Y(mK, mL) = mY(K, L), \qquad \beta + \eta = 1\,, \tag{18.20}$$

i.e. the national income changes in the same ratio as the production fund and the labour force. In English-language economic literature this is called the case of "constant returns to scale". In this expression, "to scale" refers traditionally to the fact that if *all* factors are changed *together, in the same ratio,* then the marginal return is constant.

If the sum of elasticities is 1, then the production function is homogeneous of the first degree*.

(b) The sum of the elasticities is larger than 1. In this case the national income will grow to a larger extent than to which K and L have been increased. If for instance $\beta + \eta = 1.2$, $m = 1.5$, then – if we increase the production fund and the labour force both by 50 per cent – the national income will increase not by 50 but 63 per cent. This is the case with "increasing returns to scale": increasing marginal return in the case of the increase of the factors *together, in the same ratio.*

(c) The sum of the elasticities is smaller than 1. This is the case with "diminishing returns to scale": a diminishing marginal return in the case of the increase of the factors *together, in the same ratio.*

It is not necessary now to make (a), (b) or (c) a condition of our analysis, we may express our proposition in a more general form, so that it should be valid for all three cases. For this reason we may state that the third property may be considered an acceptable working hypothesis.

Property 4 of the production function. In addition to the two factors of production, the production fund and the labour force, figuring as variants in the function, there figures in it a third $e^{\mu t}$ *factor, which grows exponentially as a function of time.*

The economic interpretation of the property is as follows:

Technical progress is *quantitative* and *qualitative* at the same time. On the one hand, $k = K/L$, the technical equipment of labour grows. The effect of this *quantitative* change is expressed by

* We wish to refer here briefly to the connection between the production functions used by us, and the Cobb–Douglas function and other production functions applied in economic literature. The original Cobb–Douglas function (see [38]) is as follows:

$$Y = A\, K^{\beta}\, L^{1-\beta}. \tag{18.21}$$

This is a *static* homogeneous function of *the first degree.*

The dynamic variation of this function has become known from R. M. Solow [160] and [161]:

$$Y = Ae^{\mu t}\, K^{\beta}\, L^{1-\beta}. \tag{18.22}$$

This is a *dynamic* function, but *also* homogeneous of the first degree.

The function in formula (18.18), which is also known from economic literature, is more *general*, because it is not bound to homogeneity *of the first degree*, to the assumption of "constant return to scale". There are other production functions in economic literature. See e.g. the function worked out by K. J. Arrow *et al.* [6].

the property of function (18.18) that at a given L more K result in a larger Y. In order to be able to perceive the *qualitative* aspect of technical progress, let us imagine for a second, that K/L, the technical equipment of labour, does not change. As time went on, the productivity of labour would still grow, because the know-how, skill, technical culture, discipline of the workers would increase, the organization of production would improve, small changes (even with an unchanged k) would increase the capacity of the machines, reduce idle time, etc. At the same time, as a result of technical progress, in the process of the continuous renewal of the production fund, the quality of the machines, of the technical equipment, improves, their output increases. Today's machine "knows more" than a machine which was acquired thirty years ago at the same cost for a similar purpose. All these changes are reflected together, in the production function, by the continuous growth of the $e^{\mu t}$ factor. This factor grows exclusively as a function of time; its growth rate is expressed by the parameter μ, by the qualitative parameter of the technical level. As time progresses the effect of K and L is "multiplied" by the $e^{\mu t}$ factor, which is increasing in time.

The utilization of the function type (18.18) has the advantage that it can be made to agree, without contradictions, with the facts that can be observed empirically.

To make this clear let us first introduce a concept: let us call the national income due to one unit of the production fund the (average) efficiency of the production fund, and let us mark it with χ:

$$\chi(t) = \frac{Y(t)}{K(t)}\,. \tag{18.23}$$

We have already spoken of one of the empirical observations when describing the second property of the production function: at a given point of time, at a fixed t, F_K, the differential efficiency of the production fund, and with it obviously χ, the average efficiency of the production fund *diminishes* while the production fund is growing. The other empirical observation is that $\chi(t)$, the average efficiency of the production fund in time is approximately constant. This is so in many countries, including Hungary*. It will later become obvious that if the (18.18) form production function, as well as other complementary assumptions, applies, then *both* properties may exist at the same time: χ and Y_K

* See the relevant statistical data in Appendix F.

are diminishing *at a given point of time*, and still constant *in time*. The (18.18) function expresses here the following simple relationship:

If we invest *today*, instead of the planned 30 billion, 31 billion forints, the efficiency of the additional 1 billion is already smaller than that of the first thirty billion – provided that the 30 billion were intended for the most efficient investments. The continuous increase of the production fund, however, in time does not entail such diminishing efficiency because this is counteracted by the quality side of technical progress, by the fact that the one billion forint worth of machines of tomorrow "know more" than the ones of today*.

Based on these considerations, the fourth property of the production function may also be considered an acceptable working hypothesis.

Besides the assumptions relating to the production function, further complementary assumptions are made for our growth model. These are the following:

Let us assume that the labour force grows exponentially in time:

$$L(t) = L_0 \, e^{\lambda} \, , \tag{18.24}$$

where

L_0 = the labour force at the starting point
λ = the growth rate of the labour force.

Let us assume that accumulation is constant in time**:

$$\alpha = \frac{\dot{K}}{Y} = \text{constant}. \tag{18.25}$$

Let us assume that the economic policy requires that the growth of the national income should be even. It assures by working out appro-

* Marxists have long criticized, especially in connection with the problems of land rent, the one-sided interpretation and the over-emphasizing of the phenomenon of diminishing returns. V. I. LENIN [98] for instance, arguing with the Russian economist N. S. Bulgakov, pointed out that in agriculture we meet diminishing returns but at a given, unchanged level of technology; the basic tendency, however, is the development of technology, of the forces of production. This is exactly what the dynamic function of the type (18.18) expresses: the diminishing return applies to the given t, yet – under the influence of the quality parameter of the technical level expressing the quality side of technical progress – the marginal efficiency of the production fund is not diminishing in time.

** The dot above the symbol is the distinguishing mark of the first derivative with respect to time, e.g. $\dot{K} = dK/dt$.

priate detailed economic plans that the growth rate of the national income, ϱ, should be unchanged in time:

$$\varrho = \frac{\dot{Y}}{Y} = \text{constant}. \tag{18.26}$$

The justification for the assumptions (18.24) and (18.26) has been verified statistically (see Appendix F). The same cannot be said of assumption (18.25): the accumulation share fluctuated quite considerably in the past. But for the future it may be stated realistically that, if economic policy requires it, the stability of the accumulation share may be assured. (Appendix F covers this question too.)

On the basis of all this, assumptions (18.24)–(18.26) qualify as acceptable working hypotheses.

18.9. Fourth Experiment: Conclusion from the Growth Rate of the National Economy. The Propositions

We now concisely sum up the simple growth model described above:

$$\begin{aligned} Y(t) &= A\, e^{\mu t}\, K(t)^{\beta}\, L(t)^{\eta} \\ L(t) &= L_0\, e^{\lambda t} \\ \alpha &= \text{constant} \\ \varrho &= \text{constant}\,. \end{aligned} \tag{18.27}$$

Within the limits of the model we may put the following propositions:

Proposition 18.4. Given assumption (18.27), both average and marginal efficiency of the production fund are constant in time.

$$Y_K(t) = Y_K = \text{constant for every } t\,, \tag{18.28}$$

$$\chi(t) = \chi \quad = \text{constant for every } t\,. \tag{18.29}$$

For the next proposition we introduce a new concept: let us call the per capita national income the a v e r a g e p r o d u c t i v i t y o f l a b o u r, and let us mark it with y:

$$y = \frac{Y}{L}\,. \tag{18.30}$$

Proposition 18.5. Given assumption (18.27), the average and marginal productivity of labour grows exponentially in time. The growth rate is equal to the difference between the growth rate of the national income and of the labour force.

$$\frac{\dot{y}}{y} = \frac{\dot{Y}_L}{Y_L} = \varrho - \lambda . \tag{18.31}$$

These two propositions can be verified appropriately by the statistical data of Hungarian economic development (see Appendix F).

From propositions 18.4 and 18.5, as well as the earlier proposition 18.2, follows:

Proposition 18.6. Given assumptions (18.27), the proportion of the rational computational rental on capital and wage rate changes in time. (A) If we fix the magnitude of the rental on capital and keep it unchanged in time, then the computational wage rate belonging to it will grow in time at a rate equal to the productivity of labour. (B) The same is valid the other way round: if the computational wage rate grows in time at a rate equal with the productivity of labour, then the rational rental on capital belonging to it must be constant in time.

The computational wage factor figuring in the general price formula (16.1) is the quotient of the computational wage rate and the actual wage rate:

$$\Omega = \frac{\omega}{w}. \tag{18.32}$$

After this, we may put an important proposition concerning the Ω wage factor figuring in the general price formula (16.1):

Proposition 18.7. Given the assumptions (18.27), if the wage rate grows at the same rate as the productivity of labour, and the computational wage rate is constant over time, the rational computational rental on capital is also constant over time.

This follows logically from proposition 18.6. If the actual wage rate grows at the same rate as the productivity of labour, and we always multiply this by an Ω wage factor constant over time, then the *computational* wage rate grows at the same rate as the productivity of labour.

$$\frac{\dot{\omega}}{\omega} = \frac{\Omega\, \dot{w}}{\Omega\, w} = \varrho - \lambda . \tag{18.33}$$

And according to proposition 18.6 (B), a γ unchanged in time is entailed.

Propositions 18.4–18.7 have so far been based exclusively on *acceptable* working hypotheses. It has been possible to verify some of our assumptions and some of our propositions statistically as well. But we have not said anything so far about the connections between γ and ϱ, the rational rental on capital and the growth rate of the national income. To put a proposition here, we have to insert a further assumption which must be qualified as a *provisional* hypothesis. We assume that the entire national income is imputed to two factors of production, K and L:

$$\gamma K + \omega L = Y. \tag{18.34}$$

I shall call this from now on the assumption of complete imputation. The assumption would obviously be unjustified if we considered other factors besides these two and sought the best combination of several factors. It would also be unjustified if our calculations referred to the most favourable formation of the structure of consumption. But as the latter is outside the scope of our investigations – for lack of a better one – this assumption may be applied.

For the further treatment of the subject, the concept of the standard distribution of national income will again be necessary. If we deal with production function (18.18), then the α^{Δ} accumulation share according to the standard distribution may be determined as follows*:

$$\alpha^{\Delta} = \frac{\beta}{\beta + \eta}. \tag{18.35}$$

We may now put the following proposition concerning the connections between the rational rental on capital and the growth rate of the national income:

Proposition 18.8. Given the assumption (18.27) and the application of the assumption of complete imputation, (A) the rational rental on capital is larger than the growth rate of the national income if the accumulation share is smaller than it would be according to the standard distribution; (B) they are equal if the accumulation share equals the one according to the standard distribution; and finally (C) the rational rental on capital is

* Insofar as we have to do with a homogeneous production function *of the first degree*, a Cobb–Douglas function, it should read $\alpha^{\Delta} = \beta$.

*smaller if the accumulation share is larger than the one according to the standard distribution**.

$$\begin{aligned} \gamma &> \varrho, &\quad \text{if} \quad \alpha &< \alpha^{\triangle} \\ \gamma &= \varrho, &\quad \text{if} \quad \alpha &= \alpha^{\triangle} \\ \gamma &< \varrho, &\quad \text{if} \quad \alpha &> \alpha^{\triangle}. \end{aligned} \tag{18.36}$$

In an earlier section we already emphasized that the standard distribution of the national income could not be considered either a necessity or a norm. It is therefore *not necessary* for γ to coincide with ϱ; it may be larger or it may be smaller.

To sum up: the magnitude of the rational rental on capital cannot be deduced directly from the growth rate of the national income; this deduction can only be made if we apply supplementary provisional working hypotheses (complete imputation; standard distribution).

18.10. Fifth Experiment: Statistical Investigation

We have attempted to estimate the parameters of the production function from the statistical data of the development of the Hungarian national economy, and to draw conclusions from these as to the magnitude of the rational γ and ω. In this connection the following proposition may be put:

Proposition 18.9. In so far as the production function has properties 1, 2, 3 and 4, the ratio of the rational computational rent on capital γK to the rational calculative wages, ωL, equals the ratio of the exponents of the production function.

$$\frac{\gamma K}{\omega L} = \frac{\beta}{\eta} \,. \tag{18.37}$$

The connection is even simpler if we assume that the production function has property 3 (a) ("constant return to scale"), i.e. it is as follows:

$$Y(t) = A\, e^{\mu t}\, K(t)^{\beta}\, L(t)^{1-\beta} \,. \tag{18.38}$$

* E. MALINVAUD [114] arrives at a similar conclusion, through the assistance of a Neumann-type model.

As we may see, this is Solow's dynamic production function, homogeneous of the first degree. Proposition 18.9 leads to the following relationship:

$$\frac{\gamma K}{\omega L} = \frac{\beta}{1 - \beta} \, . \tag{18.39}$$

If we succeeded in determining statistically the parameters μ and β, it would be a very simple matter to draw conclusions as to the ratio $\gamma : \omega$ so important to us.

For our statistical investigation we made use of function type (18. 38). Its application may be considered but a *provisional* working hypothesis; we have not verified the justification of the assumption of homogeneity of the first degree.

The statistical examination is described in detail in Appendix F. Here we wish to mention only some of its principal characteristics and conclusions.

For the purpose of the statistical investigation we transformed the function (18.38), by dividing both sides by L and transforming to logarithms as follows:

$$\log y(t) = \log A + \mu t + \beta \log k(t) \, , \tag{18.40}$$

where

$$y = \frac{Y}{L} = \text{the productivity of labour}$$

$$k = \frac{K}{L} = \text{the technical equipment of labour.}$$

We have determined the time sequence of Y, K and L back to 1950 for the entire Hungarian economy, and within this for industry too. From these we have calculated the time sequence of y and k. At first glance it may seem that, on the basis of the eq. (18.40), the parameters μ and β may be estimated by means of multiple regression analysis. But unfortunately, this could not be done. It turned out that k was very nearly an exponential function of time, i.e. $\log k$ was a linear function of t. Such a close linear relation (collinearity) between the variables $\log k$ and t, the "independent" variables of the multiple regression analysis to be performed, means that the multiple regression analysis cannot furnish an acceptable estimate. In practice, it is not possible to separate the effect of the variables k and t on the dependent variable y. We may obtain proof of the truth of this statement without going into the mathematical statistical evidence of it. Equation (18.40) is – as regards the variables $\log y$, t and $\log k$ – the equation of a plane. The object of the regression analysis would be to fit a plane to the points corresponding to the actual triplets of $\log y$, t and $\log k$. However, the close linear relation between $\log k$ and t means that the points corresponding to the actual figures essentially lie over a *straight line* of the plane $\log k$, t, so that if the validity of eq. (18.40) is assumed, the points lie along a straight line. In such circumstances, the task would be to determine the equation of the plane in the knowledge of a straight line of the plane. It is obvious however, that not one plane but an infinite number of them may be laid across a straight line, so that the problem has no definite solution*.

All this may appear to be a purely mathematical-statistical difficulty. In our view, however, this problem goes deeper. In the last resort, we wish to draw conclusions through multiple regression analysis as to the marginal efficiency of the production fund and the marginal productivity of the labour force respectively. But we could draw such conclusions from statistical time sequences only if in the history of the Hungarian economy the following phenomenon had occurred repeatedly: the production fund stagnates for some time (or approximates stagnation), while the labour force increases. Or, the other way round, the labour force stagnates from time to time (or it approaches stagnation), while the production fund grows. Or the growth of the labour force does not cease but slows down, while, let us say, the growth of the production fund quickens; or the other way round: the growth of the production fund slows down and the growth of the labour force quickens. Or the labour force is reduced while the production fund goes on growing at the accustomed rate, and so on. In general terms: if neither the growth of the labour force nor that of the production fund would approximate so closely an exponential function of time. If actual economic history had seen all these "experiments", then we could draw conclusions from the statistics, from the "experiments", to what extent the growth of national income could be attributed to the growth of the technical equipment of labour, to what extent exclusively to "time", to the increase of the level of technology. Then the statistically observed points would

* This difficulty of the regression analysis directed at the estimation of the parameters of functions of the Cobb–Douglas type was first explained by H. MENDERSHAUSEN [125] (see also J. TINBERGEN [166]).

cover a relatively wide area and it would be possible to fit a plane to them. The statistical examination cannot be carried out successfully because of the fortunate circumstance for the development of the Hungarian economy that both the production fund and the labour force as well as the national income have grown relatively regularly, at an approximately unchanged rate, exponentially. The regularity of development causes the points to gather around a straight line and do not offer an opportunity for an acceptable statistical estimate.

We have not attempted to use another production function, which would differ from the dynamic function (18.38). But we are under the impression that the phenomenon which we have just described – the regularity and approximately even rate of the growth of K, L and Y – would lead to similar difficulties in other statistical investigations based on time series*.

To sum up, *the determination of the rational rental on capital and of the wage factor cannot be carried out on the basis of a statistical estimate of the parameters of the production function, because this estimate, according to our present knowledge, cannot be made unequivocally.*

18.11. Sixth Experiment: The Determination of Computational Evaluations through Mathematical Programming

The easiest way to determine the evaluations needed for the formation of computational prices would seem to be mathematical programming**. This question will be discussed more fully in Part 5 of this book; here we only wish to refer to this possibility.

When we use a programming model for the long-range planning of the economy, we simulate, as it were, on the electronic computer the "capital market" and the "labour market"***, of which we have shown in section 18.5 that they do not exist, or only faint traces of them are to be found, in the reality of the planned economy. We execute on the

* We have not even attempted to estimate the parameters from cross-sectional data, the comparison of data from *many countries*. It can be expected that, because of the incomparability of price relations, the difficulties would be insurmountable.

** We have borrowed this idea primarily from L. V. KANTOROVICH [62] who recommended that the magnitude of the rental on capital should be determined on the basis of shadow prices to be obtained through linear programming.

In Hungary, this was recommended for the first time by GY. SIMON and GY. KONDOR [158, 159].

*** This will be described more amply in sections 25.5 and 26.4.

electronic computer those "experiments" which cannot take place in the actual development of the economy (see section 18.10) and which cannot be carried out when the plans are worked out with traditional methods (see section 18.6).

The first experimental economy-wide programming is now under way and from this we expect, among other things, that it will supply bases for the estimation of the rational rental on capital and of the rational wage factor.

It is of course clear to us that from a linear programming model, which contains numerous essential simplifications and inexactitudes compared to reality, we may only obtain approximate estimates of the justified magnitude of γ and Ω. The figures to be so obtained promise, however, to be more acceptable than our present estimates which are based on less reassuring, provisional working hypotheses.

18.12. Accounting Principles

Parallel to the description of the accounting principles applied in our calculations concerning γ and Ω, we discuss to what extent each principle is well founded; to what extent it rests on *acceptable* and to what extent on but *provisional* hypotheses. We believe that none of them is based on *unacceptable* hypotheses.

Let us first recall accounting principle 16.8 according to which the wages are not calculated at the actual level valid when the calculations are carried out but at the future level to be expected in the plan year. According to experience, the growth rate of wages more or less agrees with the growth rate of the productivity of labour. The following accounting principle can therefore be based on proposition 18.7:

Accounting principle 18.1. The computational rental on capital, γ, and the computational wage factor, Ω, are constant in time.

We compute with the same γ and Ω, whether we program for 1965 or say 1970. The principle – as we have already pointed out under the discussion of proposition 18.7 – is based exclusively on acceptable working hypotheses.

Unfortunately, any further accounting principle can only be based on auxiliary, *provisional* working hypotheses. For the lack of a better hypothesis we apply the assumption of complete imputation; i.e. we "impute" the *entire* national income, in the form of computational rent on capital and wages to the production fund and labour force; furthermore the hypothesis of the standard distribution of national income.

From these the following accounting principles follow:

Accounting principle 18.2. The magnitude of the computational rental on capital should fundamentally adjust to the growth rate of the national income. Magnitude: 0.08.*

The growth rate of the national income was in the past 10–12 years around 6 per cent. "To be on the safe side", we set the magnitude of γ slightly higher. We thought that we had to calculate cautiously and with economy first of all in respect of the production fund, the investments.

According to the assumption of complete imputation:

$$Y = \gamma K + \omega L = \gamma K + \Omega wL = \gamma K + \Omega V, \qquad (18.41)$$

where

V = the actual wage fund of the national economy.

Since Y, K, V, as well as – in accordance with principle 18.2 – γ too are now known magnitudes, we could calculate the computational wage factor:

$$\Omega = \frac{Y - 0.08\,K}{V}. \qquad (18.42)$$

This is approximately 1.25. This shows the computational wage factor to be identical with the actual one.

Accounting principle 18.3. The computational wage factor: 1.25.

To make a survey of the accounting principles easier we diagrammatically present the logical structure of our train of thought in figure 18.5, we show how we have arrived from certain hypotheses to certain propositions and then how the latter have led to the accounting principles.

* The accounting principle worked out on the basis of the highly simplifying assumptions employed in ch. 18 is, after all, in conformity with the proposition suggested in the literature mentioned in the footnote on p. 258 (i.e. both in von Neumann's model and the so-called "golden rule"). Yet, we are applying accounting principle 18.2 only provisorily and in want of a better solution – with a restless conscience, as it were – until a more adequately founded principle can be worked out.

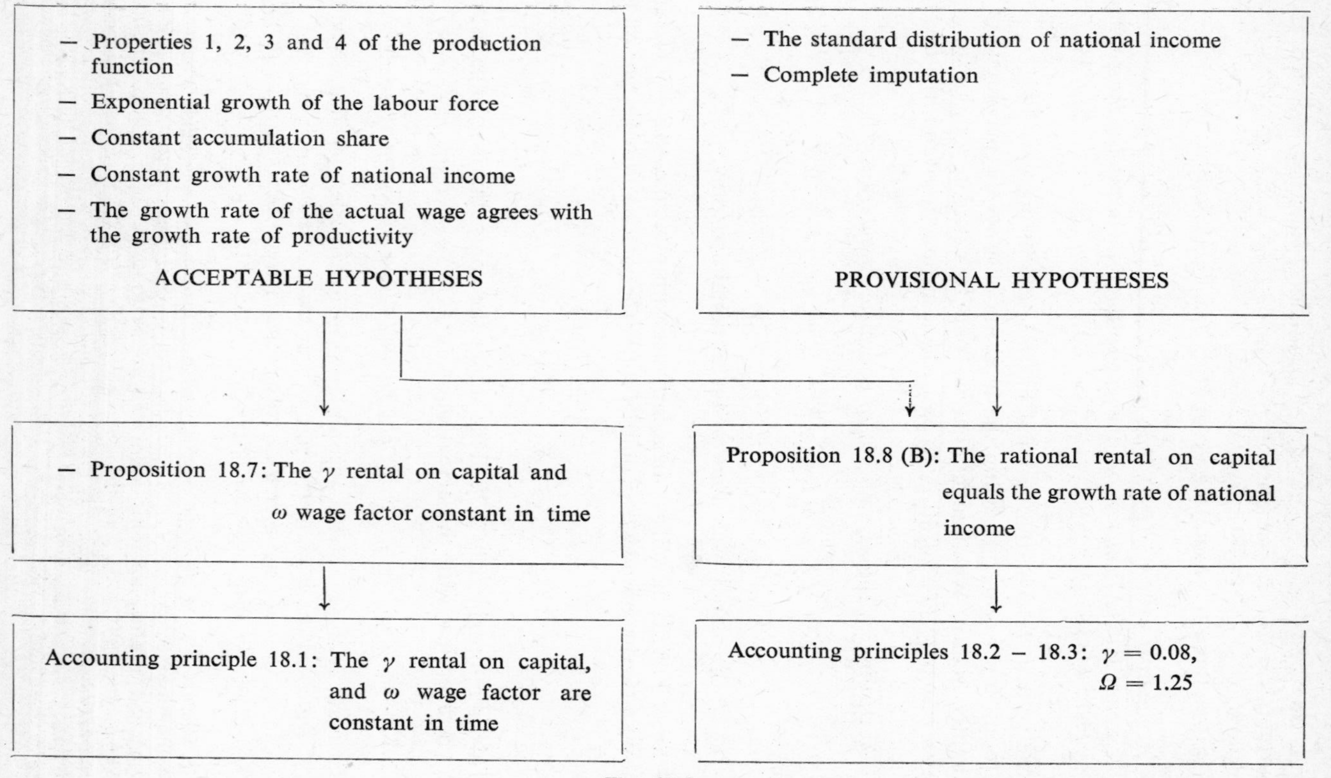

– Properties 1, 2, 3 and 4 of the production function
– Exponential growth of the labour force
– Constant accumulation share
– Constant growth rate of national income
– The growth rate of the actual wage agrees with the growth rate of productivity
ACCEPTABLE HYPOTHESES
– The standard distribution of national income
– Complete imputation
PROVISIONAL HYPOTHESES
– Proposition 18.7: The γ rental on capital and ω wage factor constant in time
Proposition 18.8 (B): The rational rental on capital equals the growth rate of national income
Accounting principle 18.1: The γ rental on capital, and ω wage factor are constant in time
Accounting principles 18.2 – 18.3: γ = 0.08, Ω = 1.25

Fig. 18.5

18.13. General Conclusions

Athough we have not succeeded in establishing satisfactorily the magnitude of γ and Ω, and have obtained in the end result but a few accounting principles based on provisional hypotheses which are not verifiable, we still believe that it was not superfluous to describe the theoretical considerations and the unsuccessful attempts at quantification.

Our experience helps us to have a clearer view of the limits of the "optimality" of our branch programming. Nothing is more dangerous in science than self-deception. When carrying out our branch programming, we could not hold – and we did not try to make the state organs that commissioned us believe – that the "optimum programs" which are to be obtained would inevitably coincide with the program most desirable from the point of view of the national economy.

With our experiments we aimed also at a defence against the pitfalls of the false explanations and mistaken theories related to the rental on capital. Appendix G provides a survey of the debate which took place in recent years about the rental on capital (interest) in a socialist economy. This debate was extraordinarily diverse and produced dozens of "theories". Numerous authors tried to create the impression that they were already able to determine satisfactorily the rental on capital which was economically justified. If the unsuccessful attempts were not good for anything else, they were perhaps useful in arousing doubt about over-facile explanations. We believe that it is preferable to see the present – unfortunately rather narrow – confines of our knowledge than to believe that we have solved a problem which has in reality been left unsolved.

If the attempts have not lead to immediate results, the lessons which can be drawn from them have shown the path most promising for further attempts: computational evaluations obtainable from mathematical programming.

From the theoretical analyses and the attempts at quantification a few practical conclusions can be drawn as well.

One is that it cannot be left exclusively to the objective function to prescribe the minimization of the computational costs to insure that the branches should utilize the production fund and labour force to the extent desirable for the balance of the national economy; if for no other reason, than because the magnitude of γ and Ω is not sufficiently firmly established. Therefore, we include in the branch models direct constraints of the resources, e.g. investment quotas and, in the latest programming, labour quotas too, etc. For the time being, for the lack of something better, we take over the magnitude of the quotas from the economic plan worked out by the traditional method, as a plan directive. This way we have "double assurance": firstly, through the constraints, and secondly, through the prescription of γ and Ω, we try to lead the branch into the channel desired by the requirement of economic balance. The application of one or the other only is insufficient. It is also possible that the two means have a contradictory effect: e.g. at a given γ, the branch does not utilize the investment quota. For this reason, further. steps will be needed here, which will be described in Part 5 of this book.

It is another practical conclusion that in view of the uncertainty of the computational evaluations, checks are needed. The next section deals with such checks.

18.14. Sensitivity Analyses

The estimates of the national economic plan, the traditional calculations of the economic efficiency of investments, and the official computational evaluations influence the choice between technologies in three ways:

(1) The national economic plan prescribes the investment quota.

(2) The official methodology prescribes a computational rental on capital.

(3) The chapter of the national economic plan dealing with technological development directly prescribes the determined directions and proportions of the development.

In our research into the cotton industry we investigated whether the three data are consistent with each other in the technological development of the cotton industry.

In one calculation, we carried out a continuous parametric programming with the following objective function (with γ as parameter):

$$C(\mathbf{x}) = \mathbf{c}'\mathbf{x} = (\gamma\,\mathbf{p}' + \mathbf{r}')\,\mathbf{x}\,, \tag{18.43}$$

where

$\mathbf{p}$ = the vector of the investment costs to the unit of the activity
$\mathbf{r}$ = the vector of the operation costs to the unit of activity.

As may be seen, the vector of the coefficients of the objective function is a *linear* function of γ.

For the purpose of our calculation, we excluded from the scope of programming of our model the broad and weft-pattern looms.

TABLE 18.3

Parametric programming in the cotton industry with the rental on capital as a parameter

Characteristics of the activity			Limited resources of convertible foreign exchange			Unlimited resources of convertible foreign exchange			
			γ-interval						
Loom	Weft-winder	Construction	2–3.6%	3.6–15.1%	15.1–91.5 %	0–6.7%	6.7–9.3%	9.3–15.1 %	15.1–91.5 %
Operation of old, less efficient loom	Old machine	In old building	330	2614	3823				3823
Speeding-up of old, more efficient loom	Old machine	In old building	3787						
Speeding-up of old, more efficient loom	New machine	In old building		3787	3787		3787	3787	3787
Shuttle-changing automatic loom	New machine	In old building	4139	2128	1017			4528	1015
Shuttle-changing automatic loom	New machine	In new building	331	615	812			919	1542
Shuttleless automatic loom	New machine	In old building				9357	5266		
Shuttleless automatic loom	New machine	In new building				568	651		
Construction (in m²)			2847	5289	6983	4203	4817	7903	13 261
Investment (in million Ft)			345 260	307 218	283 858	1 744 122	1 139 860	441 697	177 638

We carried out the calculation with two models of a different structure. In the first we computed with the output set initially and a fixed foreign currency quota, in the second we started with an increased output and assumed that any amount of foreign currency may be used.

The results are shown in table 18.3. Since all optimum programs prescribe the acquisition of new sizing, warping, and cross-winding machines, I do not show these in a separate table.

At the first programming we arrived at three, and at the second programming at four quantitative identity intervals. The differences between the identity intervals can be explained by the fact that at one programming the foreign exchange quota was limited and at the other one it was not.

Let me describe briefly another calculation. In this we compare, through a parallel calculation with the assistance of a model extending to the entire scope of programming, what the optimal program would be if we counted with a 10 per cent or a 20 per cent rental on capital. The results are shown in table 18.4.

The elements of the optimum programs – as far as the sensitivity to γ is concerned – may be put into three groups:

(a) The activities not sensitive to the magnitude of the rental on capital. These include the exchange of the sizing, warping and cross-winding machines for modern ones. These figure in all optimum programs.

(b) The less sensitive activities. These include the acceleration of old looms, which is squeezed out of the optimum program only if the γ is *very low*, because in that case all old machines have to be exchanged for new ones.

(c) Activities sensitive to the rental on capital. These include the exchange of the old looms that cannot be accelerated. In the case of a lower γ, the exchange of the machines is included, in the case of a higher γ, this activity is left out of the optimum program.

Let us now investigate more closely those parts of the program which are sensitive to the magnitude of the rental on capital.

Without going too much into detail, three kinds of investment and technological development trends can be discerned from the various programs described in tables 18.3 and 18.4.

One extreme is the "ultra-radical" trend of technological development. This applies most clearly if the rental on capital is lower than 3.6 per cent. In this case even the machines that can be accelerated have to be exchanged, and the stock of narrow machines has to be composed exclusively of the most productive – and most expensive – machines. However, for this investment program to be realized, the entire investment costs foreseen in the official plan would be required several times over.

TABLE 18.4

Parallel programming in the cotton industry with two kinds of rental on capital

Serial number	Composition of machine stock	10% rental on capital	20% rental on capital
1.	How many old, worse narrow looms shall there be in operation?	1416	3823
2.	How many old, worse narrow looms should be dismantled?	2404	0
3.	How many old looms should be accelerated?	3787	3787
4.	How many shuttle-changing narrow machines shall be acquired?	3650	1828
5.	In the broadloom machine stock	complete exchange of machinery	all old machines remain
6.	In the weft-variegating machine stock	complete exchange of machinery	all old machines remain
7.	In the sizing machine stock	complete exchange of machinery	complete exchange of machinery
8.	In the warping machine stock	complete exchange of machinery	complete exchange of machinery
9.	In the weft-winding machine stock	partial exchange of machinery	complete exchange of machinery
10.	In the cross-winding machine stock	complete exchange of machinery	complete exchange of machinery
	A few general characteristics of the optimum program		
11.	How many per cent of fabric production is supplied by automatic machines?	56.6	27.8
12.	The amount used for investments (in million Ft)	555	360
13.	Construction of new workshops (in 1000 m²)	1	7.4

The other extreme is the complete conservation of the present technological conditions. This is the optimum program if the γ is higher than 15.1 per cent. In this case all old machines would have to be kept, and only that number of automatic machines could be bought which would be needed for the foreseen production task exceeding the capacity of the existing machine stock. This trend requires the lowest investment cost but, proportionately, the most construction work.

Between the two extremes there is the trend of technological development at a moderate rate. Its characteristics are the partial exchange of looms, the gradual introduction of automation, but with the relatively cheapest automatic machines. This is the optimal program if we compute with a γ of 9–15 per cent.

The official computational rental on capital is, as I have already mentioned, 20 per cent. What happens if we apply in our model this rental?

First, the optimum program does not exhaust the investment quota allocated for the programming scope.

Second, it is conducive to a more backward, more conservative technology than the one defined in the chapter of technological development of the national economic plan. The propositions concerning the tasks set by the Second Five Year Plan declared that by 1965 the proportion of automation in the cotton spinning industry had to be raised to 35–40 per cent (see [197]). But in the case of a 20 per cent rental on capital, the optimum program assures only 28 per cent automation. This too, is only achieved because a certain degree of automation had already taken place irrevocably before the calculation was made.

As we may see, the three kinds of central estimates are not consistent. We took the stand that the investment quota and the technological development estimate were realistic, and the latter could even be surpassed, but the official computational rental on capital was unrealistically high.

CHAPTER 19

IMPORT MATERIAL COSTS. FOREIGN TRADE PRICES

19.1. The Problem Surveyed

The general formula of computational prices (16.1) contains the following factors connected with external trade:

$r^{dir}_{i,Rbl}$, $r^{dir}_{i,\$}$ = direct import material costs in Rbl or \$

$r^{indir}_{i,Rbl}$, $r^{indir}_{i,\$}$ = indirect import material costs in Rbl or \$.

Parts of direct import material costs have been accounted for in full detail, material by material, in the following manner:

$$r^{dir}_{i,Rbl} = \sum_{k=1}^{m} s^{imp}_{k,Rbl}\, g_{ki} + \bar{r}^{dir}_{i,Rbl}, \tag{19.1}$$

where

$s^{imp}_{k,Rbl}$ = the price of the kth import material import from socialist markets, in Rbl ($k = 1, \ldots, m$)

g_{ki} = material input coefficient; the amount of the kth material required for one unit of the ith product, expressed in the appropriate quantity unit

$\bar{r}^{dir}_{i,Rbl}$ = the cost of other materials not accounted for among the m individually calculated materials (but imported also from socialist markets), in Rbl.

A similar formula can be set up for materials derived from capitalist markets. In the course of the programming project for the man-made fibres industry, a total of 20 types of import materials have been accounted for individually.

In Part 4 we have been dealing so far only with the computational price system connected with production. Now it will be necessary to extend the investigation also to the outlays and revenues relating to the *foreign-trading* activities figuring in the programming models. Here we will find four types of magnitude involved:

$$s^{imp}_{k,\mathrm{Rbl}},\ s^{imp}_{k,\$} \ = \text{import price in Rbl or \$}$$

$$s^{exp}_{k,\mathrm{Rbl}},\ s^{exp}_{k,\$} \ = \text{export price in Rbl or \$}.$$

Of the magnitudes mentioned above, material input coefficients g_{ki} will not be dealt with here; their determination belongs to the domain of technological informations. Nor will we be able to say more about $\bar{r}^{dir}_{i,\mathrm{Rbl}}$ or $\bar{r}^{dir}_{i,\$}$; it is difficult to make them "tangible", owing to their residual character. In the calculations we have been striving to reduce their weight as far as possible, i.e. to calculate individually the greatest possible number of inputs.

Sections 19.2–19.5 will deal with foreign trade prices s_k. Here we will already treat jointly the prices of the direct material inputs of productive activities and those of the exported and imported products. The central problem of these sections will be the determination of prices.

Finally, section 19.6 is to deal with indirect import material costs $r^{indir}_{i,\mathrm{Rbl}}$ and $r^{indir}_{i,\$}$.

19.2. What Should Be Regarded as a Foreign Trade Price?

In the traditional efficiency calculations certain outlays and returns are calculated on the basis of "world market prices" instead of domestic prices (see ch. 2). In actual practice, however, the term "world market prices" will raise a number of problems. Most products have no uniform price on the world market. It is mainly with respect to the commodities of standardized quality, quoted in the world's big markets, that the term can be used unequivocally. These products, on the other hand, account for only a fraction of international trade. In the majority of cases, the price of a commodity will vary according to the country of supply, probably even according to the supplying firm. It may, furthermore, depend on the quantity contracted for, on the currency in which payment takes place, on the terms of payment and delivery, etc. The prices actually contracted by the organs of Hungarian foreign trade will also depend on the efficiency of the latter, on the market conditions of the deal, etc., and may considerably differ from those quoted in the financial and trade journals.

These factors of uncertainty tend to enable certain "manoeuvring" around world market prices in the traditional efficiency calculations.

Those carrying out the calculations will be in a position arbitrarily to employ a higher or lower price, according to what they wish to prove, and will be able to "authenticate" both prices. Thus, for example, one price may be that quoted in an actual contract, the other that advertised in a trade journal, and so on.

It will, accordingly, be necessary to lay down some unequivocal rules concerning the prices on which the investment calculations are based. We will not speak now of *future trends* in the price level – these will be dealt with in subsequent parts of this chapter. In all estimates of future trends the starting point will be some present price: it must, therefore, be made unequivocally clear, what should be regarded as the "present price" of a commodity. Our own calculations have been based on the following accounting principle:

Accounting principle 19.1. The foreign trade prices employed in computational price formation and pertaining to import and export activities should approach the average level of the prices paid and charged for Hungarian imports and exports, respectively.

The practical implications of this principle are the following:

(1) The basic point of departure should be *actual* prices figuring in the contracts of the foreign trade organs. They should, however, be subjected to correction in each case when it can be proved to satisfaction that a shift due to some temporary cause had occurred in one direction or the other. Lacking an actual contract price, quotations in trade journals can, with adequate precaution, be used as the basis of estimates concerning the price that would be payable or obtainable in the case of actual purchase or sale on foreign markets.

(2) The calculations should be based on the relations, quantities, transport costs as well as terms of payment, credit and delivery most current in Hungarian foreign trade.

(3) In any given program, the principles under (1) and (2) should be applied in the same way to all products concerned, in order to provide a *uniform basis* of comparison for the alternatives. For example, no export alternative should be given an advantage by applying to it the higher quotations of a trade journal while basing the other alternatives on the lower prices actually obtained by Hungarian foreign trade.

19.3 Characteristic Trends of Price Movements

We shall now turn our attention to the question of *changes* in foreign-trade prices *over time*. According to accounting principle 16.9 in our calculations an attempt was made to *take into account some characteristic trends in price movements**.

It is clearly out of the question to forecast with any precision much in advance the trend of changes in the capitalist markets. The sphere must, accordingly, be narrowed down to the changes which it will be both reasonable and possible to take into account.

Price movements on the world market constitute a highly complex phenomenon. If we tried to classify the changes we must, first of all, distinguish two main categories, viz. changes in the general level of prices in individual capitalist countries and changes in the relative prices of individual commodities and commodity groups.

The general level of prices will depend on the general tendencies prevailing in the capitalist economy (prosperity or depression, crisis) and, closely connected with that, on the (inflationary or deflationary) character of the financial policy of the country concerned. It will be expedient for those shaping *short-term foreign trading policies* in the socialist planned economy to take the general trend of prices in capitalist countries into account when deciding on what and where to purchase and to sell. On the other hand, when formulating *long-term investment policies* aimed at marking out the country's place in the international division of labour, it will not be possible to make an allowance for such trends. A general rise or fall in the price level of some foreign market will affect several sectors of Hungarian foreign trade and, through that, to some extent also a whole range of industrial branches. But these effects cannot be taken into account when facing the problem to determine the future proportions a sector will have to bear to the other sectors of the national economy. Thus, the question whether the synthetic fibre and plastics industries should be developed at a greater pace than the vehicle industry, cannot be influenced by the prognosis that price increases of an inflationary character are likely to continue over the next years in a number of capitalist countries.

* The idea was repeatedly put forward in economic literature (see e.g. M. Mandel *et al.* [117], p. 269). The Polish official methodology affords a possibility to take into account the prospective changes in the price level. "If . . . on the basis of world market trends considerable changes can be expected in the cost and price relationships figuring in the calculations, then these changes may be taken into consideration . . ." (see [183], p. 11).

Partial price changes and shifts in price proportions which occur within the general changes in the price level may again be classified into two groups. Part of the price shifts may be due to incidental fluctuations, e.g. when a big firm starts dumping the market in order to win it over from its competitors. It devolves on the foreign trading companies to take advantage of such price fluctuations in their daily business transactions – to sell when the price is comparatively high and to buy when it is relatively low. But such short-term price fluctuations cannot affect our long-term investment policies.

The other class of partial price changes and shifts in price proportions comprises the price movements which show a discernible regular *trend*. A case in point is that of the relative price levels of synthetic materials on the one hand and natural ones on the other, with the former showing a continually falling tendency in relation to the other. This is a trend which it will be advisable to take into account when formulating investment policies concerning the plastics industry as it has a real bearing on the question whether the mass production of such materials would in the long run be profitable.

Our reasoning may be summed up as follows:

Accounting principle 19.2. In our investment efficiency calculations, it will be expedient to take into account exclusively one type of change in world market prices. This type of change is characterized by relative shifts in the price level of a commodity or a group of commodities with respect to that of other commodities. The shifts are not exceptional or incidental, not merely transitory in character, but showing a lasting trend and a recurrent regularity.

19.4. Price Trends of New Commodity Types*

To illustrate the characteristic trends of price movements which it will be both reasonable and possible to take into account in the course of the investment efficiency calculations, we will discuss now in some detail the typical price trends shown by *new* commodity types.

In the course of investigations into the production of man-made fibres, the problem presented itself with considerable sharpness. On the world

* In compiling the material of sections 19.4–19.5 I had the valuable assistance of Mr. M. Tardos (Institute for Market Research) and Mr. T. Vidos (Chemical Plant Design Bureau).

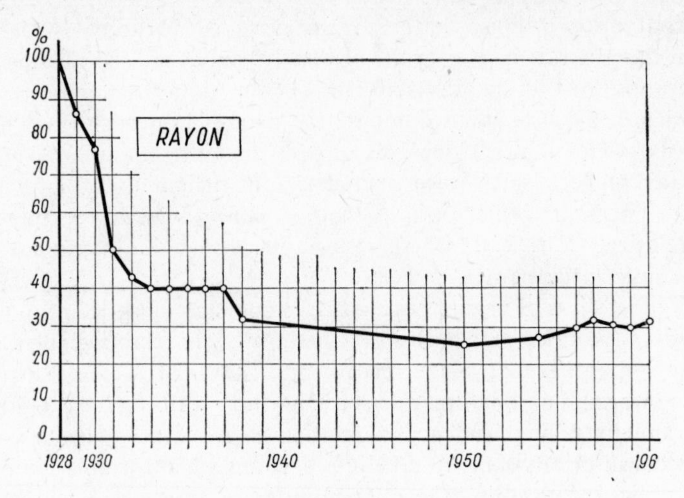

Fig. 19.1

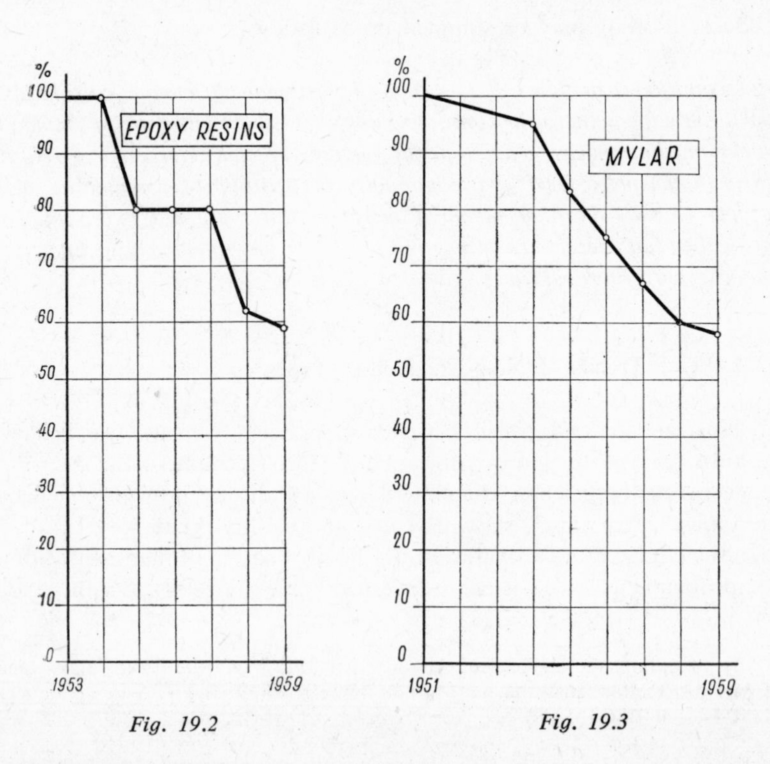

Fig. 19.2

Fig. 19.3

market, ever newer man-made fibres are making their appearance. Hungary, being actually about to set up a man-made fibres industry, is now in a position to decide whether to take up the production of some earlier type known already for several years or to launch that of some recently developed variety.

We have studied the price trends of a large number of man-made fibres and plastics types. Let us, first of all, survey the relative data.

The prices in table 19.1 are – with the sole exception of the initial prices given in absolute terms – index numbers based on the price of the product concerned in the first year of its appearance (= 100). For the sake of comparability, the data are given for each product from the first year of its appearance.

The data in the table refer to US prices and to the year of the product's appearance in the United States.

The same price index series are also presented graphically in figures 19.1–19.9.

The figures display a certain similarity. *Price trends are throughout falling*, with the price of the first year of appearance constituting in each case the highest one. As a general rule, the rate of decrease is quicker in the beginning, then it slows down and the price becomes relatively stable. This "regularity" is particularly marked in figures 19.1, 19.4, 19.6, 19.7 and 19.9 where the curve is fairly *hyperbolic*.

From the economic point of view, the falling trend of prices is easy to explain*. The new product will in the beginning command a novelty price – a kind of monopoly price. The firm first to appear on the market will strive to profit from the attraction inherent in the novelty of the product**. At this stage the price will be well above first cost. Later on a number of factors working for a decrease in price will become operative. The attraction of novelty will gradually cease and competitors will appear in the field. Supply will tend to outgrow demand***. Others, too, will try to take advantage of the high prices commanded by the novelty and will thereby only help to knock down the high price. Shocks to the capitalist economy (a depression, or even a comparatively mild recession) are likely to have an even stronger

* See H. Macskássy and T. Vidos [112].

** In American business language this price policy is called "skimming the cream" (see J. Dean [31]).

*** In our case the two factors are closely interrelated. What we have to do with is an article of clothing, the demand for which will depend on fashion and taste, e.g. nylons were more attractive when still a novelty than when they became more "common" wear.

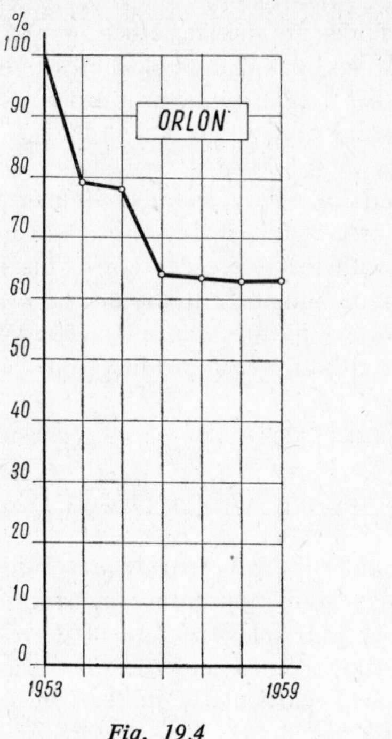

Fig. 19.4

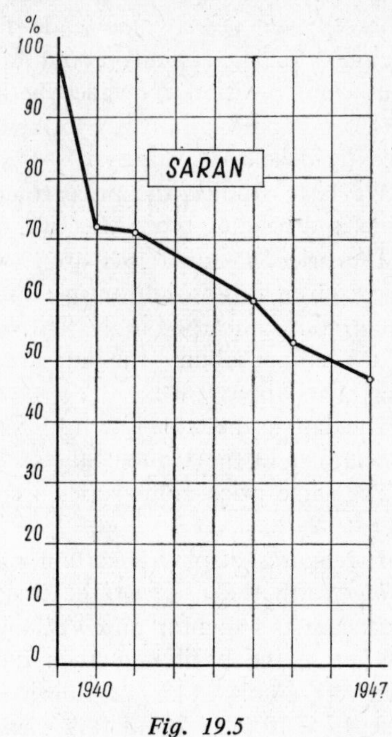

Fig. 19.5

TABLE

Time series of price indices of

Product	First year of appearance	Initial price ($/lb)	Price index								
			1	2	3	4	5	6	7	8	9
Epoxy resin*	1953	1.00	100	100	80	80	80	62	59		
Mylar (Polyester foil)*	1951	3.00	100			95	83	75	67	60	58
Orlon fibre**	1953	1.89	100	79	78	64	63	62	62		
Polyethylene*	1943	1.00	100		70	52	47	43		45	48
Polystyrol*	1938	0.68	100	84	76		43		40		38
PVC*	1934	0.78	100	76		72			67		61
Saran (Polyvinylidene-chloride)*	1939	1.25	100	72	71			60	53		47
Teflon*							60	50	36		
Viscose rayon+	1928	1.50	100	87	77	50	43	40	40	40	40

* SOURCE: [199].
** SOURCE: [193].
\+ SOURCE: for data referring to the years 1928–1938 [192]; for those referring to later years [196].

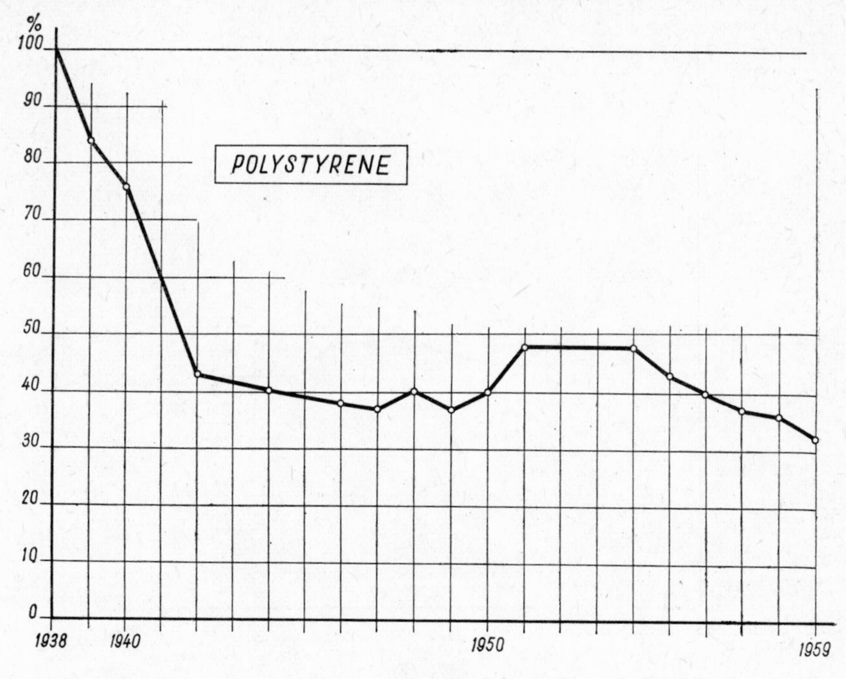

Fig. 19.6

19.1
plastics and man-made fibres

for years following first appearance (1st year = 100)																							
10	**11**	**12**	**13**	**14**	**15**	**16**	**17**	**18**	**19**	**20**	**21**	**22**	**23**	**24**	**25**	**26**	**27**	**28**	**29**	**30**	**31**	**32**	**33**
47	47	41	41	41	35	35	32																
37	40	37	40	48			48	43	40	37	36	32											
56	50	45	42		44		46	49			47	45	41	38	30								
	34	33	30			24																	
40													25				26		29	32	30	29	31

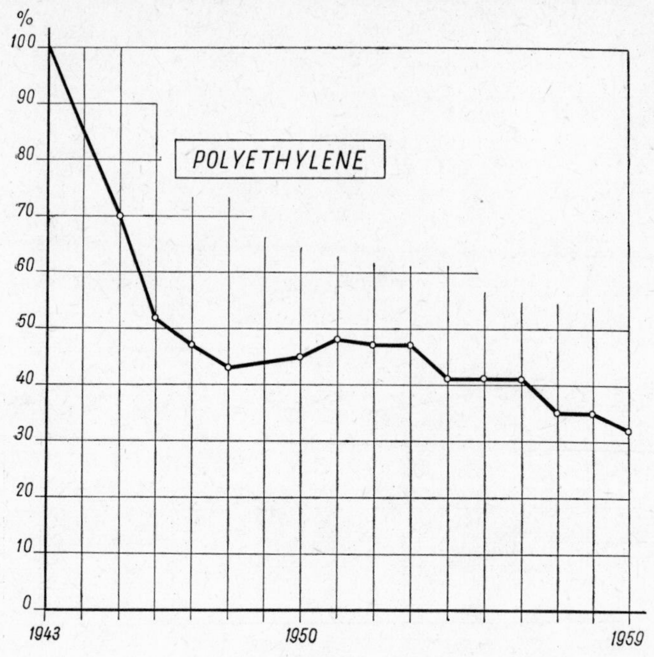

Fig. 19.7

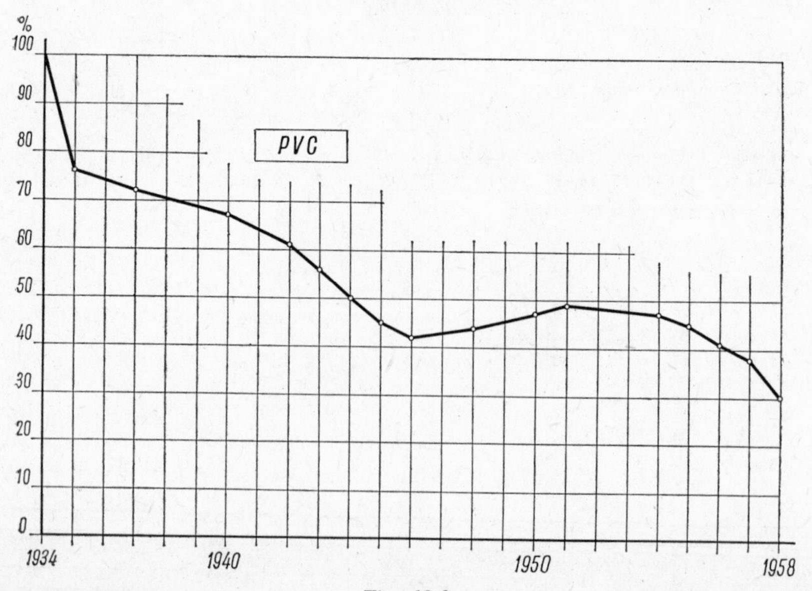

Fig. 19.8

effect, as the producers of the highly profitable products in question will try to retain their hold on the market by cutting down prices. It is in this way that they will endeavour to fight off their permanent compet-

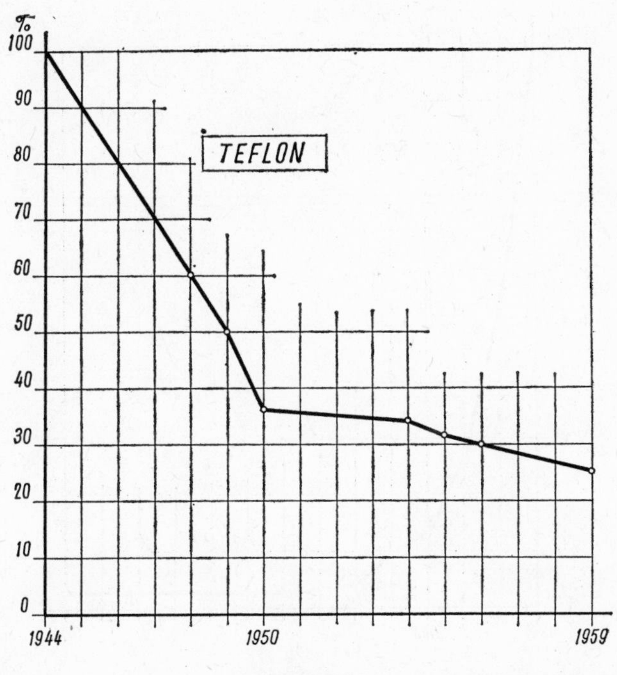

Fig. 19.9

itors – in the present case the producers of natural fibres and materials. A further factor working for a decline in prices will be the falling trend of prime costs concomitant with the growth of technological skill and the advance of research work. With the profits incorporated in the price once reduced to the level characteristic of other products, the further fall in prices will largely depend on the decrease of first costs and on the competitive position with respect to rival products (in the case of synthetic fibres and materials, the natural varieties). After the elapse of some time, the rate of decline in prices will, accordingly, tend to slow down. Let us call this relatively more stable price the n o r m a l p r i c e, in contradistinction to the considerably higher novelty price.

The concrete slope of the price curves of the individual products is, of course, not uniform. The rapidity, i.e. the steepness, of the initial fall will depend on the rate at which the factors described in the foregoing become operative and interacting. The "regularity" of the curves will be broken by incidental fluctuations.

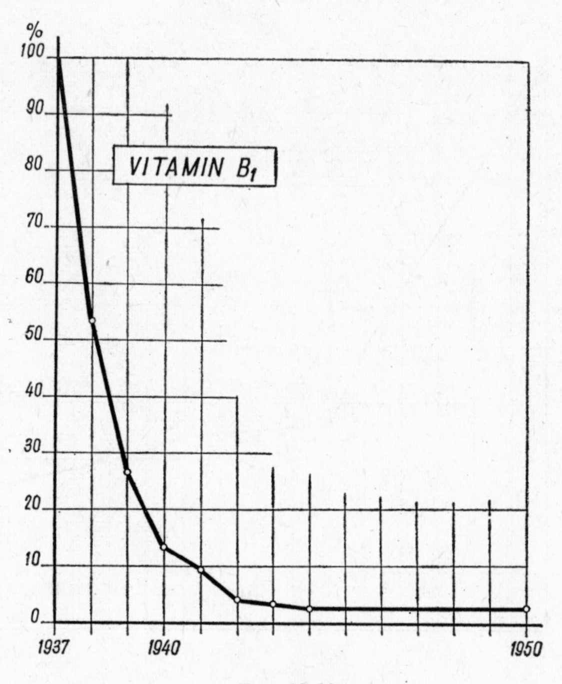

Fig. 19.10

Nor is this falling-off of novelty prices exclusively peculiar to synthetic fibres and plastics. The same phenomenon will be observed in the case of every product which, owing to its novelty, elicits an extremely keen demand in the initial marketing period. Let us take another example, that of the *pharmaceutical industry*, a highly important one from the point of view of Hungarian exports. We will now examine the dynamics of price movements in some pharmaceutical products (see table 19.2 and figures 19.10–19.16).

In the latter figures the curves approximate even more closely the regular hyperbola than in the case of man-made fibres and of plastics. The fall in the price of pharmaceutical products is more abrupt than in that of man-made fibres.

TABLE 19.2

Time series of price indices of some pharmaceutical products

Product	First year of appearance	Initial price, $	Price index for years following first appearance (1st year = 100)															
			1	2	3	4	5	6	7	8	9	10	11	12	13	14	15	16
Aureomycin	1948	15/capsule of 16.25 mg	100	66.7	40.0		34.0	34.0			34.0		12.5	11.8				
Vitamin B_1	1937	7.50/g	100	53.3	26.7	13.3	9.3	4.0	3.3	2.7					2.7			
Vitamin B_2	1937	17.80/g	100	56.2	28.1	9.6	8.4	3.9	2.2	1.1					0.6			
Vitamin B_6	1939	12/g	100	30.8	25.0	16.0	10.0	9.2	9.2	6.7	5.0							
Vitamin B_{12}	1949	2500/g	100	40.0				9.6			8.0	3.4	2.6					
Penicillin	1942	20/100 000 units	100	50.0	4.5	2.5	1.2	0.5	0.3	0.2		0.1	0.4					
Streptomycin	1945	15/g	100	24.7	16.7	6.7	2.7	1.3		1.3	1.3	0.8		0.5		0.3	0.2	0.2

* SOURCES: for data referring to the years previous to 1957 J. DEAN [31] (p. 421) and Report submitted to the United States Congress [182]; for those referring to the years after 1957, informations obtained from MEDIMPEX Foreign Trading Company.

19.5. The Forms and Bases of Estimation

From what has been said above it must be clear that by simply taking the novelty price of a new product for its future price we would commit a grave error. The novelty price is bound to decrease in future and we must, therefore, find a way to estimate the future price of the new product.

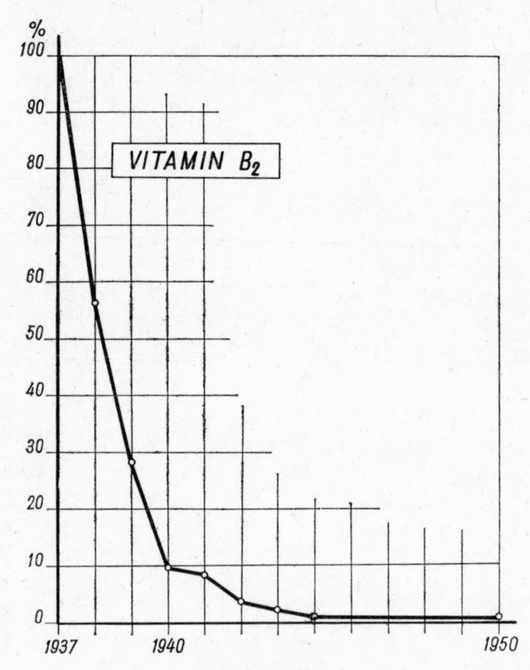

Fig. 19.11

In the course of our study of the man-made fibres industry, thirty-four forecasts of this type have been carried out*. A detailed survey of all these would go beyond the scope of this book but a short outline of some of the methodological viewpoints may prove useful in other calculations of this character. In figures 19.17 and 19.18 below, the forecasts for the price trends of terylene and acrylonitrile are presented for

* These forecasts as well as the corresponding calculations for the bauxite-aluminium industry were carried out by Mr. M. Tardos. It is partly on his records that the present section of this work is based.

the sake of illustration; the detailed data, together with those referring to a third product, are contained in Appendix B.1.

Our estimates were based on the following information:

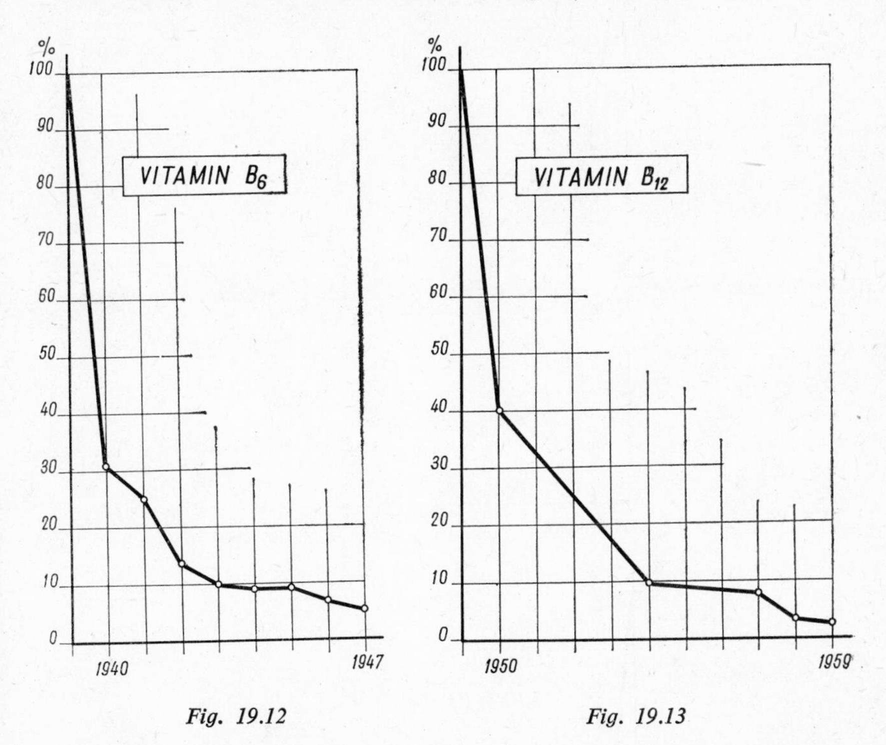

Fig. 19.12 *Fig. 19.13*

(1) The data concerning the conditions of production and the first cost of the product under investigation were compiled together with those relating to prospective new developments in technology and the new achievements of scientific research. On the basis of these data, the level of short-term variable costs of production (primarily of direct wages and material costs) was estimated. The level thus calculated may be taken as the lower limit of normal price, a level below which prices are, in the majority of cases, unlikely to fall. In the calculations we set out from the fact, established by technico-economic experience, that it usually takes a long period of time until some result of scientific research, not yet in the stage of industrial realization and with several details still unsolved, becomes a large-scale factor in the formation of foreign-trade prices. In the meantime, new methods of production may possibly

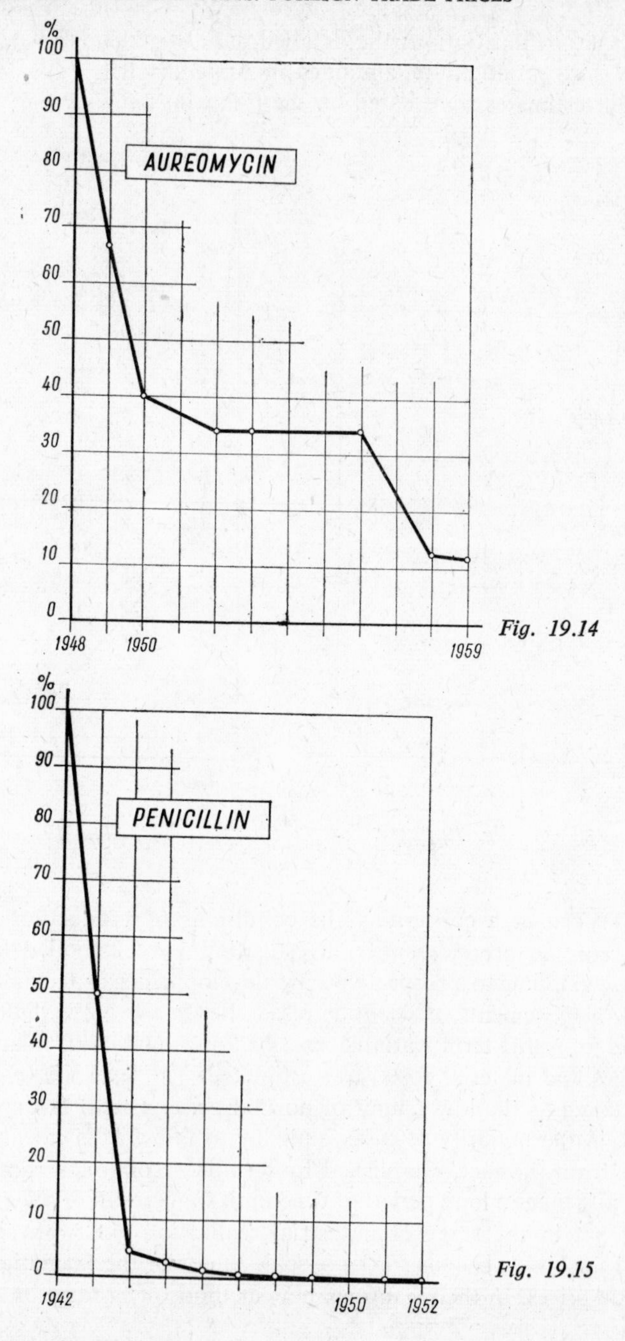

Fig. 19.14

Fig. 19.15

be discovered, but these will presumably be introduced on a large scale only during the period under investigation and will, accordingly, not become a factor in price formation.

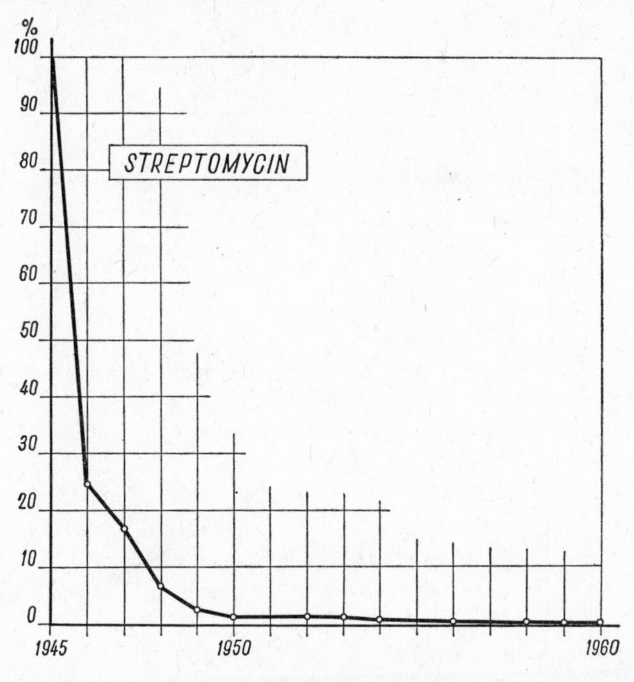

Fig. 19.16

(2) Data on price changes, covering the longest possible period in the past, were compiled.

As far as price changes are concerned, the data available consisted exclusively of domestic prices in foreign countries. After conversion into a common currency, these prices showed considerable differences from one another and were often very far from the level of Hungarian import prices. They had, therefore, to be brought to a common level. It appeared expedient, in accordance with accounting principle 19.1, to transpose the various national price series to the level of contracted Hungarian import prices. For a basis we have chosen the average prices of Hungarian import contracts in 1960. As a first step, the time series of foreign (British, American, etc.) prices were established, in index form, with 1960 = 1. As a second step, the basic price (average price of 1960 Hungarian imports) was multiplied with the price indices thus obtained. This gave us as many curves – intersecting in one point that of the average 1960 Hungarian import price – as the number of foreign price series that

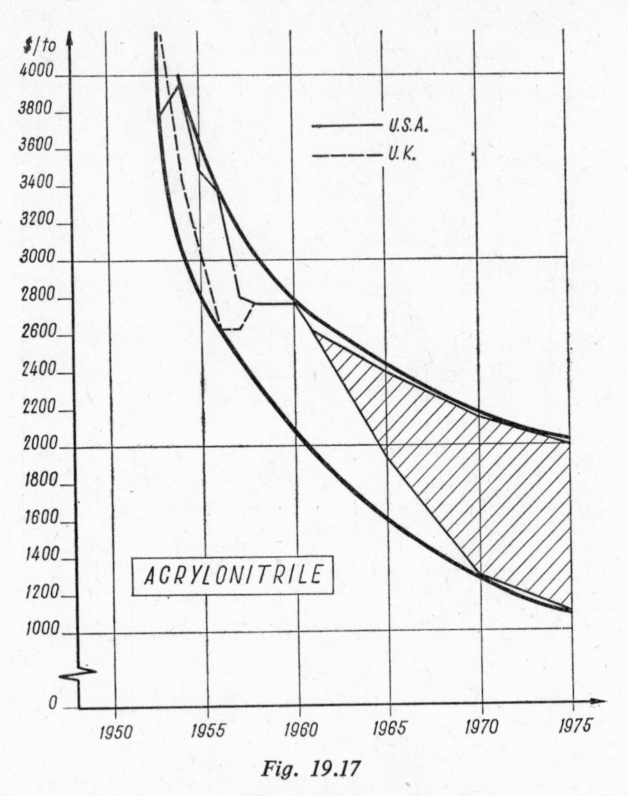

Fig. 19.17

could be established for the product in question (see the price series covering the years before 1960 in figures 19.17 and 19.18).

The data having thus been brought to a uniform level, there still remained the problem of the distortive effect on their trend of the uneven rate of price inflation in the various countries. To eliminate this disturbing factor, it appeared expedient, as a third step of adjustment, to deflate the prices, i.e. to divide each price series by the index of wholesale prices – the indicator of the rate of inflation – or, in the case of export prices, by the index of world-trade prices. This means essentially that the curve thus obtained measured the changes in the price of a given commodity in relation to the changes in the prices of all other commodities. This is in accordance with accounting principle 19.2.

When examining the shape of the price curves it appeared expedient to fit a regression function to the national price curves, or to find the envelopes between which the points obtained can be enclosed. The price

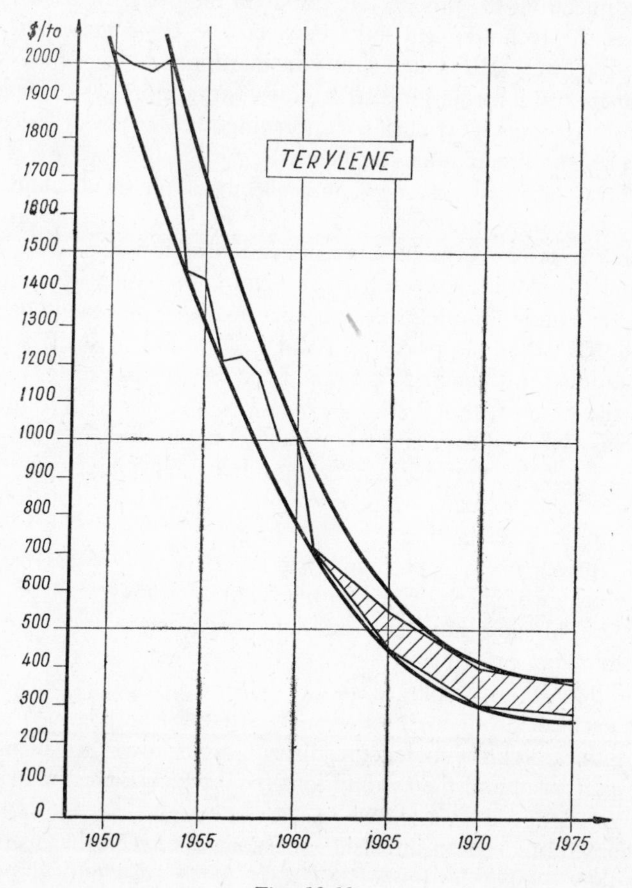

Fig. 19.18

changes were here expressed as a function of time. The trend line indicated by the regression function, or the zone enclosed by the envelopes, would then yield information as to prospective price movements.

It should be pointed out, however, that we considered the functions used to evaluate the characteristic trends of past price movements only the basis of our estimation and did not mechanically extrapolate them, project them into the future.

(3) The market position of the product in question has been examined, and the activities and price policies of the marketing firms analysed, with special regard to the possible existence of international cartels. In this connection, the prospective trends in the prices of basic materials as well as the technological links between the basic materials and the final product were also taken into consideration.

To the *special* information listed under paragraphs (1)–(3) was added some more *general* information concerning the trends of price movements. The analogous phenomena in the "price history" of new man-made fibres, new plastics, new pharmaceutical products, and of new products in general allow us to draw inferences concerning prospective trends in the price of the product under investigation.

We had to take into account the typical course of price changes but had to bear in mind at the same time that no rigid rules could be applied. From the fact that the price of synthetic fibre "A" fell off within five years one must not conclude that the process will take exactly the same time in the case of fibre "C". The shape of the price curve may differ from industry to industry and from product to product. We must, therefore, be extremely cautious in drawing our conclusions from analogous phenomena and should carefully study the special information on the product under investigation*.

In our price forecasts we endeavoured to comply with the requirements which prognoses of a scientific character may well be expected to meet**. This does not imply any ideal accuracy, only the observance of the following principles:

– The definitions employed should be unequivocal. This will enable ulterior verification of the accuracy of estimates.

– It should be possible to reproduce the reasoning on which the estimates were based and the assumptions from which the estimated magnitudes were deduced.

– There should be an intrinsic consistency between the different estimates; they should be prepared on the basis of identical principles.

What we have established for each individual time point is not a single price but an interval, a lower and an upper limit for the prospective

* In a number of cases neither technico-economic information nor the trend of price movements in past years suggested anything definite concerning the tendency of price changes. In such cases the mean value of prospective prices was estimated as being invariable over time and, to draw attention to the instability of the price level, the degree of oscillations around the present price level was set higher.

** On this subject see the important findings of H. THEIL [164].

future price. Chapters 11 and 14 described in detail the safety ranking and safety programming with the data given in "from-to" form.

We have no illusions as to the exactitude of the price forecasts. We know that the purchasing and selling prices attainable by Hungarian foreign trading companies in the capitalist markets are inevitably uncertain, a fact due to their being highly dependent on the market situation in the capitalist countries, on supply and demand on the part of the capitalist firms and on the trade cycle. There are thus a number of unpredictable factors to influence future price trends. Meanwhile, our misgivings may to some extent be relieved by a comparison with the traditional methods of efficiency calculation.

The traditional investment efficiency calculations carried out in accordance with the official methodology are not based on price forecasts but on factual data referring to some past period. True, factual data are "certain", whereas estimates are "uncertain". But the rentability of an investment will ultimately depend, among other factors, on future rather than past prices. It must, therefore, still be considered more appropriate to attempt a price forecast based on careful investigation – even if it may not come exactly true – than to extrapolate mechanically and without scrutiny a past price into the future, as done in the traditional calculations. Considering its role in the calculation, the latter procedure, too, may be called "forecasting" – but forecasting of the most naive kind.

A typical case in point is that of the investment project to enlarge the production of vitamin B_{12}. It was decided that in one of the pharmaceutical works the production of this type of vitamin should be considerably increased. The investment required a substantial sum. In 1957, when the relative calculations were carried out, the price of 1 g of vitamin B_{12} was still $ 200. Based on this price, the calculations showed the investment to be highly remunerative. By 1959, however, the price of vitamin B_{12} fell to $ 65, a fact that obviously fundamentally changed the actual rentability of the investment.

As the Hungarian saying goes, it is easy to be wise after the event. But the fall in the price of vitamin B_{12} could have been predicted – if not with full exactitude, but at least in its main trend. A look at figures 19.10–19.16 will suffice to prove this.

The above case, too, shows that instead of a routine-like and mechanical application of the actual prices it will be worth while to make a serious effort to establish a realistic estimate of prospective price trends.

19.6. The Indirect Import Material Costs

The determination of indirect import material costs is fully analogous with that of indirect production-fund requirements and of indirect costs, which have been dealt with in detail in section 17.2. Let us compose the following multiplication product:

$$r_{j,\mathrm{Rbl}}^{\mathrm{indir}} = \mathbf{r}'_{\mathrm{Rbl}}\check{\mathbf{G}}\bar{\mathbf{g}}_j, \tag{19.2}$$

where

$\bar{\mathbf{g}}_j$ = the column vector formed of the material input coefficients of one unit of the programming model's jth activity. Its components will equal in number to the sectors of the utilized I–O table

$\check{\mathbf{G}}$ = the inverse matrix of the I–O table

$\mathbf{r}'_{\mathrm{Rbl}}$ = the row vector of the cost of import materials deriving from socialist markets, in the breakdown of the I–O table.

The cost of indirect import materials deriving from capitalist markets will be determined in an analogous manner.

Unfortunately, in the case of determining indirect import material costs it will not be possible to employ price forecasts as described in sections 19.3–19.5. Here we will usually have to content ourselves with the actual foreign trade prices prevailing at the time when the I–O table was set up.

CHAPTER 20

THE COMPUTATIONAL FOREIGN EXCHANGE RATE

20.1. The Necessity of Uniform Foreign Exchange Rates

Accounting principle 20.1. All outlays and returns arising in roubles or dollars must be converted into forints at uniform rates of exchange.

This is one of the most significant differences between the computational evaluations employed in our investigations, on the one hand, and the actual price system (and partly also the official computational evaluations, the official methodology of investment efficiency calculations), on the other. Let us consider for a moment the actual price system from this angle.

Table 20.1 surveys, in a breakdown to *main commodity groups*, the forint rates at which imports in the value of 1 rouble or 1 dollar, originating from socialist or industrially advanced capitalist countries, respectively, were accounted for in 1962.

TABLE 20.1

*Actual foreign exchange rates for main commodity groups**

Main commodity group	1962 delivery price in terms of forints of imports in the value of 1 rouble (in the case of commodities originating from socialist countries)	1962 delivery price in terms of forints of imports in the value of 1 dollar (in the case of commodities originating from industrially advanced capitalist countries)
Materials	42.50	46
Machinery	44	54
Industrial consumer goods	48.30	57
Agricultural and food industrial products	43	62
Average	43.40	50

*SOURCE: Report of the Central Statistical Office [189].

Table 20.2 is based on the 1959 I–O table of the Central Statistical Office. Broken down to sectors, the table defines the actual sector averages of foreign exchange rates. (Import materials consumed by the sector, in terms of forints, divided by import materials consumed by the sector, in terms of foreign currency.) This has been related to the actual average foreign exchange rate for the national economy as a whole and the deviations from this average were grouped into class intervals.

TABLE 20.2

*Deviations of sectoral exchange rates from national average**

Average exchange rate = 100	
Sectoral exchange rates	Occurrence
Below 60	3
60– 70	1
70– 80	0
80– 90	11
90–100	19
100–110	23
110–120	12
120–130	8
130–140	5
Above 140	8
Total	90

* SOURCE: [189].

Both tables show a high degree of dispersion in the rates of foreign exchange, notwithstanding the fact that we are concerned with data that are already aggregated (main commodity groups or sectors of the national economy). The examination of the question on the product level will reveal an even greater dispersion. The domestic delivery price of imports in a value of one dollar shows a dispersion between Ft 10 and Ft 470*.

This multiplicity of foreign exchange rates in the actual price system can be justified on the grounds of various considerations. One of these may be the wish to protect some young Hungarian industry, which is still producing at high costs, against foreign competition, and to ensure that consumer enterprises do not one-sidedly prefer foreign makes to the products of the young industry. Or: to stimulate the exports of an industry with the aim of speeding up its development and thus reducing

* See Report of the Central Statistical Office [189].

its costs. Thus, when fixing the actual price, a kind of duty tax and a bonus for promoting exports is included in advance even in the cases where these elements will not ultimately appear as separate items in the financial settlement of net revenue, in the form of a duty tax and export bonus actually paid out.

Moreover, it is not only these far-reaching aims of development that play a role here. When fixing the inland, forint prices of imports, the authorities will also take into account the possibilities of substitution between the imported products and those of domestic origin as well as the role of prices in securing an equilibrium between demand and supply.

The Hungarian critics of the actual price system would argue that the dispersion of the foreign exchange rates which arise from the process of fixing actual prices was not exclusively due to rational considerations of industrial and trade policy or to the wish to secure an equilibrium, but was – at least partially – a consequence of deficiencies in the methods of price fixation. It is clearly not within the scope of the present work to take a stand on the issue and to analyze the extent to which the dispersion of exchange rates within the *actual* price system can be termed reasonable or the contrary. It should be sufficient to point out that even the divergencies which would appear reasonable enough in the short run may cause considerable disturbances in long-term calculations. When drawing up long-term investment plans, it will be no longer necessary to take the actual structure of production in Hungary, and with that the conditions of present equilibrium, as given, the aim being exactly to work out the desired changes in that structure. What is needed here is exactly to determine the products whose home production would be more profitable than their import, respectively whose production should be encouraged beyond domestic requirements in order to provide also for exports. It will not be possible to see clearly in these matters as long as the production of certain products is made to appear advantageous by accounting for the import materials required in their production at an exchange rate considerably below the average, or is, conversely, appearing in a prejudicial light owing to the higher pricing of the import materials that go into their manufacture. If we want all branches of production and all products to have *equal chances* in the efficiency calculations which determine the allocation of investment resources, we must see to it that all imports and exports are accounted for at a uniform rate of exchange.

This is one of the fundamental considerations out of which it becomes necessary to resort to computational prices and computational rates of exchange in order to evade the actual price system and the actual rates.

Besides, a certain – though not entirely consistent – tendency in this direction can also be observed in the official methodology of investment efficiency calculations. The latter prescribes that when computing the already repeatedly mentioned g_n investment efficiency formula, the numerator of the index – which gives the value of the output of the investment at world-market prices – should be calculated on the basis of a uniform computational rate of foreign exchange specifically fixed for the purpose by the National Planning Board. The same uniform computational rate of exchange should be employed also in the denominator for converting import material costs into forints. The import inputs appearing in the range of investment costs, such as e.g. the purchase of foreign machinery, should, on the other hand, be accounted for not at this computational rate of exchange but at the rates of the actual price system. The rates used for converting investment costs will thus be often 20–30 per cent higher or lower than the uniform computational rate employed when calculating market values of output and import costs.

20.2. The Economic Contents of the Rate of Exchange

Accounting principle 20.2. The computational rate of exchange should express in terms of forints the national average of domestic input required to procure 1 rouble or 1 dollar by means of exports. (The term "domestic input" is used here in accordance with chs. 16 and 18, i.e. to denote the computational wage and rent costs required by the exports.)

Why do we employ in our calculations the *average* input instead of the *marginal* input required to improve the foreign exchange balance? The decisive reason is that we do not know the latter. It was shown in the case of the computational rental on capital and of the computational wage rate, what difficulties are involved in the determination of marginal magnitudes, in the cases mentioned, of the marginal efficiency of the production fund and of the marginal productivity of the labour force, respectively. Nor is the problem any simpler in the case of the rate of foreign exchange. What would be required is, therefore, the knowledge not of a marginal input of any kind but of that required to improve the (active) balance of foreign exchange in the *optimal* program of the national economy as a whole. To obtain this it would be necessary to carry out an economy-wide programming, just as in the case of the numerical definition of the marginal efficiency of the productive fund and, with that, of the rational computational rental on capital.

The marginal input required *at present* to improve the foreign exchange balance will most likely be higher than the present-day average input. It is, however, the endeavour of top economic administration to improve both commodity structure and market distribution of exports, and to decrease domestic production costs. The marginal input which will be required *in future* to improve the balance of foreign exchange can, therefore, be expected to decrease and to approach the present-day average. As already discussed in another context (see section 17.3), here, too, marginal and average input may be expected in the long run to come closer to one another. It is, therefore, to be hoped – though there is nothing to prove that the hope is justified – that the application of accounting principle 20.2 will not lead to grave errors. Its application (and, in general, the eclecticism and inconsistency shown in the treatment of the question "marginal versus average") can be exceeded only as long as economy-wide programming does not provide a better foundation for the numerical determination of foreign exchange rates.

20.3. Determination of Foreign Exchange Rates by Means of the Input–Output Table

Our next task will be to work out, in accordance with accounting principle 20.2, also *numerically* the uniform computational rate of exchange to be used in long-term programming. The calculation can be carried out by means of the I–O table.

Let us first of all define $\check{\mathbf{c}}'$, the N-component row vector of total domestic input-content coefficients, in the breakdown of the I–O table, in terms of forints:

$$\check{\mathbf{c}}' = \gamma \check{\mathbf{p}}' + \Omega \check{\mathbf{q}}' = (\gamma \mathbf{p}' + \Omega \mathbf{q}')(\mathbf{E} - \mathbf{G})^{-1}, \qquad (20.1)$$

where

γ = the computational rental on capital
Ω = the computational wage factor
$\mathbf{p}'$ = the row vector of direct production fund coefficients
$\check{\mathbf{p}}'$ = the row vector of total production fund coefficients
$\mathbf{q}'$ = the row vector of direct effective wage contents coefficients
$\check{\mathbf{q}}'$ = the row vector of total effective wage contents coefficients (on the definition of $\mathbf{p}'$ and $\mathbf{q}'$ see section 17.2)
$\mathbf{G}$ = the inner square of the technological matrix.

The total contents vectors $\check{\mathbf{p}}'$ and $\check{\mathbf{q}}'$ are defined in such a way that they already contain also the production fund requirements and wage contents of the depreciation allowance (see section 16.4).

To carry out the calculation, the following must also be known:

$\check{\mathbf{u}}'_{Rbl}$ = row vector of total input coefficients of materials imported from socialist countries, in roubles ($\check{\mathbf{u}}'_{Rbl} = \mathbf{u}'_{Rbl}\,\check{\mathbf{G}}$)

$\check{\mathbf{u}}'_{\$}$ = row vector of total input coefficients of materials imported from capitalist countries, in \$ ($\check{\mathbf{u}}'_{\$} = \mathbf{u}'_{\$}\,\check{\mathbf{G}}$)

$\mathbf{d}^{soc}$ = column vector of exports to socialist countries, in Ft. This is a column vector of the so-called "side-wing" of the I–O table, the matrix of final output

$\mathbf{d}^{cap}$ = column vector of exports to capitalist countries, in Ft. This is another column vector of the matrix of final output

F_{Rbl} = total returns from exports to socialist countries, in Rbl

$F_{\$}$ = total returns from exports to capitalist countries, in \$.

The latter two data are known from foreign trade statistics. In the knowledge of these data, the average rouble and dollar rates for the national economy as a whole can be defined in the following manner*:

$$D_{Rbl} = \frac{(\check{\mathbf{u}}'_{\$}\, D_{\$} + \check{\mathbf{c}}')\,\mathbf{d}^{soc}}{F_{Rbl} - \check{\mathbf{u}}'_{Rbl}\,\mathbf{d}^{soc}}, \tag{20.2}$$

$$D_{\$} = \frac{(\check{\mathbf{u}}'_{Rbl}\, D_{Rbl} + \check{\mathbf{c}}')\,\mathbf{d}^{cap}}{F_{\$} - \check{\mathbf{u}}'_{\$}\,\mathbf{d}^{cap}}. \tag{20.3}$$

Formula (20.2) should be interpreted as follows:

In the denominator figure rouble earnings less rouble input, i.e. net rouble returns.

In the numerator figure the forint value of total domestic input contained in rouble exports plus the forint value, obtained by conversion at the dollar rate of exchange, of dollar imports contained in rouble exports.

Formula (20.3) can be interpreted analogously. We have thus two equations with two unknown quantities: D_{Rbl} and $D_{\$}$. The solution:

* The idea that the I–O table could be used for determining foreign exchange rates was first put forward in the Hungarian economic literature by P. HAVAS [49]. Here I undertook to develop his ideas in two directions, by the breakdown into socialist and capitalist relations (separate rouble and dollar rates) and by a more detailed elaboration of the concept of "domestic input".

$$D_{\mathrm{Rbl}} = \frac{\check{\mathbf{c}}'\,\mathbf{d}^{\mathrm{soc}}(F_{\$} - \check{\mathbf{u}}'_{\$}\,\mathbf{d}^{\mathrm{cap}}) + (\check{\mathbf{c}}'\,\mathbf{d}^{\mathrm{cap}})\,(\check{\mathbf{u}}'_{\$}\,\mathbf{d}^{\mathrm{soc}})}{(F_{\mathrm{Rbl}} - \check{\mathbf{u}}'_{\mathrm{Rbl}}\,\mathbf{d}^{\,\mathrm{oc}})\,(F_{\$} - \check{\mathbf{u}}'_{\$}\,\mathbf{d}^{\mathrm{cap}}) - (\check{\mathbf{u}}'_{\mathrm{Rbl}}\,\mathbf{d}^{\mathrm{cap}})\,(\check{\mathbf{u}}'_{\$}\,\mathbf{d}^{\mathrm{soc}})}, \tag{20.4}$$

$$D_{\$} = \frac{\check{\mathbf{c}}'\,\mathbf{d}^{\mathrm{cap}}(F_{\mathrm{Rbl}} - \check{\mathbf{u}}'_{\mathrm{Rbl}}\,\mathbf{d}^{\mathrm{soc}}) + (\check{\mathbf{c}}'\,\mathbf{d}^{\mathrm{soc}})\,(\check{\mathbf{u}}'_{\mathrm{Rbl}}\,\mathbf{d}^{\mathrm{cap}})}{(F_{\mathrm{Rbl}} - \check{\mathbf{u}}'_{\mathrm{Rbl}}\,\mathbf{d}^{\mathrm{soc}})\,(F_{\$} - \check{\mathbf{u}}'_{\$}\,\mathbf{d}^{\mathrm{cap}}) - (\check{\mathbf{u}}'_{\mathrm{Rbl}}\,\mathbf{d}^{\mathrm{cap}})\,(\check{\mathbf{u}}'_{\$}\,\mathbf{d}^{\mathrm{soc}})}. \tag{20.5}$$

The seeming complexity of the two formulae is due to the difficulty that exports to socialist countries also contain dollar inputs and, conversely, exports to capitalist countries also contain rouble inputs, and these inputs have mutual secondary effects.

The calculations carried out by P. Havas* on the basis of the 1959 I–O table of the Central Statistical Office essentially correspond to those described in accounting principles 18.2–18.3. In the course of his extremely important and many-sided calculations he computed several types of foreign exchange rates. From among these I propose to discuss the one which most closely corresponds to the accounting principles elaborated so far in chs. 16–20. He too was reckoning here with two types of domestic input, viz. with computational wage and rent on capital. The computational wage factor rate of payroll tax on which he based his calculations is 1.3 and he worked with a 7.4 per cent computational rental on capital. Both of them are very close to the computational evaluations according to accounting principles 18.2–18.3. In his calculations vector $\mathbf{c}'$ contains also the production fund requirements and wage contents of the depreciation allowance**.

The computational Ft/dollar rate arrived at in these calculations is 62.80. This rate as well as the corresponding rouble rate of exchange was used also in our programming work.

Accounting principle 20.3. The computational dollar rate of exchange is about 60 Ft/dollar.

20.4. The Program's Foreign Exchange-rate Sensitivity

In view of the uncertainty of the computational rate of foreign exchange, sensitivity tests have been carried out. As an example, let us describe here a parametric programming carried out within the framework of investigation for the man-made fibres industry.

* See P. HAVAS' more recent (1962) paper [50].

** Havas denotes this type of exchange rate $\overline{G}^{\beta}$.

We let the dollar rate of exchange run through the interval between Ft 40 and Ft 65, and obtained a total of 4 quantitative identity intervals. Table 20.3 sums up the results.

TABLE 20.3

*Parametric programming in the man-made fibres industry with the dollar rate of exchange as a parameter**

Interval of dollar exchange rate	−39.3	39.3−43.4	43.4−60.2	60.2−
Product (and technology) envisaged for production and export in the program				
Polyacrylonitrile-vinylchloride copolymer staple	H + E	H + E	H + E	H + E
Terylene staple	H + E	H + E	H + E	H + E
Nylon 6 yarn, technology "A"	H + E	H + E	H + E	H + E
Polypropylene yarn	H + E	H + E	H + E	H + E
Cellophane, in new plant	H + E	H + E	H + E	H + E
Phenol	—	—	H	H
Ethylene glycol	—	H	H	H
Polypropylene	—	—	H + E	H + E

* Signs used: H = production for home market
E = production for export.

Let us now survey some of the information yielded by the calculation.

A considerable part of the program is not sensitive to the dollar rate of exchange within the interval under investigation. The first five rows in the table above are essentially identical for the entire interval of the dollar rate which can realistically be taken into consideration. Home production and export of these five products would be preferable to import even at a Ft 35 dollar rate.

The calculation has yielded a special long-term import rentability index. For an interpretation of the latter let us take the case of ethylene glycol. In the case of the home production of this product, the highest price we will have to pay for 1 dollar saving in imports is Ft 39.30. It will therefore *not* be rentable to produce the product instead of importing it, if in other sectors of the national economy one dollar can be earned (by means of exports or savings in imports) at a rate lower than Ft 39.30. The same applies to the rest of characteristic values.

Our characteristic values are – at least approximately – comparable with the calculations which determined average input connected with exports to capitalist markets with the aid of the input–output table. According to the latter, the value of average input connected with these exports is Ft 62.80 to the dollar. As compared to that, the investment activities figuring in the program for the man-made fibres industry appear decidedly advantageous – they are considerably above the average.

An important index number: what is the characteristic value of the dollar rate of exchange above which the investment fund becomes exhausted and below which part of it remains unutilized?

From the calculations it will be clear that below the Ft 43.40 rate of dollar some 25–30 per cent of the investment fund will remain unutilized. At a dollar rate higher than Ft 43.40 it will pay to utilize the total fund earmarked for investment in the man-made fibres industry.

What is the meaning of this index number? If there exists a sector which obtains the dollar cheaper than at a rate of Ft 43.40 (by means of exports or savings in imports), it will be rentable to re-allot to it at least 25–30 per cent of the investment fund. But if there is no such sector, it will be rentable to leave the whole investment fund to the man-made fibres industry.

As made clear above, this critical value also shows that the development of the man-made fibres industry promises decided advantages, with the dollar rate of Ft 43.40 being decidedly below the average figure for the national economy as a whole, which is suitable for approximate comparisons.

The reasonable dollar rate of exchange is a most controversial point with the economists. There is, however, hardly an economist who would propose a rate below Ft 35 or above Ft 65. Now, we have seen that within this rather wide interval the greater part of the program was stable. This example too goes to show that parametric programming will often make the debate on the numerical magnitude of problematical parameters at least partly unnecessary.

CHAPTER 21

THIRD COMPARISON WITH THE TRADITIONAL METHODS

21.1. Divergences from the Actual Prices

First of all, we are going to describe now a comprehensive calculation to illustrate the high degree of divergence between the computational prices worked out on the basis of general price formula (16.1) and the actual prices. The calculation was carried out by a research team on behalf of the National Price Control Board*. The starting point was the 1959 I–O table of the Central Statistical Office, which was reduced for the purpose to 80 sectors. The changes which the price proportions would undergo if actual prices were replaced by "two-channel" prices were then calculated. The value of the rental on capital which would assert itself would be 0.1, that of the wage factor 1.22. As can be seen, the two figures come quite close to those employed in accounting principles 18.2 and 18.3. Ultimately, 80 price indices have been obtained, each of which relates to a broad group of products, to the "average product" of an individual sector. Table 21.1 shows the price indices classified into class intervals.

The table throws a light on the radical changes which the introduction of prices of the type (16.1) entails.

Table 21.2 gives a survey not of the numerical values but of the contents of the divergences between the computational price system described in Part 4, on the one hand, and the actual price system as well as the official computational evaluations, on the other.

What now were the methods and the facts at our disposal when we circumvented the actual prices?

One method was to take the requirements of non-productive domestic consumption as given and to prescribe the volume of final outputs to

* See report [194] of the National Price Control Board. The mathematical methods of the research work which constituted the basis of the report were worked out by a team consisting of research workers at the Computing Centre of the Hungarian Academy of Sciences and at the National Price Control Board, and headed by S. Ganczer.

TABLE 21.1

*Average change of prices of sectors in the case of "two-channel" prices**

Price index in per cent	Number of sectors
160.1–170	1
150.1–160	1
140.1–150	1
130.1–140	4
120.1–130	6
110.1–120	11
100.1–110	15
100.1–110	13
90.1–100	18
80.1– 90	5
70.1– 80	2
60.1– 70	2
50.1– 60	1
Total	80
The change is more than 10 per cent	52

* SOURCE: [194].

serve the purpose in an obligatory form in our programming models. *This amounts essentially to eliminating the direct effects of the actual consumer price system on the choice taking place within the model's framework*. In reality, of course, the system of consumer prices will affect the consumer's choice. Our assumption, however, was that those setting up the plans would take the consumer's preferences into account beforehand, when determining the plan directives of output for non-productive consumption.

In the application of the other method, the following sources of data where drawn upon when calculating inputs in terms of money:

(1) The macroeconomic statistical data referring to the growth of national income, production fund and labour force as well as their interrelations.

(2) I–O tables.

(3) Special estimates concerning the investment requirements of the various branches and sectors of production.

TABLE 21.2

Divergencies between the actual price system and the computational evaluations

Description of characteristics	Actual price system*	Official computational evaluations used in investment efficiency calculations**	Computational evaluations used in long-term programming
Is there any rent charged on the use of fixed capital? If so, at what rate?	None. (Recently the actual payment of rent on capital was established, but this does not affect the price)	Yes, 20 per cent	Yes, 8 per cent
Are indirect production fund requirements taken into account? If so, how?	No	Yes; with a uniform multiplier factor for the national economy as a whole	Yes; primarily by means of the I–O table, determined by activities
What rental is being charged on the use of working capital?	3 per cent	20 per cent	8 per cent
Are direct wage costs increased in relation to actual wage costs by the addition of the payroll tax?	Yes	Yes	Yes
Are wages taken as constant over time?	Yes (With the actual price system this is evident)	Yes	No

How are domestic material inputs calculated?	In the calculations which constitute the basis of price fixing, the materials utilized are accounted for at actual producer prices	(1) Material inputs are, wherever possible, accounted for at foreign trade prices, even if domestically produced (2) Material inputs accounted for nevertheless in forints are calculated at actual producer prices	(1) Material inputs are calculated partly at foreign trade prices, even if domestically produced (2) Material inputs calculated in forints are reduced to total wage contents, total import contents and total production fund requirements
Are the calculations based on a uniform rate of foreign exchange?	No; the rate of foreign exchange varies according to product group	Export returns and material input costs are calculated at a uniform calculative rate of exchange. The costs of investments originating from imports are calculated at the rates of the actual price system which vary according to product group	A uniform rate of exchange is employed

* For detailed information about the characteristics of the actual Hungarian price system see B. Csikós Nagy [25].

** See Hungarian Investments Code [195].

(4) The traditional "real cost calculations"; the determination of total wage contents, investment requirements and import contents on the basis of individual calculations.

(5) The calculations based on national foreign trading data (as well as I–O tables) and aimed at determining foreign exchange rates.

(6) The actual import purchase and export sales prices as prevailing in markets abroad.

The sources of data have been combined in several ways.

21.2. The Rational Relationship between Computational and Actual Prices

The circumvention of the actual price system was not and could not be carried out in a consistent manner. A significant part of the macro-economic statistical data is computed on the basis of constant prices derived from the actual price system at a fixed point of time; I–O tables are set up in terms of forint, etc. The navel cord connecting the computational evaluations and the computational price system with the actual system of prices has not been cut. It is only in the tale that Baron Munchhausen was able to draw himself from the marshes by his own hair. No matter how much we are aware of the various shortcomings of the actual price system, no matter how clearly we know that it may provide an erroneous orientation in decisions of long-term planning, we will not be able to avoid having recourse to some or other of its elements.

And here a number of questions of fundamental importance will pose themselves, such as:

– Will it be possible at all to completely circumvent the actual system of prices?

– Is the nature of the actual price system a matter of indifference from the point of view of *long-term* planning?

– If the actual price system were more satisfactory, could the computational prices not be dispensed with?

The analysis of the actual price system lies beyond the scope of the present work and will, accordingly, not be enlarged upon. It was none the less necessary to refer briefly to these questions in order to avoid leaving the reader with wrong impressions at the end of the section dealing with computational evaluations.

The main function of the price system consists in providing guidance in *operative*, *short-term* decisions, including the choices of higher economic administration as well as of the firms and consumers. The view is generally held that the present price system does not function adequately. *No computational price system designed to provide a basis for long-term decisions will, however, substitute for an adequate system of actual prices.*

It is a controversial question, who should set up the actual price system and by means of what methods it should be established. Should it be determined centrally or should its formation be left to the play of demand and supply, to a direct agreement between buyers and sellers? And, if determined centrally, should the prices be worked out on the basis of the traditional methods or by mathematical methods?

The determination of computational prices by means of I–O tables was discussed in detail in this book. In a separate chapter it will be shown later on how computational prices and evaluations can be derived from the so-called shadow prices of linear programming models. These techniques, however, can be used not only to determine *computational* prices but also as a help to work out *actual* prices*. Mathematical methods will enable the quantification of some fundamental evaluations such as the rental on capital, the pay-roll tax, foreign exchange rates, land rents, mine rents, customs tariffs of fundamental importance, etc. and probably even the general price indices of some basic materials and product groups. Moreover, the mathematical models can be used for the estimation of the expected effects of price reforms and for tracing the secondary effects of price changes. At the same time I am convinced that it is *not possible to construct a complete actual price system with its million prices by means of the electronic computer*. We have experienced, e.g. in connection with the allocation of production funds or investment quotas, that in certain cases we simply had to have recourse to the electronic computer for a "simulation" of the "market" (in our case, of the "capital market") in order to obtain the necessary evaluations. This, however, was done in an extremely aggregated form – the numberless details of economic reality, the host of processes taking place in production, distribution

* In Hungary, important research work is being carried out in this direction which has already borne fruit in many respects. One of the main branches of research concerns itself with the so-called "price model": the prospective effects of individual price changes or of comprehensive and general price reforms on the system of prices are analyzed with the aid of *I–O tables*. For details see e.g. [42].

Another branch of research is devoted to the problems pertaining to the utilization of the shadow prices of *linear programming models*, (see GY. SIMON and GY. KONDOR [156], [159]).

and consumption do not lend themselves to programming with the aid of the electronic computer. Consequently, the "mathematization" of price calculation will not make it unnecessary to allow – at least within certain limits – for market factors in the formation of prices.

It is thus both desirable and possible to subject the actual price system to considerable improvements. However, even the best actual price system will not enable us to *dispense with computational prices, which differ from the actual ones, when setting up long-term plans and making decisions of a far-reaching effect on the structure of the national economy.* Even the best actual price system will always tend to fit the given conditions: the country's given economic structure and the structure of external trade linked with it; the given technological level and the substitution possibilities of the given technologies; the given consumers' needs, etc. Long-term planning, on the other hand, will require computational prices which express more permanent tendencies.

At the same time it is also true that *the calculation of the computational prices required in long-term planning could be made easier and more reliable if better actual prices were available for a starting point.* In this case it would not be necessary to make the most strenuous efforts to evade as completely as possible the actual prices; our attention could be confined to forecasting the prospective changes over time and to the necessary correction of actual prices.

To sum up: the formation of computational prices based on mathematical methods must on no account weaken our efforts aimed at improving the actual system of prices. On the contrary, it is exactly the results of these efforts that can be expected to raise to a higher level the still rather primitive methods of computational price formation.

PART 5

CONNECTING ECONOMY-WIDE AND SECTORAL PROGRAMMING

Introduction

Part 2 of this volume dealt with the question of programming for individual sectors. The only links it established between the national economic plan and the sectoral programming models were the quasi-constant plan directives, the output obligations put to the sectors and the resource quotas.

Parts 3 and 4 went a step further. In them we have discussed the problem of how to define the objective function of the sectoral models in such a way as to make them instrumental in bringing the long-term program of the sector concerned toward the general optimum. The objective function should lead to sectoral decisions which will fit harmoniously into the desirable and rational proportions and the general equilibrium of the national economy, e.g. it should employ a computational rental on capital and a computational wage factor which will lead to a favourable combination of the production fund and the labour force; it should work with a safety level which ensures that the planned proportions assert themselves, etc.

We have, accordingly, endeavoured to define the objective function in such a manner that it would "direct" the sectoral decisions in accordance with the interests of the national economy as a whole.

In Part 5 which follows we shall go another step further and proceed to investigate the organic relationship between sectoral and economy-wide planning.

The relationship will first be presented on a lower level. It will be shown how sectoral programming may provide a basis for the structural decisions of higher economic administration, how it may reveal possible contradictions and disequilibria in the national plan and how it may contribute to improving the targets of the latter.

We will then deal with a higher-level relationship, describing the model of "two-level planning" which unites the mathematical models of central and sectoral long-term plans in a single comprehensive system.

So far we have treated the data taken over from the national economic plan, such as the output targets, the resource quotas, etc., as *constant* plan directives. In some of the calculations which now follow, part of the data taken over from the national economic plan will also become *variable*. These data, taken over from the central plan and treated not as constants but as variables, will be called – in contradistinction to the constant plan directives – the plan figures.

CHAPTER 22

THE CENTRAL PLAN FIGURE AS A PARAMETER

22.1. Some Practical Examples from the Material of the Sectoral Programming Projects

In the sectoral models, the output obligations of the industrial sectors concerned were taken over as plan directives from the national plan drawn up on the basis of the traditional methods. In the case of one type of model (the one for the cotton industry) these prescribed the sector's total output including exports (see formulae (5.1)–(5.3)), in that of the other type (the one for the man-made fibres industry) only the output destined for domestic consumption (see formulae (6.1)–(6.2)).

However, nobody has ever pretended – not even at the time when the calculations were being carried out – that the magnitude of these plan directives was the only imaginable, the optimum one. On the contrary, at the time of the calculations the question whether the targets of these two industrial sectors – as well as those of others – for the long-term plan periods under consideration (periods of five and fifteen years, respectively) should be raised or not, was still the subject of discussions with the organs of higher economic administration. In this connection, let us remember ch. 1 where it has been pointed out that when working out the long-term plan, *all* plan targets were in fact unknown and variable. The plan directives treated as constant in the sector model belong to the variables of the type x in the plan equation system (1.7). It was therefore most important to examine the changes which the optimal program would undergo as a function of the output obligations. In the course of our sectoral investigations a number of calculations of this type were carried out.

In the cotton industry it was primarily the output target for low-width fabrics that was the subject of controversy. This was denoted v_1 in the cotton industrial model. As a problem of parametric programming, we have determined the optimal program function $\mathbf{x}^* = \mathbf{x}^*(v_1)$. The problem is an example of what is called d u a l p a r a m e t r i c p r o g r a m m i n g – a type of problem where the vector of the constants on the right side of the constraints depends on a parameter*.

* For a discussion of the subject with respect to linear programming, see e.g. S. Gass [43].

In the course of the calculations it was assumed that neither the gross investment fund nor the capitalist foreign exchange fund were fixed and only the volume of construction was restricted. It was not necessary to define the optimal program for all possible values of v_1. It was furthermore assumed that the output obligation could not be lower than the performance which could be achieved without any further investment by the machine fleet actually in existence in the programming sector. This amounts roughly to 498 thousand million picks. This was considered as the lower limit of parameter v_1.

As a result of parametric programming we have finally obtained six qualitative identity intervals and with them six optimal program structures. Let us denote the vectors characteristic of the program structures (the vectors derived from the indices of variables figuring with a positive value in the optimal program) $\mathbf{j}^{(1)}, \ldots, \mathbf{j}^{(6)}$. The results are summed up in table 22.1.

The table gives the qualitative results of parametric programming, but over and above these quantitative results were also obtained. One of the quantitative results can even be read from the table: we know the five characteristic values of output obligation to be 660, 848, 875, 888, 894 thousand million picks. Moreover, we have an exact knowledge of the quantitative composition of the optimal program within the individual qualitative identity intervals. *But instead of being a total of constant values the optimal program can now be defined as a function of the output obligation.*

Within the individual intervals, the optimal function has a constant part which is independent of the parameter and another part which is linearly dependent on it. Accordingly, the optimal program will, in general terms now, have the following form*.

$$\mathbf{x}^* = \begin{cases} \mathbf{x}_1^{(1)} + (\lambda - \lambda_0)\, \mathbf{x}_2^{(1)}, & \text{if} \quad \lambda_0 \leqq \lambda \leqq \lambda^{(1)} \\ \mathbf{x}_1^{(2)} + (\lambda - \lambda^{(1)})\, \mathbf{x}_2^{(2)}, & \text{if} \quad \lambda^{(1)} \leqq \lambda \leqq \lambda^{(2)} \\ \dots\dots\dots\dots\dots\dots & \\ \mathbf{x}_1^{(s+1)} + (\lambda - \lambda^{(s)})\, \mathbf{x}_2^{(s+1)}, & \text{if} \quad \lambda^{(s)} \leqq \lambda, \end{cases} \tag{22.1}$$

where

λ = the parameter

λ_0 = the fixed lower limit of the parameter

$\lambda^{(1)}, \lambda^{(2)}, \ldots, \lambda^{(s)}$ = the characteristic values of the parameter

* When writing down the general formula it was assumed that no upper limit was set to the parameter by the system of constraints.

TABLE 22.1

Parametric programming in the cotton industry with the output obligation as a parameter

Symbol of program structure	$\mathbf{j}^{(1)}$	$\mathbf{j}^{(2)}$	$\mathbf{j}^{(3)}$	$\mathbf{j}^{(4)}$	$\mathbf{j}^{(5)}$	$\mathbf{j}^{(6)}$
Limits of output obligation (characteristic values of parameter), thousand million picks	498–660	660–848	848–875	875–888	888–894	894
Fate of less suitable old loom	dismantling	dismantling	dismantling	dismantling	dismantling	dismantling
Fate of more suitable old loom	speeding up	speeding up	speeding up	speeding up	speeding up	dismantling
Type of loom to replace less suitable old ones	automatic, shuttle-exchanging	automatic, shuttle-exchanging	automatic, partly shuttle-exchanging, partly shuttleless	automatic, shuttleless	automatic, shuttleless	automatic, shuttleless
Type of loom to replace more suitable old ones	—	—	—	—	—	automatic, shuttleless
Does any construction work take place?	no	yes	yes	yes	yes	yes
Type of loom to be installed in new building	—	automatic, shuttle-exchanging	automatic, shuttle-exchanging	automatic, partly shuttle-exchanging, partly shuttleless	automatic, shuttleless	automatic, shuttleless

$\mathbf{x}_1^{(1)}, \mathbf{x}_1^{(2)}, \ldots, \mathbf{x}_1^{(s+1)}$ = the part of the optimal program which is independent of the parameter, in the 1st, 2nd, ..., $(s+1)$th identity interval

$\mathbf{x}_2^{(1)}, \mathbf{x}_2^{(2)}, \ldots, \mathbf{x}_2^{(s+1)}$ = the part of the optimal program which is dependent on the parameter, in the 1st, 2nd, ..., $(s+1)$th identity interval.

The knowledge of function (22.1) of the optimal program enables us to determine the *optimal objective function value as a function of the parameter:*

$$C^* = C^*(\lambda) = \begin{cases} C_1^{(1)} + (\lambda - \lambda_0)\, C_2^{(1)}, & \text{if} \quad \lambda_0 \leqq \lambda \leqq \lambda^{(1)} \\ C_1^{(2)} + (\lambda - \lambda^{(1)})\, C_2^{(2)}, & \text{if} \quad \lambda^{(1)} \leqq \lambda \leqq \lambda^{(2)} \\ \dots\dots\dots\dots\dots\dots\dots & \\ C_1^{(s+1)} + (\lambda - \lambda^{(s)})\, C_2^{(s+1)}, & \text{if} \quad \lambda^{(s)} \leqq \lambda, \end{cases} \tag{22.2}$$

where

$C_1^{(1)}, C_1^{(2)}, \ldots, C_1^{(s+1)}$ = the part of the optimal program's objective function value which is independent from the parameter, in the 1st, 2nd, ..., $(s+1)$th interval

$C_2^{(1)}, C_2^{(2)}, \ldots, C_2^{(s+1)}$ = the part of the optimal program's objective function value which is dependent on the parameter, in the 1st, 2nd, ..., $(s+1)$th interval.

Other characteristics of the program, such as investment requirements, foreign exchange requirements, labour force requirements etc., as a function of the parameter, can be determined in a similar manner. Thus, e.g. the formula of investment requirements will be the following:

$$P^*(\lambda) = P_1^{(r)} + (\lambda - \lambda^{(r-1)})\, P_2^{(r)}, \quad \text{if} \quad \lambda^{(r-1)} \leqq \lambda \leqq \lambda^{(r)}, \tag{22.3}$$

where

$P_1^{(r)}$ = constant part of the optimal program's investment requirements in the rth interval

$P_2^{(r)}$ = the part of the optimal program's investment requirements which is dependent on the parameter, in the rth interval ($r = 1, 2, \ldots, s+1$).

Table 22.2 presents, on the basis of the above-described parametric programming for the cotton industry, the objective function values as a

TABLE 22.2

Objective function value as a function of output obligation in the cotton industry
(Objective function value in million Ft, output in million picks)

Symbol of program structure	Objective function value*
$j^{(1)}$	$2872.6 + (\lambda - 498)\ 58.5$
$j^{(2)}$	$3822 \quad + (\lambda - 660)\ 69.4$
$j^{(3)}$	$5128.2 + (\lambda - 848)\ 91.5$
$j^{(4)}$	$5372.2 + (\lambda - 875)\ 101.6$
$j^{(5)}$	$5505.7 + (\lambda - 888)\ 223.4$
$j^{(6)}$	5639

* In connection with the objective function value it should be taken into consideration that the scope of the programming calculation does not include the broad and weft-pattern looms.

function of output obligation. The same relationship is also graphically represented in figure 22.1.

As can be seen, the function represented in the figure is a periodically linear, *convex* one. By exhausting the less costly alternatives, we will be compelled to resort to more costly ones. The value of $P_2^{(r)}$ in formula (22.3) corresponds to the slope of the function represented in figure 22.1 within the rth identity interval. The part of the cost accounted for in the objective function, which depends on the parameter is thus nothing but a *marginal* cost within the identity interval in question, indicating as it does the *increment of cost as output obligation is raised by one unit.*

From what has been said it will be clear *that parametric programming of this type may play an important role in national planning.* By its aid we will be able to obtain the sector's long-term input functions as a function of the production plan, the output obligation (e.g. the long-term investment function, labour-force requirement function, foreign-exchange requirement function, etc.). We establish, of course, all the input functions at the given (actual or computational) prices used for the model.

In the man-made fibres industry no continuous parametric programming was carried out owing to the difficulties of calculation due to the concave objective function. Instead, we have approximated the solution of the problem by giving to vector $\mathbf{b}_i$ of the constants on the right side of the constraints three fixed numerical values. These vectors $\mathbf{b}_1$, $\mathbf{b}_2$ and $\mathbf{b}_3$ differ from one another in the magnitude of the estimates of domestic requirements (and in that of the other estimates which are logically

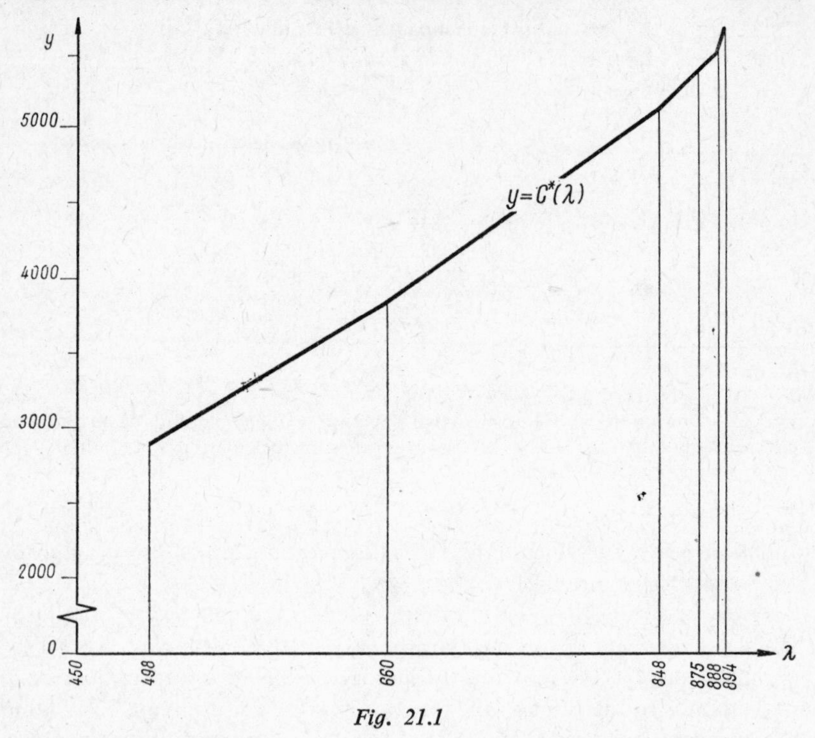

Fig. 21.1

connected with the latter). Programming was carried out on the basis of all three vectors $\mathbf{b}_i$ and our inferences were drawn from the comparison of the results.

This discrete treatment of output obligations as variable parameters was employed also in the course of programming for the cotton industry. Here the original output obligation taken over from the traditional plan was contrasted with the raised estimates which were at the time of the programming project submitted to the higher authorities as new and modified proposals*.

* The calculation differed in some basic assumptions from the *continuous* parametric programming described above and summarized in table 22.1. In the present case the capitalist foreign exchange fund remains fixed, in the former not; this includes the entire scope of programming, the former only the narrow looms, etc.

The results of the calculations are summed up in table 22.3.

TABLE 22.3

The consequences of plan modification in the cotton industry

	Unit	Original plan	Raised plan	Difference (per cent)
Production	million picks	757 050	907 348	+19.8
Total costs (objective function value)	million Ft (discounted)	5 170	6 061	+17.3
Gross investment	million Ft	555.3	1 676.9	+302
Construction requirements	m²	1 000	8 223	+722
Released manpower	number of workers	418	846	+103

From the table it becomes clear that the abolition of the constraints of some hitherto limited resources will result in total costs of the program increasing to a lesser degree than the total volume of production (cost increase of 17.3 per cent as against production increase of 19.8 per cent). Moreover, owing to increased productivity, manpower will be released in spite of the growing volume. On the other hand, it cannot be denied that investment costs show a heavy increase.

In the cases dealt with up to now, it was an output obligation that was treated as a parametric plan figure. Of course, it may be also useful to carry out investigations to examine the effects of modifying a plan figure which constitutes the constraint of some input or resource, treating it as a parameter on which the optimal program depends.

Here, too, the parameter may be treated both continuously and discretely. Let us give a simple example of the latter case. In the cotton industry model it was originally assumed that capitalist foreign exchange was available within the limits of a definite quota only. The optimal program was established on the basis of this assumption. Now we proceeded to work out the characteristic value of the capitalist foreign exchange quota beyond which the program will not require any more capitalist foreign exchange. It turned out that the maximum amount of surplus foreign exchange that would be required was Ft 48 million. Could this be allocated to the industry, the optimal program would be modified; the program would come to include the complete replacement of the pirners whereas the original optimal program envisaged partial replacement only. The surplus requirement of foreign exchange is balanced by savings: the new, modified optimal program lowers total costs – the value of the objective function of programming – by 6.3 per cent.

22.2. Economic Experimentation

The calculation in itself does, of course, not provide an answer to the question whether it was really worth while to increase the quota of foreign exchange. This will also depend on other factors (such as the country's balance of payments, etc.) which have been disregarded here. Nor will the above calculations, those of programming carried out as a function of output obligations, admit of any direct conclusion as to the reasonable magnitude of the output obligation.

It can be stated as a general rule that this type of calculation is not aimed at optimizing a plan figure awaiting the decision of higher authority. It is meant to perform a more limited role: *by indicating the consequences of a modification of the plan figure it may – as has been shown – provide a basis for the decisions of higher administration.* Nor is it simply *any kind* of consequence that will be indicated by the calculation. The raised targets may be fulfilled by the cotton industry in several ways: by purchasing more or less expensive machinery, by more or less construction, etc. Our calculation provides an answer to the question, what should the cotton industry do if (within the terms of the given model) it reacts in the *most rational* manner possible to the raised targets; what will be the *minimum* of surplus cost required to meet the raised output obligation. Likewise, it provides an answer to the question, which will be the *maximum* of saving that can be attained after the abolition of the foreign exchange quota.

In general, it can be stated that sensitivity analysis will indicate *the minimum cost arising, or the maximum saving attained, as a consequence of a modification of the plan figure, i.e. the consequences of a modification of the plan figure for the case when the programming scope reacts to this in the optimal manner within the terms of the given model.*

Whenever there is a debate on the raising of plan targets, cutting down quotas and other related problems, arguments will usually be raised for and against. These, however, are frequently of a qualitative character only, and even if they are quantitative, they will tend to pick out one or another of the consequences from a whole complex of effects. For example, those interested may point out some favourable effect in order to convince higher administration of the soundness of the modification while concealing other, less favourable effects.

Sensitivity analysis is able to show in a quantitative form the consequences of a modification of the plan figure – and not only a single effect of a modification but the whole system of consequences.

Here again, reference should be made to ch. 1, with its description of the traditional methods of plan coordination. The sensitivity tests described above cannot serve as a substitute for the planners' coordination discussions and the comparison of plan targets both within and outside of the model. But they will greatly help coordination and render it more purpose-conscious and less exploratory in character. They will help the planners to see more clearly the consequences of "knocking off" some plan target and of "stressing" another. An exact and collective analysis of the relationships is enabled by the fact that the procedure unites the individual interrelated groups of documented and auxiliary plan targets and plan equations into systems of simultaneous equations. Another reason why the sensitivity tests will yield more reliable informations concerning the consequences than the traditional methods of coordination, is that in the programming models numerous auxiliary plan targets as well as numerous auxiliary, non-documented plan equations are promoted, as it were, to the rank of variables and constraint-constants of the programming model. Their effect cannot, therefore, get lost, as it does in the course of the traditional procedure of plan coordination.

Sensitivity analysis carried out with the plan figures will afford higher economic administration the possibility of a kind of "experimentation". It will be considerably less expensive to carry out such economic experiments (as to the possible effects of raised targets, etc.) on paper than in reality. It is better to have the numerical proofs of the advantages and drawbacks of a measure in advance than to have actually to pay for possible losses.

Just as those engaged in other social sciences, the economist, too, is inclined to envy the scientist for his being able to resort to *experimentation.* Indeed, the scientist is in a position to check his hypotheses by means of experiments which can be repeated as many times as necessary. Now, mathematics has provided a tool which brings our discipline also in this respect nearer to the natural sciences. The natural scientist would change the conditions of his experiment in accordance with certain purposeful principles and would register the reactions of the test subject to the changes. We are proceeding in a similar manner when working out our program in several variants. This, as a matter of fact, amounts to what could be called a special type of *economic test series.* Changing the conditions of the experiment (the model's framework and numerical values) in accordance with certain purposeful principles, we would register the reactions of the test subject: the optimal program. The character of the experiment will, of course, differ in many respects from that of empirical experimentation in the field of the natural sciences. Our experiments will be carried out on paper only, by means of figures. They may be called "mental experiments". The two types of experiment series have, none the less, some important analogous characteristics such as *the recording of the effects of systematic changes in the conditions, the numerical measuring of these effects and, last but not least, the possibility of repetition.*

22.3. Survey of the Sensitivity Tests Carried out in Sector Programming

In the following, a comprehensive survey is given of the series of experiments and sensitivity tests carried out in the course of our programming projects for the cotton and the man-made fibres industries. This serves, in the first place, as an illustration to the first section of the chapter, showing as it does how the central plan target performed its role as a parameter. At the same time, it illustrates also the sensitivity tests made necessary by the uncertainties (connected with the technical and cost data as well as with the computational evaluations) discussed in Parts 3 and 4 of the book.

In the case of the *cotton industry* program we had been setting out from a "basic model" on which calculation (1) was based. All subsequent calculations went to modify this basic model, according to the following points of view:

(a) The basic model contained the output obligations of the original official plan, which were in certain calculations raised or treated as a parameter.

(b) In the basic model, a limit was imposed on the quotas of gross investments and capitalist foreign exchange. In certain calculations the limit was removed.

(c) In the basic model we employed our own computational rental on capital. In certain calculations, on the other hand, the official rate of 0.2 was employed or the rental was treated as a parameter.

(d) In the basic model we reckoned, in accordance with our accounting principle, with the plan year's expected wage level. On the other hand, certain calculations were based, in accordance with the official instructions, on the actual wage level of the period when the calculations were being carried out.

(e) In the basic model, our own computational rate of foreign exchange was used. In certain calculations the official computational rate of foreign exchange was instead used or treated as a parameter.

(f) In the basic model we reckoned with certain definite technical characteristics of the machinery. In one of the sensitivity tests, certain technical characteristics were treated as a parameter.

TABLE 22.4

Sensitivity tests with the cotton industry model. Deviations from the basic model

No. of computation	Output target	Were gross investment and capitalist foreign exchange expenditure bounded?	Rental on capital	Were wage increases considered?	Rate of currency exchange	Other characteristics
2					official	
3				no		
4			0.2			
5	raised					
6	raised	no			official	
7	raised	no		no	official	
8	raised	no		no		
9	parameter	no				
10			parameter			
11					parameter	
12						Technical characteristics of some machine types, as parameters
13						Price of some machines, as parameters
14						The accounting period for the sum of discounted costs as a parameter

(g) In the basic model, calculations were based on the definite prices of new machinery. In one of the sensitivity tests, the price of new machinery was also treated as a parameter.

(h) In one of the calculations we examined how it would affect the optimal program if the discounted cost amount were minimized and the calculations based on accounting periods of varying length.

Table 22.4 gives a summary of the calculations.

Within the framework of the *man-made fibres industrial project* part of the calculations was carried out with respect to a given vector $\mathbf{b}_1$ (the vector of the constants on the right side of the constraints). Most of the components of this vector were taken over as plan directives from the official plan worked out by traditional methods.

In this phase of the investigations we were working with a total of 9 concrete models. These models differed from one another in the following respects:

(a) In some special models a linear objective function was employed instead of the concave objective function (7.6) (see section 7.5).

(b) For part of our calculations no programming model was set up and the alternatives were only *ranked* according to a given rentability index.

TABLE

Sensitivity tests with the man-

No. of computation	Which vector b	Type of objective function	Programming or ranking	Dollar rate as a parameter, or fixed
1	$\mathbf{b}_1$	concave	programming	fixed at Ft 60.—
2	$\mathbf{b}_1$	concave	programming	parameter
3	$\mathbf{b}_1$	concave	programming	fixed at Ft 60.—
4	$\mathbf{b}_1$	linear	programming	fixed at Ft 60.—
5	$\mathbf{b}_1$	linear	programming	fixed at Ft 60.—
6	$\mathbf{b}_1$	linear	programming	fixed at Ft 60.—
7	$\mathbf{b}_1$	concave	ranking	fixed at Ft 60.—
8	$\mathbf{b}_1$	concave	programming	fixed at Ft 60.—
9	$\mathbf{b}_1$	concave	ranking	fixed at Ft 45.—
10	$\mathbf{b}_2$	concave	programming	fixed at Ft 50.—
11	$\mathbf{b}_3$	concave	programming	fixed at Ft 60.—

(c) In some models the dollar rate of exchange was treated as a parameter; for the purpose of other calculations again, the rate was fixed at Ft 60, on the basis of the considerations set forth in ch. 20. In one case a Ft 45 rate, usually employed in the official investment efficiency calculations, was used.

(d) Uncertain data given in "from–to" form were employed in three different ways:

– In some calculations the mean of the "from–to" interval was used.

– In other calculations the lower or upper limits of the "from–to" interval were used.

– In other calculations again, uncertain data were treated as random variables.

(e) The system of constraints does not restrict the export of the following products:

Caprolactame
Phenol
Ethylene glycol
Dimethyl terephthalate
Acrylonitrile.

22.5

made fibres industry model

Treatment of uncertain data	Unbounded material exports	Dimethylterephthalate and acrylonitrile imports	Polyacrylonitrile-vinyl-chloride co-polymer production and imports	Rental on capital
mean value	eliminated	feasible	feasible	8%
mean value	eliminated	feasible	feasible	8%
mean value	feasible	feasible	feasible	8%
mean value	eliminated	feasible	feasible	8%
mean value	eliminated	eliminated	feasible	8%
mean value	eliminated	feasible	eliminated	8%
upper and lower bounds	feasible	feasible	feasible	8%
probability variable	eliminated	feasible	feasible	8%
mean value	feasible	feasible	feasible	20%
mean value	eliminated	feasible	feasible	8%
mean value	eliminated	feasible	feasible	8%

In some calculations the export of these products was admitted, in others it was eliminated as an alternative.

(f) It was generally assumed that no obligation existed to set up vertical industries when organizing the production of polyester and polyacrylonitrile fibres, dimethyl terephthalate and acrylonitrile being available for import in unrestricted quantities. For the purposes of a calculation of special character, however, the import of the two materials was eliminated as an alternative, and it was assumed that together with the production of the fibres that of the materials must also be set up.

(g) In one of the calculations, the import as well as the domestic production of polyacrylonitrile-vinylchloride copolymer fibre was eliminated because of the questionable properties of this material in use.

(h) As a general rule, we used an 8 per cent rental on capital. In one of the control calculations, however, the 20 per cent rental prescribed in the official investment efficiency calculations was employed.

In addition to the above described nine calculations based on vector $\mathbf{b}_1$, further calculations were carried out with models where this vector was replaced by vectors $\mathbf{b}_2$ or $\mathbf{b}_3$, respectively. These vectors differed from one another primarily in the estimates concerning domestic demand and in the volume of the investment fund.

A tabular survey of the characteristics of the types of model is given in table 22.5.

CHAPTER 23

IMPROVING ON THE PLAN OF THE NATIONAL ECONOMY

23.1. Consistency Analysis

The information which the methods described in ch. 22 will yield to higher economic administration, do not contain any direct, definite recommendation. "This decision of higher administration will have this consequence, that decision that consequence" – this is approximately how the contents of the calculations mentioned above could be characterized. The methods which we are about to introduce now go a step farther, taking as they do a *stand* on the individual targets of the national economic plan.

One type of these calculations I propose to call consistency analysis. Its purpose is to ascertain whether there is consistency between the various targets of the national economic plan to bring to light the possible contradictions.

Several variants of this type of analysis are known; I shall confine myself here to the description of those used in the course of mathematical programming*.

An elementary problem of control is to ascertain whether the plan targets taken over from the plan set up by traditional methods will admit of a feasible program, e.g. whether the prescribed output obligations can be met by the allocated resources, etc.

Our sectoral investigations up to now have shown a feasible program to exist; there was no contradiction in this respect between the plan figures.

While the above test will show whether the centrally allocated resources are *sufficient* for the centrally prescribed output, another type of test is to answer the question whether the originally estimated quantities of the resources are in fact *required*. Sectoral programming may reveal the surplus resources granted to an industrial sector by central allocation.

This was the case, e.g. in the cotton industry with the construction quota taken into account as a plan directive. Construction constitutes one of the bottle-necks in the economy-wide plan. It is, accordingly,

* Consistency analysis by I–O tables was discussed in ch. 3.

most useful that the optimal program requires less construction than originally allocated to this sector in the plan based on traditional methods (see section 5.8).

23.2. The Redistribution of Resources between Two Sectors

By employing, in the course of programming carried out in different sectors, objective functions of identical economic contents and identical structure, it will become possible to investigate the circumstances which make it worth while to shift a resource allocated to one sector to another sector.

Let us compare sectors 1 and 2, e.g. the man-made fibres industry and the aluminium industry which both come under the competence of the same ministry. (The ordinal number of sectors is indicated by the suffices beside the symbols.) Let us assume that in both sectors we are working with cost-minimizing objective functions of identical structure. Programming had been completed in both sectors.

The problem of redistributing a resource is a trivial one in the case when one of the sectors has already exhausted the resource in question while in the other sector some of it is still available. In this case it will obviously be worth while to shift the remaining part to the sector where it is still needed. Thus, e.g. the optimal program for the cotton industry did not totally exhaust the construction quota – it would be worth while to allocate the remaining part to another sector which puts in a claim for it.

Now, what should be done in the case when the originally allocated resource is used up by the optimal program of both sectors? For example, let us assume that the investment quota was exhausted in both sectors and we now wished to find out *whether it would be worth while to decrease the investment quota allocated to one sector in favour of the other and, if so, to what extent should a redistribution take place.*

Let us introduce the following notation:

C_1, C_2 = the objective function value for sectors 1 and 2, respectively

$\mathbf{x}_1, \mathbf{x}_2$ = the program of sectors 1 and 2, respectively

$\mathbf{A}_1, \mathbf{A}_2$ = the matrix of the coefficients figuring in the constraint equation of sectors 1 and 2, respectively (the investment quota was omitted from the constraints)

$\mathbf{b}_1, \mathbf{b}_2$ = the constants in the system of constraints of sectors 1 and 2, respectively (here, too, the investment quota was omitted)

B = the sum of investment quotas allocated to sectors 1 and 2 originally, previous to redistribution

$\mathbf{a}'_{B1}, \mathbf{a}'_{B2}$ = the vector of the coefficients figuring in the investment quota constraint of sectors 1 and 2, respectively.

In a linear programming model the problem can be formulated as follows:

Let us define the common *optimal* program $(\mathbf{x}_1^*, \mathbf{x}_2^*)$ for sectors 1 and 2 which will, over and above the condition of non-negativity, conform to the following conditions:

$$\mathbf{A}_1 \mathbf{x}_1 = \mathbf{b}_1 \, , \tag{23.1}$$

$$\mathbf{A}_2 \mathbf{x}_2 = \mathbf{b}_2 \, , \tag{23.2}$$

$$\mathbf{a}'_{B1} \mathbf{x}_1 + \mathbf{a}'_{B2} \mathbf{x}_2 = B \, , \tag{23.3}$$

and for which the sum of the costs for the two sectors is a minimum:

$$C_1(\mathbf{x}_1) + C_2(\mathbf{x}_2) \rightarrow \min! \tag{23.4}$$

We have thus united the two programming models, leaving their separate systems of constraints unaltered and prescribing one common constraint only in the form of a common investment quota.

Problems (23.1)–(23.4) can be solved also directly, provided that the united model is not too large. Should, however, the two sectoral models even separately surpass the computation technique possibilities at our disposal, it will be practically impossible to unite the two problems in a direct manner. There is, however, a roundabout way of solving the problem and this will be described in the following:

Let λ denote the investment quota allocated to sector 1 after redistribution. The investment quota of sector 2 will, accordingly, be $B-\lambda$.

Parametric programming with parameter λ is now carried out for the two sectors separately. The parameter has λ_0 and λ^0 for lower and upper limits, respectively. The investment quota allocated to sector 1 cannot be less than λ_0, because in this case sector 1 could not comply with its own constraints, e.g. with its output obligation; nor can it be more than λ^0, for then the $(B-\lambda)$ quota would not suffice to satisfy the constraint system of sector 2.

As has been pointed out in section 22.1 above, the functions $C_1(\lambda)$ and $C_2(\lambda)$, i.e. the objective functions of optimal programs $\mathbf{x}_1^*(\lambda)$ and $\mathbf{x}_2^*(\lambda)$ belonging to parameter value λ, are in intervals linear and continuous. C_1 is monotonically decreasing, C_2 monotonically increasing. Both functions are convex (see figure 23.1).

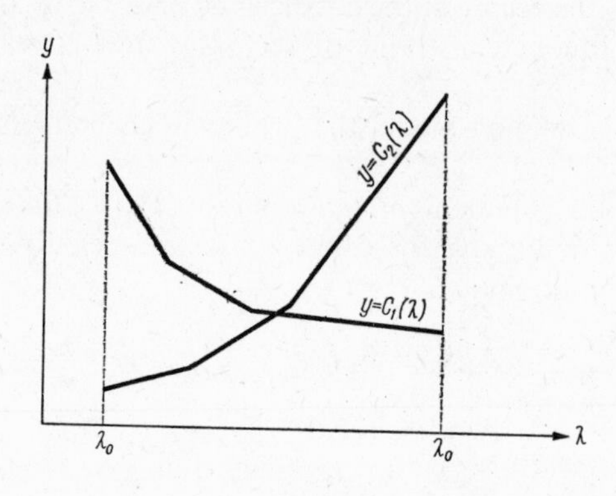

Fig. 23.1

Let $\phi_1(\lambda)$ and $\phi_2(\lambda)$ denote the corresponding marginal functions. In accordance with what has been said of functions $C_1(\lambda)$, $C_2(\lambda)$, these are in intervals constant, monotonically increasing functions; ϕ_1 is a negative, ϕ_2 a positive one. The values of these marginal functions will be determined directly by dual parametric programming. The value ϕ_1 is called the s h a d o w p r i c e of the investment quota allocated to sector 1. It will express the cost that can be saved in sector 1 as a result of a unit increase of investment quota λ. (Logically, the economic interpretation of ϕ_2 will be analogous.)

Our problem consists in determining a value λ^* for which total costs $C_1(\lambda) + C_2(\lambda)$ have a minimum value. In accordance with the above, $\phi_1(\lambda) + \phi_2(\lambda)$, the derivative of $C_1(\lambda) + C_2(\lambda)$, will also be a monotonically increasing, in intervals constant function. Let this be denoted $\Gamma(\lambda)$.

$$\Gamma(\lambda) = \phi_1(\lambda) + \phi_2(\lambda). \tag{23.5}$$

$\Gamma(\lambda)$ represents the difference between the shadow prices of the investment quotas obtained in the course of programming for the two sectors, in view of the fact that the shadow price of investment quota λ in sector 1 will be negative, and that of investment quota $(B-\lambda)$ in sector 2 positive.

Let us, furthermore, denote the right- and left-side limiting values of function $\Gamma(\lambda)$ at point λ_1 $\Gamma^+(\lambda)$ and $\Gamma^-(\lambda)$, respectively. In order to determine the most favourable distribution λ^*, various cases must be taken into consideration.

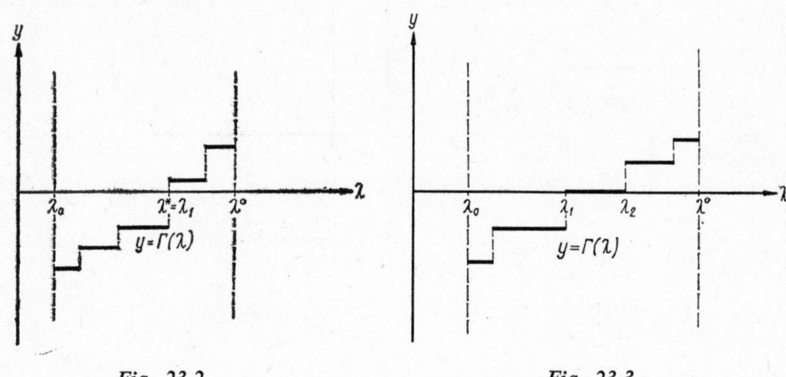

Fig. 23.2 *Fig. 23.3*

(1) $\Gamma^+(\lambda_0) < 0$, $\Gamma^-(\lambda^0) > 0$, i.e. the monotonically increasing step-function $\Gamma(\lambda)$ is negative at the lower, and positive at the upper limit of the interval in question. In this case there are two possible alternatives, viz.

(1a) For some point $\lambda_0 < \lambda_1 < \lambda^0$, $\Gamma^-(\lambda_1) < 0$ and $\Gamma^+(\lambda_1) > 0$, i.e. the function changes its sign at point λ_1. It is easy to see that in this case $\lambda^* = \lambda_1$, as $C_1(\lambda) + C_2(\lambda)$, the total cost of the two sectors, will be strictly monotonically decreasing to the left of point λ_1 and strictly monotonically increasing to its right (see figure 23.2).

(1b) Within some interval $[\lambda_1, \lambda_2]$, $(\lambda_0 < \lambda_1 < \lambda_2 < \lambda^0)$, the value of function $\Gamma(\lambda)$ is 0. In this case any point of interval $[\lambda_1, \lambda_2]$ will be optimal, because within the interval the function $C_1(\lambda) + C_2(\lambda)$ is constant, decreasing to the left of it and increasing to its right.

(2a) $\Gamma^+(\lambda_0) > 0$, or (2b) $\Gamma^-(\lambda^0) < 0$. In case (2a), $\lambda^* = \lambda_0$; in case (2b), $\lambda^* = \lambda^0$, as here $C_1(\lambda) + C_2(\lambda)$ is strictly monotonically increasing or decreasing over the whole interval (see figures 23.4 and 23.5).

(3a) $\Gamma^+(\lambda^0) = 0$, or (3b) $\Gamma^-(\lambda^0) = 0$. In these cases any value will be optimal in the neighbourhood of the corresponding limiting point, up to the next breaking point (see figures 23.6 and 23.7).

Let us revert for a moment to case (1b). Here, the investment quota was distributed between the two sectors in such a way that the shadow price of the quota allocated to sector 1 exactly equalled that of the quota allocated to sector 2. Though he two shadow prices had not been equal previous to the procedure, *the redistribution of the resource in question was carried to the point where its shadow prices became equalized in the two sectors.*

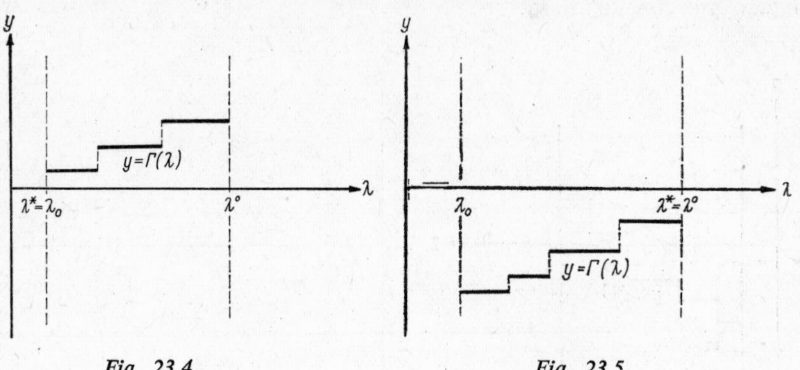

Fig. 23.4 *Fig. 23.5*

Case (1b) occurs only rarely. But even in case (1a), which may be considered the most typical, one can speak of the "equalization" of shadow prices in a certain broader sense of the term. With the optimal distribution of λ^*, either investment quota λ allocated to sector 1, or investment quota $(B-\lambda)$ allocated to sector 2, will have a characteristic value. Let us assume the latter case, i.e. that step function $\phi_2(\lambda)$ shows a discontinuity, a new "grade" at λ^*. In case (1a) (considering always absolute values only*), left-side limiting value $\phi_2^-(\lambda^*)$ which precedes the "grade" is

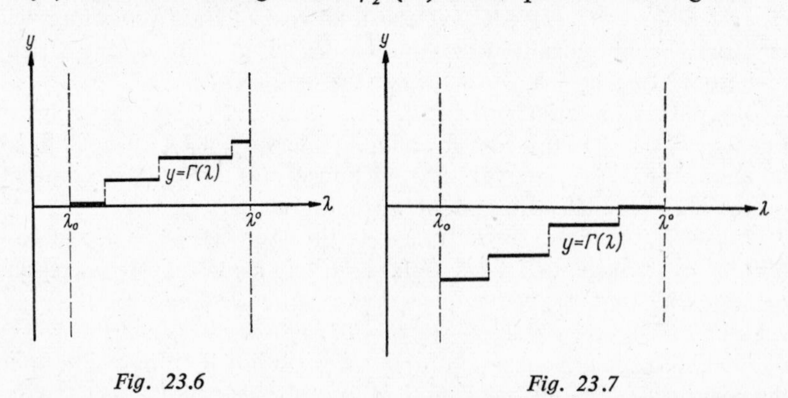

Fig. 23.6 *Fig. 23.7*

* In view of the fact that ϕ_1 and ϕ_2 will differ in sign, one being the shadow price of λ and the other that of $(B-\lambda)$, it is logically the magnitude of absolute values that must be compared.

smaller than $\phi_1(\lambda^*)$, right-side limiting value $\phi_1^+(\lambda^*)$ which follows the "grade" is greater than $\phi_1(\lambda^*)$. The shadow price belonging to "grade" λ^* itself may be considered as one that can take any value between $\phi_2^-(\lambda^*)$ and $\phi_2^+(\lambda^*)$. Therefore, as

$$\phi_2^-(\lambda^*) \leqq \phi_2(\lambda^*) \leqq \phi_2^+(\lambda^*), \tag{23.6}$$

and

$$|\phi_2^-(\lambda^*)| \leqq |\phi_1(\lambda^*)| \leqq |\phi_2^+(\lambda^*)|, \tag{23.7}$$

it is possible that

$$|\phi_2(\lambda^*)| = |\phi_1(\lambda^*)|. \tag{23.8}$$

In this broader sense of the term we may speak also here of an "equalization" of shadow prices as a result of redistribution*.

The procedure of redistribution described above will usually not require the carrying out of parametric programming for all possible values of λ. Departing from the original optimal program determined for the two sectors independently of each other, it will generally be sufficient to proceed to the second or third next characteristic value in order to define the optimal redistribution of the resource in question.

The *fundamental idea* behind the procedure is evident: it will not be worth while to employ in sector 1 a resource of the economy which could be more fruitfully used and which could save more cost in sector 2. The procedure described above enables the enforcement of this principle, utilizing for the purpose the results obtained in sectoral programming. It constitutes, accordingly, more than a mere redistribution of a resource, and this for the following reasons:

The redistribution is carried out not simply between two sectors but between the optimal programs of the two sectors. What we want to determine is the common optimum of two partial optima.

The redistribution is carried out in such a way that all other constraints of the model are satisfied. Thus, among others, output obligations will remain in force. Other planned proportions in the national economy will thus not be affected by the redistribution.

The results of the redistribution can be measured numerically by the change in the value of the sum of the two sectors' objective function.

What has been said above indicates at the same time the limits of the procedure. It does not provide an absolute guarantee that the general

* I am not dealing here with cases (2a), (2b) and (3b) which may be considered as exceptional.

optimum that will be determined in the redistribution as determined by the system of constraints of the two sectoral models. This problem, however, leads up already to the subject-matter of the next chapter.

The present chapter has been dealing with the question *how sectoral programming can be used for the purpose of criticizing the national economic plan "from below"*, and how the analysis of a *part* (a sector or two sectors compared with one another) may provide a basis for proposals aimed at the improvement of the *whole* (the national plan). We shall now proceed further and draw the problems of economy-wide planning also into the orbit of our investigations.

CHAPTER 24

THE MODEL OF "TWO-LEVEL PLANNING"*

CO-AUTHOR:
TH. LIPTÁK

24.1. The Course of the Discussion

As the preceding parts of this book have shown, the application of mathematical methods to long-term planning has taken place along two lines in Hungary during the past years. One line has been that of long-term programming for sectors of industry, of which examples have been presented in chs. 5 and 6. The other line has been the application of input–output tables to long-term planning (see ch. 3). The first mathematical tools used in Hungary for the preparation of *national* plans were static Leontief models. It is, however, a familiar fact that the input–output table is not suited for optimization and is merely designed to achieve correct proportions between the sectors.

A survey of the situation thus leads logically to the next step: procedures must be worked out which make it possible to optimize, but this time for the whole of the national economy. This is a requirement frequently voiced by the practical planners, and indeed the Hungarian literature has contained proposals to this effect**. The ideas put forward to date have, however, not been able to cope with the basic difficulty of solving this problem, viz. that we may either prepare a highly compact programming model, in which case the possibilities of choice are very much restricted and the extreme aggregation and over-simplifications endanger the utility of the calculation's results, or else we work out a very large-scale model that is free of these faults, but in this case the numerical computing

* The model of two-level planning was worked out as part of a broader research project, commissioned by the National Planning Board. The aim of this project was to examine the mathematical methods that could be applied in practice to planning for the national economy, under the given circumstances. The point of departure of the project was J. KORNAI [74] on linking the central and sectoral programming problems (1961). The essential features of the method of two-level planning with respect to the problem of economy-wide planning, were set out (1962) in J. KORNAI and TH. LIPTÁK [80]. TH. LIPTÁK [102, 103] has generalized the method and reported the results of this work.
Other publications in the course of the project were [81] and [82].

** See, for instance, GY. SIMON and GY. KONDOR [156].

of the problem can not be carried out, even with the most powerful electronic computers.

In our research we have aimed to overcome precisely this difficulty. The solution must obviously be sought in decomposing the large-scale programming problem. This idea has more than once been mooted in the literature of planning*. Mathematical methods have, moreover, been developed for the decomposition of linear programming problems of certain special forms**. It has seemed to us, however, that it is worth while to search for other methods.

The planning problem may at the outset be stated as a single linear programming problem that is too large to be solved with the given computing facilities. This will henceforth be called the overall central information problem (OCI problem, for short). The OCI problem can be decomposed into component problems that may be solved by the separate "sectors" and which are coordinated by the "centre" through distributing the constraints (resources, materials, manpower, etc.) among the various sectors. Since, according to this method, the planning takes place alternately on two levels, in the centre and the sectors, organically linked with one another and continuously supplementing and correcting each other, we have called this procedure two-level planning.

In the programming models for sectors of industry described in the preceding chapters, the constants on the right-hand sides of the constraints have included certain plan directives adopted from plans worked out by the traditional method, e.g. the output targets, resource bounds, etc. These programming projects certainly suggest the idea that it would be worth while to compare the results of sector programming and use them to amend the directives and quotas adopted from the plan for the national economy. The purpose of the present procedure is to lend an organized form to such comparisons and the national plan correction to be based on them, thus *organically to link up the programming carried out at sector level.*

This research project was highly relevant to the current practical requirements of planning Hungary's national economy. In the course of

* Reference may here be made to the works of L. V. KANTOROVICH [62], R. FRISCH [40] and W. TRZECIAKOWSKI [168].

** See e.g. G. B. DANTZIG and P. WOLFE [28, 29]. At the Cambridge Conference of the International Economic Society in summer, 1963, E. MALINVAUD [115] advanced some highly noteworthy ideas on the partial decentralization of the national planning problem. He used the decomposition procedure of Dantzig and Wolfe as one method.

the work, however, a procedure of more universal validity was developed. A *general model* was worked out, which is presented in Appendix H. A general model makes it easier to furnish certain definitions and to prove the mathematical propositions. A general model can also provide a basis for applications of the method to the solution by decomposition of other general linear programming problems, beyond the problem of planning the national economy which was the point of departure of this work.

In the present chapter it is intended, on the basis of the propositions proved in Appendix H, to present a concrete economic application of the method of two-level planning to the problems of national long-term planning.

The course of the treatment is as follows:

In ch. 24 the problem of long-term planning is discussed through a relatively simple, schematic model. The constraint system and the treatment of investments are highly simplified, the objective function is set with the aim of optimizing the country's foreign currency balance, without any particular economic explanation, etc. All this is done in order to make it easier to introduce the reader to the basic ideas of two-level planning. Chapters 25–27 will then return to the problematic features of the schematic model described in ch. 24. They will go more deeply into the economic problems previously left open, and resolve some of the simplifying assumptions.

The discussion begins with the presentation of some of the basic ideas of the method in section 24.2. In section 24.3 the central model, in sections 24.4 and 24.5 the sector model, are described. Sections 24.6 and 24.7 set out and define the rules of iteration. In section 24.8 the problem is interpreted in terms of the theory of games.

24.2. Imitation of the Usual Course of Planning

The present method is to a certain extent an imitation of the usual course of planning. The National Planning Board on the basis of economic policy requirements and general information about the sectors, works out a provisional plan proposal that contains general targets and plan figures for the sectors. The centre undertakes a provisional distribution of the available resources, materials, manpower, etc. among the sectors, and at the same time allocates their output targets. Now the sectors, through their own detailed calculations and according to their actual circumstances, "fill in" the quotas and render the central targets concrete. While doing so, they also propose changes to the NPB. This phase is usually termed "counter-planning". On the basis of this counter-planning, the NPB modifies its original targets and again sends these down to the sectors (see the plan coordination process described in section 1.4). The method to be described is an attempt to assist this process of "planning and counter-planning", through objective criteria.

The procedure also simulates the usual practice of planning from another point of view. It frequently happens that the centre sets the sectors certain tasks, and asks them to report with what degree of economic efficiency the tasks can be carried out. The sectors express the efficiency of their activities by means of various "economic efficiency indices", whose structure is centrally prescribed (see ch. 2). Our method incorporates this "reporting back" process in a unified system. The sectors at each step report back one kind of economic efficiency index – the shadow prices obtained from programming – to the centre, to evaluate the tasks set from there.

24.3. The Central Model*

The process of planning is directed by the c e n t r e – in practice by the NPB. There are altogether n sectors. Each sector is responsible for one group of products: in the subsequent discussion we shall, for brevity's sake, speak of p r o d u c t s in place of product groups. The activities of the sector include not only the domestic production of the product concerned and the investment needed for production, but also the export and import of the product. For example the programming scope of the man-made fibre model treated in ch. 6 may be considered as one such sector, comprising as it does the output, investment, import and export

* While in the general model described in Appendix H the point of departure was the OCI problem, in this presentation of the concrete model we shall immediately proceed to the two-level problem obtained from the OCI problem. Both criterion (H.17) and the simplifying remarks (H.21)–(H.27) have been observed in formulating the set of feasible central programs. The various components of the central program and the sector programs are designated by different letters, in accordance with their economic nature, and their sign has also been chosen to furnish the simplest notation.

The reader may check the concrete planning model to be described here against Appendix H, to establish that it is a *special case* of the *general model* described in the Appendix H, moreover that the corresponding OCI problem is solvable and the polyhedral game derived from it is regular.

activities associated with man-made fibres and with the intermediary materials necessary for their manufacture. Long-term plans are worked out for a plan term, consisting of altogether T periods.

It is not intended with the help of this model to determine all the targets of the national economic plan. The point of departure is an existing plan for the economy, worked out by the "traditional", non-mathematical methods and checked through input–output tables. Certain targets of this plan are adopted as constants for our programming model. These are called plan directives.

The centre sends the sectors three kinds of plan figures*:

(1) The centre sets the ith sector the task of providing a certain quantity of product for domestic requirements in the tth period. This is symbolized by v_{it} and called a supply task ($i = 1, 2, \ldots, n$; $t = 1, 2, \ldots, T$). The centre does not prescribe whether the sector should meet the desired quantity from home production or imports – this will be determined by the sector program. The sector program must, moreover, decide whether the sector also wishes to export, over and above meeting the domestic requirement.

(2) The centre assigns to the ith sector a certain quantity of the jth product during the tth period. This is denoted by z_{ijt} and called the material quota ($i = 1, 2, \ldots, n$; $j = 1, 2, \ldots, n$; $j \neq i$; $t = 1, 2, \ldots, T$). The material quota includes both the material produced at home, and also imports of the jth material.

(3) The centre makes a certain labour force available to the ith sector for the tth period. This is denoted by w_{it} and called the manpower quota.

The plan figures are the variables of the central program. The constants figuring in the constraint system of the central program are plan directives. These are:

(1) d_{it}, which is the external consumption of the ith product, needed in the tth period. This comprises both personal and communal consumption, including also unproductive investments. It does not, however, comprise either exports, or (apart from certain exceptions) the productive investments. (We shall return to the exceptions later).

(2) V_{it} is the upper bound of the ith supply task in the tth period. (This bound has no real economic meaning; its introduction is only necessary for the mathematical algorithm.) There is no practical diffi-

* The notions used agree with the terminology so far used. For a definition of the plan directive see ch. 4, and of the plan figures see the introduction to Part 5. The plan directive is a number adopted as a *constant* from the central plan, the plan figure is a central plan target that is regarded as a *variable*.

culty about determining the quantity that the mass of products needed to meet the domestic requirement will certainly not exceed.

(3) W_t is the manpower quota available to the national economy for productive work during the tth period.

We shall call those central programs (v_{it}, z_{jit}, w_{it}) feasible, where

$$\sum_{\substack{j=1 \\ j \neq i}}^{n} z_{jit} + d_{it} = v_{it} \leqq V_{it}, \qquad i = 1,\ldots, n; \; t = 1,\ldots, T, \qquad (24.1)$$

$$\sum_{i=1}^{n} w_{it} = W_t, \qquad t = 1,\ldots, T, \qquad (24.2)$$

$$v_{it} \geqq 0, \; z_{jit} \geqq 0, \; w_{it} \geqq 0, \; i = 1,\ldots, n; \; j = 1,\ldots, n; \; j \neq i; \; t = 1,\ldots, T \qquad (24.3)$$

24.4. The Primal Sector Model

The variables figuring in the programming model of the ith sector may, according to their economic nature, be graded into several groups:

(1) Reproductive activities. These are understood to mean the unchanged, continued operation of the output capacities for the ith product which already existed at the beginning of the plan term. (In the man-made fibres model for instance, the production of viscose fibre in an old plant, the production of cellophane in an old plant – were of this type.) On the basis of the technical characteristics, e.g. whether a plant is backward or advanced, several activities of this kind can be included in the model. Let x_{ikt} denote the planned volume of the kth reproductive activity of the ith sector during the tth period* ($x_{ikt} \geqq 0$, k = repr**, $t = 1,\ldots, T$).

(2) Investment activities. This concept is understood to include both the establishment of new capacities, and also the production to take place with the new capacities. Various *types* of investment

* Both here and in the case of the other variables (with the exception of the investment activities), the unit of volume is the natural unit suited to measure the quantity of the product per 1 interval, or else Ft per 1 interval. It must be the same as the unit used for the ith product in the central product balance concerned with it (24.1).

** The numbers of the variables will not be stated either here, or with the other groups of sector variables. Instead, suitable abbreviations after the suffix k will refer to the nature of the activity, e.g. k = repr, k = inv, etc.

activity, distinguished according to technical or economic characteristics (e.g. the technology to be used, the use of imported or home-made machinery, etc.), may be incorporated in the model. Moreover it is possible within a given type of investment activity (e.g. the establishment and operation of a specified plant in a given way), to distinguish several investment activities according to the period *when the investment commences*. We shall let a separate investment activity correspond to each such alternative. Let x_{ik} denote the volume of the kth investment activity in the ith sector* ($x_{ik} \geqq 0$, $k =$ inv).

(3) Export activities. Several kinds of export activities can figure in the model, distinguished by their economic characteristics, e.g. according to markets, countries, etc. Let x_{ikt} denote the volume of the kth export activity of the ith product in the tth period ($x_{ikt} \geqq 0$, $k =$ exp, $t = 1, \ldots, T$).

(4) Bounded import activities. This group includes only those import activities that compete with the domestic productive activities belonging to groups (1) and (2), are able to replace them, and where the import volume is bounded by some external market factor. Various kinds of activity can figure in the model, distinguished by economic characteristics, e.g. markets, etc. Let x_{ikt} denote the volume of the kth bounded import activity, importing the ith product in the tth period ($x_{ikt} \geqq 0$, $k =$ imp, $t = 1, \ldots, T$).

(5) Unbounded import activities. These are import activities which, similarly to the import activities figuring in group (4), compete with domestic production, but where the volume is not limited by either external market factors, or other circumstances. In some sectors we may be fully justified in assuming realistic opportunities for unbounded import activities. In other sectors this kind of free, unbounded import activity does not in fact exist. This type of variable will, however, be made to figure in these sectors too, as a fictitious auxiliary variable. The nature of the present method requires the insertion of an import variable with no upper bounds in each sector model, but the programming procedure which is applied, automatically eliminates these variables from the

* Since, according to the above definitions, an investment activity does not apply to a particular period, for those series of investment actions that take place throughout the full plan term the volume x_{ik} is distinguished from the other variables by the fact that it does not contain the suffix "t". The volume of an investment activity is accordingly measured by the quantity in natural units or in Ft of the product produced during one plan period by the plant, once it has been established and is working to full capacity. The unit of the product is identical with the unit used in the central product balance, according to (24.1).

program. Unbounded import is the 0th activity of the sector model. Let x_{i0t} denote volume of unbounded imports in the ith sector during the tth period ($x_{i0t} \geqq 0$, $t = 1, \ldots, T$).

The constraints prescribed for the ith sector program may – apart from the constraint of non-negative values – be divided into two main groups. One group of constraints makes sure that the sector complies with the plan figures received from the centre. The first constraint is that:

$$v_{it} \leqq \sum_{\substack{k=\text{repr,exp,}\\ \text{imp,0}}} f_{ikt}\, x_{ikt} + \sum_{k=\text{inv}} f_{ikt}\, x_{ik} \leqq V_{it}, \qquad t = 1, \ldots, T. \tag{24.4}$$

The output coefficient f_{ikt} figuring in the constraint is defined as follows in the case of the different sector activities:

(1) For reproductive activities $f_{ikt} = 1$.

(2) For investment activities $f_{ikt} \geqq 0$, but for at least one t, $f_{ikt} = 1$. As the result of a unit of investment activity a unit of capacity will at some time, but at the latest during the last period, be established, which will be able to produce unit quantity of the ith product during one time interval. The previous production on the other hand, will depend on when the investment commences and how much "warming up" is needed, before it achieves normal operation. Let us assume that in the case of the kth investment activity a definite time schedule applies to the product output, and, as we shall see, to the expenditures*. Let us assume moreover, that after full-scale operation is achieved, the capacities established through the investment will always be utilized to the nornal extent. Thus if f_{ikt} is equal to 1 for a particular t, then it will also be 1 for the $(t + 1)$st, $(t + 2)$nd, etc. periods. In this respect, therefore, this group of activities differs from the reproductive activities, for in their case we did not assume that the existing old capacities need necessarily be utilized.

(3) For export activities, $f_{ikt} = -1$.

(4) and (5) For bounded import activities and for unbounded imports, $f_{ikt} = 1$.

* For example, let the chemical industry have the sector model with the index number $i = 3$, and let its 17th variable be the construction of a particular new chemical plant in such a way that the investment activity begins during the 2nd period, furnishes 60 per cent of its ultimate capacity during the 3rd period, and operates at full capacity by the 4th period. In this case $f_{3,17,1} = 0$, $f_{3,17,2} = 0$, $f_{3,17,3} = 0.6$, $f_{3,17,4} = 1$, $f_{3,17,5} = 1$. On the other hand, for the 18th variable, which is technologically identical but commences one period later, the coefficients are: $f_{3,18,1} = f_{3,18,2} = f_{3,18,3} = 0$, and only $f_{3,18,4} = 0.6$, $f_{3,18,5} = 1$. This kind of treatment of investments bears some similarity to the way in which R. FRISCH [40] handles the various "channels" of investment activities.

The next series of constraints associated with the central plan figure is that

$$\sum_{\substack{k=\text{repr,exp,}\\ \text{imp, 0}}} g_{ijkt}\, x_{ikt} + \sum_{k=\text{inv}} g_{ijkt}\, x_{ik} \leqq z_{ijt}\,, \tag{24.5}$$

$$j = 1,\ldots,n;\ j \neq i;\ t = 1,\ldots,T.$$

The material input coefficient g_{ijkt} is the following for the different sector activities:

(1) For reproductive activities $g_{ijkt} \geqq 0$. The technological character of production determines whether the jth material is required or not. This material requirement comprises both the needs of current operation, and also the material requirements of the general repair, replacement and overhaul activities needed to maintain the old capacity or achieve its simple reproduction.

(2) For investment activities $g_{ijkt} \geqq 0$. This comprises the products (e.g. machines) required by the investment during the years of establishing the new capacity, moreover the products needed for current production and for the maintenance and replacement of the established capacity once the investment has become operative. As with the output, it is here also assumed that for the kth investment activity there is a definite time schedule of material requirements.

(3) (4) and (5). For all foreign trade activities $g_{ijkt} = 0$.

Finally the last constraint associated with the central plan figures is

$$\sum_{\substack{k=\text{repr,exp,}\\ \text{imp,0}}} h_{ikt}\, x_{ikt} + \sum_{k=\text{inv}} h_{ikt}\, x_{ik} \leqq w_{it}, \qquad t = 1,\ldots,T. \tag{24.6}$$

The labour force coefficient h_{ikt} is the following for the different groups of activities:

(1) For reproductive activities $h_{ikt} > 0$. No production can take place without manpower.

(2) For investment activities $h_{ikt} \geqq 0$. Before operation begins it is 0, after this it is positive. Here too, the numerical value obeys a time schedule.

(3), (4) and (5) For the foreign trade activities $h_{ikt} = 0$.

Beyond the conditions that assure compliance with the central plan figures, it is also possible to set up special constraints, characteristic of the sector's particular circumstances. Reproductive activities are bounded by the upper limit of the existing capacity. For instance constraints (6.8) and (6.9) of the man-made fibre model are of this type.

Some investment activities, such as the modernization of existing plants, are bounded, e.g. constraint (6.7) of the man-made fibre model. In some sectors domestic production is bounded by our natural resources. Certain export and import activities are bounded by market factors, e.g. constraint (6.3) of the man-made fibre model. The special constraints may be written in the following general form*:

$$\sum_{t=1}^{T} \sum_{\substack{k=\text{repr,exp,}\\ \text{imp,0}}} a^0_{ilkt}\, x_{ikt} + \sum_{k=\text{inv}} a^0_{ilk}\, x_{ik} \leqq b^0_{il}\,, \qquad l = \text{spec}\,. \tag{24.7}$$

The objective of programming for the ith sector is that

$$\sum_{t=1}^{T} \sum_{\substack{k=\text{repr,exp,}\\ \text{imp,0}}} s_{ikt}\, x_{ikt} + \sum_{k=\text{inv}} s_{ik}\, x_{ik} \longrightarrow \max!\,, \tag{24.8}$$

i. e. the maximization of the sector's objective function, on the left-hand side of (24.8). In this expression s_{ikt} and s_{ik} are the foreign currency returns from the activity concerned. These are the following, for the various groups of activities:

(1) and (2) For reproductive and investment activities the foreign exchange returns are generally 0. One exception is the type of productive and investment activity that requires non-competitive imports, which cannot be produced at home. The costs of the non-competitive imports are accounted for as negative foreign currency returns. Naturally in the case of investment activities the foreign exchange returns comprise the costs of all the non-competitive imports arising throughout the plan term.

(3) For export activities the foreign exchange returns are positive.

(4) and (5) The foreign exchange returns of import activities are negative. In so far as the unbounded imports are merely a fictitious variable, they are allocated very high negative foreign exchange returns. It is also assumed of the returns of foreign trade activities that

$$\max_{k=\text{exp}} s_{ikt} \leqq \min_{k=\text{imp,0}} (-s_{ikt}), \qquad t = 1, \ldots, T. \tag{24.9}$$

On the national scale that central program may be regarded as optimal, where the sum of the maximal sector objective function values is a maximum.

* The abbreviation l = spec expresses the fact that (24.7) lists all the special constraints. For the unbounded import variables $a^0_{il0t} = 0$.

24.5. The Dual Sector Model

In the dual of the ith primal sector problem according to (24.4)–(24.8), with the central progam (plan figures) given as $(v_{it}, z_{ijt}, w_{it})$, let ν_{it} be the shadow price of the supply task v_{it}, ζ_{ijt} that of the material quota z_{ijt}, and ω_{it} that of the manpower quota w_{it}. Let $\varkappa_{it}$ denote the shadow price of the upper boundary V_{it} of the ith supply task, and σ_{il} that of the boundary b_{il}^{0} figuring in the lth special constraint. Then with the sector shadow price system $(\nu_{it}, \zeta_{ijt}, \omega_{it}, \pi_{it}, \sigma_{il})$ as the dual variable, the ith dual sector problem assumes the following form*:

$$f_{ikt}(\varkappa_{it} - \nu_{it}) + \sum_{\substack{j=1\\ j\neq i}}^{n} g_{ijkt}\zeta_{ijt} + h_{ikt}\omega_{it} + \sum_{l=\text{spec}} a_{ilkt}^{0}\sigma_{il} \geqq s_{ikt},$$

$$k = \text{repr, exp, imp, } 0; \quad t = 1, \ldots, T. \tag{24.10}$$

$$f_{ikt}(\varkappa_{it} - \nu_{it}) + \sum_{\substack{j=1\\ j\neq i}}^{n} g_{ijkt}\zeta_{ijt} + h_{ikt}\omega_{it} + \sum_{l=\text{spec}} a_{ilk}^{0}\sigma_{il} \geqq s_{ik},$$

$$k = \text{inv}; \; t = 1, \ldots, T. \tag{24.11}$$

$$\nu_{it} \geqq 0, \zeta_{ijt} \geqq 0, \omega_{it} \geqq 0, \varkappa_{it} \geqq 0, \sigma_{il} \geqq 0,$$

$$j = 1, \ldots, n, \; j \neq i; \; t = 1, \ldots, T; \; l = \text{spec}. \tag{24.12}$$

$$\sum_{t=1}^{T}\left(V_{it}\varkappa_{it} - v_{it}\nu_{it} + \sum_{\substack{j=1\\ j\neq i}}^{n} z_{ijt}\zeta_{ijt} + w_{it}\omega_{it} \right) + \sum_{l=\text{spec}} b_{il}^{0}\sigma_{il} \longrightarrow \min! \tag{24.13}$$

What is the economic content of the shadow prices in our case?

(1) The shadow price of the supply task expresses the amount by which the foreign exchange returns of the ith sector would rise, if the supply task of the sector were reduced by one unit**, while the other bounds figuring

* On the dual problem of linear programming see, for instance, S. Karlin [63], S. Gass [43], or B. Krekó [90].

** Strictly speaking both here and with the other bounds, the shadow price expresses the yield change not per unit change of the constraint, but for a sufficiently small change. It is only for the sake of easier comprehension that we speak of the unit change, which is a more concrete, practical concept.

in the constraints of the sector model remained unchanged. This may be regarded as a kind of "supply price" of the *i*th product.

(2) The shadow price of the material quota expresses the amount by which the foreign exchange returns of the *i*th sector would rise, if the quota of the *j*th material allocated to the sector were increased by one unit, while the other bounds of the sector model remained unchanged. This may be regarded as a kind of "demand price" of the *j*th product.

(3) The shadow price of the labour force quota expresses the amount by which the foreign exchange returns of the *i*th sector would rise, if the labour force quota of the sector were increased by one unit. This may be regarded as a computational "wage".

Some of the remaining shadow prices also have plausible economic interpretations, e.g. the shadow prices of the upper bounds of exports and imports may be regarded as "tariffs", the upper bounds of the existing productive capacities as "lease dues", the bounds of the natural resources as "rent", etc.

It is thus possible to furnish an economic interpretation of the dual problem.

It is a familiar property of the shadow prices obtained in dual programming that the optimal objective function value belonging to the optimal program of the primal problem is fully "imputed" to the bounds. In the present case the minimum of the evaluation of the bounds at shadow prices is exactly equal to the maximum of the returns from the activities.

Let us for a moment assume the following: The centre actually gives the sector the resources at the "price" corresponding to the shadow price reported back by the sector, and at the same time demands of the sector that it should not operate at a loss. If the sector reported back "rosy" shadow prices that were too high (e.g. if it said that a rise in the labour force quota would lead to higher surplus returns than it is actually capable of achieving according to the optimal program), then the sector will operate at a loss. The minimization of the evaluation of the bounds as the optimization requirement of the model, expresses the idea that we must beware of *over-estimating* the modification of the bounds figuring in the constraints and the effect of this modification on the objective function.

This requirement on the objective function is supplemented by another requirement, expressed in the constraint system of the dual problem. This may actually be regarded as the familiar "non-profit condition". Let us take for example a productive activity that is not charged with noncompetitive import costs, i.e. where $s_{ikt} = 0$. Constraint (24.10) in this case means that the production costs (evaluated at shadow prices), minus the income due to the output intended to discharge the supply task, also evaluated at shadow prices, cannot be negative. In other words this activity of the sector cannot yield a profit.

The minimization of the evaluation of the bounds at shadow prices in the dual problem, together with the non-profit conditions, express an attitude of caution and responsible restraint in forecasting the consequences of the activities.

24.6. The Course of Programming

We shall first briefly outline the course of the programming, then present the rules of the procedure in mathematical form.

The programming begins with the centre prescribing the supply tasks, the material quotas and the labour force quotas for the sectors.

If the central plan figures were the best possible ones, the programming would now in fact be concluded. This, however, is by no means certain. It is possible that the centre did not succeed "at the first try" in working out the best central plan figures. The centre therefore wishes to gauge the correctness of its distribution of supply tasks, material and labour force quotas. To do this, it requests reports from the sectors, which have to furnish figures on how efficiently they are able to utilize the materials and manpower allocated by the centre.

It is for the purposes of this reporting-back process that the sectors solve the dual problem. They determine the shadow prices of the central plan figures (also the shadow prices of the bounds figuring in their own special constraints), and on their basis report to the centre. This report is a kind of reflection – a "marking" – of the original central program. Let us assume that it turns out that the shadow price of the labour force quota in sector 1 is 100, while in sector 2 it is 50. It stands to reason that the labour force quota of sector 2 must then be curtailed in favour of sector 1. Or else it turns out that the shadow price of the electric power quota in sector 3 is 60, but that in sector 9 it is only 20. It is then worth while re-allocating some of the electric power from sector 9 to sector 3.

These rearrangements lead to the preparation of a new central program. The sectors are sent new central plan figures. The sectors once more determine the shadow prices of the new central plan figures. The centre accordingly again corrects the central program, once more sends down modified plan figures to the sectors, and so forth. The procedure consists of several steps; each step comprises a central program correction, and a sectoral dual programming process or shadow price determination.

In the course of the *iterative process* which will be discussed in detail later, information flows in two directions – new sets of central targets

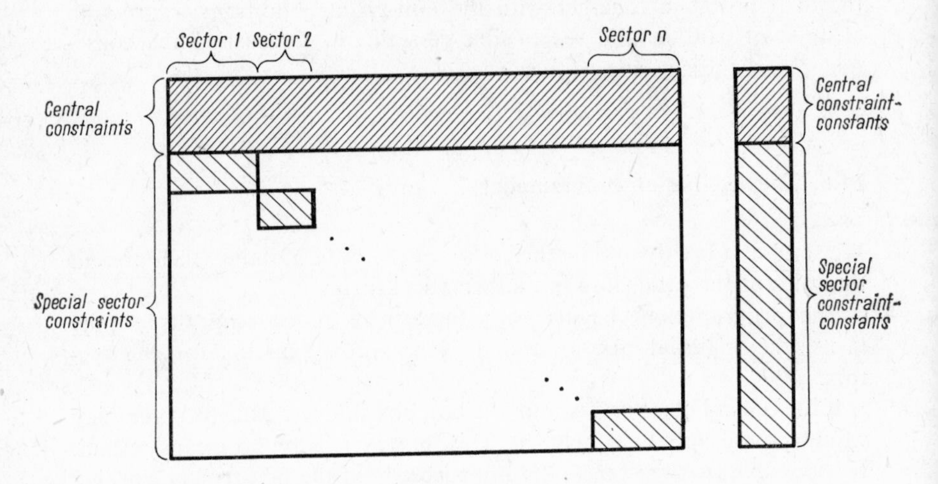

Fig. 24.1

flow from the centre to the sectors, and new sets of shadow prices flow from the sectors to the centre. This, in fact, is why the procedure has been called two-level planning. To use the familiar terms of cybernetics, the model represents a control system that operates with "negative feedback". The shadow price system obtained by programming the sectors, furnishes a feedback that achieves the continuous correction of the instructions emanating from the centre.

It will be proved in Appendix H that this procedure is *convergent*, and that the optimum may be approached to any required accuracy.

At each step it is possible to supply an upper estimate of the maximum amount by which the objective function value of the program determined in the step concerned, is less than the optimal objective function value. In other words, it is possible to state the maximum savings that a continuation of the steps of the programming process could still achieve. If these maximum potential savings are no longer too large, the process may be halted. It is possible to prescribe a figure in advance – a kind of "tolerance value" – so that if the objective function value in a particular step does not differ from the optimal value by more than δ, then the computing can be halted and the program called quasi-optimal, or δ - o p t i m a l.

In our view this is sufficient for all practical purposes. In practice it is not necessary to have an exact solution of the problem and to achieve the ultimate optimum. It is enough to have a well-defined approximation*.

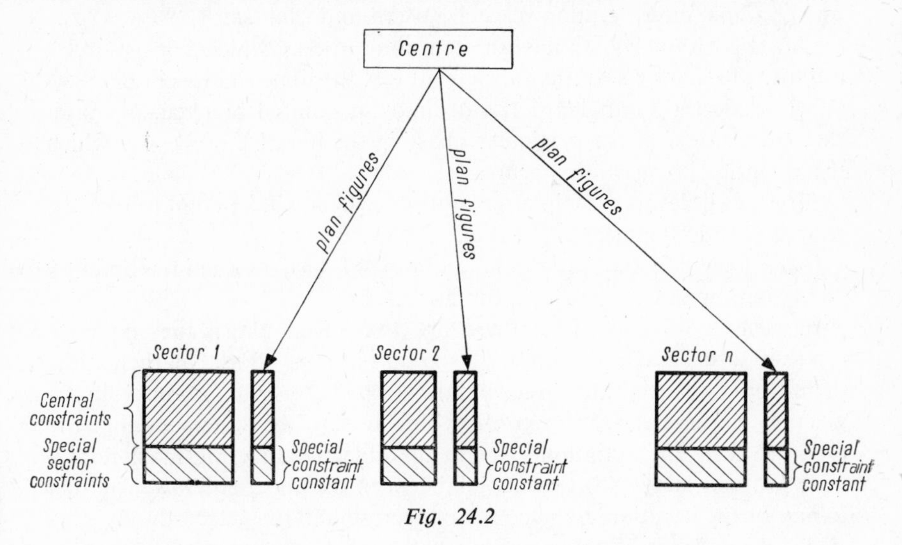

Fig. 24.2

Before proceeding to a more detailed discussion of the course of computation, we try to explain the model of two-level planning by diagrams. Figure 24.1 shows the OCI problem before decomposition. The big rectangle is the matrix of the coefficients in the constraints. The empty field represents those blocks where exclusively zeros are figuring. The strip stretching above across the matrix represents the coefficients of the central constraints; the smaller blocks along the diagonal represent the coefficients of the special sector constraints. The structure of the column on the right side, i.e. of the vector of constraint-constants corresponds to the structure of the coefficient matrix.

The next diagram, figure 24.2 shows the decomposition of the problem by the two-level planning model. The big **O**-blocks are omitted. The lower part of the vector of the sectoral constraint-constants (thinly striped) remains unchanged in the whole course of the procedure. The upper part of the column (striped in heavy lines) represents the central plan figures, which are modified from phase to phase.

* Let us recall, for instance, that a considerable part of the initial data is not exact (see Part 3 of this book). This in itself is sufficient reason to avoid exaggerating the importance of whether the exact solution of the programming problem for the national economy has in fact been achieved.

24.7. Detailed Description of the Algorithm

In the detailed description of the algorithm we will endeavour to give also an economic interpretation of each notion and each step*.

Our algorithm constitutes an iteration process which consists of a number of p h a s e s. In the subsequent text the upper indices in brackets ( ) beside the symbols, or the ordinals in pointed brackets ⟨ ⟩ indicate the number of the particular phase in the iterative process in which the quantity in question occurs.

First of all, let us explain a few notions which will be employed in the course of describing the algorithm.

One of these is the e x a m i n a t i o n o f t h e t e r m i n a b i l i t y of the iteration. This is carried out as follows:

In each individual phase there are two given data: the u p p e r o p t i m u m and the l o w e r o p t i m u m. Both mathematical definition and economic interpretation of these two notions will be given later on. Let us here confine ourselves to the statement that the OCI problem, the optimum value of the objective function in economy-wide programming will certainly fall between the upper and lower optima in any of the iterations. The control of terminability is, accordingly, carried out by means of ascertaining whether the difference between upper and lower optima was greater than a predetermined critical value δ. If so, the calculation should be continued; if not, it can be terminated.

The other notion which will be encountered rather frequently is that c l o s i n g of the calculation. By this, the following is meant.

As will be clear from the foregoing, the sectors will in each phase of the iteration solve the *dual* programming problem of the sector model; it is on the basis of this that they will report to the centre. In the "sector store", on the other hand, the primary program belonging to the last received dual program will also be preserved**.

The centre has, on the basis of the examination of the iteration's terminability, decided to terminate the calculation, it will instruct the sectors to determine the *primal* optimal program obtained in the last phase***.

* Those interested exclusively in the mathematical or computational aspects of the problem will find a more concise description in Appendix H and in other publications such as [102] and [103].

** As known, in the case of employing the simplex algorithm, this will "automatically" issue from row "z" of the simplex tableau. See S. KARLIN [63], pp. 169–170.

*** Later on, we will revert to the question that what we are dealing with here is the primal program belonging to the *preliminary* dual optimal program.

The total of these programs constitutes the δ-optimal program of the economy-wide programming problem, the final determination of which is equivalent to closing the calculation.

Having introduced these two notions, let us now proceed to describe the course of the algorithm. In the calculation we may depart from any central program $(v_{it}^{(1)}, z_{ijt}^{(1)}, w_{it}^{(1)})$. We will pass over the 1st, 2nd, ... phase and begin with the Nth phase.

Each individual phase is composed of four steps at the most, although, as will be shown, the closing of the calculation may be reached before all four steps have been made.

Step 1. This takes place at the centre. First of all, the terminability of the calculation must be examined. For the purpose we must know $\Phi^*\langle N-1\rangle$, the upper optimum of the $(N-1)$th phase, as well as $\varphi^*\langle N-1\rangle$, the lower optimum of the $(N-1)$th phase. There are two possible cases, viz.

Case 1.1.

$$\Phi^*\langle N-1\rangle - \varphi^*\langle N-1\rangle \leqq \delta .$$

The iteration can be terminated. The calculation is closed.

Case 1.2.

$$\Phi^*\langle N-1\rangle - \varphi^*\langle N-1\rangle > \delta .$$

The calculation must be continued. In this case the following programming problem must be solved in the centre: let us maximize the central objective function

$$\sum_{i=1}^{N} \sum_{t=1}^{T} \left\{ v_{it}^*\langle N-1\rangle\, v_{it} + \sum_{\substack{j=1\\ j\neq i}}^{n} \zeta_{ijt}^* \langle N-1\rangle\, z_{ijt} + \omega_{it}^* \langle N-1\rangle\, w_{it} \right\} \tag{24.14}$$

subject to constraints

$$\sum_{\substack{j=1\\ j\neq i}}^{n} z_{jit} + d_{it} = v_{it} \leqq V_{it}, \quad i = 1,\ldots,n;\ t = 1,\ldots, T, \tag{24.15}$$

$$\sum_{i=1}^{n} w_{it} = W_t, \quad t = 1,\ldots, T, \tag{24.16}$$

$$v_{it} \geqq 0,\ z_{jit} \geqq 0,\ w_{it} \geqq 0,\ i = 1,\ldots, n;\ j = 1,\ldots,n;\ j \neq i;\ t = 1,\ldots, T. \tag{24.17}$$

It will be clear that the constraint system of this programming problem is identical with the originally set constraints. Now, the objective function prescribes that the *computational return* of the plan figures sent to the sectors should be maximal. This calculative return is computed on the basis of the shadow prices sent up by the sectors. The content of the objective function could be formulated in the following words: "Let us believe the sectors that the plan figures allotted to them will actually bring the national economy as much as they have reported them to bring – and let the return be maximal as computed on that basis!"

This central programming problem is one of rather extensive dimensions. Fortunately, it can be divided into easily solvable "microprogramming problems". There are two types of the latter: one that is connected with the product balances of the type (24.15) and another that is connected with the manpower balances of the type (24.16). Let us examine the two types separately.

One of the microprogramming problems formulates the *provisional* production and distribution of the ith product for the tth period:

$$\left.\begin{array}{l} \sum\limits_{\substack{j=1 \\ j\neq i}}^{n} z_{jit} + d_{it} = v_{it} \leqq V_{it} \\ z_{jit} \geqq 0, \quad j = 1,\ldots,n;\ j \neq i;\ v_{it} \geqq 0 \\ \sum\limits_{\substack{j=1 \\ j\neq i}}^{n} \zeta^{*}_{jit} \langle N-1 \rangle z_{jit} - v^{*}_{it} \langle N-1 \rangle v_{it} \rightarrow \max! \end{array}\right\} \begin{array}{l} i = 1,\ldots,n \\ t = 1,\ldots,T. \end{array} \qquad (24.18)$$

The solution of the problem is the following:

(a) if $\max\limits_{j\neq i} \zeta^{*}_{jit} \langle N-1 \rangle < v^{*}_{it} \langle N-1 \rangle$,

then

$$v^{(N)}_{it} = d_{it}, \quad z^{(N)}_{jit} = 0, \qquad j = 1,\ldots,n, j \neq i. \qquad (24.19)$$

(b) if $\max\limits_{j\neq i} \zeta^{*}_{jit} \langle N-1 \rangle = \zeta^{*}_{j_0it} \langle N-1 \rangle \geqq v^{*}_{it} \langle N-1 \rangle$,

then*

* If shadow price $\zeta^{*}_{jit} \langle N-1 \rangle$ is in several sectors both maximal and not less than $v^{*}_{it} \langle N-1 \rangle$, then $V_{it} - d_{it}$ may be distributed among them in any arbitrary portion.

$$v_{it}^{(N)} = V_{it}, z_{j_0it}^{(N)} = V_{it} - d_{it}, z_{jit}^{(N)} = 0, \ \ j = 1,\ldots, \ n, j \neq i, j \neq j_0. \quad (24.20)$$

The logic of the solution is quite simple. Shadow price v_{it}^* of the supply task may be considered as the "supply price" of the product; shadow price ζ_{jit}^* of the material quota as its "demand price". Now, there are two fundamental cases, viz.:

(a) The supply price is higher than any of the demand prices. In this case the decision will be that none of the sectors should be given anything of it and only the requirements of external consumption d_{it} should be secured.

(b) The other case is when the highest demand price is higher than the supply price. In this case the maximum $(V_{it} - d_{it})$ quantity should be secured for productive utilization, and the whole should be allocated to the sector which promises the highest demand price.

This will most probably appear an absurd principle: either nothing – or all to the same sector? However, as will be seen later in Step 3, the actual distribution will be less extreme than this.

Let us now approach the second microprogramming task, that of the provisional distribution of the national manpower quota. Here, the problem is the following:

$$\left.\begin{aligned} &\sum_{i=1}^{n} w_{it} = W_t \\ &w_{it} \geqq 0, \qquad i = 1,\ldots, n \\ &\sum_{i=1}^{n} \omega_{it}^* \langle N-1 \rangle \ w_{it} \to \max! \end{aligned}\right\} t = 1,\ldots, T. \quad (24.21)$$

In this case the solution is even more simple:

if $\max\limits_{i} \omega_{it}^* \langle N-1 \rangle = \omega_{i_0t}^* \langle N-1 \rangle$, then*

$$w_{i_0t}^{(N)} = W_t, w_{it}^{(N)} = 0, \qquad i = 1,\ldots, n; \ i \neq i_0. \quad (24.22)$$

This means that in the course of the provisional distribution the total manpower quota of the national economy is allotted to the sector which promised the highest ω_{it}^* computational wage rate.

* If the shadow price $\omega_{it}^* \langle N-1 \rangle$ is equally maximal in several sectors, W_t may be distributed at will among these sectors.

When all microprogramming problems have been carried out, Step 1 is completed.

Step 2. This step, too, is carried out in the centre. With the provisional distributions completed, the sum of the maxima obtained from the microprogramming tasks must be computed. Let us denote this sum $\Phi^{\#}\langle N\rangle$. Then*

$$\Phi^{\#}\langle N\rangle = \sum_{t=1}^{T} \left\{ \sum_{i=1}^{n} \left[\left(\max_{j\neq i} \zeta^{*}_{jit}\langle N-1\rangle - v^{*}_{it}\langle N-1\rangle \right)^{+} . V_{it} - \right.\right.$$

$$\left.\left. - v^{*}_{it}\langle N-1\rangle\, d_{it} + \max_{i} \omega^{*}_{it}\,\langle N-1\rangle .\ W_{t} \right] \right\} . \qquad (24.23)$$

To this a sum $\sum_{i=1}^{n} \Phi^{0}_{i}\langle N-1\rangle$ must now be added. Let us call this latter sum the s p e c i a l o p t i m u m c o m p o n e n t, whose more precise definition and economic interpretation shall be deferred.

Now it will be possible to calculate the upper optimum in the Nth phase:

$$\Phi^{*}\langle N\rangle = \Phi^{\#}\langle N\rangle + \sum_{i=1}^{n} \Phi^{0}_{i}\,\langle N-1\rangle . \qquad (24.24)$$

It will be recalled that at the beginning of Step 1 already we examined the terminability of the iteration, but at that stage by means of the upper optimum $\Phi^{*}\langle N-1\rangle$ obtained in the $(N-1)$th phase. At the present stage, however, a new $\Phi^{*}\langle N\rangle$ upper optimum is available for the repeated control of the iteration's terminability.

Case 2.1

$$\Phi^{*}\langle N\rangle - \varphi^{*}\langle N-1\rangle = \delta .$$

The iteration can be terminated, the calculation is closed.

Case 2.2

$$\Phi^{*}\langle N\rangle - \varphi^{*}\langle N-1\rangle > \delta .$$

* α^{+} is used to denote the positive part of α: $\alpha^{+} = \max\,(0, \alpha)$. Accordingly, $\alpha^{+} = \alpha$ if $\alpha \geqq 0$, and $\alpha^{+} = -\alpha$ if $\alpha < 0$.

The calculation must be continued, the aim being to obtain realistic and reasonable distributions instead of the extreme and one-sided provisional ones. This is achieved by "mixing" in the appropriate proportion the provisional distributions now obtained with the earlier ones.

The new central programs to be sent down to the sectors will be obtained on the basis of the following formulae:

$$\left.\begin{aligned} v_{it}^{*}\langle N\rangle &= \frac{N-1}{N}\, v_{it}^{*}\langle N-1\rangle + \frac{1}{N}\, v_{it}^{(N)} \\ z_{ijt}^{*}\langle N\rangle &= \frac{N-1}{N}\, z_{ijt}^{*}\langle N-1\rangle + \frac{1}{N}\, z_{ijt}^{(N)}, \; j=1,\dots, n,\; j \neq i \\ w_{it}^{*}\langle N\rangle &= \frac{N-1}{N}\, w_{it}^{*}\langle N-1\rangle + \frac{1}{N}\, w_{it}^{(N)}. \end{aligned}\right\} \begin{aligned} i &= 1,\dots,n \\ t &= 1,\dots,T. \end{aligned} \tag{24.25}$$

The provisional, "extreme" plan figures were not marked with an asterisk, but the above ones are; this is the distinctive symbol of the fact that what we have here to do with are already real plan figures to be sent down to the sectors. As can be seen, "mixing" means here that we calculate the weighted arithmetic mean of the provisional microprogram now obtained and the central plan figure employed in the preceding step*.

With Step 2, the centre's tasks in the Nth phase have been completed. It was shown that the operations to be carried out in the centre are quite simple and would not even require the use of the electronic computer. The task consists in comparing various magnitudes, in working out

* This is actually the simple arithmetic mean of the microprograms obtained up to now. For, reversing formula (24.25), in the case of e.g. $v_{it}\langle N\rangle$ we obtain the following:

$$\begin{aligned} v_{it}\langle N\rangle &= \frac{N-1}{N}\, v_{it}\langle N-1\rangle + \frac{1}{N}\, v_{it}^{(N)} = \\ &= \frac{N-1}{N}\left(\frac{N-2}{N-1}\, v_{it}\langle N-2\rangle + \frac{1}{N-1}\, v_{it}^{(N-1)}\right) + \frac{1}{N}\, v_{it}^{(N)} = \\ &= \frac{N-2}{N}\, v_{it}\langle N-2\rangle + \frac{1}{N} v_{it}^{(N-1)} + \frac{1}{N}\, v_{it}^{(N)} = \dots = \\ &= \frac{1}{N}\left(v_{it}^{(1)} + v_{it}^{(2)} + \dots + v_{it}^{(N-1)} + v_{it}^{(N)}\right). \end{aligned} \tag{24.26}$$

arithmetic means, etc. All these operations may be carried out separately and do not make it necessary to burden the memory of the electronic computer with a mass of data.

Step 3. This is already taking place in the sectors. The sectors will carry out their programming tasks in possession of the plan figures $v_{it}^*\langle N\rangle$, $z_{ijt}^*\langle N\rangle$ and $w_{it}^*\langle N\rangle$ just received from the sectors. They will carry out the dual programming task described in formulae (24.10)–(24.13), where the new plan figures just received from the centre figure as objective function coefficients*. From the calculation, the sector will obtain the following informations:

(a) *Provisional* sector shadow prices, the solutions $\nu_{it}^{(N)}$, $\zeta_{ijt}^{(N)}$ and $\omega_{it}^{(N)}$ of the dual programming problem.

(b) Objective function value $\varphi^{(N)}$ pertaining to the optimal program. Summing up all sector optima $\varphi_i^{(N)}$, we obtain the *lower optimum* of the OCI problem in the Nth phase:

$$\varphi^*\langle N\rangle = \sum_{i=1}^{n} \varphi_i^{(N)} . \tag{24.27}$$

(c) The *provisional special sector optimum component:*

$$\Phi_i^{0(N)} = \sum_{t=1}^{T} V_{it}\, \varkappa_{it}^{(N)} + \sum_{l=\text{spec}} b_{il}^0\, \delta_{il}^{(N)} . \tag{24.28}$$

The name of this magnitude may be somewhat long, but its content is quite simple: it constitutes the computational return of V_{it}, the upper bound of the supply task and of the bounds of the special sector constraints, valued at shadow prices. In this component are summarized all computational returns which are *not* charged to the centrally allocated plan figures but to the undistributed bounds of constant magnitude throughout the course of the iteration.

Step 4. The *provisional* sector shadow prices obtained in Step 3 fail to give a realistic idea of how the sector is able to "manage" the plan figures allocated to it by the centre. Realistic valuation will again require the "mixing" of the provisional sector shadow-price system with the shadow-price systems obtained in earlier phases. This is carried out as follows:

* From the computational point of view it will be expedient to use for the calculation the optimal simplex tableau of the programming carried out in the previous, $(N-1)$th phase.

$$\left.\begin{aligned} v_{it}^*\langle N\rangle &= \frac{N-1}{N}\, v_{it}^*\langle N-1\rangle + \frac{1}{N}\, v_{it}^{(N)} \\ \zeta_{ijt}^*\langle N\rangle &= \frac{N-1}{N}\, \zeta_{ijt}^*\langle N-1\rangle + \frac{1}{N}\, \zeta_{ijt}^{(N)},\ j=1,\ldots,n; j\neq i \\ \omega_{it}^*\langle N\rangle &= \frac{N-1}{N}\, \omega_{it}^*\langle N-1\rangle + \frac{1}{N}\, \omega_{it}^{(N)} \end{aligned}\right\} t=1,\ldots,T. \qquad (24.29)$$

The asterisks marking the "mixed" sector shadow prices thus obtained signify the fact that these are no longer merely provisional, but shadow prices that may actually be sent up to the centre. It was shown in Step 1 that it is on these that the calculations at the centre are based; it is these that are used as objective function coefficients.

The provisional special sector optimum components obtained here must be "mixed" in a similar way with the components obtained in the previous phases:

$$\Phi_i^0\langle N\rangle = \frac{N-1}{N}\Phi_i^0\langle N-1\rangle + \frac{1}{N}\Phi_i^{0(N)} \qquad (\Phi_i^0\langle 1\rangle = \Phi_i^{0(1)}). \qquad (24.30)$$

This is the "special optimum component" which was required according to formula (24.24) to work out the upper optimum but whose closer interpretation it was not possible to give at that stage.

Now that Step 4 has been described, the notions must have become clear whose explanation had been deferred in the course of the exposition, viz.:

The upper optimum: the sum total of the computational returns charged to the central plan figures, valued at mixed sector shadow prices (24.25), plus the undistributed returns charged to the constant sector bounds, valued equally at sector shadow prices (24.28) and (24.30).

The lower optimum: the sum total of the optimal subjective function values of sector-level dual programming problem (24.27).

Looking now back on the tasks carried out on a sector level: first, in Step 3, "regular" linear programming has to be carried out, e.g. by the simplex method; then, in Step 4, the operations to be carried out are also most simple, e.g. averaging.

At the end of Step 4, shadow prices $v_{it}^*\langle N\rangle$, $\zeta_{ijt}^*\langle N\rangle$ and $\omega_{it}^*\langle N\rangle$ as well as sector optimum $\varphi_i^{(N)}$ and mixed special optimum component $\Phi_i^0\langle N\rangle$ are sent up by the sector to the centre. With this, the Nth phase of the iteration is closed.

24.8. Interpretation of the Problem in Terms of the Theory of Games

The basis for the procedure was the fact that the task was approached as a game-theoretical problem. The restatement of the programming done in two-level planning as a zero-sum two-person game, may be found in Appendix H. We might well be satisfied to regard this as a transformation of purely mathematical significance, in that the present procedure utilizes propositions and calculating methods that happen to have been worked out as part of the theory of games. This would lead us not to attach independent economic meaning to the game-theoretical features.

It is a noteworthy fact, however, that in the case of the economic planning model, the statement of the problem in terms of the theory of games reflects actual economic relations. The fact is that the situation originally already shows some analogy with strategic games. Both players are in possession of certain information, but they cannot alone take fully satisfactory decisions, because to do so they would require to know the information of the other player as well. The centre has a broad purview, but it has no detailed knowledge of the special problems (e.g. the technical and cost figures for the various sectors, the special conditions limiting choice within the sector, etc.), which are known to the sectors. Or put the other way round, the sectors see many details, but they have no ability to survey the broad interrelations that can only be clear to the centre. Just as in strategic games, the situation which evolves depends on both players. Both the centre and the sectors clearly know that the actions of the other "player" also exercise a great influence on the situation. Under such circumstances both players seek the relatively most reassuring strategy for themselves. This strategy is the minimax solution of the game.

In the present model the acceptance of the minimax strategy means the following:

Let us presume that the centre is "omniscient" and is in possession even of those special detailed items of information that are usually only known accurately to the sectors. In this case, if ideal computing facilities were available, it would itself be able centrally to elaborate the optimal program for the national economy (the optimal OCI program). The program thus determined would have a certain objective function value and result in optimal economic returns (the OCI optimum).

If, on the other hand, the centre (both in this model and in real life) is, due to deficient information, unable itself, without the collaboration of the sectors, to determine the optimal program for the economy, then the returns of the economy will be less than the optimal value. Thus in consequence of decisions taken "independently" of the sectors, relative losses will be incurred. The centre strives cut to the losses.

At the opposite end, the sectors are unable themselves, without the directing and coordinating activity of the centre, to achieve the optimal program for the economy. In the case of decisions taken "independently" of the centre, they will necessarily furnish a faulty evaluation of the resources and quotas allocated to them. Let us again presume for a moment, as was done earlier in defining the dual objective function, that the sectors are made to pay a "penalty" for the surplus allocated to them due to the over-estimation of resources and quotas. Under such circumstances, a biased evaluation, i.e. a biased shadow price system, would result in a grave loss to the sector. The sectors would then obviously strive to make this loss as small as possible.

It may thus be seen that both sides strive to reduce a specific kind of relative loss. The centre's aim is that as little as possible should be lost of the optimal returns of the economy, the sector's that the optimal evaluations should be surpassed by as little as possible. The minimax solution is achieved when both players succeed in eliminating this relative loss.

Several procedures may be used to determine the minimax strategy. One familiar method is that of *fictitious playing*. The two-level planning procedure uses this fictitious playing to solve the problem. The two players – only on paper, of course – "play a game". The centre "moves" – it issues a set of central plan figures to the sectors. Next the sectors together "move", by reporting back a set of shadow prices. Now the centre "moves" again, and so forth. Thus the players approach the solution of the game, which is the optimal program.

Let us assume – taking a highly exaggerated example for easier understanding – that we have come to the tenth step. It has turned out that the shadow price of the current quota is highest in sector 6. Should we then, having noted this, take away the current quota of all the sectors, to give all the current to sector 6? This would be palpably absurd.

Such extreme corrections must in all cases be avoided. As the tenth correction in the central program is carried out, we must not forget the lessons learned from Steps 9, 8, 7, etc., of the fact, say, that in the ninth step it was not sector 6 but sector 4 which reported the most favourable shadow prices for current, in the eighth step sector 1, and so forth. The proposed method, that of "fictitious playing", is based precisely on the consideration of "remembering" the earlier step at each new step. The strategies obtained in the successive steps are therefore "mixed" according to definite rules, discussed in section 24.7. In the case of the previous example we would therefore, instead of the extreme move of transferring the whole power quota, merely correct the distributions already obtained in the earlier steps, in favour of sector 6. The strategy of giving all the current to sector 6 would thus be "mixed" in the ratio of 1 : 9 with the earlier power distribution strategies, i.e. the power quota of sector 6 would be augmented by 10 per cent of the total power quota, at the expense of the other sectors.

Similarly the sectors also "mix" the shadow prices obtained in the successive steps with those of the earlier steps, thus gradually approaching the optimal shadow price system.

This gradual process of correction (the "mixing" of strategies) makes sure that the successive steps should not lead to oscillations between extreme programs that are absurd from the practical point of view, but that the cautious correlation of the programs should result in a continuous approach to the optimum.

24.9. The Treatment of Investments in the Model

The two-level planning model as described in ch. 24 exceeds to some extent the boundaries of the subject of this work, affording as it does the possibility of a certain choice of time – in contrast with the models discussed hitherto which were always confined to programming for the structure of the plan year.

The determination of the program is tantamount to decision-making, among others, on the following points:

– The time when an investment activity should be started. As a matter of fact, the various alternatives resulting in the same output and identical in input structure, differing from one another exclusively in starting time of the investment project (and, of course, in the time of going into operation), may be treated in the model as separate variables.

– The duration of the investment activity. As a matter of fact, even the alternatives which concur with one another, in addition to the above, also in the starting time of the investment project may be treated in the model as separate variables, the difference between them consisting in the fact that with one of them construction takes two years, with another three years; or that one of them will start production at full capacity in the second year of operation, another in the third year only, and so on.

– The time when a reproductive activity should be stopped.

– The cases when imports should be substituted for domestic production (or conversely), or exports should take place.

At the same time it must be obvious that even in this form our model leaves several problems of time choice out of consideration.

Thus, for example, determining the schedule of private and public consumption is not considered a decision problem of our model. The relating targets – and their most important part, the dynamics of raising the standard of living – are taken over as constant plan directives from the official plan based on traditional methods.

Nor can the question, how to ensure further economic development *after* the plan period, be considered a decision problem of our model. Here again, the Gordian knot of this extremely difficult problem is cut with a single sword-stroke: the conditions of development in the farther future are ensured by the adequate definition of the constraints in accordance with the stipulations of the official plan. In practice, this is achieved by a combination of the following methods.

(1) It is prescribed obligatorily, by means of constraints, that certain investment projects should be started within the plan period – even such as will by the Tth period as yet not contribute to the growth of the objective function – provided that this is required for further development after the Tth period.

(2) For certain projects which are to start towards the end of the plan period, resources are "kept in reserve", i.e. the input requirements of certain "transitory" projects to be concluded after the Tth period are made to appear among the targets d_{it} of external consumption. In such cases the input requirements will have to be defined only summarily and it will not be necessary at this stage to take a stand as to which concrete projects should be started towards the end of the plan period.

Actually, both methods will nevertheless necessitate the setting up of certain targets to ensure the transition between the plan period and the one following it, and to outline the structure of the "transitory" projects to be concluded after the plan period. It is, though, from the programming project itself that the desirable structure of investments ought to emerge*.

* The difficulty may be eased by resorting to some type of iteration, of multistep calculation. Setting out from *a priori* assumptions concerning the trend and sectoral structure of the optimal program's investments, we base the constraints associated with transitory investments on these assumptions. After programming is carried out, we proceed to investigate whether the trend and structure of the investment projects brought in "voluntarily" by the optimal program (especially as far as the first stages are concerned) differed essentially from what had been assumed when defining the constraints associated with transitory investments.

This is one more reason for fixing the greatest possible length for plan period T. The longer the long-term plan period, the less will the targets of the later stages affect the program of the first ones. And yet, from the point of view of actual action it is these latter that count most.

There is a further question that poses itself in connection with the objective function described in ch. 24, the maximization of foreign currency returns.

From the point of view of the national economy it is not indifferent whether the surplus foreign currency obtained as a result of programming will be available at the beginning of the plan period or only at its end. It will, therefore, be expedient to maximize the *discounted* amount of foreign currency returns. The rate of interest to be employed in discounting is obvious here: it should equal either the rate of interest asked for on credits granted by Hungary (provided that an extension of credits granted can be realistically envisaged), or that payable on Hungary's foreign debts, – in particular, on the most burdensome debts which are repayable first, provided that it is the repayment of debts that is primarily envisaged. As a matter of fact, it is warranted to set out in our model from the assumption that the surplus foreign currency obtained as a result of programming will be used either for credit granting or for debt repayment and will thus bear compound interest to the benefit of the national economy.

If so, new constraints associated with transitory investments will have to be defined, this time already on the basis of data obtained from the optimal program. It is to be hoped that with sufficient professional routine it will be possible to eliminate essential contradictions between the trend and structure of investments brought in "voluntarily" by programming and those "forced in" by means of the constraints associated with transitory investments.

CHAPTER 25

THE FUTURE OF MULTI-LEVEL PLANNING

25.1. Aspects of the Model of Two-level Planning

The model of two-level planning as described in ch. 24 lends itself to analysis and further development from several points of view.

(1) It may interest the *mathematician* to know what is the significance from the viewpoint of the theory of games and the theory of mathematical programming, of the propositions elaborated in connection with the model and given in Appendix H; to what extent may these propositions constitute a starting point for further theoretical investigations, etc. However, these problems transcend the scope of the present book*.

(2) From the point of view of those *engaged in computation techniques* it may be of interest to know how far the algorithm described in ch. 24 can be employed in actual practice. This is briefly treated in section 25.2.

(3) Sections 25.3 and 25.4 may concern the *planner*, as they discuss the question of how far can two-level planning be used in planning for economic activities and prices, and what is its place in the system of planning.

(4) Section 2.5 approaches the problem from the viewpoint of the *theoretical economist* and poses the question: to what extent can we regard two-level planning as the abstract model of a centrally planned and directed economy?

The present chapter gives, of course, a few general ideas only in answer to questions (2), (3) and (4) – a detailed exposition of the problems presented will require further extensive study.

25.2. Computation-technical Properties of the Algorithm

On the basis of the algorithm described in ch. 24 and Appendix H, some numerical experiments have been carried out**. Though these have as yet

* On this subject see [103].

** The experiments have been carried out by Gy. Tarnay and S. Frivaldszky within the framework of a research project connected with national-level economic programming.

not been completed, some important facts may be derived from the results obtained up to now.

From the point of view of computation techniques, an interesting comparison offers itself between the Dantzig–Wolfe decomposition method*, (the most widely-known procedure for the decomposition of large programming models) and the fictitious playing method described in ch. 24. In the following, the first shall be called the DW method, the second the FP method.

The FP method has the important advantage over the DW method that under it the operations carried out on the central level are considerably more simple as regards computation techniques. They consist exclusively of microprogramming problems, i.e. the carrying out of calculations of the simplest type separately with each of the central constraints. There will thus be practically no limit set to the number of constraints by the store capacity of the electronic computer. As the OCI model may be broken down into any number of sector models, it may be stated that *with the application of the FP method the dimensions of the OCI problem are not restricted by the store capacity of the computer.*

With the application of the DW method, on the other hand, "regular" linear programming must be carried out which does not lend itself to decomposition into microprogramming problems. The number N of the constraint constants of this central linear programming problem will depend on the following:

$$N = m + n, \tag{25.1}$$

where

m = the number of centrally treated product and resource balances. (In the terminology of ch. 24: the number of central constraints.) This corresponds to the number of rows running through the whole matrix in the upper zone in figure 24.1

n = the number of sectors.

A limit will thus be set to the dimension of the central model by the greatest programming problem which the computer is able to solve without decomposition. Under the circumstances prevailing in this country the limit is: $N \leqq 100$.

In the case of an OCI problem of large dimensions, it must be broken down into a great number of sectors, i.e. n will be large and this in turn

* See [28] and [29].

will reduce the possible size of *m*. Or, conversely, if for any reason *m* must be chosen higher, this will in turn reduce the possible number of sectors, i.e. ultimately the possible dimension of the OCI model.

With the application of the DW method, the limits of the *store capacity* of the available computers will thus come to the fore.

The DW method has, none the less, three decided advantages over the FP method, viz.:

(1) The DW method is finite, the FP method is not.

(2) Experiments carried out up to the present have shown that with the DW method convergence was more rapid*.

(3) The DW method is a *monotonic* procedure with the value of the objective function improving with each phase of the iteration, whereas in the case of the FP method the optimum is approached with fluctuations.

I would consider advantage (3) the most important, at least as far as our economy-wide programming experiments are concerned. With our problem (but this applies equally to several other instances of application) a known official program based on other than mathematical methods is given beforehand. It is *in relation to this program* that we want to achieve an improvement. The point is not when to reach the exact optimum or its immediate neighbourhood – it has repeatedly been pointed out in this book how relative this notion of optimality was anyhow. What really matters is to obtain an improvement in relation to the given official program at the earliest possible stage. In the case of a monotonic convergent method, such as the DW method, this stage can be reached comparatively rapidly. In the case of the FP method, on the other hand, it is usual at the beginning of the iteration for the value of the objective function to fluctuate strongly.

As a conclusion it may be stated that from the point of view of the speed of the convergence – and especially from that of the rate of improvement that can be achieved in relation to a given program – the DW method must be considered more advantageous.

* Experiments have been carried out with the aim of modifying the "mixing rules" described in ch. 24 and in Appendix H. The most efficient method turned out to be the one where in the course of provisory distribution (see formulae (24.19), (24.20) and (24.22)) not everything was allotted to the sector which promised the most advantageous shadow price but the rest of the sectors were also given a share, each in proportion to the shadow price reported by it.

According to information, similar experiments to accelerate to progress of convergence in fictitious playing are being carried out in the USSR too. So far, no final evaluation of the experiments has taken place.

Our comparative experiments have as yet not been completed. In the first experimental calculation, which will be dealt with below, the DW method will most probably be employed first and only later will it be possible to proceed to a practical application of the FP method.

25.3. The First Experimental Calculation

Commissioned by the National Planning Board, a large research team is actually engaged in the preparatory works of the first experimental economy-wide programming project*. The model is destined to provide a help in working out the long-term plan for the years 1966–1970. The principle aim is to test the method itself and to gain practical experience. It is, however, desirable that some of the numerical results of programming should prove to be utilizable in practical planning. Practical preparations for an economy-wide programming project were launched in 1964. Here, I will confine myself to describing a few principal characteristics of the model, and even this rather with the purpose of giving the reader an idea as to the modifications a *theoretical* model (in the present case the project outlined in ch. 24) is likely to undergo in the course of its first *practical* testing.

(1) In the course of the first experimental calculations, in contrast with the procedure described in ch. 24, no multi-period programming could as yet be undertaken. Owing to the difficulties of data compilation and of the calculations themselves, programming will be carried out – just as in the case of the sector projects described earlier in this book – only for the last plan year of the long-term planning period. This is a regrettable concession and it is to be hoped that in later calculations it will be possible to carry into effect our plans concerning a multi-period model.

(2) The first calculation does not embrace the whole domain of the national economy. Some 40 sector models are expected to be constructed, among them those embracing the major part of power supply, mining, the light, food and building industries, railway communications and agriculture. Other important branches of the national economy, such as the engineering and chemical industries, on the other hand, figure only with part of their activities.

* The research project is directed by the author, with 14 different research institutes and computing centres participating in it. The work is supervised by the Scientific Section of the National Planning Board and the Computing Centre of the Hungarian Academy of Sciences; the sector models are worked out by the responsible sector research institutes and computational centres.

(3) It was our endeavour to bring the framework of our model as near as possible to the index system of the traditional planning methodology. I wish to recall here the main groups of the traditional index system as surveyed in ch. 1. They will (at least within the scope embraced by our programming project) appear in their major part in the model:

Product balances (among the constraints).
Investment balances* (among the constraints).
Manpower balances (among the constraints).
Balances of external payments and of foreign trade (partly among the constraints, partly in the objective function).
Priority investments (among the activity variables).

In our model – just as in the sector programming model – several relationships appear among the constraints which would in the index system of the traditional planning methodology figure only among the non-documented, and frequently ignored, plan equations. Cases in point are the various export sales constraints, import purchase constraints, capacity constraints, etc.

Thus the model advances on the path started with sector programming: *it unites into a system of simultaneous equations the numerous (documented as well as auxiliary, non-documented) plan variables and plan equations of the traditional planning methods.*

The model's framework makes it, accordingly, possible to take over several pieces of data (directly or with more or less modification) from the plan based on the traditional methods. On the other hand, the results of our calculations, too, will in this manner become comparable with the traditional plan.

25.4. The "Pyramidal" Network of Programming Models

Up to this stage it has been my endeavour to draw conclusions from research work already concluded or from projects actually in course. Now I propose to depart – to the extent of a few ideas – from this principle and to describe the future of mathematical planning as I see it, utopian as it may appear to the reader.

* As our model is not of the multi-period type we are compelled to base our calculations on aggregate investment quotas, in contrast to the model described in ch. 24 where there figured instead the balances of concrete machinery, buildings and other investment goods intended to be utilized in a definite period of time.

Let us imagine a network of computing centres connected in a pyramid*. On the apex we have the computing centre of the National Planning Board; below it, at mid-level, those of the leading institutions of the individual sectors; at bottom level, the computing centres of the minor units (trusts and enterprises) subordinate to the individual leading institutions.

I have no intention of entering into detail as to how many levels will be required** (this depends on the country's dimensions, economic situation etc.), nor as to the principles of organizational structure, whether it thould be based on sectoral or territorial division; whether it is the subsequent or the adjacent phases that should be connected, etc. All I want to point out is that the network is *multi-level* and pyramidal; the lower levels include more units than the higher ones.

At each level, all units will have to construct a mathematical programming model embracing their activities and the constraints prescribed. The units which compose the pyramid are connected by suitable means of telecommunication, e.g. by a telex network. The result, the information output, of calculations carried out with one model provides the basic data, the information input, for one or more of the other models. Here again, I do not wish to go into any detail about the exact character of this information which may consist of final output obligations, material quotas, resource quotas, shadow prices, plan estimates, etc. On the basis of the information received, the units will continuously correct the individual parameters of their models and carry out improvements to their plan.

It is my opinion that *one of the main paths of development in planning methods leads in the direction of establishing the model pyramid outlined above.*

All this may rightly seem to be a utopia at a stage like the present when we are still about to work out the methods of the experimental application of the first *two*-level model. There are, however, real prospects for the implementation of the above ideas, prospects which fundamentally depend on our progress in establishing a wide computer basis and in training specialists in mathematical planning.

Here, a short digression will be permissible. At the time when this book was in print in 1965, extensive discussions were taking place in Hungary

* The term "pyramidation" is used by R. FRISCH [40] in a sense which is to some extent analogous with the above.

** It has not been proved – but may be proved, I believe – that just as in the case of *two*-level planning, a convergent algorithm is conceivable also for *multi*-level models.

between the representatives of top management, the economic planners and the theoretical economists over the questions relating to the "mechanism" of the economy. Mechanism is meant here as a broad collective term including the entire system of planning, economic management and the institutional forms of the economy. To mention but a few of the questions under discussion: which of the economic indicators should be drawn into the orbit of planning and which should be left out? What should be the role of directives in economic management? (Or, in the terminology of the French planners: to what extent should planning be imperative and to what extent indicative in character?) What should the price system be like?

Now, in the course of these discussions there arose also the question, what should be the role of planning based on mathematical methods in the national economy. From the wide variety of views, let me mention but two characteristic ones.

One opinion could be summed up in its crudest form as follows:

"The allocation of resources and with it price formation should be left to the mechanism of the market. Centralized economic planning did in the past not prove sufficiently rational – it should, therefore, be restrained within narrow bounds or even abandoned altogether. Nor can the introduction of mathematical methods alter these negative features of planning. The models of mathematical economics are unrealistic and cannot be considered anything but an interesting intellectual pastime entirely out of contact with the actual functioning of the economy".

It will be worth while to point out that such views are not unequivocally associated with some political attitude. I have heard them voiced in Budapest by socialists and in London by persons who were certainly nothing of the kind.

In my opinion, such views are behind the times and anachronistic. They are both overrating the perfection of the market mechanism and underestimating the achievements of modern science. When in the 1930's the concept of socialism was discussed by western economists, Professor Hayek could still raise the argument against Barone's mathematical model of the socialist economy that in actual practice it would be impossible to solve the enormous number of equations involved by means of mathematical tools*. The three decades that have since passed witnessed significant changes. Sufficient to mention only four closely interrelated achievements:

* See F. A. HAYEK [51].

(1) the extensive spread of punched-card machines, of the modern methods of data processing and storing;

(2) the appearance of high-capacity electronic computers and the incredibly rapid growth of their efficiency;

(3) the elaboration and steady improvement of numerical methods and algorithms suited to solving large equation systems; and, finally,

(4) the application of decomposition methods enabling the combination and joint solution of mathematical models composed of large equation systems.

These achievements went a long way towards extending the sphere of decisions where mathematical models may play a part, i.e. the sphere of strictly rational, exact planning.

The other opinion could be summarized as follows:

"The highly centralized system of economic administration as developed up to now under socialism should be maintained together with the central planning of partial economic processes down to the most minute detail and with the central fixing of all prices – but all this should from now on be carried out by means of mathematical programming. A country-wide network of computing centres should be set up, linked with one another, and the whole economy should then be subjected to detailed planning based on mathematical models."

If the former view can be characterized as a naive 19th-century notion, a naively optimistic belief in the market mechanism – the latter view is certainly a naive 20th-century notion, a naively optimistic belief in the computer. Its representatives include mathematicians who have never directly experienced the infinitely intricate character of economic reality, or practical economists whose knowledge of mathematical methods, operation research and programming derives from promotional literature, and who are not aware of the fact that this discipline is still more or less in its infancy. Only those who are themselves engaged in the practical application of mathematical planning methods will know how far such models are from perfection. Immense efforts will be required even in the construction and solution of an equation system where only several hundred product aggregates are involved, with but one or two technological variants to each, and where a few thousand relationships within the economy are only taken into consideration. Even in a small country as Hungary the Price Control Board will in the course of a general price adjustment fix the price of several hundred thousand products. As mentioned in ch. 1, the number of plan figures and indices set by the National Planning Board and the economic ministries in the course of drawing up a five-year plan is estimated to run to seven digits. And yet, these examples refer only to the mass of figures to be handled at some given data – in connection with a general price adjustment scheme or with the drawing up of a five-year plan. Actually, the economy is in continuous movement; all external conditions are continually changing and decisions will, accordingly, have to be made continually. One cannot know what the 21st century might bring – but *for the time being* it would still be illusory to believe that every decision could be "mathematized".

In my opinion a modern economy – and especially a socialist economy – can dispense neither with planning nor with the market mechanism. What is needed is, however, not the "happy mean" of the two, not their "convex combination" with 50 per cent of market mechanism and 50 per cent of planning, both in half-developed, half-disintegrated form. Both should function in their fully developed form. In the human organism certain functions are controlled by the autonomous nervous system, others by the central nervous system. It would give rise to grave difficulties if the control of, let us say, breathing or the temperature of the body were to devolve on the central nervous system; this would absorb our mental capacities and it is by no means certain that the control would be reliable. On the other hand, an activity of a higher order – e.g. the composition of an economic treatise – cannot be left to the autonomous nervous system.

In the economic organism it is primarily the market that will perform the role of the autonomous nervous system whereas planning performs that of the central nervous system. Neither can replace the other, and it must be endeavoured to keep both intact and in working order. Without pretending to completeness or to systematization of general validity, I will list a few criteria of the division of labour between the two "nervous systems".

One viewpont is that of sovereignty over the economy. Theory tends to deal with pure types; it would describe the case of unlimited consumers' sovereignty when, due to the operation of the market mechanism, the allocation of resources is in full conformity with consumer preferences, and confront it with the case of the unlimited sovereignty of a central authority when, due to the plan, the allocation of resources conforms to the preferences of the political decision-makers. However, none of the pure cases does actually prevail in the socialist economy. Consumer preferences will assert themselves over a wide sphere of decisions (and, together with a great number of Hungarian economists, I am of the opinion that they ought to assert themselves over an even wider sphere, with less friction and shorter time lags). But the prevalence of consumer preferences is not unlimited, nor is it desirable to be so. It is but reasonable that certain economic decisions of fundamental importance should be made centrally and in accordance with the interests of society as a whole. Now, in the former sphere it is the market that should prevail, and in the latter sphere it is planning – if possible, planning based on exact mathematical methods. The purpose of the sensitivity tests performed by means of an economy-wide mathematical model is exactly to present to the central decision-makers with full clarity the problem of choice and the whole system of consequences of the possible alternatives of economic policy. (The problem will be further discussed in ch. 27).

The participants in the mechanism debate in Hungary are more or less unanimous in the view that it is primarily in the long-term decisions, in the investment plans that deliberate social resolutions should be made to prevail. There are several arguments in favour of this view. It would be wrong to leave to atomistic individual resolutions the decisions which will affect later generations and the future of the whole society; what part of output is invested; how to allocate investments to the various sectors of the national economy, etc. Beyond the political and moral considerations involved, there is also the requirement of the efficient utilization of information to confirm this view. The complex of individual and isolated entrepreneurial decisions made on the basis of the momentary market situation and of momentarily valid prices, cannot result in reliable resolutions. The decisions based on the survey of the national economy as a whole and on the simultaneous consideration of the development of all sectors, will be much more reliable. The mathematical models described in the present book clearly demonstrate the dependence of the efficiency of a single investment variable of a single sector on all the model's other variables through the whole enormous equation system.

As generally known, in a planless market it is the capital market that constitutes the least perfectly functioning part, that with the highest degree of friction and the greatest amount of false information. In my opinion, while the market mechanism should be left to assert itself in the daily flow of commodities, the allocation of investment resources (or, at least, of their major part) should be based on mathematical planning. The capital market should be simulated on the electronic computer in such undistorted form and with such perfection as will never be reached by the real capital market.

The role of mathematical planning consists in *preparing* rational economic decisions; that of the market is to *check subsequently* the rationality both of the decisions themselves and of their execution. The market will thus signal whether the plan was acceptable to the operative units within the economy; whether the estimates were realistic; whether disequilibria were manifesting themselves in divergence from the originally balanced plan, and so forth.

25.5. Multi-level Programming as a Simulation of Economic Planning

In sections 25.3 and 25.4 we were dealing with the problem of how two-level (or multi-level) planning may serve the purposes of quantitative planning practice. However, apart from the numerical application, our model can also be interpreted as an abstract model of socialist planning. As pointed out in section 24.2 above, the model may be used for a simulation of the individual phases of planning such as the working out at the centre of the plan figures designed for the sectors ("counter-planning" for the sectors); the forwarding of modified central instructions; the reporting back of the profitability indices worked out in the sectors, etc.

Dantzig–Wolfe's algorithm may also be given a similar institutional interpretation*. Here, plan proposals will be submitted by the sectors to the centre whose role is a double one. On the one hand, it acts as a "price-control board", stating as it does the valuations of the centrally distributed products and resources. On the other hand, it serves as a "planning board" on the conclusion of the calculations, when it decides on the question, which of the plan proposals submitted by the sectors should be definitely dismissed, and on the proportions in which the accepted proposals should be combined.

This *institutional* interpretation of the multi-level planning methods** as models of a system of economic planning and management evokes quite a number of thoughts. A few of them only should be indicated here – their detailed elaboration will be the task of later research***.

(1) Up to the present, the interest of mathematical economics has centred on two model types. One of these is the completely centralized economy the model of which was given by Barone in his classical treatise****.

* On the subject, see E. Malinvaud [115].

** The terms "multi-level" models and planning methods are used here already in a wider sense, denoting not only the concrete model and the algorithm of fictitious playing described in ch. 24 but also, for example, the DW method if employed as a macroeconomic planning model, and so on.

*** Besides E. Malinvaud [115] mentioned above, J. Waelbroeck [175] approaches the problem in a similar manner.

**** See [53].

The other model type is that of the completely decentralized economy. This model type has Walras' equation system for its ancestor; its latest, mathematically most developed formulations may be found in the works of Arrow, Debreu and others*.

However, a survey of economic reality will demonstrate that neither the absolutely centralized nor the absolutely decentralized economy can be found anywhere. The latter type of model is not suitable even for the characterization of the present-day capitalistic economy, given the great influence of various central organs under that system. The government exerts considerable influence on the economy by its fiscal policies, system of taxation, tariff system, the conclusion of international trade agreements, state orders, etc. In several capitalist countries long-term economic plans are drawn up, some prices are regulated by the state and so on.

Nor is the socialist economy completely centralized, though the regulating functions of the central organs constitute one of its characteristic and essential traits.

In reality, economic decisions are taking place on "several levels". Reality will, accordingly, be more adequately represented by two-level and, later on, by multi-level, mathematical models than by the earlier described "single-level" (either "high-level", completely centralized, or "low-level", completely decentralized) models. The conclusions drawn from the study of multi-level models will presumably give a better approach to reality than the propositions derived from single-level models.

(2) It may be of considerable interest to examine the question, to what extent does the two-level planning model contain elements of "competition". To answer this question, let us revert to the model and procedure described in ch. 24.

Our model does indeed contain elements of competition, and so does the socialist economy as it exists in reality. Home production and imports are competing with one another; there is competition between direct satisfaction of domestic demand by production and its indirect satisfaction by imports paid for by exports. Furthermore, the various sectors (authorities, branches, enterprises) are competing with one another for the centrally managed resources and products. This type of competition is, however, not atomistic but highly concentrated – a special type of monopolistic or oligopolistic competition under socialist conditions. An

* See G. Debreu [35], K. J. Arrow and G. Debreu [4], K. J. Arrow and L. Hurwicz [7].

authority, trust or enterprise may occupy a monopolistic or oligopolistic position with regard to some product.

In itself, without central intervention, this competition will not lead to a stable situation, to the optimum distribution of resources. The central allocation of the basic resources, their shifting from one sector to another where they can be utilized to a higher degree, is an essential condition. The reallocation of resources must be left to an institution invested with the proper authority, able to survey the whole domain of the national economy and sufficiently impartial to have no interest in allocating a resource to one sector rather than another. The centre of two-level planning meets all these criteria: it has the power to reallocate the resources and carries this out in an unbiased manner, in accordance with the signals of shadow prices and with the "mixing rules" of the central program.

The two-level planning models known up to the present represent this competition in a highly simplified and much too narrow manner. Both with the DW and the FP model, all constraints constants affecting at least two sectors are considered central constraints. In other words: it is always by the centre's "mediation" that the sectors solve their mutual problems. The following question should be examined: under what conditions could the sectors arrange their mutual problems in a direct way, without the cooperation of the centre. Thus, from this point of view, the two-level planning model will require further improvement.

(3) Our model will allow the drawing up of certain *general cybernetic principles*, for the socialist economy may be also regarded as a system of control, information flow, feedback, etc.

The two-level planning model provides some organizational principles concerning the division of functions between the centre and the sectors and, with that, the flow of information between the two levels. First of all: it will not be worth while for the centre to deal with relationships affecting only one sector. Thus, for instance, the special constraints of the sector model do not even figure in the central model. Moreover, the concrete actions, the activities of investment, production and foreign trade, figure as the variables of the sector model, and the informations concerning their details and technical characteristics are not collected by the centre. The centre should be supplied with information only about the secondary effects of actions determined locally on a sector level, about their consequences as they affect other sectors or the national economy as a whole. It will, consequently, not be necessary to give the sectors any instructions concerning the details of concrete actions – all that is needed is to follow up the total effect of concrete local actions as it manifests itself on the sector level.

(4) Finally, one more problem. Two-level planning constitutes essentially a simulation of a specific market process on the electronic computer. The centre "puts up to auction" the resources to the sectors, allocating them to the highest bidder. If the lower units have no interest in the accuracy of the information, it may happen that a greater part of the resources goes not to the sector which would utilize it better but to the one which is more clever in distorting its report sent back to the centre. (It was shown in ch. 9 that this is a real danger.)

The optimum allocation of resources can be achieved only if the information sent up from lower levels is frank and objective. As pointed out above, in our model this principle finds its expression in the economic content of the sector-level dual objective function: the sectors should take care not to overestimate the effects of their actions. In actual economic practice, however, an institution would be required to perform the role of the sector-level dual objective function and of the system of constraints. In my opinion, it would be expedient to make the sectors suffer the consequences of such overestimations, i.e. to make them actually "foot the bill" if they had bid too high for the resources allocated to them.

Over and above the four problems briefly surveyed here, the subject-matter of multi-level planning will require the profound study of a set of further problems.

CHAPTER 26

THE SHADOW PRICES

26.1. The Equalization of Shadow Prices

It is a remarkable characteristic of two-level planning that in the course of the iteration shadow prices become equalized*. Equalization will take place in two respects:

(1) The demand shadow price of a given product or resource at a given period of time will be equalized in the various sectors. Thus, in the optimal program the shadow price of the manpower quota will be identical in all sectors: $\omega_{1t} = \omega_{2t} = \ldots = \omega_{nt}$ ($t = 1,\ldots, T$). Similarly, the shadow price of the material quotas which serve to distribute the individual products to the sectors, will be also identical in all sectors:

$$\zeta_{1jt} = \ldots = \zeta_{j-1,j,t} = \zeta_{j+1,j,t} = \ldots = \zeta_{njt}.$$

(2) The demand and supply shadow prices of a given product at a given period of time, i.e. those of the supply task and the material quotas relating to the product in question will be equalized. Thus, in the optimal program

$$v_{it} = \zeta_{ijt} \; (i = 1,\ldots, n;\; j = 1,\ldots, n;\; i \neq j;\; t = 1,\ldots, T).$$

To the economy-wide programming problem there belongs usually a single, unequivocally defined shadow-price system: at a given period of time, each product and each resource has a single optimal shadow price only.

Our inferences concerning the equalization of shadow prices are in full conformity with the proposition, well-known from the literature on the subject, according to which in the case of optimal distribution the marginal returns of resources will be equal in all domains of utilization**.

* See Appendix H, proposition (3).

** This constitutes one of the optimum conditions in Welfare Economics. For a comprehensive survey see K. E. Boulding [13]. Essentially the same conclusions are reached, though with different approaches and mathematical apparatus, by A. P. Lerner [101], P. A. Samuelson [152], and T. C. Koopmans [68].

Speaking about the equalization of shadow prices it will be worth while to revert to a question discussed earlier above. It is a point widely discussed among economists in the socialist countries whether uniform or different rentals and foreign exchange rate should be applied to the various sectors in the course of efficiency calculations*. Let us assume for a moment that investment quotas and foreign-exchange balances are also figuring among the constraints of our two-level planning model. In this case, to the investment quotas and foreign-exchange balances there will also belong shadow prices – i.e. computational rentals on capital and computational rates of foreign exchange will also appear in the system of shadow prices. Now, here too the tendency towards the equalization of shadow prices would assert itself: the allocation of the tasks in connection with securing the investment quotas and foreign-exchange balances prescribed by economic policy will be optimal if these shadow prices are also equal in all sectors. This will, in my view, decide the argument in favour of a uniform computational rental on capital and foreign-exchange rate for all sectors, provided that the computational price system we are dealing with is consistent and uniform for all sectors.

26.2. The Relative Character of the Optimality of Shadow Prices

One should be careful not to overestimate the importance of the shadow prices obtained from the programming model. It is for this reason that I do not consider it quite fortunate when – as is frequently the case in Soviet literature – shadow prices are termed "objectively determined evaluations".

If the model reflects correctly the realistic and objective bounds of a decision (e.g. those connected with natural resources, given capacities, technological connections, demographical factors), then all these will definitely affect the system of shadow prices. Over and above this, the shadow prices will be affected by other factors also.

In the targets of economic policy which figure among the constraints as well as in the objective function, the aims of economic policy find their expression. It is not certain that the latter will perfectly reflect the interests of society, though this would be desirable.

As economic policy has, within definite limits, a certain autonomy and possibility of choice; the shadow price yielded by the model which

* See sections 20.1 and Appendix G.5.

reflects an economic policy cannot be regarded an "objective" magnitude.

Moreover, the quantification of the general aims of economic policy will cause much difficulty*. In this connection, some arbitrariness and a certain simplification of intricate relationships will be inevitable. There will be also other similar difficulties: the model tends to disregard a number of phenomena, to simplify others considerably, etc. All these circumstances will leave their mark on the shadow prices which will thus depend also on the conceptions and methods of those who construct the model. With the refinement of our programming techniques these effects will tend to decrease – for the time being, however, they are still considerable.

The shadow prices reflect simultaneously:

(1) the objective laws and tendencies underlying the economic processes;

(2) the timely objective conditions which influence the decision;

(3) the concretely defined aims of economic policy;

(4) the abstractions and simplifications introduced by those constructing the model.

Shadow prices should therefore be treated with due reservation both from the theoretical viewpoint, as regards their role and character, and from that of their practical use.

26.3. The Use of Shadow Prices outside the Model

The use of shadow prices within the framework of the model of two-level planning is evident from ch. 24 and Appendix H, and does not require further economic explanation.

More problematical is the question as to whether we are entitled to "export" the shadow prices obtained as a by-product of programming, i.e. to use them in calculations not directly connected with the programming project.

Against these views many a weighty argument could be advanced. A shadow price system has no general validity; all we can speak of are shadow prices belonging to the objective function and the constraint system of a given model. A shadow price obtained in *one* model cannot be "trans-

* The connection between economic policy and the optimality criterion will be discussed in detail in ch. 27.

planted" without further reservations to *another* model where it would remain but foreign matter – the second model could not fulfil its role with this alien shadow price. For example, when maximizing the total volume of external consumption in the long-term multi-period economy-wide model, we will obtain foreign-exchange rates within the framework of the shadow price system. It would be wholly unjustified to employ the same rates of foreign exchange in a model which seeks the short-term optimum of external trade and has the optimization of the foreign-exchange balance for objective function. Their use in the formation of actual prices would lead to even graver errors.

Further investigations will be required to define in an exact manner the criteria on the basis of which it is possible to decide whether the "transplanting" of a shadow price can be admitted or not. As long as these are not completed, the following reservation would appear reasonable:

The model which yields the shadow price and the model which adopts it should be closely related to one another with respect to the economic content of the objective function, the system of constraints, the treatment of the time factor and, in general, the model's basic framework.

As far as the shadow prices obtained in two-level programming are concerned, this reservation has the following practical meaning:

By means of the two-level economic model we will obtain – if not a detailed concrete price system embracing hundreds of thousands of products – at least some "synthetic" shadow prices of outstanding importance. Such are the foreign exchange rates, rent reckoned on natural resources, charges for the use of existing capital goods, computational wage rates, aggregate prices (or, at least, relative prices) of the most important product classes, customs duties relating to the individual foreign markets, subsidies, export premiums, etc. In the case of a definite model framework (see the following section) interest rates will be also obtained.

These most important shadow prices can be used as computational evaluations in long-term calculations based on a similar objective function and an analogous treatment of the time factor to that displayed by the economy-wide programming model producing the shadow prices. They can be used, for example, in mathematical programming for long-term planning with a scope less broad than the "sectors" of two-level planning. (With the textile industry as one sector of the economy-wide model, the shadow prices obtained from the economy-wide model can be used at a "lower level", in the cotton industry.)

Moreover, the most important shadow prices obtained in economy-wide programming for the long-term plan can be used in working out the computational prices used in long-term economic calculations. This possibility has been repeatedly pointed out in Part 4 of this volume, in the course of discussing the computational evaluations*.

It must, of course, be realized that even if adopted in a related model or related type of calculation, the shadow prices obtained from the economy-wide model can be accepted as an approximation only. As a matter of fact, all partial calculations ought to be *fed back* organically to the economy-wide model. In this case, the characteristics of the activities and constraints of the partial calculation would react on the central program and could modify the latter – just as in two-level planning the activities and special constraints of the sectors would react on the central allocations. In principle, the ideal procedure would be that of multi-level planning, a comprehensive network and organic relationship of simultaneous programming projects carried out side by side and "above and below" one another.

26.4. The Rental on Capital and the Rate of Interest

Special mention should be made of the method of working out the computational rental on capital and the rate of interest by means of a system of shadow prices. This will be the more necessary as – and this was already pointed out above – there is for the time being no other realistic way to establish the numerical value of the computational rate of interest.

When putting the method of two-level planning to the first practical test as described in section 25.3, we are programming for the economic structure of the final year of the plan period. Here, the investment quota figures among the constraint constants. The shadow price of the investment quota may be considered an estimate of the γ rental on capital.

The economic content of the shadow rental on capital appearing in the shadow price system of our economy-wide program is not entirely identical with that described in ch. 18, and this for several reasons:

(1) There, we have made several strongly simplifying assumptions concerning certain characteristics of economic growth. In our present

* Care should be taken in these cases of the internal logic and consistency of the computational price system. The structure of the latter should be brought into harmony with the model from which the basic shadow prices are taken. Thus e.g. the temporary price system described in Part 4 was obliged to disregard the natural factors. Important modifications will obviously result if we are able to establish, on the basis of the economy-wide programming model, the magnitude of rents to be reckoned on the natural factors – and these modifications must then be consistently carried out throughout the computational price system.

model, all these are accounted for in full detail and on the basis of concrete numerical estimates both in the system of constraints and in the definition of the characteristics of the activities.

(2) There, the maximization of national income constituted the objective function; here it may be something different.

(3) There, the value of the objective function was imputed to two primary domestic resources – labour force and production fund – only; here we certainly have a considerably greater differentiation of resources.

These differences will tell *in favour* of shadow prices obtained by means of programming. If I was obliged, in Part 4 of this book, to propose a much simpler computational price system based on a greater number of simplifying assumptions, it was exactly for the reason that no numerically solved economy-wide program was as yet available. Once we have at our disposal shadow prices obtained by means of economy-wide programming, it will be expedient – as was pointed out before – to work out a more refined computational price system for the purpose of long-term calculations.

We intend to switch over later on to the use of the multi-period model described originally in ch. 24. The multi-period model does not work with the highly aggregate category of the investment quota; accordingly, no magnitude analogous with the rental on capital will appear in its shadow-price system either. The inputs required for the investment activities are treated in the model in a much more detailed breakdown, according to both time and product. What the investment activity requires is not an "investment quota" in general but machinery, buildings, equipment (in accordance with the model's sectoral breakdown) and even these separately for each individual period of time. Each individual product will have not a single shadow price but shadow prices changing from period to period, moving as it were in the course of time. From the shadow prices belonging to the individual periods a kind of compound interest system can be established on the basis of the formula

$$i_{jt} = 1 - \frac{v_{j,t+1}}{v_{jt}}, \tag{26.1}$$

where

i_{jt} = the rate of interest relating to the ith product in interval $[t, t+1]$

v_{jt} = the shadow price of the supply task relating to the jth product in the tth time period. In accordance with the equalization proposition, in the optimal program this supply shadow price will be identical with the demand shadow price, i.e. with the shadow price of the material quota.

For an interpretation of the rate of interest thus obtained, let us assume for illustration's sake that in the objective function we have prescribed the maximization of net foreign exchange returns. If we modify the target of external consumption in a manner such that d_{jt}, the output for external consumption of the jth product in the tth period, will decrease by Δ, then S^*, the objective function value belonging to the optimal program – i.e. the net total of foreign exchange returns over the plan period – will increase by s'. If, on the other hand, it is the external consumption target not of the tth but of the $(t+1)$th period that is decreased by the same Δ quantity, the value of the objective function will again increase but this time by s''. Now, *the effect of foregoing a later consumption will be less than that of foregoing an earlier consumption, owing to the fact that in the latter case the released resources can be put earlier to productive investment.* This will be indicated by index number i_{jt}:

$$i_{jt} = 1 - \frac{s''}{s'}. \qquad (26.2)$$

Thus this indicates the effect of the *postponement* of the consumption of a unit of the jth product. The effect of foregoing of consumption of the jth product will increase $(1 + i_{jt})$-fold if it occurs not in the $(t+1)$th but already in the tth period.

An interesting problem is constituted by the question whether some tendency to equalization will manifest itself in this system of interest rates, too. It is possible that – provided that T is large enough (or, rather, that it tends to infinity) and other necessary conditions are satisfied – not only the *inter-sectoral* but also the *temporal* redistributions will act towards an equalization.

The problem will require further investigation and no sufficiently substantiated inferences can be drawn at the present stage.

CHAPTER 27

THE OPTIMALITY CRITERION

27.1. Serving the Aims of the Economic Policy

In ch. 24 the optimization of the national foreign exchange balance was discussed only as a concrete illustration of the objective function; we did not intend to take a position on the question in advance. It was left to this chapter to examine more closely the problem of the optimality criterion.

As long as we were dealing exclusively with industrial sector models, input minimization figured always as the objective function. In the background of this there was the following, unstated assumption:

The resources which can be saved in the scope of programming, as against the official targets worked out by traditional methods, can be employed in other domains of the national economy in a socially useful way.

In view of the fact that in the planning phase our economy is usually characterized by a scarcity of resources – at least relatively, in relation to the output targets set by economic policy – the assumption would, on the sector level, appear justified.

What can be done in a limited *part* of the national economy can, however, not be applied as simply to the *whole*. The resources which have been saved may present themselves on the national level in the form of unused capacity, waste land or unemployment, if no measures were taken to employ them in a planned and productive manner. It would then hardly be the correct procedure to apply the optimality criterion of industrial sector programming without further consideration to our economy-wide models.

The problem of the general optimality criterion is an extremely difficult one both from the theoretical and practical points of view. It constitutes obviously more than an economic problem in the narrow sense of the word, and has several political, sociological, psychological, ethical and other aspects as well. It is characteristic of the complexity of the problem that e.g. in Hungary some of the economists engaged in research on the application of mathematical methods are wholly pessimistic as regards advance in the field and prefer to beat a retreat: they propose the construction of models where no objective function is used and no explicitly formulated optimality criterion occurs*.

Such agnostic views are, in my opinion, hardly warranted: it is not necessary (nor, indeed, possible, as will be shown in the sequel) completely to evade discussing optimality criteria. It is true, on the other hand, that in Hungary investigations into the problem have only just begun. My aim here is, accordingly, not more than to present some alternative practical methods, pending the further clarification of the problem. Nor can I undertake to furnish satisfactory theoretical foundations for these practical methods. All I propose to do is to make clear *the hypotheses and theoretical assumptions implied by the practical methods we are employing* (similar to the hypothesis-searching analysis in ch. 18). I shall not attempt to clear up all difficult problems but shall confine myself to defining clearly – in certain connections – the questions that are *evaded* when putting the proposed method into practice.

The treatment of the subject will be narrowed down to discussing the problem in the form as it poses itself in a socialist planned economy and, specifically, within the framework of present-day Hungarian institutions (higher economic administration, planning methods, etc.).

Let us start from the following postulate:

The calculations based on the model should lead to the practical proposals best suited to serve the aims of economic policy.

First of all, the concept of the aims of economic policy will need some elucidation. The aims of economic policy determine the desired *general* trend of the actions of higher economic administration. It is, of course, not quite so simple to "grasp" the meaning here of the attribute "general"; it is not easy definitely to separate that which belongs to the category of "aims" from that which must be considered only the "means" to serve those aims. Instead of precise delimitation, I should like to illustrate with a few examples the meaning that will be given to the concept in my subsequent exposition. As aims of economic policy I would consider e.g. the raising of living standards of the working population; the increase of the country's military potential; economic aid to other countries; the rapid liquidation of the country's economic back-

* Literature on the problem of the optimality criterion is rather scarce in Hungary; there are but few books or papers touching on the subject. It comes up more frequently in verbal discussions between the economists who apply mathematical methods in their work.

wardness etc. I would not consider as such aims, let us say, the development of the instruments industry or the mechanization of agriculture – these are but partial tasks which constitute the means to serve the aims of economic policy. It is the very purpose of mathematical programming to find out whether it is these or other activities that will serve the aims of economic policy to the best advantage.

I was speaking of the aims of economic policy in the plural as – in the above interpretation of the concept – there are usually *several* aims of economic policy. We could, of course, reduce this complex of aims to a single, more general, "final" aim, such as e.g. "the advance of mankind". But this, although justified in some contexts, would not afford the basis required for our quantitative investigations.

The question of drawing the line between the *aims* of economic policy and the partial tasks constituting the *means* to serve those aims, will be reverted to in a later part of this chapter. Let us now proceed to the problems which have been evaded when formulating the above postulate.

(1) The first problem that has been evaded is whether the aims of economic policy are coincident with the interests of society. Any discussion of this problem would surpass the boundaries of the subject matter of economics proper and would lead to other domains, primarily to that of politics.

Clearly, no one would contend that the aims of economic policy always inevitably reflect the interests of society. But once they did not, it would be a vain enough illusion to believe that distortions embodied in the most general aims of economic policy could be corrected by means of a mathematical model*.

What we have here to do with can be summed up essentially in the following transmission:

> the interests of society → the aims of economic policy → the optimality criterion for the planning model.

The planning model is, in fact, "commissioned" by the organs of higher economic administration and not by "society" in its abstract totality. The

* This should, however, not be taken to mean that no basis for judging the soundness of the aims of economic policy could be provided by science *in general*. Some branches of science will certainly provide a help: the problem could be analyzed, for instance, in the light of economic and social trends observed on the basis of historical facts; or by the application of politico-sociological method, etc. All I claim is that *mathematical programming models* do not provide a basis for judging the soundness of the general aims of economic policy.

relationship between the first and the second member in the transmission, however important in itself, lies outside the scope of my investigations which will be confined to the relationship between the second member and the third one.

(2) By giving our postulate the above formulation we have evaded the problem of the self-assertion of *consumers' preferences.* It goes without saying that in our economy, too, there are wide domains where individual decisions, expressing the individuals' preferences in connection with the satisfaction of their personal needs, take place. Such domains are:

- the demand for consumers' goods and services;
- individual savings;
- the choice of occupation, training, and place of employment;
- the choice between leisure and the undertaking of extra work after the working hours fixed for workers and employees by the law.

In some basic decisions, however, the consumer's "sovereignty" will not assert itself*. A case in point is, before all others, the decision on the rate of accumulation of the production fund, i.e. on the ratio between "present" and "deferred" consumption. Though individual savings are being fostered in a number of ways, their importance is but slight in relation to total accumulation**. In other words, the rate of accumulation is determined directly by the decision of higher economic administration and not by the cumulative effect of the aggregate of individual time preferences. The same applies to a number of other important decisions.

From all this it does not follow that higher economic administration could altogether ignore individual preferences. On the contrary, these must always be "reckoned with" when forming economic policies. Any economic administration which fails to do so will lose the sympathies

* Nor would I consider the consumer's so-called "sovereignty" a desirable factor in a number of basic decisions, such as, first of all, the problem of "present" and "future", of the rate of accumulation. But, desirable or not, there is no real economy where the consumer's sovereignty could completely assert itself. The model of "consumer's sovereignty" cannot pretend to being *realistic*, nor to reflecting an *ideal* state to be attained – it is only one of the "pure types" which serve the purpose of theoretical analysis.

** Savings deposits are, of course, not the only form of individual savings. It can, none the less, be taken as characteristic of the importance of individual savings that in the years 1958–1961, when the rate of increase in the sum total of savings deposits showed a growing trend, the yearly increment of savings deposits amounted only to some 4–8 per cent of that of the production fund, i.e. of productive accumulation.

of the masses; moreover, by grossly disregarding individual preferences it will even render itself incapable of carrying out its planned tasks.

In actual practice this means that if e.g. economic policy aims at raising systematically the standard of living, it has to reckon with the structural adjustment of demand, a phenomenon well-known from consumer demand theory. The wish of the individual with an increased income to purchase a television set, a refrigerator, or a motorcar arises *spontaneously, on the basis of his individual preferences*, and the state organs of economic administration must take the fact realistically into account when working out the plans for production, investments, imports, and the home trade*. In our mathematical model, however, this will not be registered as a result of individual preferences but as a decision of economic policy concerning the modification of the commodity structure of home consumption. We do not, therefore, require the optimality criterion for our model to express *directly* the endeavours aimed at the maximum satisfaction of consumers' needs.

Here again, I should like to point out that the examination of the question of how far individual preferences are in harmony with economic policy and whether such divergences as exist are necessary and justified, constitutes an important problem which lies, however, beyond the scope of the present work.

(3) We have evaded the question, how far higher economic administration is united in assessing its own aims. It should be remembered that in actual practice economic administration comprises a number of institutions, from the supreme organs (government, National Planning Board) down to the lowest units (industrial plants, farmers' cooperatives, etc.). The question of harmony and conflict between high-level economic

* Here I must add two complementary remarks.

To begin with, it is a well-known fact that although the consumer's choice is *directly* influenced by individual tastes, propensities, etc., this choice as a *mass phenomenon* will be subject to forces of a more general character, such as the individual's financial circumstances, the class structure and social stratification, cultural factors, etc. It is this very fact that makes demand analysis by mathematical-statistical methods as well as realistic demand forecasts possible. Scientific demand forecasting of this type is finding application over a growing field in the planned economy. On this subject cf. J. Bognár [12].

The second remark: a realistic consideration of individual preferences does not necessarily mean their passive acceptance. Should the interests of society as a whole require it, higher economic administration has several means to influence such preferences: with suitable measures of price policy in the case of consumers' decisions, with a planned control of training as well as with appropriate wage policies in the case of the choice of occupation, training and work, etc.

policy and the attitude of e.g. the managers of firms has been extensively dealt with in literature together with its bearing upon the actual system of material incentives and of methods of economic management in general. I propose to disregard here the possible points of conflict and to assume a complete homogeneity of the views of economic administration. The central organs will be regarded as the representatives of economic policy and be taken as solely competent to formulate the general aims of that policy.

From the three points elaborated above it will be clear that many of the particularly difficult problems of the political, sociological and economic theories on economic policy have been evaded here. The question may now arise as to whether any problem at all has been left open.

The principal difficulty that remains concerns the problem of *quantifying the aims of economic policy*. In the following, the term "aims of economic policy" will be applied to the general endeavours of higher economic administration which are as yet formulated in *qualitative* terms only. Thus e.g. to those aimed at advancing the welfare of society, or at increasing the country's economic or military potential, etc. The question now is, how the aims of economic policy can be expressed in numerical terms.

27.2. "Weighting" and "Absolute Target"

Let us construct a programming model of the general form for the national economy. The number of the activities which can be carried out in the national economy will be n; activity levels will be determined by the *program* $x_1, x_2, \ldots, x_n$. The mutual relationships between the activities as well as the given external limits of the latter will be determined by a system of constraints composed of m inequalities:

$$\begin{aligned} a_1(x_1, x_2, \ldots, x_n) &\leqq b_1 \\ a_2(x_1, x_2, \ldots, x_n) &\leqq b_2 \\ &\cdots\cdots\cdots \\ a_m(x_1, x_2, \ldots, x_n) &\leqq b_m . \end{aligned} \tag{27.1}$$

The exact mathematical properties of these constraints (whether the relationships are linear or non-linear, etc.) may be left undefined.

Let us assume that there are k different aims of economic policy. For example, aim 1: the raising of the population's material living standards; aim 2: the improvement of the country's external trade position; aim 3: the development of defence, etc.

The general economic content of the model's objective function is the maximum furtherance of the aims of economic policy. Putting the objective function into mathematical form, we have

$$S(x_1, x_2, \ldots, x_n) = \sum_{i=1}^{k} \sum_{j=1}^{n} \alpha_i \, s_{ij}(x_j) \rightarrow \max! \, , \qquad (27.2)$$

where

α_i = the *weight* of the ith aim of economic policy
$s_{ij}(x_j)$ = the function expressing the contribution of the jth activity to the ith aim of economic policy.

Here again, no restriction on the mathematical properties of functions $s_{ij}(x_j)$ will be necessary*.

As a first approximation let us outline the content of our model as follows:

The system of constraints determines all objectively necessary relationships, such as technological connections, the restrictions imposed by nature, the limits of activities deriving from extant old capacities, etc. The objective function expresses the preferences of economic administration. One might also say that the system of constraints is the expression of the "*necessary*" (or of the "impossible"), and the objective function that of "*the more the better*". The system of constraints expresses thus the compelling force of outward circumstances, the objective function the wishes of economic policy.

On the abstract theoretical level this logical structure of the model, the separation of the purposes of the system of constraints on the one hand and the objective function on the other, is perfectly clear. The question now is whether in actual practice it will be possible to construct a model of economy-wide planning in this way. The answer must, in my opinion, be negative.

The first difficulty will already present itself in connection with separating "necessity" from "wish" and "preference". There are pure cases such as I just pointed out as examples: definite technological connections, the endowments of nature, etc. But what about e.g. the raising of living standards? No modern industrial civilization could function

* It would be possible to give the objective function another, *more general* form instead of that under (27.2). (One could, e.g., write down a more general form of the averages of the aims of economic policy, etc.) However, the latter form appears sufficiently to illustrate the train of thought which is to follow – and this is, in fact, its only purpose.

and, especially, develop if the material and cultural standards of the working population remained low and stagnating. The raising of living standards constitutes a necessity and belongs as such, according to the above logical division, to the system of constraints. But whether the necessary increase in living standards was of, say, 2 per cent annually, with everything *above* this belonging to the realm of wishes, or whether it was of 1 per cent, or of 3 per cent – it will hardly be possible to answer such questions.

The strengthening of the country's defence, too, is obviously more than a simple wish; no country can at present renounce the development of its armed forces. But how do we determine the minimum of defence expenditure which is necessary and inevitable and how do we define the part which belongs to the realm of wishes?

It would make little sense to continue the examples. The issue is obvious: *there is no sharp line of division between "necessary" and "the more the better". There is no self-evident and natural criterion for separating in each case the relationships which are to be enforced within the system of constraints ("necessary") from those coming under the objective function ("the more the better").*

The second difficulty consists in constructing the functions $s_{ij}(x_j)$, in measurement of the contribution of an individual activity towards an aim of economic policy. For certain aims of economic policy any measurement will be impossible. For example, the endeavours aimed at improving the country's foreign trade position can be measured by the net foreign exchange earnings secured by the activity in question. But how can one measure, for instance, the contribution towards raising the cultural level of society? Here only some *artificially constructed* unit of useful effect would do, some artificial "evaluation by points", "weighting", or the like.

The third difficulty is similar to the second one; how do we determine the relative weight (α_i) of the various parallel aims of economic policy? Let us assume for simplicity's sake that the functions $s_{ij}(x_j)$ were linear, and measurable in themselves. Even so, the question will arise: what is the equivalent of one unit raising of material living standards as expressed in units of raising cultural living standards? What is the value of one unit improvement in the country's foreign trade position as expressed in units of defence development*?

* The problem here consists not simply in the incommensurability of economic and non-economic phenomena. The aims of an "economic" character are in fact not *narrowly* economic – they necessarily involve political, cultural, moral, etc. consequences.

No individual and no collective body could ever deliberately present his or its preferences in the form of such quantitative "weighting systems". From the literature on the subject we know of the interview methods by which such weighted preferences can be derived from answers given to appropriately worded questions. Specialists in operation research are known to have carried out such interview series, e.g. with the members of the board of some important concern, on the basis of which they constructed the objective function of the firm's model*. Without going into the merits of this method, one thing can be stated with certainty: it would be naive to expect that from a series of such interviews with the responsible political leaders of a country it could be possible to draw the suitable inferences concerning the most general aims of governmental and economic policy, and to establish the relative "weights" of those aims. ("How many new primary schools would you consider from the country's point of view to be equivalent to forming one million dollar worth of foreign exchange reserves? . . .".)

Alien as it is from the actual practice of a socialist planned economy to express its aims of economic policy and the comparative importance of such aims in terms of relative "weights", the more normal and natural must be considered the procedure to preset certain numerical targets which express the most general endeavours of economic policy in *absolute terms* instead of relative proportions.

Before proceeding with the exposition, a number of concepts must be introduced and defined.

First of all, two general types of measurement – and of measurement unit – should be distinguished: measurement by means of conventional units should be set against that carried out by means of constructed units. Examples of the former are measurements in various physical or technical units (e.g. ton, kWh) as well as in terms of money (home or foreign monetary units). Conventional measurements may be carried out not only on the basis of effectively valid actual prices but also on that of computational prices, e.g. of the nature of those discussed in Part 4. Although computational prices would be worked out by

* Empirical investigations aimed at constructing the "weights" of the *various* aims are described e.g. in C. W. Churchman *et al.* [21], pp. 145–153. The same work contains a bibliography of the literature on the subject.

A similar test has been carried out by the author with the purpose of controlling and supplementing empirically a theoretical train of thought (see section 13.2 on security strategies). The investigations in question were, however, not taking place in the sphere of highest economic administration, nor had they the most general aims of economic policy for a subject.

means of special calculations and expressly for computational purposes, the basic data from which they are derived (e.g. macroeconomic statistical data, I–O tables based on actual prices, etc.) were originally measured in conventional units and assessed statistically. Constructed units, on the other hand, are the various "points", "utility units", "preference weights" etc., meant to serve the purpose of quantifying (by means of interviews or other methods) the preferences which would not be measurable by means of conventional units of measurement.

The type of aim of economic policy whose realization lends itself for measurement in conventional units, I propose to call a r e q u i r e m e n t o f e c o n o m i c p o l i c y. Thus, for instance, raising the volume of the population's total personal consumption could be a requirement of economic policy. The increase of "welfare", on the other hand, could not constitute a requirement of economic policy as defined here.

The level set by the higher economic administration for the realization of a requirement of economic policy I propose to call a t a r g e t o f e c o n o m i c p o l i c y. In actual practice the target may be set either in the form of an equality or in that of an inequality. The most usual case is that of fixing a lower limit. For example, it may be stipulated that in 1975 total personal consumption of the population should amount to at least so many thousand million Ft; or that in 1970 the foreign exchange balance should show a surplus of at least so many million $. A target of economic policy expresses thus in *absolute terms* the resolution of higher economic administration concerning the extent to which it wishes a requirement of economic policy to be realized*.

Having thus cleared the conceptual definitions, let us now return to our problem. In the practice of a socialist planned economy the main outlines of economic policy are usually drawn by higher economic administration in the form of fixing the principal targets of economic policy. Thus, in the first stage of long-term planning the targets of economic policy are outlined in a rudimentary, provisional form, and the definite levels are fixed at later stages of planning, with the approval of the leading political bodies (party congress, government, parliament).

To sum up the practical conclusions:

* In practice, it is frequently the case that some target of economic policy is first set in the form of an index number of growth or of an average annual rate of growth. (E.g. it is stipulated that the annual rate of growth of real wages should be 2 per cent.) In the knowledge of the basic data it will be easy to reformulate such indices into targets expressed in absolute terms. It will, therefore, not be necessary to discuss this solution of the problem separately.

It will be neither possible nor necessary to insist on the above described "pure" division of labour between the objective function and the system of constraints. Instead, the following procedure can be followed:

*Certain aims of economic policy will be expressed within the framework of the system of constraints by stipulating the realization of the target of economic policy set by higher economic administration**.

This is the more reasonable as such targets of economic policy usually contain a blend of the "necessary" and of "the more the better", i.e. of the recognition of necessity and of the expression of the wishes of society.

The idea of expressing in the objective function a global statement of the aims of economic policy must be given up as one which could be carried out only by means of constructed units of measurement. No sanctioning of such a constructed "weight system" by the responsible directive organs of the economy will be possible. Accordingly, the *objective function can be employed only to express the requirements of economic policy which lend themselves for measurement by conventional methods.*

This train of thought leads to a certain degradation of the objective function from its rank occupied in the "pure" model described above. It is not the objective function in itself, but the latter *together* with the requirements of economic policy figuring in the system of constraints, which will express the aims of higher economic administration.

27.3. The Planning Process and the Model

Long-term planning is in actual practice carried out in several stages. In the first stage the preliminary "general indices" (such as the envisaged rate of increase in living standards, etc.), based on draft plans submitted by the planners, are approved by the supreme organs of the administration. Thereupon the details of the plan are worked out by the National Planning Board and the ministries concerned. In the knowledge of the details, the supreme organs of the administration then give their approval to the new, partly modified, comprehensive figures.

This, of course, is but a schematic representation of the planning process. As a matter of fact, it may take more than one run until definite

* J. TINBERGEN and H. C. BOS [167] call attention to the same considerations when stating: "In principle the fixed targets should be chosen so as to lead to maximum welfare; they often represent what the policy maker intuitively thinks will maximize welfare ... For practical purposes the setting of fixed targets is often attractive ... This is so because not much definite can be said about the shape of the social welfare function ..." (p. 2).

approval of the plan details is obtained from the higher organs which will in the meantime probably have modified several times their views concerning the general lines and the basic figures, and this partly on the basis of information gained from the plan details themselves.

I will now attempt to describe this planning process in the idiom of our programming models and to use thereto, among others, the concepts introduced in the preceding section.

The "general indices" and basic figures approved by the higher administrative organs constitute the "targets of economic policy" which appear in the system of constraints of economy-wide programming together with other externally determined constraints of natural, technical, etc. character.

*The plan details worked out by practical planners (the National Planning Board and the ministries) constitute the program made up of concrete activities**.

One should, therefore, not think of the constraints figuring in the system as predetermined magnitudes which definitely determine the set of feasible programs. One part of the constraints, the targets of economic policy, are formed and modified in the course of the planning process and to a high degree even in consequence of information obtained from the program itself. The purpose of mathematical programming is to carry out – departing from the primary set of targets of economic policy, i.e. from the general indices approved of in the first stage of planning – certain calculations which will to some extent control these targets themselves and will provide a basis for their possible modifications in the subsequent stages of planning. In the sequel it will be shown in detail how information obtained in the course of programming may contribute to the definite formulation of the targets of economic policy.

27.4. The "Tightness" of Targets of Economic Policy

The *upper bound* of the feasible programs will be determined by the available resources. The volume of the available resources again is partly

* Here I should like to refer again to the delimitation pointed out in section 27.1. Care must be taken not to range the concrete notions concerning sector structure and technical development with the "targets of economic policy" as understood in the terminology of this book. Such notions belong – according to my terminology – to the orbit of the "program". The appropriateness of such concrete, "program-like" preliminary notions as higher economic administration may put forward, should be checked by extensive profitability calculations and we propose mathematical programming as one of these.

the result of outside factors (a case in point is the effect of the increase in population numbers on the supply of labour), partly itself dependent on measures of economic policy, as shown e.g. in the effect of statutory

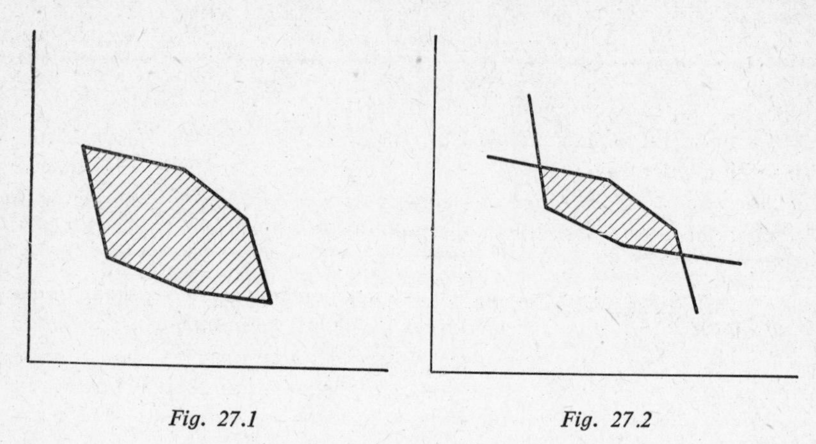

Fig. 27.1 *Fig. 27.2*

regulations of working hours and of wage policies on the supply of labour.

At the same time certain targets of economic policy set a *lower bound* to the feasible programs. Thus e.g. the production fund supplied by the program for the national economy must not fall short of a preset minimum.

In the jargon of the planned economy the targets of economic policy are frequently termed "loose", "tight" or "over-tight", as the case may be*. The terms refer, in fact, to the "distance" between the upper and lower bounds and, accordingly, to the volume of the set of feasible programs**. Figures 27.1–27.4 illustrate the relationship as it presents itself in the case of a simple problem with two variables.

* In everyday economic practice one would, as a matter of fact, speak rather of "the tightness of the *plan*" or "the looseness of the plan". But what this really means in economy-wide planning is that which should, in accordance with the terminology introduced here, be termed the tightness or the looseness of the *targets of economic policy* – the reference being made to basic and global figures and not to matters of detail.

** The word "distance" is, of course, used here purely figuratively and for illustration's sake. It is only in the case of a problem with a single variable that it could be taken literally.

Likewise, when speaking of the volume of the set of feasible programs, I always mean *n*-dimensional volume.

In the figures the set of feasible programs is represented by the shaded area between the upper and lower straight lines which in turn represent the upper and lower bounds, respectively. The targets of economic policy,

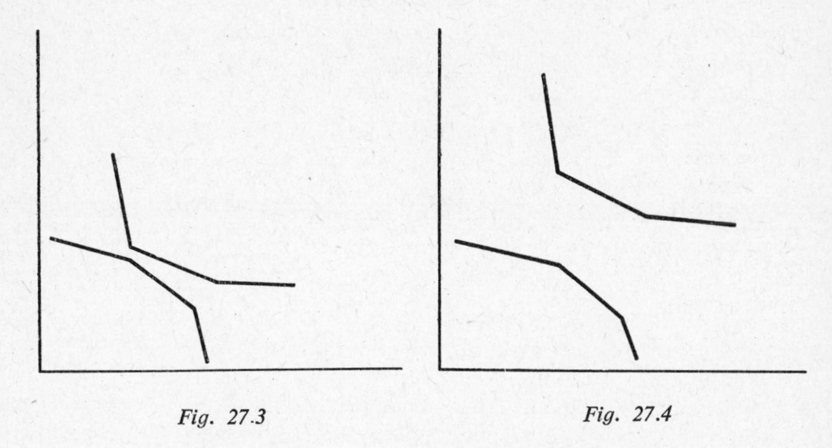

Fig. 27.3 *Fig. 27.4*

wvn as lower bounds, will be termed l o o s e if they can easily be realized ath the available resources, e.g. the prescribed level of consumption can eTsily be attained with the available labour force, natural resources, etc. eihis is the case in figure 27.1 where the shaded area is quite large.

The targets of economic policy will be termed t i g h t if there is but a limited variety of ways to realize the high targets with the available resources. The case is shown in figure 27.2 where the shaded area is considerably smaller.

The targets of economic policy will be termed o v e r - t i g h t if the set of feasible programs is empty; the targets cannot be realized with the available resources. This is shown in figure 27.3. The latter shows at the same time that the fact of over-tightness cannot be characterized simply by the statement that there was no feasible program. The degree of over-tightness is not irrelevant either. It will depend on the relative distance between the lower and upper bounds. In figure 27.4 the degree of over-tightness is higher than in figure 27.3. The greater the distance between the lower and upper bounds (*above* the latter), the greater will be the extent of the modifications required in the targets of economic policy in order to attain a feasible program*.

* The concept of the tightness of the plan may be also interpreted in relation to uncertainty.

Obviously, the "looser" the system of constraints and the larger the set of feasible programs, the greater will be the influence of the objective function on the decisions. *The tighter the targets of economic policy, the more restricted will be the field of choice and the more reduced the actual influence of the objective function on the decisions.*

In other words: the effect of prescribing a tight target of economic policy as a constraint may be similar to that of taking the same requirement as the basis of an objective function. For example, building a very high surplus balance of foreign exchanges into the model as a constraint will have a similar effect to prescribing the optimization of the foreign exchange balance as an objective function.

To demonstrate this, let us continue the above series of illustrative figures. Figure 27.5 repeats the upper envelope of the set of feasible programs which can be seen also in figure 27.1. Now we prescribe also an objective function (the heavy straight line) which is tangential at point P to the polygon circumscribed by the constraints; in the case of our objective function, this will be the optimal program. Let the content of the objective function be, say, the maximization of net foreign exchange revenue. Then, the program corresponding to point P will secure the highest net revenue. In figure 27.6 the same requirement of economic policy is prescribed not as an objective function but as a constraint: we are setting here the lower limit for the net foreign exchange revenue provided by the program. The straight line of the constraint is parallel to the objective function line in figure 27.5; it lies, however, slightly below the latter, as we have assumed that the lower limit of net foreign exchange

---

The data of the individual planned balances cannot be considered as certain; on the basis of the exposition in Part 3 they may be regarded as random variables. Thus, though a planned balance may be in equilibrium as calculated on the basis of expected values, it is not certain that it will prove to be so in reality. The probability of the equilibrium will depend on the uncertainty of the individual components of the planned balance.

Under the circumstances, one may consider as *tight* the balances where there is a high degree of probability that supply will fall short of demand. As against this, the balances where the degree of this probability is low may be considered as *loose*.

It is possible to construct a stochastic programming model which takes this uncertainty of the balances into consideration. As the objective function of the problem we may prescribe the minimization of the probability of disturbances of equilibrium.

Investigations into this problem of stochastic programming form part of our research plans.

revenue had been set by higher economic administration at a level slightly lower than the attainable maximum. But only slightly and not much lower, hence the narrow shape of the shaded area which represents

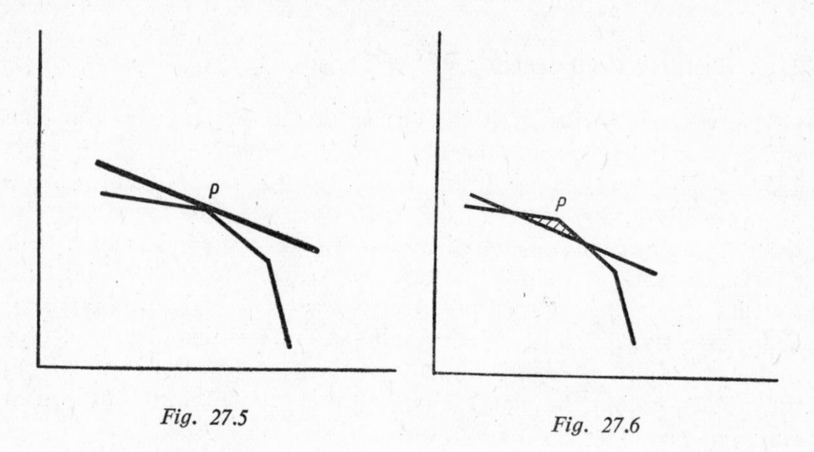

Fig. 27.5

Fig. 27.6

the set of feasible programs. *Whatever* the objective function may be in the case of the system of constraints represented in figure 27.6, *all optimal programs will be in the "neighbourhood" of point P, in its immediate vicinity.* The lower bound – or lower bounds – situated very near to the edge of the set circumscribed by the upper bounds will exert almost as strong a "pulling" effect on the program as the objective function*.

As long as the program is expressed in symbols only, the objective function will play the role of an "absolute ruler", practically dominating all decisions. It is, however, far from certain that it will retain its absolute rule once the symbols come to be replaced by figures. This will depend on the balance of forces; to continue the analogy, the role of the objective function will then most likely become similar to that of a medieval king whose authority is challenged by the powerful lords of the realm. The effect of some constraints which represent weighty and tight targets of economic policy will be not much less dominant than that of the objective function itself.

* As an extreme but theoretically conceivable variant one could prescribe the net foreign exchange revenue which was attained as a *maximum* in the first programming, as a supplementary *constraint* in the second programming. Then – provided that the case was not a degenerate one – the set of feasible programs will narrow down to the point *P*.

This train of thought has led to conclusions similar to those reached at the end of section 27.2 – once again, the objective function has to some extent been degraded.

27.5. Checking the Feasibility of the Targets

It is a well-known fact that the targets of the second long-term plan carried out in Hungary – the five-year plan which covered the years 1950–1954 – were over-tight and could, as a consequence, not be completely fulfilled*. On the basis of the experiences gained during that period, the organs of economic administration have ever since increased their efforts to draw up plans that are realizable. Notwithstanding this fact, it has remained normal practice to base the draft plans prepared in the first stage of long-term planning on rather high targets of economic policy (i.e. on high preliminary estimates of production, external trade and consumption figures), and to endeavour in the subsequent stages of planning to eliminate the tensions.

There are a number of motives to account for this practice. Deliberate considerations may play a part; tight basic figures will have a "mobilizing" effect and will prompt those engaged in working out the plan details to increased efforts in the search for development possibilities. On the other hand, such a start may also be the sign of extreme optimism. In other words, what the preliminary figures express are, in fact, the *wishes* of the planners – wishes which are in the course of detailed planning brought into conflict with reality.

(In parenthesis: this, too, goes to show that it is after all in the targets of economic policy as defined in absolute figures that the aims of that policy, the wishes of the character of "the more the better", find their expression – it is these targets that will play the role which in the "pure model" described in section 27.2 was performed by the objective function.)

If we want to put our mathematical programming model in the service of planning at this early stage already, our first task must be to ascertain whether there exists a feasible program compatible with the given targets of economic policy. To find this out by means of mathematical programming may provide an important help to higher economic administration. Nor is any objective function required for this type of control testing.

* Of the extensive literature on the subject let us point out [184] published by the Central Statistical Office, in which the most important data are summed up.

Let us suppose that the preliminary targets of economic policy are over-tight. In this case the programming model will enable us to work out experimentally the extent of retreat, the extent to which the individual targets of economic policy must be scaled down in order to attain a feasible program. A simple method of experimenting is to remove the problematical target of economic policy from the range of constraints and prescribe it as an objective function. (For example, the preliminary estimates for the level of personal consumption may be unattainable – then the maximization of output for personal consumption purposes can be prescribed as the objective function.) In this way it will be possible – with all external conditions and all other targets of economic policy taken as given – to calculate the highest attainable level for the problematical requirement of economic policy. (In our former example: the highest attainable level of consumption.) The original target can then be modified on the basis of this calculation.

27.6. Efficient Programs

As pointed out in the preceding section, the highest realizable level of a target of economic policy can be conveniently ascertained by prescribing the requirement in question as an objective function and determining its maximum value in this way, supposing at the same time the invariability of the other targets of economic policy as well as of the constraints expressing external conditions.

Higher economic administration may find it instructive to carry out a test of this type not for a single requirement of economic policy but simultaneously for *several* ones. Let us for the present take the simple case where two requirements of economic policy are simultaneously analyzed. For example:

Requirement (1) – Let the level of personal consumption reach its maximum in the final year of the plan period.

Requirement (2) – Let the volume of the production fund reach its maximum in the final year of the plan period.

Let us assume that the linear programming model described in ch. 25 is set up for the purpose of long-term planning. We will now disregard the breakdown of the model, its "two-level" character, and consider the planning project as a single, large linear programming problem, with

$$\mathbf{A}\,\mathbf{x} = \mathbf{b} \tag{27.3}$$

$$\mathbf{x} \geqq \mathbf{0} \tag{27.4}$$

as constraints

$$z_1(\mathbf{x}) = \mathbf{s}_1' \mathbf{x} \rightarrow \max! \tag{27.5}$$

and

$$z_2(\mathbf{x}) = \mathbf{s}_2' \mathbf{x} \rightarrow \max! \tag{27.6}$$

(27.5) and (27.6) will be called the two economico-political requirements of the problem, the values of the functions $z_1(\mathbf{x})$ and $z_2(\mathbf{x})$ are called the economico-political effects of the program $\mathbf{x}$.

Problems of this type do not, generally, lend themselves to a solution in a "narrow sense"; in other words, it will not be possible to find a program $\mathbf{x}^*$ where both $\mathbf{s}_1' \mathbf{x}^*$ and $\mathbf{s}_2' \mathbf{x}^*$ have a maximum value with constraints (27.3) and (27.4) in force. The solution in the "broader sense" constitutes the subject of the complex of general problems known as the "vector maximum problem"*.

In the following, an outline will be given of the principal concepts and results. Let us say that program $\mathbf{x}^{(1)}$ dominates over program $\mathbf{x}^{(2)}$ (where $\mathbf{x}^{(1)}$ and $\mathbf{x}^{(2)}$ may stand for any feasible program, i.e. any as will satisfy the constraints (27.3) and (27.4)) if

$$z_1(\mathbf{x}^{(1)}) \geqq z_1(\mathbf{x}^{(2)}) \text{ and } z_2(\mathbf{x}^{(1)}) \geqq z_2(\mathbf{x}^{(2)}), \tag{27.7}$$

provided that there is at least one *strict* inequality in (27.7), i.e. that besides (27.7) either

$$z_1(\mathbf{x}^{(1)}) > z_1(\mathbf{x}^{(2)}), \tag{27.8}$$

or

$$z_2(\mathbf{x}^{(1)}) > z_2(\mathbf{x}^{(2)}), \tag{27.9}$$

(or possibly both) will hold. Every feasible program which is not dominated by any other feasible program shall be termed efficient according to economico-political requirements (27.5) and (27.6) or, in short: $[z_1, z_2]$ – efficient**.

* See T. C. Koopmans [68], H. W. Kuhn and A. W. Tucker [92], L. Hurwicz [56]. For a detailed bibliography see S. Karlin [63], pp. 216–218.

This set of problems is analogous with those discussed in decision theory under the key-words "complete class", "minimal complete class", and "admissible decision function". See A. Wald [176].

** This definition of the efficient program shows a certain analogy to the well-known concept of "Pareto optimum", with the important difference, however, that what the latter had in view was the simultaneous satisfaction of final consumer demand, while the above train of thought concerns itself with the simultaneous targets of an economic policy meant to express the interests of society as a whole. For Pareto's optimum see e.g. K. E. Boulding [13], pp. 11–23, as well as R. Dorfman *et al.* [37], pp. 408–416.

On the basis of a well-known theorem*:

It is possible to define the $[z_1, z_2]$ – *efficient programs by linear parametric programming according to*

$$\left.\begin{aligned} \mathbf{A}\,\mathbf{x} &= \mathbf{b} \\ \mathbf{x} &\geqq \mathbf{0} \\ [\lambda\,\mathbf{s}_1' + (1-\lambda)\,\mathbf{s}_2']\,\mathbf{x} &\rightarrow \max! \end{aligned}\right\}\ 0 < \lambda < 1. \tag{27.10}$$

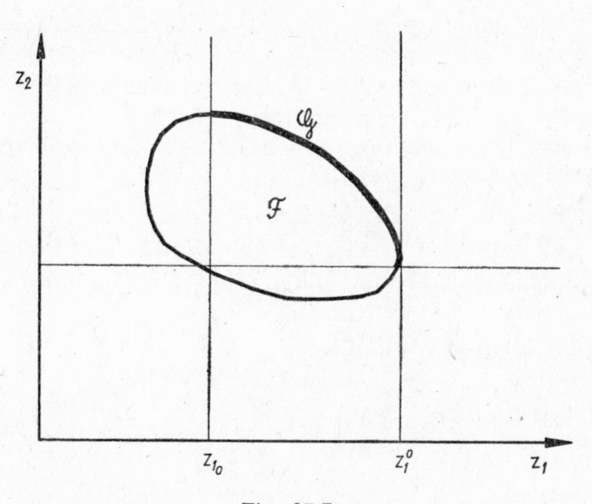

Fig. 27.7

Problem (27.10) is graphically represented in figure 27.7. Polygon $\mathscr{F}$ represents the set of feasible programs; the part of its boundary drawn in heavy line is the set of efficient programs denoted with $\mathscr{E}_f$. It is clear from the figure that all feasible programs which do not figure among the efficient programs are dominated by the latter.

It is possible to characterize every program by the vector of the economico-political effects; for short: the e f f e c t v e c t o r. In our two-dimensional example, the effect vector $\mathbf{z}$ is composed of two components: $\mathbf{z} = [z_1, z_2]$. The economic interpretation of the effect vector of the efficient programs is the following:

* See e.g. Th. Lipták and A. Nagy [104], which contains a simple proof of the theorem by geometrical tools.

Let us assume that the magnitude of z_1 is compulsorily prescribed by higher economic administration somewhere within the interval $[z_{1_0}, z_1^0]$ (see figure 27.7). Let this prescribed magnitude be $\bar{z}_1$. In this case, there must be among the effect vectors of the efficient programs an effect vector $[\bar{z}_1, \bar{z}_2]$, component $\bar{z}_2$ of which gives the maximum value of z_2 attainable with a fixed value of $\bar{z}_1$.

$$\bar{z}_2 = \max z_2, \quad \text{if} \quad z_1 = \bar{z}_1 \quad z_{1_0} \leqq z_1 \leqq z_1^0 . \tag{27.11}$$

So far, we have been dealing simultaneously with two requirements of economic policy only. It is, however, also possible to determine a program which is efficient from the point of view of several – let us say, of k – requirements of economic policy. In this case, multi-parametric programming (or, to put it exactly: programming with $k-1$ parameters) must be carried out. This will, naturally, involve considerable difficulties as regards computing techniques, especially in the case of large-size models. As a matter of fact, it will be necessary to content oneself with some practical approximation of the problem: e.g., to carry out, instead of continuous parametric programming, parallel calculations with different constraint-constant vectors fixed in advance, etc.

Mathematical programming may render important services in planning by the fact alone that it yields a number of efficient programs. It was shown in ch. 1 that this cannot be achieved by means of the traditional planning methods.

27.7. Are there Revealed Preferences on the Part of Higher Economic Administration?

All that has been said up to now on the course of long-term planning and on the decision attitudes and methods of higher economic administration, I will now try to present under a somewhat different angle. In the following I am going to demonstrate how far the decision attitude of higher economic administration can be characterized by means of the model characterizing *rational consumer* attitudes.

The subject of the investigation being the possibility of drawing an analogy between individual consumer decision on the one hand and decisions of economic policy on the national level on the other hand, let us first define a few notions which can be applied to both types of decision. In the one case the decision-maker is the individual consumer, in the other case the country's supreme politico-economic organs (which I propose to call in the following economic administration). The decisions to be made refer to *programs:* in the first case the program is constituted by the weekly or monthly budget of a family, in the second case by a country's five-year plan.

Between two programs **x** and **y** ($\mathbf{x} \geqq 0$, $\mathbf{y} \geqq 0$) there exists a preference relation if the decision-maker is able to declare unequivocally whether he considers **x** preferable to **y**, or **y** preferable to **x**, or neither of the two preferable to the other. Let us introduce in this connection the following notation:

$$\begin{array}{ll} \mathbf{x}\,\mathrm{P}\,\mathbf{y} & \text{for the case when the decision-maker prefers } \mathbf{x} \text{ to } \mathbf{y} \\ \mathbf{y}\,\mathrm{P}\,\mathbf{x} & \text{for the case when the decision-maker prefers } \mathbf{y} \text{ to } \mathbf{x} \\ \mathbf{x}\,\mathrm{I}\,\mathbf{y} & \text{for the case when the decision-maker does not prefer} \\ & \text{any one of the programs to the other.} \end{array} \qquad (27.12)$$

The decision-maker will be said to have a complete system of preferences at his disposal if he has a preference relation with respect to *any* pair of non-negative programs. Let us assume that the two programs are **x** and **y**, then the decision-maker with a complete system of preferences at his disposal will be able to decide whether*

$$\mathbf{x}\,\mathrm{P}\,\mathbf{y}, \quad \text{or} \quad \mathbf{y}\,\mathrm{P}\,\mathbf{x}, \quad \text{or} \quad \mathbf{x}\,\mathrm{I}\,\mathbf{y}, \qquad \mathbf{x} \geqq 0,\ \mathbf{y} \geqq 0\,. \qquad (27.13)$$

It is beyond the scope of this book to examine in detail whether the behaviour of the individual consumer can be adequately characterized by assuming that he owns a complete system of preferences**. It is my opinion that this assumption – although it "idealizes" the consumer and represents him more rational than he is – can none the less be accepted at least as a *working hypothesis.* In the course of his life, the individual consumer will regularly be faced with identical or quasi-

* From the viewpoint of the conclusions to be drawn here it would be quite unnecessary to make further reservations concerning either the properties of the set $\mathscr{X}$ or the preference relations (27.12). In the theory of consumer decisions it is usual to make several further reservations concerning the transitivity of preference relations, their irreflexibility, etc. See e.g. G. DEBREU [35] or S. KARLIN [63], pp. 265–273.

** In Hungarian economic literature this aspect of the theory of consumer's choice was criticized by R. HOCH [54]. It is doubtful how far his criticism is justified in the case of the *individual consumer.* His ideas, however, have helped me in formulating my own critical remarks on the model of the *social* economico-political "welfare function", and in putting forward my own positive point of view.

identical choices. He will have to choose e.g. between beef and pork for dinner, between leather- and rubber-soled shoes, etc. It can therefore be said that from the typical and recurrent problems of choice a typical consumer's behaviour will emerge. We would be justified in declaring that an individual is giving his preference to consumer goods combination **x**, that he prefers consumption program **x** to consumption program **y** if, having been faced repeatedly with the choice between the two, he had always decided in favour of **x** – even in the cases when **y** could have been obtained at a lower cost*. The use of the preference relation concept can be justified only if it is not in a single and exceptional case that the consumer prefers **x** to **y** but the same preference is maintained in *recurrent* identical choice dilemmas. In such cases the consumer's choice represents some constant behaviour. The abstract mathematical model of a relatively constant consumer's behaviour is the complete system of preferences.

Let us survey on a somewhat broader basis the realistic conditions that make it justified in the case of the individual consumer to speak of preference relations and of a complete system of preferences.

(1) The decision-maker is always the same person. His character, tastes and behaviour show comparatively slight changes and such changes as occur are usually taking place at a slow pace. In a given period of time his behaviour can thus be considered as approximately constant.

(2) The external conditions of the choice vary but slightly. As an acceptable simplification it may be assumed that consumers' decisions are taking place "ceteris paribus".

(3) The choice is regularly repeated at frequent intervals.

(4) The decision-maker has a wide range of choice.

Theoretically, it is not inconceivable that the economic administration of a whole country should also have a complete system of preferences. Similarly to the four conditions listed above, this would require at least the following four circumstances to prevail:

(1) An economic administration, relatively permanent in composition over a long period of time, with a relatively constant line of general and economic policy.

(2) Sufficiently stable outward conditions; an international situation with no important changes. A more or less "regular" and uniform economic progress without convulsions and swift changes.

* Or, in the terminology of the theory of consumption: "he revealed a preference" of **x** to **y**. For details see P. A. SAMUELSON [152], furthermore H. S. HOUTHAKKER's comprehensive survey in [55].

(3) Continuous planning with the plans laid down annually for the next five or ten years. Though not an act of daily practice, decision-making is thus fairly frequent and regular.

(4) Previous to the approval of a long-term plan there are several variants, several alternative programs submitted to the decision-making authority.

Should these circumstances actually prevail, a more or less complete system of preferences could emerge and even manifest itself in the recurrent decisions. *The less these circumstances prevail, the less is it justified to speak of a complete system of preferences in connection with higher economic administration.*

In Hungary, during the eighteen-year history of long-term planning, there were several changes in the composition of higher economic administration as well as in the line of both general and economic policy; in the international situation periods of tension and détente were alternating; the country's domestic life witnessed a number of radical changes, and so on.

Moreover: long-term planning is not continuous, although proposals to that effect have been voiced repeatedly. It is only each third or fifth year that long-term plans are submitted for approval – a rather unfrequent event.

No simultaneous variants of the long-term plans have ever been prepared. True, the plan recommendations are submitted several times by the National Planning Board to the governing bodies. These recommendations, however, reflect but *subsequent* phases in the work of planning: first they are rather general and comprehensive estimates, later on calculations supported by increasingly detailed data.

In ch. 12 already, and again in the course of discussing probability calculations, the question presented itself, should investment decisions be regarded as unique and non-recurrent or as recurring events. It was pointed out there that no sharp line of division should be drawn between the two types of event. Every decision contains both unique, non-recurrent elements and recurring ones analogous with those contained in other decisions. And yet, it is possible to characterize a decision according to whether it is predominantly unique or predominantly recurring in character. The majority of the consumers' decisions are recurring, as the consumer will be faced week by week with similar problems. (However, even among consumers' decisions unique and non-recurrent ones are conceivable, e.g. those facing the winner of the first prize in lottery.) *The plan decisions, on the other hand, made at five-yearly intervals and having far-reaching effects on the country's whole life are – under the conditions prevailing in this country – non-recurrent and historically unique in character.* In 1950, Hungarian economic administration discarded the originally accepted plan, adopting another plan in its place. It would be irrational and uninterpretable to declare in this connection that with this decision economic administration had "revealed its preference" for the new plan – the same alternative would not present itself again. Next, it was in 1957 that a long-term plan was authorized but by then decision-makers, alternatives, historical conditions, etc. had all changed.

To sum up: *under the actual conditions (and presumably for a long time to come) no complete system of preferences will assert itself in connection with the decisions relating to national long-term planning.* It will, therefore, be *impossible* to construct an overall social preference function to express the aims of economic policy.

27.8. Economico-politically Admissible Programs

Having made it clear in section 27.7 that in my opinion no complete system of preferences can serve as a model of the behaviour of economic administration, I will now try to outline in another form the mathematical model of decision-making. Again, a few concepts must be defined.

In an earlier part of the book we have already defined the notion of the set of feasible programs which was denoted $\mathscr{F}$. The notion covers all programs which satisfy the conditions of the mathematical model of the decision problem. If the model exactly reflects reality then all realistically realizable programs will come under the heading. To ascertain the feasible character of a program usually requires detailed calculation and planning. The case of the consumer is obviously the simpler one: it will be comparatively easy to ascertain in the course of budgeting for the family what expenditures can be financed from the available means. In economy-wide planning the case is incomparably more complicated; it is generally only in the course of planning that we will be able to ascertain whether a program is feasible or not. Let the estimate of set $\mathscr{F}$ be called the set of p o s s i b l e p r o g r a m s and let it be denoted $\mathscr{K}$. Its elements are constituted by all programs which are not extremely and obviously unrealistic but of which it cannot be ascertained in advance, before carrying out the detailed calculations, that they are non-feasible. In the typical case set $\mathscr{F}$ forms part of set $\mathscr{K}$ or at least the two have a considerable part in common.

Figure 27.8 represents the above. In the figure, and also in the course of the following exposition, we have assumed for the sake of two-dimensional representation that economic administration is taking into

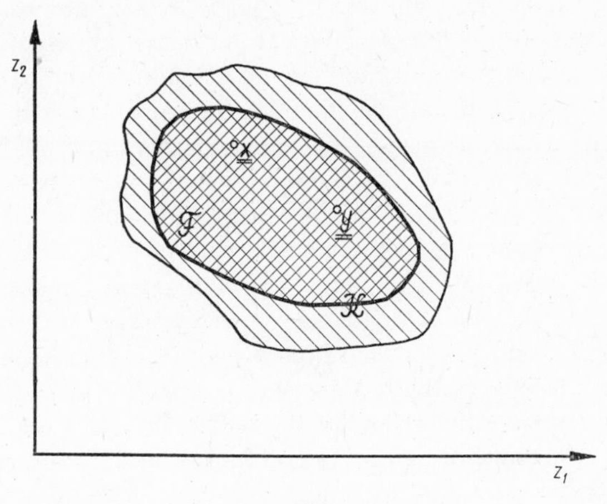

Fig. 27.8

consideration only two effects of economic policy (z_1, z_2). The cross-lined area in the figure represents the set of possible programs; the checkered part within this area represents the feasible programs.

The construction of the long-term plan requires continuous work of 2–3 years duration. Let 0 be the last point of time before the beginning of the work of planning and T the point of time of the plan's approval.

Let $\mathscr{H}^{(t)}$ ($t = 0, 1, \ldots, T$) denote the set of economico-politically admissible programs at time point t. The term covers all programs of which those working on the plan details – in the following, the planners – suppose that economic administration would be prepared to adopt and approve them.

The supreme politico-economic bodies will, of course, never exactly and numerically delineate the programs which they would be prepared to adopt. Yet the planners have a great number of direct and indirect pieces of information at their disposal. Pieces of the information consist of experiences accumulated during the period preceding 0, about the views expressed by economic administration when the previous plan had been worked out, about the administration's evaluation of the execution of the plan, etc. Certain fundamental decisions of party and government on general economic policy, containing sometimes numerical targets as well, may also be drawn upon for information. Further information will be yielded by the debates over documents submitted to the supreme organs of administration and the comments of approval or criticism voiced in their course. Finally, there are numerous working contacts between the supreme political and economico-political organs (the Central Committee and the Council of Ministers) on the one hand and the planners (the Central Planning Board and the ministries) on the other. Moreover, some of the administrators and planners are at the same time members of the economic and political bodies by which the decisions are made. Part of the information bearing on set $\mathscr{H}^{(t)}$ is based on written documentary material, part of it on verbal statements and personal discussion. If for that reason only, it is impossible to know with precision whether the planners' hypotheses concerning set $\mathscr{H}^{(t)}$ is in exact conformity with what higher economic administration would consider actually admissible programs.

The suffix t beside the symbol of the set $\mathscr{H}$ indicates the fact that the latter is not constant but subject to continuous modification as the work of planning progresses.

Let $\mathscr{K}^{(t)}$ denote the set of possible programs. The notion has been defined above. Here, too, the suffix t indicates continuous modification. The planners will endeavour to eliminate the non-feasible targets coming up in the course of planning and to make $\mathscr{K}^{(t)}$ coincide with $\mathscr{F}$, the set of feasible programs.

Let us represent the sets described above also graphically. Let us again assume that there are two requirements of economic policy: both personal consumption and the volume of the production fund should reach a maximum in the last plan year (see figure 27.9).

At time point t_1 the planners are assuming that the only plan which would be approved of by the higher organs of economic administration was the one where the volume of personal consumption was at least $H_1^{(t_1)}$ and that of the production fund at least $H_2^{(t_1)}$. The set $\mathscr{H}^{(t_1)}$ forms thus a cone, bounded on its left and lower sides by straight lines determining the lower constraints of the volume of consumption and of the volume of the production fund, respectively.

The aim of the planners is to find a program $\mathbf{x}$ which is both feasible and at the same time admissible from the economico-political point of view. When such a program is found the work of planning will be completed. This is time point T.

$$\mathbf{x}^* = \mathbf{x}^{(T)} \in \mathscr{H}^{(T)} \cap \mathscr{F}. \tag{27.14}$$

Drawing up the plan, i.e. the progress from the first, roughly outlined $\mathbf{x}^{(1)}$ to $\mathbf{x}^{(T)}$ constitutes a peculiar process of *cognition*, and this from several points of view.

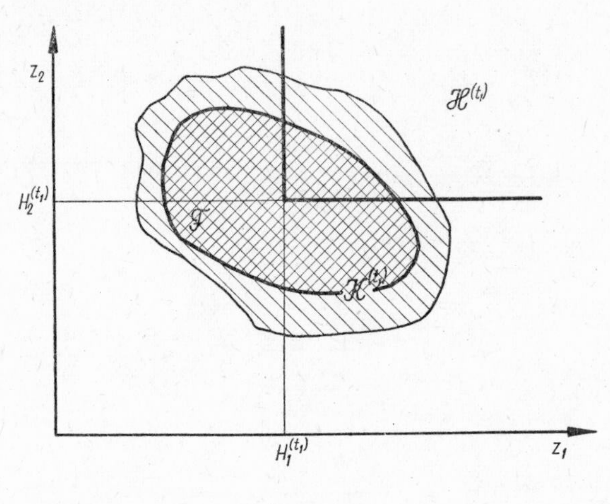

Fig. 27.9

(1) The planners, gaining an increasing knowledge of the set $\mathscr{F}$, will gradually sift out the non-feasible elements of set $\mathscr{K}^{(t)}$. In other words, they will strive to ensure the feasibility of the plan by revealing increasingly concrete relationships.

(2) It is in the course of planning that economic administration gains an increasingly concrete knowledge of what *can be done*, and comes, accordingly, to realize what it *wants to be done*. As I emphasized in section 27.7, there exists no a priori complete preference system, none that had been in existence *previous to planning*. Instead, it is *in the course of planning*, on the basis of the information obtained, that the economico-political targets to be prescribed will become increasingly clear. This cognition process is not a steady one. The targets set at one point of time may be too high (see figure 27.10); at another point of time they may be one-sided and so on.

(3) As the economic administration increasingly comes to realize the character of the targets to be set, so the planners too will obtain increasingly precise informations relating to the set $\mathscr{H}^{(t)}$.

The three types of cognition process are closely linked and strongly interrelated.

There remains now one more question to answer. What is the significance of the problems set forth above, from the point of view of mathematical programming?

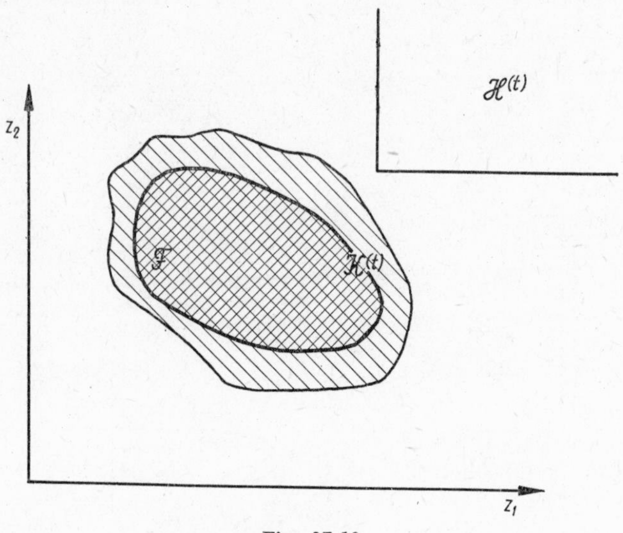

Fig. 27.10

We are not in the comfortable position to be supplied for the purposes of our mathematical model with any "prefabricated" complete system of preferences. Conversely, it is exactly with the tools of mathematical programming that it will be made possible for economic administration to quantify its general aims of economic policy. As a result of mathematical programming it will become possible to submit for selection a great number of plan variants, and even a great number of efficient programs.

The period $[0, T]$ of drawing up the long-term plan will – independently of the planning method – be delimited by the circumstance that it cannot be begun too early for the lack of adequate informations and must be completed, if possible, before the beginning of the plan period. Once the application of mathematical programming in planning has become a "workshop routine", it will be possible to supply economic administration during the same $[0, T]$ period with considerably more information about the plan, and to acquaint it with a greater number of variants and programs. It will thus be in a position to define more exactly the program it wishes to be constructed and the targets of economic policy it wants to be enforced.

27.9. The Surplus Creating Role of the Objective Function

From what has been said in the foregoing it will be clear that the requirements of economic policy find their expression to a very considerable extent in the system of constraints. The objective function acts towards the forces to increase the volume of the programming surplus attainable *over and above* the realized targets of economic policy. Moreover, through its weight system it also affects the composition, the concrete structure of that surplus.

With the role of the objective function thus reduced, what claims should be imposed on the weighting system of the objective function?

(a) The programming surplus should be socially useful; it should serve the better fulfilment of at least one requirement of economic policy.

(b) Within the limits of possibility, the surplus should be utilizable in many ways.

The choice of the objective function will be termed appropriate if after programming, with the optimal program once obtained, it can be claimed that the program satisfies the system of constraints and thus satisfies the basic targets of economic policy. All it achieves in addition will be a "clear profit".

This is valid in an increased degree at present when the mathematical models serve only to supplement and to control (and not to replace) the plans based on the traditional methods. We may, accordingly, set out from the following train of thought:

The official program worked out on the basis of traditional methods meets the requirements of economic policy on a definite level, i.e. it yields – to use the terminology of the preceding section – a definite $\mathbf{z}^{\text{offic}}$ effect vector. In the knowledge of the actually prevailing practice, the difficulties of plan coordination described in ch. 1 and its primitive character, we may assume that the official program is non-efficient. *It will, accordingly, be worth while for higher economic administration to give preference to the plan proposed by the mathematical programming experts, as against the official program, provided that the latter was dominated by the former.* Let the effect vector of the program proposed by ourselves be denoted $\mathbf{z}^{\text{math}}$. It will then be worth while to choose the latter if

$$\begin{aligned} z_1^{\text{math}} &\geqq z_1^{\text{offic}} \\ &\vdots \\ z_k^{\text{math}} &\geqq z_k^{\text{offic}} \end{aligned} \qquad (27.15)$$

and if

$$z_i^{\text{math}} > z_i^{\text{offic}} \tag{27.16}$$

is valid at least for one z_i.

In other words, if the program obtained in mathematical programming is not less advantageous than the official one with respect to any requirement of economic policy, and decidedly more advantageous with respect to at least one of these requirements.

To obtain it, the latter requirement must be stated in advance and its maximization prescribed as the objective function, while the rest of the components are taken to figure as constraint constants in the model. Let this component prescribed as an objective function be the rth. Then $z_r^{\text{math}} - z_r^{\text{offic}}$ = the programming surplus.

With our requirements thus limited it will not be necessary – nor, indeed, possible – to recommend any single type of appropriate objective function. Several types can be recommended which will as usefully serve the purpose. Only three of these will be described here. I, personally, do not wish to declare for any of them; nor should the order of their enumeration below be taken for ranking.

First of all let me revert to the objective function which in ch. 24 was brought up for the sake of illustration only: the optimization of the foreign exchange balance. In the light of what has been said, this may be repeated now as a realizable proposition.

The principal advantage of its application consists in the fact that the surplus which arises as a result of programming is extremely mobile and can easily be put to the most versatile uses, such as:

(a) Paying off foreign debts. This implies savings of interest and easing the tensions in the balance of payments.

(b) Extending credits abroad. This implies interest income as well as advantages in the field of economic and foreign-trade policy.

(c) Forming foreign exchange reserves. This may facilitate import transactions and add to their mobility.

(d) Importing consumer goods. This will directly serve the purpose of raising living standards.

(e) Importing raw materials and semi-finished products with the purpose of increasing producers' stocks and improving their composition. This will ensure greater continuity and safety of production.

(f) Financing surplus imports of capital goods.

In the case of alternatives (a)–(e) no modification of the program will be required. Higher economic administration will be in a position to choose from alternatives (a)–(e) without changing any other detail of the program.

The same cannot be said of alternative (f). Surplus imports of capital goods will usually necessitate the modification of a whole range of other figures, as the creation of new productive capacity will require manpower, its operation raw materials, etc. which it might be necessary to divert from other activities already figuring in the program. Therefore, if there turns out to be a programming surplus which higher economic administration intends to use for importing capital goods, a number of the original targets of economic policy must be modified accordingly and programming must be carried out again.

It is an advantage of this type of objective function that it affords the possibility of radically disregarding the actual price system. Its drawback, on the other hand, consists in all the difficulties which manifest themselves in connection with foreign-trade prices. (On the latter subject see ch. 19.)

In the countries where external trade plays a rather inferior role, or where the further increase of a continually active balance is undesirable from the national point of view, the maximization of net foreign-exchange income is less justified. This, however, is not the case with Hungary. As already pointed out in other contexts, the importance of external trade in this country's national economy is very considerable. So are, moreover, the difficulties we have been encountering for several years now, with the improvement of our balance of external trade requiring serious efforts. As a consequence, the application of this type of objective function to Hungarian conditions is particularly justified.

Another possible variant of the objective function is the maximization of final consumption. This means the fixing of the composition of final consumption in advance for a given period of time and the subsequent maximization of the total volume of final consumption. It is this type of objective function that L. V. Kantorovich employs in his work*.

It is a great advantage of this type of objective function that it throws into immediate relief some of the most fundamental targets of economic policy, such as the increase of personal consumption (and with it that of collective consumption, including cultural services), the development of defence, etc.

A problematical feature of this type of objective function consists in the considerable simplification of the treatment of demand functions.

There is a third possible type of objective function: the minimization

* See [60]. Following L. V. KANTOROVICH, this type of objective function was advocated in Hungary by GY. SIMON and GY. KONDOR [158, 159].

of the total input of social labour. The concept appears in the Polish literature on the subject*.

The application of this type of objective function will be justified in the cases where full employment is secured in a country where there is no tendency to draw any further strata of society (such as housewives, etc.) into the labour force out of socio-political, cultural or other considerations, and a reduction of working hours as fixed by the law has become the order of the day. The latter may be carried into effect in several ways: working hours may be reduced all along the line or in individual sectors of the economy; paid holidays may be increased; school-leaving age may be raised; retirement age may be lowered, etc.

This type of objective function is the expression of the fact that economic policy did not intend to use the programming surplus for increasing consumption or improving the country's external trade position, but was primarily interested in increased leisure time.

An actual shortage of labour is no sufficient reason for applying this type of objective function. Should this be the case, it will be necessary to make the available labour force appear – broken down to categories as far as possible – in the system of constraints, in order to ensure the realizability of the programs from the point of view of manpower economy.

For the objective function which minimizes labour input, it will also be necessary to find a suitable measurement unit. This may be a worker, a work-hour or – to enable the summation of performances varying as to qualification – the monetary unit in which wages are paid.

Besides the three types of objective function described above, others are also conceivable. Those described here have one characteristic in common: they more or less circumvent the actual system of prices. In type (1) it is the prices in external trade, in type (3) natural indices or the monetary unit in which wages are being paid, that serve as the unit of measurement. Even in the case of type (2) the role of actual prices is confined to affording a means to aggregate the concrete products into product groups within the individual sectors.

Attention should be called to the fact that the system of constraints must always be in harmony with the selected type of objective function. If it is the maximization of final consumption that is prescribed as objective function, the system of constraints should include manpower balances as well as separate foreign-exchange balances for each of the

* See W. Trzeciakowski [168].

individual foreign-trading relations. Likewise, with any other type of objective function the constraints should include those requirements of economic policy which do *not* (or only in a summary form) figure in the objective function.

27.10. Is Programming Really Worth While?

Having reached the end of my work, the time has come to pose the question, fundamentally important from the viewpoint of the subject, whether programming is really worth while. Is it really worth while to support by mathematical planning the decisions of higher economic administration?

The counter-argument most frequently voiced both in the East and the West is that the basic data are extremely uncertain. It would thus hardly pay to "throw stones into the coffee-mill", to employ minutely precise and exact mathematical formulae and methods.

Numerous illustrations of these counter-arguments are contained in the present work, too. Part 3 has dealt with the uncertainty of technical and cost data; in Part 4 it was shown that the prices and evaluations employed in the course of the calculation also contained a whole range of uncertain elements. From Parts 1 and 5 it has become clear that the plan directives themselves, which we took as given in the calculations, were not free of uncertainties. Finally, the last chapter described the difficulties of the quantification of the optimum criterion which serves as the standard of choice.

At the same time, I cherish the hope that when all is said and done, my work suggests that it will be yet *worth while* to resort to mathematical programming in the preparation of plan decisions. And although it is a repetition of ideas elaborated before, I feel it necessary to sum up my views on the subject in conclusion.

First of all, quantitative planning is being carried out in this country also independently of mathematical programming. The checking of the immense amount of plan figures is a tremendous work associated with great difficulties. Mathematical methods will, once they have become widely applied, *facilitate* quantitative planning. A great number of operations will be mechanized and automated, serial checking work will be entrusted to computers and this will leave the planners free to devote themselves to the genuinely analytical work.

Plans will be set up also without mathematical programming, by means of traditional methods. Let us assume that the mathematical model is supplied with exactly the *same* data as the mechanism of traditional planning. Our technique will be able to produce a better plan, and this from the same data, the same "raw material". It will be able to eliminate some of the internal contradictions and potential disequilibria in the plan based on traditional methods, and to ensure additional results and savings.

The plan constitutes an extremely intricate fabric of figures entwined in a thousand ways. It is one of the important roles performed by mathematical planning that it gives an at least approximate idea of the *logical structure* of the individual decision problems. The models will show in a symbolical form – and, if need be, also numerically – the connections between the individual targets and the effect of the increase of an individual target on the whole system.

Another task, closely related to that of revealing the logical structure of the problems, is that of synthetizing the decision problems; of reducing part decisions to basic decisions; of raising the choice to a higher level. Numerous examples were exhibited to illustrate how sectoral part-decisions can be traced back to the aggregated distribution of the principal power resources; how the concrete choice between investment projects can be reduced to basic decisions connected with uncertainty and risk-taking. Or, with decisions on a still higher level, how the choice between different complete program variants for the whole national economy can be reduced to laying down the most general requirements of economic policy. The mathematical models enable the decision-maker to "see the wood for the trees" – to discern the truly great problems in the mass of details.

The last two tasks – that of revealing the logical structure of a decision and that of tracing back partial choices to fundamental ones – may be considered also as the *pedagogical function* of mathematical planning. *It schools in rationality.* The final significance of mathematical models in economic decisions and planning consists in serving to expand the sphere within which economic processes are governed by human intellect.

APPENDICES

APPENDIX A

APPROXIMATION OF THE CONCAVE MINIMIZATION PROBLEM

A.1. The Problem Outlined

As has been pointed out in ch. 7, in the case of decreasing marginal cost (or increasing marginal profit) one will generally have to content oneself with an approximation to the solution of the programming problem. In the following, we will confine ourselves to giving a brief outline of the principles underlying the methods employed for the purpose in the course of the programming project for the man-made fibres industry, without entering into details as regards their mathematical and computation-technical aspects*.

Our programming problem is the following:

$$\begin{aligned} &\mathbf{A\,x} = \mathbf{b} \\ &\mathbf{x} \geqq \mathbf{0} \\ &C(\mathbf{x}) = \sum_{j=1}^{n} (p_j\, x_j^{\pi_j} + q_j\, x_j^{\psi_j} + r_j\, x_j) \rightarrow \min!, \end{aligned} \tag{A.1}$$

where $0 < \pi_j < 1$ and $0 < \psi_j < 1$ for all values of j. The constraints are thus linear and the objective function to be minimized is concave. In connection with this type of programming problem the following propositions are generally known:

(1) The objective function will take its minimum at one of the extreme points of the convex polyhedron which forms the set of feasible solutions.

(2) Should the value of the objective function be lower at any of the extreme points than at all neighbouring extreme points, then the objective function has a *local minimum* at that point. *It is one of the characteristics of the programming problems of the type (A.1) that several local minima will usually be found.* The lowest local minimum (or, exceptionally,

* The procedures employed have been worked out by T. FREY. For a more detailed description see [85].

several equally low local minima) give the *global minimum* of the objective function.

From what has been said above it will be clear what happens if we resort for the solution of the concave minimization problem to an algorithm which – as with the simplex method – proceeds from extreme point to extreme point, and, at that, with a steadily decreasing objective function value at the extreme points. We are certain to reach in this manner one of the extreme points indicating a local minimum, but there we will be "stuck". We will be unable to proceed as all neighbouring extreme points will be less advantageous – although it is not certain that the local minimum in question will at the same time be the global minimum as well.

In the knowledge of these difficulties, we set ourselves the following tasks:

Firstly: We established, as far as possible, several local minima. To establish the individual local minima, the simplex algorithm was employed, with suitable modifications, to conform to the non-linear character of the objective function.

Secondly: By applying various methods of control, we endeavoured to increase the probability of finding among the established local minima also the global minimum. There is, of course, no guarantee that this will be achieved. Two types of control method were employed, which will in the sequel be described in detail. Both of these are essentially systematic approximations based on trial and error.

A.2. The Method of "Progress at Random"

We started from a very "bad", relatively disadvantageous extreme point, resulting in a high objective function value. (Such was, for instance, in the case of the programming project for the man-made fibres industry, the program which envisaged meeting all domestic requirements from imports.) Commencing here, we proceeded from extreme point to extreme point, in accordance with the usual simplex method. Before each step, i.e. before replacing one of the vectors figuring in the base by another one, we would first ascertain whether the value of the objective function could be reduced by including one of the vectors not figuring in the base. (Or, with the notation generally employed in the literature on the simplex method: to ascertain, which are the vectors for which $z_j - c_j$ figuring in the last row of the simplex tableau has a positive value.) From among the vectors coming into consideration, we would determine the one to be included on the basis of *random selection with uniform distribution.* The random figures are generated on the electronic computer. This is essentially different from the usual applications of the simplex algorithm where the vector to be included is, as a rule, selected on the basis of strictly defined criteria, e.g. the vector is selected, the inclusion of which would reduce the value of the objective function to the largest extent*.

It will thus be decided at random, how, proceeding from what extreme point to what extreme point, the local minimum should be reached. Progress will be considerably slower here than if we were proceeding from extreme point to extreme point on the basis of selection according to the usual criteria.

Having established one local minimum we would return to the initial very "bad" extreme point, and start again progressing at random towards some local minimum. The progress being at random, another local minimum may be reached.

Naturally, the method will achieve the "scanning" of several local minima only if the initial extreme point had in fact been a very "bad" one, with an extremely high objective function value. Only such a start will provide a basis for the expectation that in proceeding from extreme point to extreme point several local minima will (and among them the global minimum might) be reached.

A.3. The "Curving" of the Objective Function

To apply the other method, it will be necessary to transform to some extent the objective function and to insert a parameter. This parameter has no independent economic significance; it serves exclusively as a help to reach several local minima.

The objective function now assumes the following form:

$$C(\mathbf{x}) = \sum_{j=1}^{n} \{\lambda(p_j x_j^{\pi_j} + q_j x_j^{\psi_j}) + r_j x_j\} . \tag{A.2}$$

The original objective function will be obtained with parameter value $\lambda = 1$.

The considerations underlying this method can be visualized by the diagram of a problem with two variables. The cross-lined polygon

* See e.g. S. GASS [43], p. 56.

represents the set of feasible solutions. The isocost line touches the polygon in extreme point P. This is the originally established local minimum, in the position when parameter $\lambda = 1$. This shall be called in the sequel the *original* local minimum (see figure A.1).

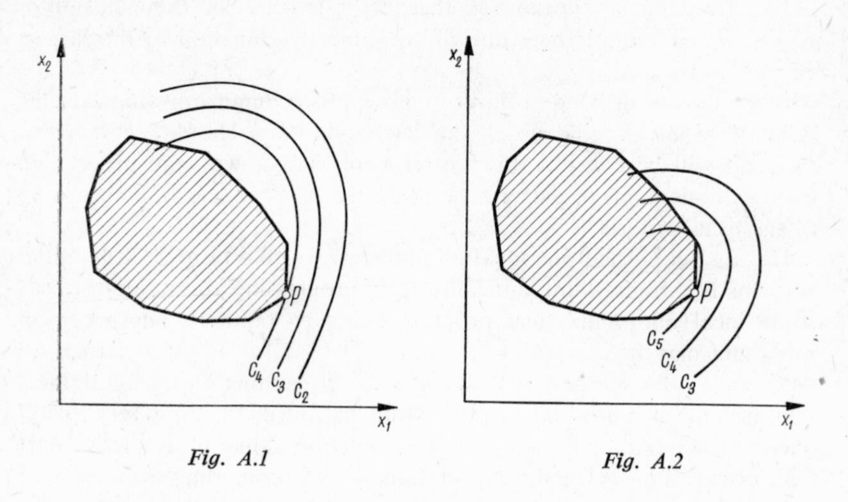

Fig. A.1 *Fig. A.2*

What happens now if we start increasing the value of the parameter? The isocost lines will "curve in", and then – at some characteristic value, some critical point of the parameter – the isocost line, of a now obviously changed objective function value, which passes through point P, will also pass one of the polygon's nearest extreme points. This is shown in figure A.2.

Let us denote this characteristic value of the parameter λ'. We will now proceed as follows:

We will fix the parameter at λ', and start with the new objective function to establish a new local minimum. Let $C'(\mathbf{x})$ denote the new objective function and P' the extreme point representing the corresponding new local minimum. In our progress towards the new local minimum we would now at every extreme point establish the value of the original objective function $C(\mathbf{x})$ (with parameter $\lambda = 1$) for that point. Finally, we select on the way between P and P' the extreme point $\overline{P}$ at which the original objective function $C(\mathbf{x})$ has a minimum value. It is possible that $P = \overline{P}$; in this case the experiment did not succeed. Let us assume, however, that $P \neq \overline{P}$, i.e. the minimum value of the original objective function was either at P' or at one of the extreme points on the way between

P and P'. Then, we will have to examine whether when starting from $\bar{P}$ the value of the original objective function $C(\mathbf{x})$ could not be further decreased. Should this prove *impossible*, then the place of the local minimum is $\bar{P}$ itself. Should a further decrease prove *possible*, then we will continue the optimization until a new local minimum is reached.

As pointed out before, the experiment may not lead to a local minimum which is more advantageous than the original one. In this case a new experiment would be made.

For the new experiment we would again return to extreme point P, the place of the original local minimum, but would now "curve" the objective function in a different way. Now we will not make the non-linear costs of all variables dependent on the parameter – only the non-linear costs of *part of* the variables will depend on the parameter. The non-linear costs of the other part of the variables, and the linear costs of all variables, will be independent of the parameter. The non-linear costs of the variables which in the course of the preceding experiment were first included in the basis will now *not* be made to depend on the parameter.

Having transformed the objective function, we start again increasing the parameter and repeat the experiment as described above in order to obtain a new local minimum more advantageous than the one belonging to the original extreme point P.

The experiment may be repeated several times, according to the choice of the variables which non-linear costs are made or not made dependent on the parameter. Similar experiments may be carried out with the value of the parameter reduced below 1 which is equivalent to "straightening" the isocost lines.

Both methods – that of "progressing at random" as well as that of "curving" the objective function – were employed in parallel. This has permitted the scanning and the comparison of several local optima. Ultimately, the lowest local minimum was accepted as an approximation to the global minimum. Repeated experiments have proved the procedure to result in an acceptable approximation, although the real global minimum has probably not been found.

APPENDIX B

FROM THE MATERIAL OF THE PROGRAMMING PROJECT FOR THE MAN-MADE FIBRES INDUSTRY

Appendix B contains part of the computational material of the programming project for the man-made fibres industry. A complete documentation of the calculations was given in the final report on the research work (see [85]). No survey of the source of the data utilized in the project nor their detailed explanation will be given here; these too will be found in the final report.

Some mathematical aspects of the research work will also be described in Appendix B.

B.1. Some Examples of Forecasting the Trend of World-market Prices

To illustrate the exposition contained in section 19.5, the procedure for forecasting the price trends of benzol, terylene and acrylonitrile will be described below*.

The actual price data for the years 1938–1960 are contained in tables B.1–B.3.

In section 19.5, paragraph (2) of the discussion on the bases of estimation has been dealing with the methods of deriving from the nominal price data the adjusted prices required for our purposes. These prices are given in the tables under the headings marked "adjusted"; it was on the basis of the same adjusted prices that figures 19.17 and 19.18 were established.

The following passages are part of the explanation of the price forecasts as given in the memorandum referred to above.

(1) Up to World War II, *benzol* was for all practical purposes derived from coal-tar or furnace gas. In the years that followed World War II,

* These forecasts, together with the correlation estimates given in section B.2 were taken over from M. Tardos' memorandum on the final report of the research project for the man-made fibres industry.

TABLE B.1

Trends in benzol prices

Country	USA		United Kingdom		France	
Source of data	[196]	–	[196]	–	[196]	–
Character of price	nominal	adjusted	nominal	adjusted	nominal	adjusted
Unit	c/gall	$/to	d/emp.g.	$/to	NF/to	$/to
Year						
1938	15.10	86.70			14.70	89.60
1950	25.90	71.20			220.70	62.10
1951						
1952						
1953	38.33	99.00	52.25	69.10	418.60	89.40
1954	40.00	103.30	55.00	70.70	418.70	91.00
1955	36.00	92.50	60.67	75.00	418.70	91.00
1956	36.00	90.00	61.00	75.40	418.70	87.60
1957	36.00	89.20	66.25	82.00	423.00	83.60
1958	33.70	81.20	63.00	82.80	437.90	77.10
1959	31.00	74.60	63.00	82.00	500.00	84.40
1960	34.00	82.00	63.00	82.00	500.00	82.00

TABLE B.2

Trends in terylene prices

Name of product	Dacron		Terylene	
Country	USA		United Kingdom	
Source of data	[196]	–	[196]	–
Character of price	nominal	adjusted	nominal	adjusted
Unit	c/lb	c/kg	d/lb	c/kg
Year				
1953	180	380	210	423
1954	160	394	162	343
1955	157	349	162	302
1956	136	338	140	264
1957	141	280	140	264
1958	141	277	140	280
1959	136	277	140	277
1960	136	277	140	277

TABLE B.3

Trends in acrylonitrile prices

Country	USA	
Source of data	[200]	–
Character of price	nominal	adjusted
Unit	c/lb	$/to
Year		
1950	40.5	2030
1951	44.5	2000
1952	43.0	1980
1953	43.0	2010
1954	31.0	1450
1955	31.0	1430
1956	27.0	1210
1957	28.0	1220
1958	27.0	1170
1959	27.0	1000
1960	27.0	1000

the production of aromatic products, with benzol among them, has shifted from the coal basis to the petroleum basis. In this field, the US are leading, with 67 per cent of their benzol production actually derived from petroleum. The production costs of benzol are, accordingly, determined by those connected with the extraction and refining of petroleum, with pyrolisis and dehydrogenization.

It was possible to work out the American, British and French prices for benzol. Their trend shows considerable fluctuations, due to changes in supply and demand over the decade under investigation. On the close of World War II, when the process of synthetic benzol production was still hardly known, prices began to soar. The rise, due to limited supply, lasted from 1950 to 1954. From 1954 on, as a consequence of the spread of petrochemical methods in benzol production, a decline in benzol prices can be observed in almost every country. A rise over recent years was registered in the United Kingdom only, where the petrochemical process has so far not been introduced and a considerable demand for benzol persists. The fall in benzol prices was concomitant with the spread of the process of deriving benzol from petroleum and the decline is likely to continue as a consequence of the end of the benzol shortage.

Transposed to the Hungarian import price level, the American, British and French benzol prices as deflated between 1954 and 1960 can be enclosed within two hyperbolae. According to our forecast, the movement of benzol prices beyond 1960 is likely to remain within these two hyperbolae. The maximum values of the benzol price can be expected to correspond to the ($y = 77.45 + 27.2\,(1/x)$) values of a hyperbolic regression function established on the basis of the deflated US prices as transposed to the Hungarian import price level. As a consequence of a probable fall in petroleum prices it may be assumed that deals will be contracted at a price level lower than the hyperbola values indicated above, and that prices will approach the values of the lower hyperbola which constitutes the bounds of the prices of recent years. Benzol prices will thus vary between 60 and 80 $/ton. The trends reckoned within the course of the calculations were substantiated by Hungarian export experiences in 1961.

(2) *Terylene* fibres have witnessed a rapid decline in price over the past period. The rate of fall in prices was quicker than e.g. in the case of nylon fibres. This situation can be explained by the fact that polyester production was launched at a later time only and the period under investigation reflects therefore to a higher degree the first phase of a period of price decline due to the end of monopolistic relations of production. The decline of prices is, accordingly, likely to continue at a quicker rate than in the case of nylon fibres and the price curve can be expected to flatten out at a later stage only.

The adjusted British and American prices can easily be enclosed within two hyperbolae which will begin gradually to flatten out from their steep fall after 1970 only. According to our forecast, import prices of polyester fibres will over the period between 1960 and 1980 move within the bounds of the two hyperbolae.

Our price forecasts have also been checked by means of calculations concerning variable costs.

(3) The prices of *acrylonitrile* have been falling off at a largely uniform rate over the past decade. At present, revolutionary changes are taking place in the technology of acrylonitrile production. The Sohio process has enabled the manufacture of acrylonitrile from propylene and ammonia, eliminating thus the difficulties connected with the hydrogen cyanide process and considerably decreasing the cost of production. As a consequence of the introduction of this new technology, acrylonitrile prices in the US have in 1961 decreased by 40 per cent.

The adjusted 1950–1961 American price data of acrylonitrile could be enclosed within two hyperbolae. In our opinion, the prices within the bounds of the two hyperbolic functions are likely to prevail also over the period between 1962 and 1980. Our forecasts were based on the American price level in the period that followed the 1961 decline and it was around that value that we have set the minimum level of prices.

TABLE B.4

Price forecasts

Year		Benzol	Terylene	Acrylonitrile
1961	Actual price	70	2630	715
1970	Lower limit	60	1300	300
	Mean value	70	1750	350
	Upper limit	80	2200	400
1975	Lower limit	60	1100	280
	Mean value	70	1500	320
	Upper limit	80	1900	360

The price forecasts for the above three products are given in table B. 4.

Altogether, price forecasts for 34 different products have been worked out in a similar manner.

B.2. Correlation Estimates

For the purpose of the stochastic calculations, estimates were made of the correlation between the prices of various products. It was not without strong reservations that we established these estimates; we did so only with the purpose of enabling us to carry out an experimental calculation on the basis of numerical data of a provisional character.

First of all, the correlation between the price trends of some products were established for the period 1953–1960.

The correlation between statistically observed data of a past period could, however, provide a *starting point of informative character* only for the estimates on future correlations. In this connection, we had to consider the fact that a certain degree of "parallelism" between the trends of related products was already taken into account when establishing our price forecasts in "from-to" form. Thus, for instance, the forecasts of the prices of terylene and of orlon fibre were based on the assumption that the prices of both products would fall simultaneously. Correlation is, therefore, meant to express nothing but the fact that if, with both respective price intervals showing a falling trend, one product can be found in the lower part of its interval, there is a growing probability that the other, too, will take up a position in the lower part of its own price interval.

The estimates for 1975 are given in table B. 5.

TABLE B.5.

Correlation estimates

1st product	2nd product	Correlation coefficient
Orlon	Polyacrylonitrile-vinylchloride copolymer	0.9
Orlon	Terylene	0.5
Polyacrylonitrile-vinylchloride copolymer	Terylene	0.5
Orlon	Polypropylene staple	0.5
Polyacrylonitrile-vinylchloride copolymer	Polypropylene staple	0.5
Nylon 6 yarn	Polypropylene yarn	0.5
Terylene	Polypropylene staple	0.5
Polypropylene staple	Polypropylene yarn	0.8
Rayon staple	Rayon yarn	0.6
Caprolactame	Nylon 6 yarn	0.6
Ethylene glycol	Dimethyl terephthalate	0.6
Dimethyl terephthalate	Terylene staple	0.6
Acrylonitrile	Orlon	0.7
Acrylonitrile	Polyacrylonitrile-vinylchloride copolymer staple	0.7
Benzol	Phenol	0.5*
Benzol	Paraxylol	0.5
Cellulose for staple	Rayon staple	0.6
Cellulose for staple	Cellophane	0.6
Cellulose for yarn	Rayon yarn	0.6
Sulphur	Sulphuric acid	0.8

* On the basis of actual figures, no correlation between the prices of benzol and phenol could be observed. This position can, however, be assumed to change in the future as a consequence of the spread of synthetic phenol production.

B.3. Expected Value and Standard Deviation of the Stochastic Cost Function

In contrast to the notation used in ch. 6 where the model of the man-made fibres industry was originally described, here the activities will be defined by means of two suffices. The first suffix will be "1" for productive, "2" for import and "3" for export activities ($k = 1, 2, 3$). The second suffix will give the ordinal number of the productive, import or export activity in question ($j = 1, 2, \ldots, n_k$).

Ordinal numbers were also given to the materials used in the man-made fibres industry for which the world-market prices were worked out individually and which were *not* produced by the model's activities. (For their list see section 6.2.) These will be called in the following priority materials, and referred to by suffix "4". Their number is n_4.

We have thus obtained four groups of product:

(1) those yielded by productive activities;
(2) those yielded by import activities;
(3) those yielded by export activities;
(4) the priority materials.

The expected value of the objective function in the case of realization of program $\mathbf{x}$ will be

$$C(\mathbf{x}) = \sum_{j=1}^{n_1} \left[P_j \cdot \left(\frac{x_{1j}}{X_{0j}} \right)^{\pi_j} + Q_j \cdot \left(\frac{x_{1j}}{X_{0j}} \right)^{\psi_j} + r_j\, x_{1j} \right] + \tag{B.1}$$
$$+ \sum_{j=1}^{n_2} s_{2j}\, x_{2j} + \sum_{j=1}^{n_3} s_{3j}\, x_{3j}\,,$$

where

X_{0j} = the plant size fixed for the jth productive activity ($j = 1, \ldots, n_1$)

P_j = the expected value of random variable P_j. This random variable represents the rent on capital according to the investment cost of the jth productive activity ($j = 1, \ldots, n_1$) with an assumed X_{0j} fixed plant size

Q_j = the expected value of random variable Q_j. This random variable represents the annual operational wages cost of the jth productive activity ($j = 1, \ldots, n_1$) with an assumed X_{0j} fixed plant size

π_j, ψ_j = the degression exponents of the jth productive activity ($j = 1, \ldots, n_1$)

r_j = the expected value of random variable r_j. This random variable represents other (non-wage) cost per unit product of the jth productive activity ($j = 1, \ldots, n_1$). This will be called in the following the proportional operation cost

s_{2j}, s_{3j} = the expected value of random variables $\mathsf{s}_{2j}, \mathsf{s}_{3j}$. These random variables represent the unit costs of the jth import activity ($j = 1, \ldots, n_2$) and the jth export activity ($j = 1, \ldots, n_3$), respectively, i.e. the unit price of imports, or, in the case of export, the unit price of exports. (The latter is negative.)

Proportional operation cost r_j ($j = 1, \ldots, n_1$) will require special explanation. It can be defined as follows:

$$\mathsf{r}_j = \sum_{h=1}^{n_4} g_{jh}\, \mathsf{s}_{4h} + k_j + \mathsf{e}_j, \qquad j = 1, \ldots, n_1, \tag{B.2}$$

where

g_{jh} = material input coefficient, the amount of the hth priority material ($h = 1, \ldots, n_4$) required for one unit of the jth productive activity ($j = 1, \ldots, n_1$). It is assumed to be constant

s_{4h} = the unit price of the hth priority material ($h = 1, \ldots, n_4$). This is a random variable

k_j = the proportional cost, not accounted for in the range of priority material costs ($\sum_h g_{jh}\, \mathsf{s}_{4h}$), per unit of the jth productive activity ($j = 1, \ldots, n_1$). For example, the cost of the auxiliary and maintenance materials accounted for at other than world-market prices. This is also assumed to be constant

e_j = a random variable the expected value of which is 0. This represents the uncertainty involved – *over and above* that of the world-market prices – in the estimates which serve to determine the proportional operation cost of the jth productive activity ($j = 1, \ldots, n_1$). This means that on the one hand the world-market prices of the utilized priority materials are uncertain, a circumstance expressed in the fact that s_{4h} ($h = 1, \ldots, n_4$) is a random variable. In addition, the material input coefficient referring to the priority materials, the consumption of materials of domestic origin accounted for at other than world-market prices etc. are also uncertain. This latter uncertainty is expressed in the random variable e_j.

Expected value r_j figuring in (B.1) will, accordingly, be

$$r_j = \sum_{h=1}^{n_4} g_{jh} s_{4h} + k_j, \quad j = 1, \ldots, n_1. \tag{B.3}$$

Let us now proceed to the definition of the standard deviation. The correlation coefficients required for the purpose will be denoted as follows:

$\varrho_{ij,hl}$ = the coefficient measuring the correlation between the unit prices of the jth product of the ith group and the lth product of the hth group. Thus e.g., $\varrho_{2j,4l}$ denotes the coefficient which measures the correlation between the price of the product imported by the jth import activity and that of the lth priority material.

The variance of the cost function of program $\mathbf{x}$ can be given as follows (the left-hand column contains the interpretation of the individual rows):

The economic relationships expressed	
rent on capital and wages costs of the productive activities	$\sum_{j=1}^{n_1}\left[\sigma^2_{P_j}\cdot\left(\frac{x_{1j}}{X_{0j}}\right)^{2\pi_j} + \sigma^2_{Q_j}\cdot\left(\frac{x_{1j}}{X_{0j}}\right)^{2\psi_j}\right]x^2_{1j} +$
proportional cost of the productive activity	$+\sum_{j=1}^{n_1} a_j^2 x_{1j}^2 +$
the cost of foreign-trading activities	$+\sum_{j=1}^{n_2}\sigma^2_{s_{2j}}\, x^2_{2j} + \sum_{j=1}^{n_3}\sigma^2_{s_{3j}}\, x^2_{3j} +$
the correlation between the priority material costs of the productive activities	$+2\sum_{\substack{j,h=1\\ j<h}}^{n_1} b_{jh}\, x_{1j}\, x_{1h} +$
the correlation between the priority material costs of the productive activities and the cost of foreign-trading activities	$+2\sum_{j=1}^{n_1}\left[\sum_{h=1}^{n_2} c_{j,2h}\, x_{1j}\, x_{2h} + \sum_{h=1}^{n_3} c_{j,3h}\, x_{1j} x_{3h}\right]+$ (B.4)
the correlation between the costs of import activities	$+2\sum_{\substack{j,h=1\\ j<h}}^{n_2}\varrho_{2j,2h}\,\sigma_{s_{2j}}\,\sigma_{s_{2h}}\, x_{2j}\, x_{2h} +$
the correlation between the costs of the import and export activities	$+2\sum_{j=1}^{n_2}\sum_{h=1}^{n_3}\varrho_{2j,3h}\,\sigma_{s_{2j}}\,\sigma_{s_{3h}}\, x_{2j}\, x_{3h} +$
the correlation between the costs of import activities	$+2\sum_{\substack{j,h=1\\ j<h}}^{n_3}\varrho_{3j,3h}\,\sigma_{s_{3j}}\,\sigma_{s_{3h}}\, x_{3j}\, x_{3h}\,,$

where

$$a_j^2 = \sum_{i,l=1}^{n_4} g_{ji}\, g_{jl}\, \varrho_{4i,4l}\, \sigma_{s_{4i}}\, \sigma_{s_{4l}} + \sigma^2_{ej}, \quad j = 1,\dots, n_1\,, \tag{B.5}$$

$$b_{jh} = \sum_{h,l=1}^{n_4} g_{ji}\, g_{hl}\, \varrho_{4i,4l}\, \sigma_{s_{4i}}\, \sigma_{s_{4l}}\,, \quad j, h = 1,\dots, n_1;\ j < h\,, \tag{B.6}$$

$$c_{j,ih} = \sum_{l=1}^{n_4} g_{jl}\, \varrho_{4l,ih}\, \sigma_{s_{4l}}\sigma_{s_{ih}},\ j = 1,\dots, n_1;\ i = 2, 3;\ h = 1,\dots, n_4. \tag{B.7}$$

In objective function (14.1) we have the standard deviation, i.e. the square root of (B.4).

APPENDIX C

THE EFFECTS OF THE CONCENTRATION AND THE SCATTERING OF THE ACTIVITIES

by

TH. LIPTÁK

In the following, the effects of the concentration and the scattering of the activities will be illustrated by means of an extremely simplified model.

We have a linear programming model with a single resource (this may be, for instance, the investment fund). The scope of the individual activities will be measured by their participation in the resources. The general objective will be the minimization of costs.

Let us, therefore, assume that in the linear programming problem

$$x_1 + \ldots + x_n = 1; \tag{C.1}$$

$$x_1 \geqq 0, \ldots, x_n \geqq 0; \tag{C.2}$$

$$\mathsf{c}_1 x_1 + \ldots + \mathsf{c}_n x_n \rightarrow \min!, \tag{C.3}$$

the coefficients $\mathsf{c}_1, \ldots, \mathsf{c}_n$ are independent random variables with expected values and standard deviations

$$c_i = M(\mathsf{c}_i) \quad \text{and} \quad \sigma_i = D(\mathsf{c}_i), \quad i = 1, \ldots, n, \tag{C.4}$$

respectively.

Problem 1

Let us minimize, instead of (C.3), the expected value.

Since

$$M\left(\sum_{i=1}^{n} \mathsf{c}_i x_i\right) = \sum_{i=1}^{n} c_i x_i, \tag{C.5}$$

it is clear that the optimal one will be the program where total capacity is given for the variable which has a coefficient of minimum expected value:

$$x_{i_0}^* = 1, \qquad x_i^* = 0, \qquad i \neq i_0, \tag{C.6}$$

where

$$c_{i_0} = \min_{1 \leqq i \leqq n} c_i . \tag{C.7}$$

Problem 2

Let us minimize the standard deviation of objective function $\sum_{i=1}^{n} c_i x_i$. The same result will be obtained as if the variance

$$D^2\left(\sum_{i=1}^{n} c_i x_i\right) = \sum_{i=1}^{n} \sigma_i^2 x_i^2 \tag{C.8}$$

were minimized. Let us employ Cauchy's inequality

$$\left(\sum_{i=1}^{n} a_i b_i\right)^2 \leqq \left(\sum_{i=1}^{n} a_i^2\right)\left(\sum_{i=1}^{n} b_i^2\right) \tag{C.9}$$

with choice $a_i = \sigma_i x_i$, $b_i = \sqrt{x_i}$. From (C.8) and (C.1) we obtain:

$$D^2\left(\sum_{i=1}^{n} c_i x_i\right) \geqq \frac{\left(\sum_{i=1}^{n} \sigma_i x_i \sqrt{x_i}\right)^2}{\sum_{i=1}^{n} x_i} = \left(\sum_{i=1}^{n} \sigma_i x_i \sqrt{\bar{x}_i}\right)^2. \tag{C.10}$$

An equality is only possible, i.e. $D^2(\sum_{i=1}^{n} c_i x_i)$ can only have a minimum value if $\frac{a_1}{b_1} = \ldots = \frac{a_n}{b_n}$, i.e.

$$\sigma_1 \sqrt{x_1} = \ldots = \sigma_n \sqrt{x_n}, \text{ or}$$

$$\sigma_1^2 x_1 = \ldots = \sigma_n^2 x_n . \tag{C.11}$$

Comparing this with (C.1) and (C.2) we have

$$x_i^* = \frac{\sigma_i^{-2}}{\sum_{k=1}^{n} \sigma_k^{-2}}, \qquad i = 1, \ldots, n . \tag{C.12}$$

for the components of the optimal program.

In other words, standard deviation will have a minimum value in the case of the program which allocates the capacity to the individual variables in a proportion inverse to the variance of the coefficients of the objective function. Minimum value of the standard deviation will be

$$\sigma^* = \left(\sum_{i=1}^{n} \sigma_i^2 \, x_i^{*2} \right)^{\frac{1}{2}} = \left(\sum_{i=1}^{n} \sigma_i^{-2} \right)^{-\frac{1}{2}} . \tag{C.13}$$

If

$$\sigma_1 = \sigma_2 = \ldots = \sigma_n = \sigma , \tag{C.14}$$

then the optimal program under (C.12) is uniformly distributed:

$$x_1^* = x_2^* = \ldots = x_n^* = \frac{1}{n} \tag{C.15}$$

and

$$\sigma^* = \frac{\sigma}{\sqrt{n}} . \tag{C.16}$$

As a general conclusion: the minimization of the expected value will induce a concentration of the activities, the minimization of standard deviation will induce their scattering.

APPENDIX D

COMPOUND INTEREST FORMULAE

D.1. The Rental Formula

The annual computational cost of a productive and investment activity was determined in the computational price system discussed in Part 4 as follows:

$$C = \gamma P + R, \tag{D.1}$$

where

C = annual computational cost
γ = the rental on capital
P = non-recurrent investment costs
R = annual working costs.

(D.1) is called the *rental formula*. This simplest formula can be employed without hesitation in all cases where there are no considerable differences between the dynamics of the outlays and results of the alternatives; where investment times for each alternative are short (and approximately equal) in duration, whereupon production can start immediately, with results and outlays constant over time. This applies e.g. to the cases where exclusively variants of machine replacement are being compared.

Owing to the difficulties pointed out in section 16.4 we were, unfortunately, compelled to employ the rental formula also where this was in fact not entirely justified. In certain calculations, however, compound interest formulae were also employed, at least for the purpose of parallel control tests.

D.2. Investment Cost with Interest Added

When the case is not one of mere replacement of machinery which can be carried out in many sectors even within hours, but of setting up a new plant – a project involving technical designing, construction, the purchase and the coordinated mounting of new machinery, etc. – then the investment may require several years.

From the point of view of the national economy it cannot be indifferent for how long the production fund is blocked without producing. Let us call the period which elapses from the beginning of an investment project until its going into operation the completion period. This will be accounted for by the application of the compound interest formula*:

$$\tilde{P} = \sum_{t=1}^{\tau} P(t)\,(1+i)^{\tau-t}\,, \qquad \text{(D.2)}$$

where

$\tilde{P}$	=	investment cost with interest added
1st year	=	the year of the beginning of the investment, the first year of the completion period
τth year	=	the last year of the completion period
$P(t)$	=	investment cost in the tth year
i	=	the rate of interest.

If, therefore, for two alternatives which are to go into operation at the same date, the value of $\Sigma P(t)$ is identical but that of τ is not so, preference will be given to the alternative whose completion period is shorter.

The investment cost with interest added, obtained in this way, can be substituted for investment cost P in formula (D.1).

It should be pointed out here that the official methodological instructions concerning the efficiency of investments are also making use of

* This relationship is emphasized by the Soviet economist T. Khachaturov [65]. He takes a stand for the application of the compound interest formula: "If the provisions aimed at automation and mechanization differ from one another with respect to the length of the planning, execution and introduction periods, then the effects of the time factor on the comparison of the variants in the economic sense of the word must be taken into consideration. The economic consequences of any shortening or lengthening of the time limits set for putting the provisions into operation must be reflected in corrections of the investment amounts required, taking into account the average effect that could be achieved by productive investment in other branches of the national economy. The practical meaning of this is that if according to one variant the investments are to take place at a later date, their dimensions will not be equivalent with those of the investments which are taking place at the given moment. To be measurable against present investments, the investments of coming years must be multiplied with the coefficient $k = 1/(1+\Delta)^t$.

the concept of interest added when taking into account the completion period*. The official formula is

$$\tilde{P} = \sum_{t=1}^{\tau} P(t)\,(1 + i(\tau - t)). \tag{D.3}$$

In the official formula (D.3) the adding of interest is *linear*, whereas in (D.2) it is *exponential*. In the case of identical interest rates, a stronger time preference asserts itself in the exponential formula. The weight of earlier arisen costs as against that of later costs is greater here than in the linear solution.

D.3. Costs Discounted

If, after the investment is put into operation, the results and outlays are not constant over time, not even approximately, and there is a difference between the alternatives as regards the dynamics of operational results and outlays, the formulae discussed above will not meet the case. In such cases the well-known formula of costs discounted should be applied**:

$$\tilde{C} = \sum_{t=1}^{T} C(t)\,(1 + i)^{-t}, \tag{D.4}$$

where

$\tilde{C}$ = costs discounted
T = the length of the accounting period
$C(t)$ = the costs arising in the tth year.

The length of the accounting period is an arbitrarily determined magnitude. The calculations where the above formula was used were generally based on an accounting period of 25–30 years. This parameter will to some extent affect the results of the calculation. Its effect is, however, not significant as – owing to discounting – the costs arising at the end of the accounting period will have but little weight. Thus, for instance, the discounted value of 1 Ft arising in the 30th year will, in the case

* See Investments Code [195].

** As the present book generally employs *cost* functions, for the sake of uniformity only the formula of costs discounted is given here. For application to returns the formula can be transformed accordingly.

of an interest rate of 8 per cent, amount to 0.099 only. Control calculations to check the modificatory effects of the length of the accounting period on the optimal program have, at any rate, been carried out, e.g. in the course of programming in the cotton textile industry. The calculations have shown the optimal program insensitive to this variable.

The sectoral models described in chs. 5 and 6 are not destined to determine the optimal time distribution, the optimal schedule of the activities. In the calculations where the formula of costs discounted has been applied we had, nevertheless, to introduce certain assumptions concerning the time distribution of the activities, in order to enable an objective comparison between the alternatives. We have therefore assumed all capacities brought into being by investment to go into operation in the last year of the plan period considered in the program. This is like starting runners with different speeds at different points of time, in order to make them reach the finish exactly at the same time. When working out the discounted value of costs, the investment activities characterized by longer completion periods will thus be at a disadvantage from this point of view as compared with those completed within shorter periods.

Other formulae of interest computation are also known*; for our calculations, however, those described in the foregoing have proved adequate.

D.4. The Rate of Interest Used in Compound Interest Formulae

Accounting principle D.1. The rental γ in the rental formula is equal to the interest rate (i) *in the compound interest formulae.*

This identity is not self-evident and can be accepted as an approximation only. It does not directly follow from the propositions in ch. 18, as the model described there laid the emphasis on the choice between labour force and production fund at the *identical moment*, allowing thus of a direct inference only on the rental γ, whereas the compound interest formulae are, as a rule, connected with problems of the *choice of time.*

* See e.g. E. SCHNEIDER [154] and F. LUTZ and V. LUTZ [111].

In place of a demonstration I shall have to confine myself to presenting in a simplified example the train of thought which leads to accounting principle D.1.

The cost of a definite investment activity is computed by means of two different formulae: rental formula (D.1) and discounted cost formula (D.4). Characteristics of the investment activity in our example are the following:

(1) All investment costs will arise simultaneously, in the 0th year.

(2) Operation costs are constant over time.

These assumptions must be made if only because without them the application of the rental formula (D.1) could not be justified.

With these assumptions once made, the following proposition can be stated:

Proposition D.1. The rental formula and the formula of costs discounted will result in the same combination of investment and operation costs, provided that the same rental on capital (γ) and rate of interest (i) is used in both formulae and that the accounting period in the latter formula is taken as infinite.

Proof. Costs according to the rental formula will be:

$$C = R + \gamma P\,, \tag{D.5}$$

where

R = operation costs over one year
P = non-recurrent investment costs.

We assume that $i = \gamma$. Therefore we apply γ also in the formula of costs discounted.

Costs according to the discounted costs formula will be:

$$\tilde{C} = P + \sum_{t=1}^{T} R\,(1 + \gamma)^{-t}\,. \tag{D.6}$$

Summarizing now the working costs according to the summation formula for geometric series, we get the discounted value of costs:

$$\tilde{C} = P + R\,\frac{(1 + \gamma)^T - 1}{\gamma(1 + \gamma)^T}\,. \tag{D.7}$$

The expression figuring here as a coefficient of R has the following properties:

$$\frac{(1+\gamma)^T - 1}{\gamma(1+\gamma)^T} \to \frac{1}{\gamma} \quad \text{as} \quad T \to \infty. \tag{D.8}$$

Accordingly

$$\tilde{C} = P + \frac{1}{\gamma} R \quad \text{as} \quad T = \infty. \tag{D.9}$$

Obviously, the ratio between P and $1/\gamma R$ in formula (D.9) is identical with that between γP and R in formula (D.5).

Proposition D.1 will exactly hold only for the case when T is infinite. In practice, however, the accounting period can without hesitation be taken as finite; if T is sufficiently long, the difference will be negligible. If e.g. in the formula of costs discounted, the accounting period is 30 years and $i = 0.1$, in the rental formula the value of γ should be 0.105, in order that both formulae suggest the same combination of investment and working costs.

The two examples described above prove that accounting principle D.1 can be accepted at least as an approximation. I had to treat this question in special detail because it had been contested in the Hungarian debate from several sides. It is also worth mentioning that it is essentially principle D.1 that is being employed both by the Hungarian and Soviet official instructions concerning the methodology of investment efficiency calculations*.

* Soviet methodology makes the application of both formulae (D.1) and (D.2) obligatory, on the basis of an identical rate of interest (see [180]). In Hungarian methodology, formulae (D.1) and (D.3) are used, also on the basis of an identical interest rate (see Investments Code [195]).

APPENDIX E

PROOFS OF THE PROPOSITIONS RELATING TO THE RENTAL ON CAPITAL

by

P. Wellisch

In the following, proofs will be given of the propositions, contained in ch. 18, relating to the computational rental on capital and to the computational wage rate.

The assumptions and propositions themselves will not be repeated here; on the basis of references they will be easily found in the chapter in question.

As regards the more obvious propositions requiring no proof, we will content ourselves with pointing out the formulae from which they follow.

Propositions 18.1 and 18.2

Both propositions follow from the assumed properties 1 and 2 of the production function $Y(K, L)$*.

Let us consider the condition

$$Y(K, L) = Y^*, \tag{E.1}$$

given for function $Y(K, L)$. The well-known theorem on implicit functions ensures that if our assumptions are valid, any of the variables in equation (E.1) can be expressed as a function of the other one. Thus e.g. from (E.1)

$$L = G(K). \tag{E.2}$$

It is also known that our assumptions allow the function $G(K)$ to be differentiated, and its derivative will be

$$G'(K) = -\frac{Y_K[K, G(K)]}{Y_L[K, G(K)]}, \tag{E.3}$$

* For the sake of accuracy, let it be pointed out that we have assumed the validity of properties 1 and 2 for all positive values of K and L. With this assumption, all our propositions are valid for the positive orthant $K > 0$, $L > 0$. The assumption of positivity is not an important restriction from the economic point of view.

where Y_K and Y_L denote the partial derivates of function $F(K, L)$. Let us now consider the problem of determining the constrained extremum defined by (18.6). Considering (E.2) besides condition (E.1), the function

$$C(K, L) = \gamma K + \omega L, \tag{E.4}$$

may also be written in the form

$$C(K, L) = H(K) = \gamma K + \omega G(K). \tag{E.5}$$

As $G'(K)$ exists, $H(K)$ can also be differentiated:

$$H'(K) = \gamma + \omega G'(K). \tag{E.6}$$

However, in accordance with property 2, $G'(K)$ and thus also $H'(K)$ are strictly monotonic decreasing functions. Accordingly, for $H(K)$ to have a minimum at point $K = \bar{K}$, the necessary and sufficient condition to be satisfied is that

$$H'(\bar{K}) = \gamma + \omega G'(\bar{K}) = 0. \tag{E.7}$$

(E.7) can, in turn, be satisfied if, and only if,

$$\frac{\gamma}{\omega} = -G'(\bar{K}), \tag{E.8}$$

.e. employing (E.3)

$$\frac{\gamma}{\omega} = \frac{Y_K[\bar{K}, G(\bar{K})]}{Y_L[\bar{K}, G(\bar{K})]} = \frac{Y_K(\bar{K},\bar{L})}{Y_L(\bar{K},\bar{L})}. \tag{E.9}$$

Proposition 18.3

This will be seen immediately to be true if in (18.15) the quotient (Y_K/Y_L) is replaced by (γ/ω) in accordance with (18.8).

Propositions 18.4 and 18.5

Integrating (18.26) we have

$$Y = Y_0 e^{\varrho t}. \tag{E.10}$$

Substituting this into (18.25) and integrating again, we have

$$K = K_0 e^{\varrho t} \tag{E.11}$$

and thus

$$\chi(t) = \frac{Y}{K} = \frac{Y_0}{K_0} = \chi(0) = \chi \,. \tag{E.12}$$

On the other hand, employing (18.24) we get

$$y = \frac{Y}{L} = \frac{Y_0\, e^{\varrho t}}{L_0\, e^{\lambda t}} = \frac{Y_0}{L_0}\, e^{(\varrho - \lambda)t}. \tag{E.13}$$

The marginal efficiency of the production fund:

$$Y_K = \frac{\partial Y}{\partial K} = \beta\, A\, e^{\mu t}\; K(t)^{\beta-1}\, L(t)^{\eta} = \frac{\beta Y}{K} \,. \tag{E.14}$$

The marginal productivity of the labour force:

$$Y_L = \frac{\partial Y}{\partial L} = \eta\, A\, e^{\mu t}\; K(t)^{\beta}\, L(t)^{\eta-1} = \frac{\eta\, Y}{L} \tag{E.15}$$

or, employing (E.12) and (E.13):

$$Y_K = \beta \chi \,, \tag{E.16}$$

$$Y_L = \frac{\eta\, Y_0}{L_0}\, e^{(\varrho - \lambda)t} \,. \tag{E.17}$$

(E.12) and (E.16) prove proposition 18.4; (E.13) and (E.17) prove proposition 18.5.

Propositions 18.6 and 18.7

A trivial proof of these propositions was given in ch. 18 above.

Proposition 18.8

Obtaining the derivative of (E.11) with respect to t, we have

$$\dot{K} = \varrho\, K_0\, e^{\varrho t}. \tag{E.18}$$

Substituting this into (18.25) and employing (E.10) we have

$$\varrho\, \hat{K}_0\, e^{\varrho t} = \alpha\, Y = \alpha\, Y_0\, e^{\varrho t}, \tag{E.19}$$

from which ϱ can be expressed as

$$\varrho = \alpha \frac{Y_0}{K_0} = \alpha\chi . \tag{E.20}$$

On the other hand, from (E.14) and (E.15) it follows that

$$Y_K K + Y_L L = (\beta + \eta) Y . \tag{E.21}$$

However, in the case of the validity of the total imputation assumption (18.34), equalities (E.21) and (18.8) will unequivocally determine the magnitude of γ. Under these conditions

$$\gamma = \frac{Y_K}{\beta + \eta}, \tag{E.22}$$

or, employing (E.16)

$$\gamma = \frac{\beta}{\beta + \eta}\chi . \tag{E.23}$$

Let us furthermore take into consideration equality (18.35). By the way, this follows from (18.16), if we substitute into it both (E.14) and (E.15), and express $\alpha^\triangle$. Then, finally, we have

$$\gamma = \alpha^\triangle \chi . \tag{E.24}$$

Combining this with (E.20), proposition 18.8 can be read off.

Proposition 18.9

If, on the basis of (18.8), Y_K/Y_L is substituted for γ/ω, and (E.14) and (E.15) are taken into consideration, we obtain (18.37).

APPENDIX F

THE STATISTICAL EXAMINATION OF MACROECONOMIC GROWTH PROCESSES

CO-AUTHOR:
P. WELLISCH

F.1. Aim of the Examination

The aim of this statistical examination is two-fold. First, an attempt is made to verify some of the assumptions of the theoretical model described in ch. 18. Partly the assumptions themselves will be considered, and partly the propositions set out in ch. 18. For if one or other of the propositions may be statistically verified, then this makes it probable that the initial assumption made in deducing the proposition was also justified.

The other aim of this examination was to make an attempt at numerically determining the parameters of the production function (18.38) described in section 18.10. It will be seen that this attempt did not yield a positive result, but its negative lessons are also useful in drawing certain conclusions.

Only post-1949 figures have been examined. It would have been impossible to compare pre-1945 data with those for the post-1949 period, because of the profound changes in the social and economic structure accompanied by corresponding ones in the price system as well*. The period between 1945 and 1949, involving a big inflation and then the extraordinary situation attendant on repairing war damages, is again not suitable for a study of the processes of "normal" economic growth.

In analyzing the figures for 1949–1962, those for the year 1956 have in some calculations (in determining averages and regression equations) been omitted, due to the extraordinary gap in the production.

The greater part of the figures are based on those of the Central Statistical Office (CSO), and the remainder on those of the National Planning Board** (NPB).

* An effort has been made by K. KÁDAS [61] to establish numerically the parameters of a Cobb–Douglas type production function on the basis of pre-1945 figures for Hungarian industry.

** This opportunity is taken to thank A. Nyilas and M. Somogyi (CSO) as well as Dr. J. Rácz (NPB), for their valuable support.

F.2. The Growth of National Income, of the Production Fund and the Labour Force

The following data are examined:

The national income $Y^{(E)}$ *of the economy.* This, in accordance with the statistical practice of the socialist countries, comprises the contributions of industry, building, agriculture, transport and home and foreign trade. Unlike the statistical practice of most capitalist countries, it does not comprise the non-productive services, e.g. most of the services rendered

TABLE

Time series of the national income, the

Quantity	Symbol	Unit	1950	1951	1952	1953
National income of economy	$Y^{(E)}$	1000 million Ft	74.7	87.4	85.7	97.0
Production fund, net, of economy	$K_n^{(E)}$	1000 million Ft	.	178.1	197.0	215.6
Labour force of economy	$L^{(E)}$	1000 persons	.	3506.5	3633.9	3621.9
National income, industry's contribution	$Y^{(I)}$	1000 million Ft	33.0	38.8	45.9	51.1
Production fund, net, of industry	$K_n^{(I)}$	1000 million Ft	47.4	51.9	58.8	69.0
Production fund, gross, of industry	$K_g^{(I)}$	1000 million Ft	72.3	79.1	89.7	99.3
Labour force	$L^{(I)}$	1000 pers.	789.6	803.3	896.3	939.1
Ratio of net and gross industrial production fund	$K_n^{(I)}/K_g^{(I)}$	per cent	65.6	65.6	65.6	69.5

* SOURCES of the figures:

$Y^{(E)}$, $Y^{(I)}$ 1950–1961. Statistical Yearbook, 1961 [188]
1962. Direct information from CSO

$K_n^{(E)}$, $K_n^{(I)}$ Figures for fixed funds:
1950. Estimated, by calculating back from the gross figure
1951–1957. Statistical Yearbook, 1957 [185]
1958. Direct information from CSO
1959–1962. Periodic Statistical Publications [190]
Figures for circulating funds: Direct information from CSO

by health and cultural institutions, the activities of the state apparatus, etc.*.

Industry's contribution $Y^{(I)}$ to the national income. This is plainly analogous to the national income of the economy.

The net production fund $K_n^{(E)}$ of the economy. This comprises the following:

1. The productive fixed capital of the economy – the value of the machines, equipment and buildings participating in production,

F.1.

production fund and the labour force

1954	1955	1956	1957	1958	1959	1960	1961	1962
93.0	101.3	90.4	111.4	118.4	126.5	139.3	147.4	155.2
237.1	253.4	272.5	276.4	298.6	336.0	353.7	376.9	402.5
3712.0	3777.3	3852.6	3862.6	3940.0	3984.1	3994.2	3920.5	3878.0
49.7	55.4	47.0	57.0	64.1	69.3	80.2	88.5	95.6
79.8	87.0	95.1	98.1	106.7	118.8	126.4	136.8	147.6
110.4	119.6	129.3	139.6	147.0	158.4	170.2	185.3	201.1
1069.9	1111.1	1124.4	1099.6	1184.0	1224.0	1291.5	1330.0	1360.4
72.3	72.7	73.5	70.3	72.6	75.0	74.3	73.8	73.4

To make the figures comparable, the earlier figures were multiplied by price indices; the price indices were furnished by the CSO

$K_g^{(I)}$ — Figures for fixed funds:
1950–1958. RÁCZ [145]
1959–1962. Periodic Statistical Publications [190]
The figures for circulating funds correspond to those used for $K_n^{(I)}$

$L^{(E)}$, $L^{(I)}$ — Direct information from CSO.

* In the subsequent text the suffix (*E*) will denote figures for the economy, the suffix (*I*) those for industry.

i.e. in the creation of the national income defined above. The value is here a net one, i.e. the depreciation of the fixed resources must be subtracted from their original value, but the value of general repairs, of their renovation, must be added.
The value of the fixed capital does not include the prices of sites, of land and of natural resources. It comprises only the reproducible elements of the stock of fixed capital.

2. The productive working capital of the economy. This includes:
   2.1. Stocks of materials, semi-processed and finished products.
   2.2. The stock of unfinished products.
   2.3. The stock of unfinished investments.

Industry's net production fund $K_n^{(I)}$. This is plainly analogous to the net production fund of the economy.

The gross production fund $K_g^{(I)}$ *of industry.* This differs from the net production fund in that the stock of fixed resources is considered at its gross value, i.e. the original value of the fixed resources is *not* reduced by allowing for depreciation.

TABLE

Time series of the more

Quantity	Symbol	Unit	1950	1951	1952
Labour productivity of economy	$y^{(E)}$	1000 Ft/head	.	24.9	23.6
Technical equipment of labour according to net production fund, for the economy	$k_n^{(E)}$	1000 Ft/head	.	50.8	54.2
Efficiency of production fund, for the economy	$\chi^{(E)}$	Per cent	.	49	44
Labour productivity of industry	$y^{(I)}$	1000 Ft/head	41.8	48.0	51.2
Technical equipment of labour according to net production fund, for industry	$k_n^{(I)}$	1000 Ft/head	60.0	64.2	65.6
Technical equipment of labour according to gross production fund, for industry	$k_g^{(I)}$	1000 Ft/head	91.6	97.8	100.1
Efficiency of net production fund in industry	$\chi_n^{(I)}$	Per cent	70	75	78
Efficiency of gross production fund in industry	$\chi_g^{(I)}$	Per cent	45	49	51

This figure is not available for the economy as a whole.

The productive labour force $L^{(E)}$ *of the economy.* This comprises the labour forces of all the sectors taking part in producing the national income $Y^{(E)}$.

The labour force $L^{(I)}$ *of industry.* This comprises the total industrial labour force.

The figures measured in value terms, i.e. those for the national income and the production fund, are presented at comparable prices, actually at the prices on January 1st, 1959. The figures for earlier periods were rendered comparable by means of price indices. It is appreciated that this procedure never yields absolute accuracy, but the basic trends which the data show are not, it is thought, appreciably affected.

The figures on the national income comprise a whole year's national income (these are flow-data), while those on the production fund and the labour force always relate to the situation on January 1st (they are stock-data).

The figures are summarized in table F.1.

F.2

important production ratios

1953	1954	1955	1956	1957	1958	1959	1960	1961	1962
26.8	25.1	26.8	23.5	28.8	30.1	31.8	34.9	37.6	40.0
59.5	63.9	67.1	70.7	71.6	75.8	84.3	88.6	96.1	103.8
45	39	40	33	40	40	38	39	39	39
54.4	46.5	49.9	42.3	51.8	54.1	56.6	62.1	66.5	70.3
73.5	74.6	78.3	85.6	89.2	90.1	97.1	97.9	102.9	108.5
105.7	103.2	107.6	116.4	127.2	124.2	129.4	131.8	139.3	147.8
74	62	64	49	58	60	58	63	65	65
51	45	46	36	41	44	44	47	48	48

It is questionable whether, for the purposes of this theoretical model, calculations based on the gross or the net fixed capital are the more justified. The literature devotes much space to the deficiencies of both methods, so that in fact both sets of figures should only be accepted with due reservations.

Recently, since the revaluation of fixed capital in 1954, the two sets of figures have become fairly compatible. The last row of table F.1 shows that the ratio of the two kinds of figures has, over the last nine years, varied little from 72–73 per cent. This fact reduces the importance of the problem of choosing between them.

F.3. The More Important Production Ratio Figures

The time series for labour productivity, the technical equipment of labour and the efficiency of the production fund are presented in table F.2.

With respect to this table it is primarily the figures on the efficiency of the production fund that require some comment.

(1) One problem is due to the fact that these ratios compare a figure relating to a *period of time* (the national income) with a figure for a particular *point of time* (the production fund at the beginning of the year). The production fund as it exists at the beginning of the year contains elements that do not actually take part in producing the national income of the subsequent year; e.g. the portion of the stock of uncompleted investments that will only become operative during the course of the year, or ones that will not become operative at all during the year. At the same time the production fund may be augmented during the course of the year with respect to the initial stock, by facilities that will become productive during the current year.

In this context it becomes necessary to examine the ratio of investments that do not become operative, compared to the total production fund. This is shown in table F.3.

It may be seen that the stock of uncompleted investments is not too large – their proportion does not vary greatly. In consequence, the conclusions here deduced are not essentially influenced by this problem.

(2) The time series of the efficiency of the production fund may be influenced by a change in the composition by products of the national income. In this respect J. Rácz has conducted control calculations for industry. He has determined the ratio figure $\chi_g^{(I)}$ by two methods:

(a) by calculating the data for each year according to the actual pattern of production; and

TABLE F.3

*Stock of investments not put into operation**

Quantity	Unit	1958	1959	1960	1961
1. Net production fund of the economy	1000 million Ft	298.6	336.0	353.7	376.9
2. Stock of investments not made operative, of the economy	1000 million Ft	18.4	21.3	24.1	25.5
3. Proportion of investments not made operative, for the economy (2/1)	Per cent	6.2	5.9	6.8	6.8
4. Net production fund of industry	1000 million Ft	106.7	118.8	126.4	136.8
5. Stock of investments not made operative, of industry	1000 million Ft	10.9	13.4	14.7	16.1
6. Proposition of investments not made operative, for industry (5/4)	Per cent	10.2	11.3	11.6	11.8

* SOURCE: Statistical Yearbook, 1961 [188].

(b) by calculating according to the unchanged 1960 pattern of production*.

Table F.4 shows the time series obtained for the ratios of the figures calculated according to methods (a) and (b).

The table shows that the ratio of the two kinds of figure varies very little with time. Consequently this problem too, may for practical purposes be neglected.

There are no similar figures for the economy as a whole. It may be assumed that here the effect of pattern changes, of the composition by products, is more powerful.

(3) It has already been pointed out in section 18.3, when commenting on formulae (18.3)–(18.5), that a normal utilization of the fixed capital

* See [145]. Rácz determined his figures for χ by sectors of industry, then calculated their weighted mean. The weighting was not according to the actual proportions of the industrial sectors which change year by year, but according to unchanged proportions for the year 1960.

TABLE F.4

*Effect of changes in the product pattern**

Year	The actual efficiency of the industrial production fund, *per* its assumed efficiency (for the case of unchanging pattern), per cent
1950	100.4
1951	99.3
1952	97.6
1953	96.3
1954	98.1
1955	98.1
1956	99.1
1957	97.8
1958	100.0
1959	101.2
1960	100.0

* SOURCE: J. RÁCZ's work [145].

is presumed. In this respect too, the calculations of J. Rácz are relevant*. In the course of his investigations he set out from the statistically observed figures for the jobs that may be staffed any time. This figure he multiplied by the number of possible working hours during the year, thus obtaining a figure for the "annual calendar time fund". This he then compared to the working hours actually performed by the physical workers of industry. The quotient of the two figures may be regarded as the extensive utilization index of the fixed capital (see table F.5).

Apart from the initial year of 1950, the degree of utilization is quite stable, varying from 32–35 per cent, without any particular trend to increase or diminish. (The maximum that could be attained in practice, would be 50–60 per cent.) The quotient of industrial national income per production fund thus reflects the productivity of production funds whose utilization is of *average* extensiveness.

* See [145].

TABLE F.5

*Extensive utilization of industrial fixed capital**

Year	Per cent
1950	29.0
1951	32.9
1952	35.4
1953	35.4
1954	34.2
1955	33.7
1956	31.2
1957	32.2
1958	33.2
1959	34.6
1960	35.3

* SOURCE: J. RÁCZ [145].

F.4. The Time Series Relating to the Utilization of the National Income

The following figures are presented:

The accumulation share $\alpha_n^{(E)}$ *of the economy.* This has been calculated as follows:

$$\alpha_n^{(E)} = \frac{K_n^{(E)}(t+1) - K_n^{(E)}(t)}{Y^{(E)}(t)}. \tag{F.1}$$

It has thus been assumed that this year's accumulation (the increment of the production fund) is sliced off the current year's national income. This is a justified assumption since, as we have seen, the stock of investments that have not yet become operative is also regarded as a part of the production fund, so that in this sense the current year's increase of the production fund does in fact take place at the expense of this year's national income.

The industrial accumulation share – net $\alpha_n^{(I)}$ and *gross* $\alpha_g^{(I)}$. This is plainly analogous to $\alpha_n^{(E)}$.

Two kinds of average have been calculated from the accumulation shares.

Let the number of years of the period under investigation be T. One average is the arithmetical mean of the accumulation shares of the individual years:

$$\bar{\alpha} = T^{-1} \sum_{t=1}^{T} \alpha(t) . \tag{F.2}$$

The other average is the quotient of the total growth in the production fund over the whole period by the total national income of the whole period:

$$\tilde{\alpha} = \frac{K(T) - K(1)}{\sum_{t=1}^{T-1} Y(t)} . \tag{F.3}$$

The index of real wages of workers and salaried employees. The scope of the term "workers and salaried employees" is on the one hand narrower, and on the other broader, than the $L^{(E)}$ category of our theoretical model, and the corresponding time series for $L^{(E)}$ in table F.1. The workers and salaried employees do *not* include those peasants, craftsmen and shopkeepers, who are not cooperative members. At the same time the term does include those workers and salaried employees who are engaged in spheres other than production. Nevertheless this is the only continuously recorded statistical figure available, and it may thus be used at least as an approximation.

The figures are presented in table F.6.

It is only with respect to the accumulation shares that some further remarks are necessary at this stage. The table shows that the annual figure α did not prove to be particularly stable over the past ten or fifteen years of Hungarian economic development. This is one reflection of the several radical changes in economic policy that took place in the years 1950–1960.

Owing to fluctuations in the rate of accumulation, the assumption of growth model (18.25) described in sections 18.8 and 18.9, according to which the rate of accumulation is constant in the flow of time, is rather problematical. We none the less believe that Hungarian statistical data do not provide conclusive evidence to warrant the dismissal of the assumption. In the future the relative stabilization of the accumulation share is realistically feasible and indeed desirable, since radical changes – whether increases or decreases – involve all kinds of repercussions and losses.

TABLE F.6

*Time series of the accumulation share and the index of real wages**

Year	Accumulation share (for expansion of the net production fund of the economy) $\alpha_n(E)$ Per cent	Accumulation share (for expansion of the net production fund of industry) $\alpha_n(I)$ Per cent	Accumulation share (for expansion of the gross production fund of industry) $\alpha_g(I)$ Per cent	Index of real wages (1949 = = 100)
1950	.	.	.	101.3
1951	.	..	21	89.7
1952	22	18	27	82.3
1953	22	22	21	87.0
1954	22	21	22	102.3
1955	18	14	19	106.0
1956	19	15	18	118.3
1957	4	6	22	139.7
1958	20	15	13	145.4
1959	32	19	18	153.1
1960	14	11	17	156.0
1961	17	13	19	156.3
1962	17	12	18	.
Arithmetic mean of the annual accumulation shares ($\bar{\alpha}$)	18.5	16.0	18.1	—
Total accumulation share of the whole period ($\tilde{\alpha}$)	17.5	16.7	18.7	—

* SOURCE of columns 1, 2 and 3 in table F.1, column 4 is from the Statistical Yearbook, 1961 [188].

The other remark is that the accumulation share is rather high, compared for instance with the accumulation shares in various capitalist countries (see table F.7).

TABLE F.7

*The accumulation share in capitalist countries**

Country	Period	Accumulation share, per cent
Australia	1921–22 – 1937–38	8.8
Germany	1891–1913	18.0
Great Britain	1891–1913	11.1
Hungary	1925–26 – 1936–37	4.8
Sweden	1913–1930	11.2
U. S. A.	1884–1924	13.3
	1919–1929	10.8
	1929–1942	6.3

* SOURCE: E. D. DOMAR [36], p. 68.

F.5. Regression Analysis

The figures presented in sections F.2–F.4 were used to set up the regression equation of the variables which are most important for the purposes of theoretical analysis. Corresponding to the assumptions of the theoretical model set up, an exponential function was adopted whose general expression is:

$$Z(t) = B_0 e^{\Lambda t}, \tag{F.4}$$

or in logarithmic form:

$$\log Z(t) = \log B_0 + \Lambda t . \tag{F.5}$$

Accordingly we estimated the linear regression of the logarithms of the different variables on time.

In order to see how closely the regression function fits the fact figures, the correlation coefficient between the logarithms of the different variables and time, was also determined.

The national income, production fund and labour force functions of the national economy – both the empirical figures and the regression functions – are shown in figures F.1–F.3.

The characteristics of the regression functions of the national income, the production fund and the labour force with respect both to the economy and industry, are presented in table F.8. This also comprises the characteristics of the regression functions of the main relative figures

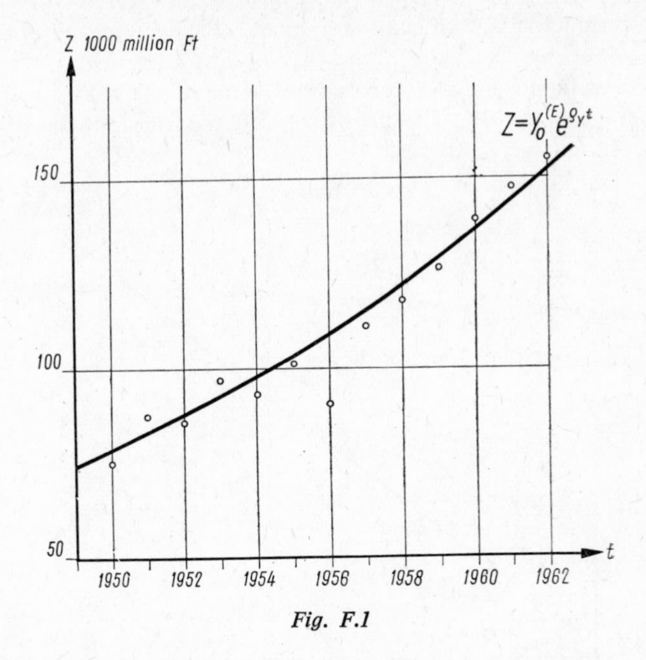
Z 1000 million Ft
150
100
50
1950
1952
1954
1956
1958
1960
1962
t
$Z=Y_0^{(E)}e^{\varrho_Y t}$

Fig. F.1

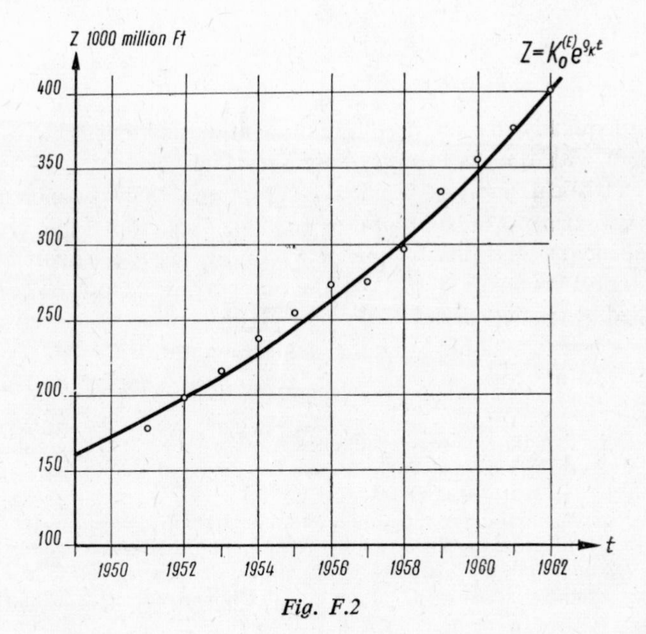
Z 1000 million Ft
400
350
300
250
200
150
100
1950
1952
1954
1956
1958
1960
1962
t
$Z=K_0^{(E)}e^{\varrho_K t}$

Fig. F.2

(labour productivity, technical equipment, efficiency of the production fund)*.

Table F.8 far-reachingly corroborates some of the basic assumptions and findings of ch. 18. The growth of all the variables listed above,

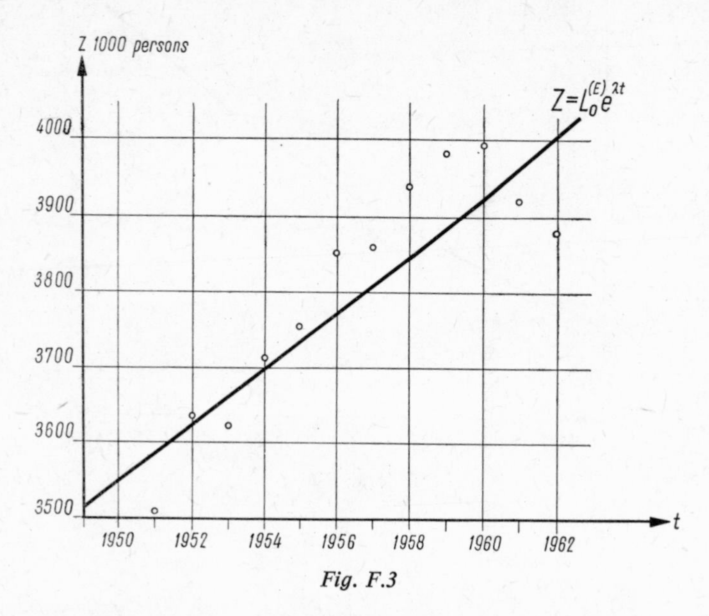

Fig. F.3

can be adequately characterized by exponential functions. The correlation coefficient with time is in every case very high**.

The statistical analysis verified assumption (18.24), concerning the growth of manpower, assumption (18.26), concerning the growth of national income and proposition 18.5, concerning the growth of labour productivity. Proposition 18.4, on the other hand, cannot be considered as verified by the data series of the past 10 or 12 years. Theoretically, the average efficiency should – under definite conditions – be constant in the flow of time; the data, however, go to show that in the Hungarian

* The starting time of the calculations was the year 1949. The values of the coefficients in table F.8 accordingly furnish the points of the regression functions belonging to the year 1949.

** The exponential approximation is least adequate in the case of the variation in the labour force; here a linear approximation would be just as good. In order, however, to facilitate the mathematical treatment of the model, it is preferable to use an exponential approximation for the labour force, as with the other variables.

TABLE F.8

Parameters of the regression functions

Function	Symbol	Regression equation for the economy			Regression equation for industry		
		Coefficient (B_0)	Exponent (A)	Correlation coefficient	Coefficient (B_0)	Exponent (A)	Correlation coefficient
National income	Y	74.3	0.055	0.985	33.6	0.078	0.980
Production fund, net	K_n	159.9	0.071	0.996	45.7	0.093	0.991
Production fund, gross	K_g	.	.	.	69.7	0.083	0.996
Labour force	L	3515	0.010	0.898	785.1	0.045	0.971
Labour productivity	y	0.0211	0.045	0.960	0.0428	0.033	0.891
Technical equipment of labour according to net production fund	k_n	0.0455	0.061	0.994	0.0455	0.048	0.994
Technical equipment of labour according to gross production fund	k_g	.	.	.	0.0888	0.038	0.986
Efficiency of net production fund	χ_n	0.465	−0.016	--0.793	0.735	−0.015	−0.646
Efficiency of gross production fund	χ_g	.	.	.	0.482	−0.005	−0.301

economy the growth of national income was slower than that of the production fund. The regression function of the average efficiency of the production fund has a negative exponent, i.e. efficiency has decreased with time. For closer examination of this problem the means and coefficients of variation of the indices on the efficiency of the production fund have been determined and set out in table F.9.

TABLE F.9

Means and coefficients of variation of the efficiency of the production fund

	Mean (per cent)	Coefficient of variation (per cent)
Production fund of the economy, net $\chi_n^{(E)}$	41.1	8.3
Production fund of industry, net $\chi_n^{(I)}$	65.6	10.6
Production fund of industry, gross $\chi_g^{(I)}$	46.6	6.4

Nevertheless it is not necessary in our view to modify the assumption on the stability in time of the efficiency χ of the production fund, as set out in the theoretical model, for the following reasons.

A systematic decrease in the efficiency of the production fund is a negative phenomenon, due to the familiar errors committed in economic policies*. It is not a necessary feature, and cannot be regarded as permanent.

Thus for instance the figures for the Soviet Union show the following: during the period of 1950–1960 the national income grew by an average of 10.3 per cent a year, the fixed production fund by only 9.4 per cent**. The data relating to working capital are not known but it may be assumed that the latter did not grow at a greater pace than the national income, or, if so, not to an extent that would have fully compensated for the slower

* In the terms of the growth model described in sections 18.8 and 18.9: The efficiency of the production fund will decrease if the chosen rate of accumulation α is of a magnitude for which no adequate μ can be secured, i.e. if the qualitative factors of economic progress (technical culture, the professional training of workers and managers, etc.) is not keeping level with the pace of accumulation.

** See [181].

growth of the fixed capital. If this assumption is true, then in the USSR the efficiency of the production fund has grown over this decade. It will not be an error if, for the *future*, we do not expect a continuation of this adverse process in Hungary (the regular decrease of the efficiency of the production fund), but instead presume at least constant efficiency. In any case in this model the constancy in time of the efficiency χ is not an *assumption*, but an economic policy *requirement* (more exactly: it is a consequence of the requirement that the national income should grow constantly, if the other assumptions of the model hold). Now this is by no means an extravagant requirement, for it would not be absurd even to require a growing efficiency.

At the same time the rate of decrease according to table F.8 is quite small (between 0.5 and 1.5 per cent). The correlation with time is not very close, nor is the standard deviation high, especially in the case of the industrial gross production fund*. This too, indicates that stability in time of the efficiency of the production fund is not an over-simplification compared to the actual situation.

Regression analyses were also carried out with respect to real wages, in three ways:

Calculation 1. The regression equation was calculated on the basis of all the figures for the period investigated.

Calculation 2. The regression calculation was carried out without the figures for those years when – in consequence of the economic policy errors committed in the early fifties – real wages decreased.

Calculation 3. The annual average rate of the rise in real wages between the first and the last year of the period examined, was determined.

The figures are shown in table F.10.

TABLE F.10

Regression equations of the changes in real wages

	Calculation 1	Calculation 2	Calculation 3
Coefficient of regression equation	83.5	94.1	100.0
Exponent of regression equation (The rate of growth)	0.054	0.044	0.037
Coefficient of correlation with time	0.885	0.910	.

* It is also possible that evaluation errors, e.g. too low depreciation rates, have played a part in the decrease of efficiency of the net production fund.

In connection with the growth model described in sections 18.8 and 18.9 it was assumed in formula (18.31) that the growth rate of actual wages was identical with that of the productivity of labour. This assumption is appreciably substantiated by the extent to which the growth rate of real wages obtained by calculation 2 (which sifts out the irregular effects), approximates the growth rate of labour productivity of the economy. The former is 4.4, the latter 4.5 per cent.

F.6. Estimation of the Parameters of the Production Function

The question was examined as to whether it was possible to determine the parameters of the production function from the macroeconomic figures presented above.

It is here best to return to the form (18.40) of the function:

$$\log y(t) = \log A_0 + \mu t + \beta \log k(t)\,. \qquad \text{(F.6)}$$

As pointed out in section 18.10, it was not possible to give an estimate of parameters μ and β of the production function by means of regression analysis. There is a close linear relationship (a collinearity) between variables $\log k$ and t*.

* Of the economists of the socialist countries, as far as we know J. PAJESTKA [140] was the first to attempt a statistical estimation of the parameters of a Cobb–Douglas type production function. This work is in many respects noteworthy and thought-provoking. In our view, however, the author was only able seemingly to overcome the difficulties which he also mentions, caused by the collinearity between the variables.

Pajestka's procedure can be described with the notations of our model in the following terms:

Firstly it is a priori assumed that $\mu = 0$, i.e. a production function of the type $Y = K^\beta L^{1-\beta}$ is determined. (By choice of the right units, the constant factor may be obviated.) This is the "classical" Cobb–Douglas form of the production function, without the Solow modification and the inclusion of a dependence on time. Thus a value (obviously very high) for β is found and fixed. This, however, thus becomes an arbitrary magnitude, devoid of independent economic significance.

Next, regression analyses are carried out with the following function:

$$Y = A_0 e^{\theta t} K^\beta L^{1-\beta}.$$

After such antecedents the factor $A_0 e^{\theta t}$ expresses only the systematic deviation in time of the fitted function from the empirical figures. This is therefore a kind of indicator of the statistical error of the fitted function, devoid of any independent economic meaning, as W. SADOWSKI has pointed out in a critical article [151].

It may thus be said that the better the statistical data verify some of the assumptions and propositions of our model (particularly on the regular, exponential nature of growth), the less they are appropriate to serve as a basis for the unique numerical evaluation of the model, or at least for estimating the parameters of the production function.

In place of a simultaneous estimation of the parameters β and μ, we shall have to be content with determining the relation between them on the basis of the statistical data. For according to the regression analysis for y and k,

$$\log y = \log \widehat{y_0} + (\widehat{\varrho_Y} - \widehat{\lambda})\, t\,, \tag{F.7}$$

$$\log k = \log \widehat{k_0} + (\widehat{\varrho_K} - \widehat{\lambda})\, t\,, \tag{F.8}$$

where

$\widehat{\varrho_Y}$ = the growth rate of the national income

$\widehat{\varrho_K}$ = the growth rate of the production fund

$\widehat{\lambda}$ = the growth rate of the labour force.

All the data marked with the circumflex sign (^) are estimates of the parameter concerned, based on regression analysis.

Substituting (F.8) and (F.9) in (F.6), the following relations are obtained*

$$\widehat{\mu} = (\widehat{\varrho_Y} - \widehat{\lambda}) - \widehat{\beta}(\widehat{\varrho_K} - \widehat{\lambda}) = \begin{cases} \text{for the economy} \\ 0.045\text{–}0.061\,\widehat{\beta} \\ \text{for industry} \\ 0.033\text{–}0.048\,\widehat{\beta} \end{cases} \tag{F.9}$$

and for

Pajestka's θ and the μ in our production function play a formally identical role. In their content and economic significance on the other hand, they are completely different magnitudes. Our parameter μ expresses one feature of technical advance, whose numerical value we are, however, unable to define unequivocally. Pajestka's parameter θ on the other hand expresses a systematic statistical error within a production function whose parameters have been fixed according to *a priori* considerations.

* In this determination of the parameters μ and β, the only assumption used is that the production function is of the type (F.6). The other assumptions of ch. 18 are not used here.

$$\hat{\beta} = \frac{\hat{\varrho}_Y - \hat{\lambda} - \hat{\mu}}{\hat{\varrho}_K - \hat{\lambda}} = \begin{cases} \text{for the economy} \\ 0.738\text{–}16.393\,\hat{\mu} \\ \\ \text{for industry} \\ 0.688\text{–}20.833\,\hat{\mu}\,. \end{cases} \tag{F.10}$$

Formulae (F.9) and (F.10) may be used to calculate $\hat{\mu}$ for any value of $\hat{\beta}$ and *vice versa.* This is shown in table F.11.

TABLE F.11

Parameters of the production function

$\hat{\beta}$	$\hat{\mu}$ for the economy (considering the net production fund)	$\hat{\mu}$ for industry (considering the net production fund)
0.10	0.039	0.028
0.12	0.038	0.027
0.14	0.036	0.026
0.16	0.035	0.025
0.18	0.034	0.024
0.20	0.033	0.023
0.25	0.030	0.021
0.30	0.027	0.019
0.40	0.021	0.014
0.50	0.014	0.009
0.60	0.008	0.004
0.70	0.002	−0.001
0.75	−0.001	

To evaluate the results of the table, let us apply the hypothesis of a standard distribution of the national income. According to the actual figures for the past years, this would mean a β of about 0.16–0.18 on the national scale. The corresponding annual growth rate of the factor $A\,e^{\mu t}$ is about 3.4–3.5 per cent.

APPENDIX G

A SURVEY OF THE DISPUTE ON THE RENTAL ON CAPITAL

G.1. Character of the Survey

Few questions of our discipline have been more widely discussed by the economists than those relating to the rate of interest. For over a century, hundreds of authors have been engaged in controversies over the problem as it presents itself under capitalistic conditions. Nor were the discussions less extensive or the views put forward less widely varied in the case of the computational rental on capital and interest rate employed in socialist economic planning.

The following survey is to serve the purpose of an outline rather than of detailed polemics. My own positive point of view has been made clear in ch. 18; it implicitly contains the critique of other views too. It will be left to the reader to compare my views with those of other authors in detail; I, for my part, wish to confine myself to occasional short references.

My principal aim consists in giving a survey of the characteristic views whose representatives should, however, be named only by way of illustration. Nor does this survey pretend to completeness; it will be limited to the opinions put forward in the USSR and in Hungary*.

For uniformity's sake my *own* terminology and notation system, used throughout this book, should be employed instead of those of the authors under review.

The various opinions can be classified according to a number of different viewpoints. The first of these is constituted by the economic relationships from which the computational rental on capital is theoretically derived. In this respect two main groups may be distinguished:

(1) the views which relate the computational rental to the production of national income, i.e. to the categories of production;

(2) those which relate it to the distribution of national income, i.e. to the categories of distribution.

* For the survey of the debate going on in the USSR I have drawn on Gy. Simon and Gy. Kondor [158].

G.2. The Views Connected with the Production of National Income

1.1. The rational computational rental on capital equals the (average) efficiency of the production fund: $\gamma = \frac{Y}{K}$.

This view was represented, among others, by T. Khachaturov, a well-known Soviet economist whose theoretical work was largely instrumental in bringing this problem to the fore of economic research and practice in the socialist countries*.

The assumption can be justified only in the extreme case, if the growth of national income is kept in strict proportion with that of the production fund, i.e. if there is no possibility of substitution between the production fund on the one hand and labour on the other. In the last analysis this means that the growth of national income will depend *exclusively* on investments, independently of the labour force available.

The principle under 1.1 relates the computational rental to the *average* efficiency of the production fund. There are several other views (see below, under 1.2, 1.3 and 1.4) which take various types of *marginal* efficiency for their starting point.

1.2. The computational rental should be fixed to equal the efficiency of the least efficient investment which is still necessary and which can still be covered out of the investment fund of the national economy. The advocates of these views propose to arrange the investment alternatives according to the diminishing order of their respective efficiency indices and to determine, by advancing in the series, the point where the investment fund is exhausted; the efficiency index of the last alternative still covered by the fund should then be accepted as the computational rental on capital**.

The principle is an inaccurate and somewhat naive approximation of the – in itself correct – principle which equates the computational rental with the marginal efficiency of the production fund. The notion of the marginal efficiency of the production fund involves the enforcement of the principle of *ceteris paribus*. It expresses the value of $\partial Y / \partial K$, i.e. the change in national income in the case when K changes by a small unit only and L does not change at all. Yet in the above case of sequencing the "last" alternative will require an increase not only in the production fund but also in the labour force.

* See T. Khachaturov [65].

** In Hungary, this view is represented e.g. in the articles of M. Mandel *et al.* [117] and of J. Varga [172].

Nor is the conception of ordering in itself realistic. In ch. 8 it was shown in detail why simple ordering will not suffice to meet practical efficiency requirements. As a matter of fact, the requirements of equilibrium may make it necessary to draw the alternatives of lower efficiency, too, into the orbit of planning. Moreover, section 18.5 discussed the fundamental problems and difficulties of the "mechanism of capital market".

1.3. The rental charged both on existing production funds and on new investments should be based on the system of shadow prices in the economy-wide linear programming model. The computational evaluations will be furnished by the shadow prices belonging to the constraints of productive capacity and of investment resources.

As already mentioned, in the USSR these views are held by L. V. Kantorovich as well as by V. V. Novozhilov*. In Hungary similar opinions have been voiced by Gy. Simon and Gy. Kondor**.

These views are very close to the viewpoint outlined in the present work. It is generally known that the shadow prices of resources in linear programming problems express the marginal returns of these resources.

However, it must be emphasized that this is but an *approximation****, though a necessary one and comparatively the best under actual conditions. The system of shadow prices obtained from the linear programming model must of necessity bear the "birth-marks" of the model from which it was derived: the simplifications due to the assumption of linearity, the inaccuracies concomitant with aggregation, the problematical character of the selection of the objective function, etc. The shadow prices thus obtained must not, therefore, be overrated.

1.4. M. Turánszky, an Hungarian author, would establish a relationship between the rental and the labour-releasing effect of the production fund****. The idea is, in my opinion, a sensible one. In this case, however, it is the ratio between the marginal efficiency of the production fund and the marginal productivity of the labour force that must be established, and that at the optimum point where both the available production fund and the available labour force are just used up (see relation (18.8)).

It was shown that on the basis of the available Hungarian statistical data this ratio cannot be numerically determined. To attain numerical solutions, Turánszky is working here with arbitrary assumptions,

* See L. V. Kantorovich [62] and V. V. Novozhilov [138].

** See Gy. Simon and Gy. Kondor [158] and [159].

*** This was one of our reasons for trying to follow this direction in our investigations (see Part 5 of the present work).

**** See M. Turánszky [169].

representing e.g. the labour-releasing effect of the production fund by that of the mechanization of plant cultivation, etc. His numerical inferences are therefore, notwithstanding the appropriateness of the basic idea, lacking in foundation.

1.5. In his work referred to, Turánszky raises another important issue when seeking to determine the respective roles of the production fund and of labour in the growth of national income. The problem is undoubtedly related to some extent to the conceptions expounded in ch. 18. Being, however, unable to solve the problem of imputation, Turánszky again resorts to arbitrary assumptions, similarly as in the case described under 1.4. He makes an attempt to determine the "investment-free growth of national income" on the basis of inferences drawn from a series of statistical data on the effects of innovations and inventions. But these data do not admit of any inference bearing on the problem under investigation – i.e. on the imputation ratios – and the numerical results attained by this method of estimation are again lacking in foundation*.

1.6. The computational rental would equal the rate of growth in the productivity of labour: $\gamma = \dot{y}/y$. In the Soviet debate this view is represented by S. G. Strumilin and P. Mstislavsky**.

In section 18.4 it was shown that the value of the rational computational rental was not independent of trends in the productivity of labour. The relationship is, however, of a different character.

It is not impossible for the rational rental to be identical with the rate of growth in labour productivity, but it is not necessary***. Nor can this ratio be considered as desirable or advisable for any reason. This definition of the rational computational rental must therefore be termed unmethodical.

* M. Turánszky deserves credit as one of the pioneers in Hungary of the calculations on the efficiency of investments and of the application of a computational rental in these calculations. His work has exerted considerable influence on the officially developed forms and methods of investment-efficiency calculations – this is the reason why I dwelt at some length on his views.

The opinions surveyed under 1.4 and 1.5 are correct in their surmises. The numerical conclusions drawn are, however, based on insufficiently grounded assumptions. These – in my view unfounded – computations have also worked towards fixing the computational rental at the extremely high value of 20 per cent in Hungary.

** See S. G. Strumilin [163] and P. Mstislavsky [130].

*** It will be worth while to take the following into consideration. In the case of the standard distribution of national income and of a production function of type (18.38), the rental can only equal the rate of growth in labour productivity if $\lambda = 0$. i.e. if the labour force remains stationary – a rather unrealistic assumption.

G.3. The Views Connected with the Distribution of National Income

As a preliminary already I should like to emphasize that these views are for their major part erroneous in the point of departure. The problem of a rational ratio between the computational rental and the wage rate should be approached from the *production* side; it is here that the possibilities of substitution, the ratio between marginal efficiency of production fund and marginal productivity of labour, etc. will become manifest. The distribution of national income is essentially independent of this; under the conditions of a socialist planned economy it will largely depend on the decisions of the organs of economic management.

2.1. The rational computational rental should equal the quotient of net income and the production fund. This opinion was voiced in the Soviet debate by I. S. Malishev*, and in the Hungarian debate by E. Megyeri**.

The theoretical error contained in this view needs no further comment. It should be pointed out, however, that its realization would lead to an absurdly high rate of interest which would put a check on technical progress.

2.2. The rental should equal the quotient of the part of national income allocated to accumulation, defence and administration on the one hand and the production fund on the other. The rest of national income, which serves directly or indirectly the purposes of personal consumption, should be imputed to labour.

This view is represented by A. Stepankov***.

Figuratively, this view could also be interpreted as though claiming that accumulation as well as the maintenance cost of defence and administration should be covered out of the "returns" of the production fund, and all other consumption out of the "returns" of labour.

This will possibly lead to a γ/ω ratio which is accidentally rational. Possibly – but not certainly. It may be justified to cover the expenditure on public education out of the "returns" of the production fund, or, inversely, the cost of public administration out of those of labour, etc. All net income which is not allocated to accumulation will in some direct or indirect form serve the purpose of consumption in the broadest sense

* See I. S. Malishev [116]. The views of Malishev are directly connected not with the investment-efficiency debate but with the problems of price formation.

** See the review of E. Megyeri's lecture in [198].

*** See A. Stepankov [162].

of the word*. Any limit drawn here can be only arbitrary. Nor would such a limit be relevant from the point of view of the question under investigation, as the γ/ω ratio will be determined by other factors.

2.3. The rental should equal the part of national income allocated to accumulation of the production fund.

This view is advocated by V. S. Nemchinov in the USSR and by T. Nagy as well as Zs. Esze in Hungary**.

This interpretation of the rental is practically equivalent with the – explicit or implicit – application of the hypothesis of a standard distribution of national income. The hypothesis once applied, the rational rental will equal the rate of growth of the production fund, i.e. (assuming a uniform rate of growth) the ratio between accumulation and the production fund (see proposition 18.8 (B)).

In the absence of a more suitable solution, practically the same hypothesis has been applied in our own programming computations (see accounting principles 18.2 and 18.3). This is, in my opinion, acceptable provided that we bear in mind that the computations were based on a hypothesis only, that they are of a provisional character and that they should at a later stage be revised. From the paper of T. Nagy and Zs. Esze it will be clear that they considered this a provisional solution.

G.4. Distribution and Optimality

The survey in some detail of an opinion of recent standing should afford an opportunity to discuss some questions of principle not dealt with up to now.

Gy. Simon and Gy. Kondor essentially concur in the views reviewed under 1.3 and 2.3; their point of departure is, however, slightly different***. According to these authors, the standard distribution of national income, which I would consider an auxiliary and provisional hypothesis, constituted a definitely desirable and advisable goal. Their train of thought could be outlined as follows.

All parts of the national income – the allocations both to accumulation and to consumption – will ultimately serve the purpose of further growth. Rising standards of living, safeguards to public health, public education, etc. will all be instrumental in rendering the contribution of the working people to the growth of national income more efficient.

* The trends in indirect consumption additional to money wages in Hungary are discussed in detail by E. Jávorka and J. Berényi [59].

** See V. S. Nemchinov [132] and T. Nagy and Zs. Esze [131].

*** See [159].

National income should, as a consequence, be distributed in a way that its allocation results in every domain in the same increment to national income. The marginal returns of the allocations aimed at "labour-force development" and of those aimed at "production-fund development" should be equal. As a result of this type of allocation of national income all factors of production – both the "human" and the "objective" factors – will receive their own marginal returns, the working people in the part of national income released for consumption, the production fund in that allocated to accumulation.

This optimally allocated national income will grow at the rate of ϱ. Obviously, the part of national income reserved for accumulation – the surplus production fund – will also secure a return rate ϱ.

In this interesting train of thought important and realistic concepts are, in my opinion, mixed with a kind of narrow "economism" and utilitarianism.

True, the part of national income released for investment will also ultimately affect consumption. No modern industrial civilization could perform properly its functions with a poor and uneducated labour force. The development of public education, science, public hygiene and general culture, together with improved material standards of living, are essential factors in the systematic and continuous increase of the productivity of labour and in technical progress. The neglect of these requirements will – as events in Hungary in the period between 1949 and 1953 have clearly shown – have detrimental effects, among other things, on the national economy as a whole.

The division of national income into accumulation and consumption allocations can, notwithstanding these facts, not be interpreted as a simple problem of economic optimization, because of the following considerations.

The effect on national income of the allocations aimed at "labour-force development" is practically non-measurable. It is not possible exactly to foresee the growth in national income which would be brought about by differences of 1–2 per cent in the increase of real wages.

The reason for this can be found, among other things, in the fact that labour discipline, initiative, the wish to study and the development of culture and science are not exclusively dependent on increases in real wages and consumption, i.e. on direct economic factors, though the basic importance of these cannot be denied, but tend to be influenced by a set of other – political, sociological, cultural, moral, etc. – factors as well. To "separate" the effects of increased consumption from the joint effects of the other factors will be practically impossible. There are periods conceivable in the life of a nation (e.g. a patriotic war) when people will be stirred to maximum exertion even at lower living standards, and others again when they will be indifferent and lacking in enthusiasm in spite of advancing welfare.

And one more moral aspect of the question. In a socialist society, the purpose of "labour development" is not the improvement of production. Man does not exist here for the sake of production – the case is exactly the reverse. For moral reasons, parts of the national income must be put to certain uses – such as caring for the blind and for invalids, town planning, the protection of monuments, etc. – which will not practically react on the further growth of national income.

My reason for discussing this point in some detail was that it afforded an opportunity to make it clear that in my opinion the decisions concerning the *distribution* of national income must in a socialist society be separated from the question of the marginal returns of the individual factors of production. In a centrally directed socialist planned economy the distribution of national income (especially between the two main allocation groups of accumulation and consumption) constitutes a complex political, economic, sociological and moral problem the solution of which will require decisions of a *political* character.

G.5. Other Questions under Debate

In sections G.2–G.4 the views put forward in the course of the dispute were classified according to the economic categories with which they related the computational rental. There are, however, other classification viewpoints as well.

(a) Some of the participants in the debate wish to connect the computational rental on new investments simply with the actual price system. Others again have realized that the problem can be consistently dealt with only within the framework of a price system where rental is calculated in every phase of production on the fixed (old or new) production fund. The latter view is advocated by the majority of the authors mentioned already previously in other connections, such as L. V. Kantorovich, V. S. Nemchinov* in the USSR, M. Turánszky, T. Nagy and Zs. Esze, Gy. Simon and Gy. Kondor in Hungary.

* In this connection special mention must be made of the proposals of V. S. Nemchinov [132] which cover, among other things, the question of rents calculated on scarce natural goods. This is a problem which I had to disregard in my own investigations although I am fully aware of its importance.

(b) Another controversial question is whether different rentals should be calculated in the various branches, or a uniform rate should be applied over the whole domain of the national economy. The former view was advocated by T. Khachaturov in the USSR and by Gy. Gerle* in Hungary; the latter one by I. S. Malishev in the Soviet debate and by M. Turánszky in this country.

There is a divergence in this respect between the Soviet and the Hungarian methodological instructions concerning the official computational evaluations to be applied to investment efficiency calculations**. The former envisage different rentals for the different branches of production, while the latter prescribe the use of a uniform rental.

From what has been said in ch. 26.1, it should be clear that I, for my part, advocate the use of a uniform rental in every model in which the production fund as well as the investments meant to increase it are treated as grouped aggregates and in which computational prices are applied according to price formula (18.1).

The economists who are for the application of different rentals in the different branches would mainly argue that a uniform rental might make the development of such branches to appear *unprofitable* which are of primary importance from the point of view of the general proportions of the national economy***.

These fears are, however, justified only as long as planning for the proportions of the national economy (by means of the balance method) and investment-efficiency calculations (by means of efficiency indices) are carried out separately from one another. Programming, as has already been pointed out earlier, makes it possible to eliminate this duality, as in the model the required proportions between the branch under investigation and the other branches of the economy can from the very beginning be taken into consideration. The purpose is served by final output obligations in the system of constraints. The fact that certain proportions of production are from the very beginning fixed in the programming model in the form of output obligations and product balances, acts as a *restriction on the influence of the rental on capital*. Under these conditions, the rental will primarily affect the proportions and combinations between the various types of input, especially those between more up-to-date technology, machinery and equipment pro-

* See Gy. Gerle [44].

** See the official Soviet methodological instructions [180] and the Hungarian Investments Code [195].

*** See e.g. T. Khachaturov [65].

curable by investment on the one hand and direct labour on the other (cf. ch. 25).

(c) The participants in the debate resorted to various methods in laying the numerical foundations of their proposals. The majority tried to use aggregated macroeconomic statistical data. As has been shown, this method will, according to present knowledge, not yield definite results.

Some would propose trying to base the deductions on microeconomic data and to conclude on the reasonable value of the computational rental on capital from the efficiency indices of some isolated investment alternatives.

Other authors finally propose to define the numerical value of the computational rental by means of mathematical programming. In my opinion, too, this seems to be the most workable method.

APPENDIX H

THE GENERAL MODEL OF "TWO-LEVEL PLANNING": "TWO-LEVEL PROGRAMMING"

by

TH. LIPTÁK

H.1. Introduction

During the course of the elaboration of the method of two-level planning, it turned out that the ideas and conclusions arising from the special problem of planning could be far more simply and lucidly put into mathematical form if the model was treated in somewhat more general terms. It became evident, moreover, that it would be "easier to prove the harder" and that in such a model the mathematical arguments could also be treated in a simpler fashion. Finally, a decomposition technique was found that may be applied to any (solvable) linear programming problem, and where the iteration of the fictitious play in the model after decomposition is convergent. The procedure is, in this general case, called "two-level programming".

The method will in this Appendix be discussed according to the following arrangement. In sections H.2–H.11 it is assumed that the original linear programming problem, called the "overall central information problem" (OCI problem, for short), is in some way decomposed into parts called "sectors", whose programming is coordinated by a "centre". After introducing some other terms and notation, certain "regularity" assumptions are made, and theorems deduced, which are valid under these conditions and permit the solution of the original problem to any required degree of accuracy by means of the separate, iterative solution of the subproblems. The steps of the iteration are outlined and the general "equalization" tendency of the mixed shadow prices is discussed. Finally section H.12 presents a decomposition and embedding technique whose use guarantees the fulfilment of the regularity conditions necessary for the application of two-level programming for any (solvable) linear programming problem. It also makes it possible for the linear programming at the centre only to solve problems that may be carried out trivially, by setting coefficients in the order of magnitude.

Since it is not the object of this Appendix to undertake an exhaustive treatment of the mathematical details, the aim in the latter section has been confined to a clear description of the decomposition and embedding technique to be used, and of the algorithm of two-level programming. Readers interested in the rigorous proofs are referred to other publications*.

H.2. The Overall Central Information Problem

Let

$$\begin{aligned} \mathbf{A}\,\mathbf{x} &\leqq \mathbf{b}, & \qquad \mathbf{y}'\mathbf{A} &\geqq \mathbf{c}', \\ \mathbf{x} &\geqq 0, \quad \text{and} & \mathbf{y} &\geqq 0, \\ \mathbf{c}'\mathbf{x} &\rightarrow \max! & \mathbf{y}'\mathbf{b} &\rightarrow \min! \end{aligned} \tag{H.1}$$

be the canonical forms** of the primal and dual versions respectively, in the OCI problem of the general model.

The primal variable of the OCI problem (the vector $\mathbf{x}$) is called the *OCI program*, the dual variable (the vector $\mathbf{y}$) the *OCI shadow price system.* Let X denote the set of feasible *OCI programs,* and X^* the set of *optimal OCI programs,* moreover let Y be the set of feasible *OCI shadow price systems* and Y^* the set of *optimal OCI shadow price systems*, i.e.

$$\begin{aligned} \mathsf{X} &= \{\mathbf{x} : \mathbf{Ax} \leqq \mathbf{b}, \quad \mathbf{x} \geqq \mathbf{0}\}, \\ \mathsf{X}^* &= \{\mathbf{x}^* : \mathbf{x}^* \in \mathsf{X}, \quad \mathbf{c}'\mathbf{x}^* = \max_{\mathbf{x} \in \mathsf{X}} \mathbf{c}'\mathbf{x}\}, \end{aligned} \tag{H.2}$$

$$\begin{aligned} \mathsf{Y} &= \{\mathbf{y} : \mathbf{y}'\mathbf{A} \geqq \mathbf{c}', \quad \mathbf{y} \geqq \mathbf{0}\}, \\ \mathsf{Y}^* &= \{\mathbf{y}^* : \mathbf{y}^* \in \mathsf{Y}, \quad \mathbf{y}^{*\prime}\mathbf{b} = \min_{\mathbf{y} \in \mathsf{Y}} \mathbf{y}'\mathbf{b}\}. \end{aligned} \tag{H.3}$$

Let it be assumed that the OCI problem is *solvable*, i.e. that an optimal OCI program exists: i. e.

$$\mathsf{X}^* \neq \mathsf{O}.$$

* See [82] and [103]. The application of "two-level programming" to a problem whose economic content is completely different to that of the model described in ch. 24 of this work – that of a short-range optimum calculation for foreign-trade – is described in [104].

** The primal-dual versions of all linear programming problems can be transformed into the symmetrical form (H.1).

It is known* that there then also exists an optimal OCI shadow price system: $\mathsf{Y}^* \neq \mathsf{O}$, moreover, the maximum value of the objective function in the primal version and the minimum value of the objective function in the dual version are equal – their common value is the *optimum* Φ of the OCI problem:

$$\max_{\mathbf{x} \in \mathsf{X}} \mathbf{c}'\mathbf{x} = \min_{\mathbf{y} \in \mathsf{Y}} \mathbf{y}'\mathbf{b} = \mathbf{c}'\mathbf{x}^* = \mathbf{y}^{*\prime}\mathbf{b} = \Phi, \quad \mathbf{x}^* \in \mathsf{X}^*, \mathbf{y}^* \in \mathsf{Y}^* . \tag{H.4}$$

The solvability of the OCI problem is, incidentally equivalent to the assumption that a feasible OCI program and a feasible OCI shadow price system also exist**,

$$\mathsf{X} \neq \mathsf{O} \quad \text{and} \quad \mathsf{Y} \neq \mathsf{O} . \tag{H.5}$$

H.3. Sector Partitioning

Let

$$\mathbf{A} = [\mathbf{A}_1, \ldots, \mathbf{A}_n], \quad \mathbf{x} = \begin{bmatrix} \mathbf{x}_1 \\ \vdots \\ \mathbf{x}_n \end{bmatrix}, \quad \mathbf{c}' = [\mathbf{c}_1', \ldots, \mathbf{c}_n'] \tag{H.6}$$

be a mutually corresponding partitioning of the matrix **A**, the OCI program **x** and the OCI objective function vector $\mathbf{c}'$ in the primal version of the OCI problem. Then in place of (H.1) the equivalent forms

$$\begin{array}{lll} \mathbf{A}_1\mathbf{x}_1 + \ldots + \mathbf{A}_n\mathbf{x}_n \leqq \mathbf{b} & & \mathbf{y}'\mathbf{A}_1 \geqq \mathbf{c}_1' \\ \mathbf{x}_1 \geqq \mathbf{0} & & \quad \ddots \\ \quad \ddots & \text{and} & \mathbf{y}'\mathbf{A}_n \geqq \mathbf{c}_n' \\ \mathbf{x}_n \geqq \mathbf{0} & & \mathbf{y} \geqq \mathbf{0} \\ \mathbf{c}_1'\mathbf{x}_1 + \ldots + \mathbf{c}_n'\mathbf{x}_n \rightarrow \max! & & \mathbf{y}'\mathbf{b} \rightarrow \min! \end{array} \tag{H.7}$$

may be used.

* See e.g. A. I. GOLDMAN and A. W. TUCKER [46], Corollary 1A, p. 60.
** See e.g. A. I. GOLDMAN and A. W. TUCKER [46], Theorem 2, p. 61.

If the sum of the vectors $\mathbf{u}_1, \ldots, \mathbf{u}_n$ (of the same size as the constraint vector $\mathbf{b}$) is itself $\mathbf{b}$, i.e. if they satisfy the *constraint vector partitioning condition*

$$\mathbf{u}_1 + \ldots + \mathbf{u}_n = \mathbf{b} \tag{H.8}$$

then the vector

$$\mathbf{u} = [\mathbf{u}_1', \ldots, \mathbf{u}_n']' \tag{H.9}$$

composed of them is called a *central program*, the vector $\mathbf{u}_i$ is the *ith sector component* of the central program $\mathbf{u}$, while the *ith sector problem under the central program* $\mathbf{u}$ (or, under the sector component $\mathbf{u}_i$) is understood to mean the linear programming problem

$$\left.\begin{array}{ll} \mathbf{A}_i\mathbf{x}_i \leqq \mathbf{u}_i,\ \mathbf{x}_i \geqq \mathbf{0}, & \mathbf{c}_i'\mathbf{x}_i \rightarrow \max! \\ \mathbf{y}_i'\mathbf{A}_i \geqq \mathbf{c}_i',\ \mathbf{y}_i \geqq \mathbf{0}, & \mathbf{y}_i'\,\mathbf{u}_i \rightarrow \min! \end{array}\right\} i = 1, \ldots, n\,. \tag{H.10}$$

In (H.10) $\mathbf{x}_i$ is the *ith sector program*, while $\mathbf{y}_i$ is the *ith sector shadow price system.* In the ith sector problem under the sector component $\mathbf{u}_i$, let $\mathsf{X}_i(\mathbf{u}_i)$ stand for the set of *feasible sector programs*, $\mathsf{X}_i^*(\mathbf{u}_i)$ for the set of *optimal sector programs*, moreover Y_i for the set of *feasible sector shadow price systems*, and $\mathsf{Y}_i^*(\mathbf{u}_i)$ for the set of *optimal sector shadow price systems*, i.e.:

$$\begin{aligned} \mathsf{X}_i(\mathbf{u}_i) &= \{\mathbf{x}_i : \mathbf{A}_i\mathbf{x}_i \leqq \mathbf{u}_i,\ \mathbf{x}_i \geqq \mathbf{0}\} \\ \mathsf{X}_i^*(\mathbf{u}_i) &= \{\mathbf{x}_i^* : \mathbf{x}_i^* \in \mathsf{X}_i(\mathbf{u}_i),\ \mathbf{c}_1'\mathbf{x}_i^* = \max_{\mathbf{x}_i \in \mathsf{X}_i(\mathbf{u}_i)} \mathbf{c}_i'\mathbf{x}_i\} \end{aligned} \tag{H.11}$$

$$\begin{aligned} \mathsf{Y}_i &= \{\mathbf{y}_i : \mathbf{y}_i'\mathbf{A}_i \geqq \mathbf{c}_i',\quad \mathbf{y}_i \geqq \mathbf{0}\} \\ \mathsf{Y}_i^*(\mathbf{u}_i) &= \{\mathbf{y}_i^* : \mathbf{y}_i^* \in \mathsf{Y}_i,\quad \mathbf{y}_i^{*\prime}\mathbf{b} = \min_{\mathbf{y}_i \in \mathsf{Y}_i} \mathbf{y}_i'\mathbf{b}\}. \end{aligned} \tag{H.12}$$

H.4. Evaluable Central Programs

Let us find the condition for the solvability of all the sector problems. Since it follows from (H.12) and (H.3) that

$$\mathsf{Y} = \mathsf{Y}_1 \cap \ldots \cap \mathsf{Y}_n, \tag{H.13}$$

and because according to the assumption made with regard to the solvability of the OCI problem (H.5) states that $\mathsf{Y} \neq \mathsf{O}$, we have

$$\mathsf{Y}_i \neq \mathsf{O}, \quad i = 1, \ldots, n\,. \tag{H.14}$$

Hence two necessary and sufficient conditions may be deduced for the solvability of the ith sector programming problem under $\mathbf{u}_i$.

The first, from the theorem quoted in footnote** of p. 489, is that

$$\mathsf{X}_i(\mathbf{u}_i) \neq \mathsf{O}\,. \tag{H.15}$$

The second is that $\mathbf{y}_i'\mathbf{u}_i$ is bounded from below* on the set Y_i. This latter statement is best put in another form. Let

$$\mathsf{Y}_i = \mathbf{Y}_i^{\Delta} + \overline{\mathbf{Y}}_i^{<} = \tag{H.16}$$
$$= \{\overline{\mathbf{Y}}_i\mathbf{q}_i + \mu_i\,\overline{\mathbf{Y}}_i\,\overline{\mathbf{q}}_i : \mathbf{q}_i \geqq \mathbf{0},\quad \overline{\mathbf{q}}_i \geqq \mathbf{0},\ \mu_i \geqq 0, \mathbf{1}'\mathbf{q}_i = \mathbf{1}'\,\overline{\mathbf{q}}_i = 1\}$$

be the canonical decomposition** of the convex polyhedral set Y_i. Then the boundedness of $\mathbf{y}_i'\,\mathbf{u}_i$ on the set Y_i may be written in the form

$$\overline{\mathbf{Y}}_i'\mathbf{u}_i \geqq \mathbf{0}. \tag{H.17}$$

Let those central programs for which all the sector problems are solvable, be called *evaluable central programs.* According to (H.8) and (H.17) the set $\dot{\mathsf{U}}$ of the evaluable central programs can be written in the form:

$$\dot{\mathsf{U}} = \left\{\begin{bmatrix}\dot{\mathbf{u}}_1\\ \vdots \\ \dot{\mathbf{u}}_n\end{bmatrix} : \dot{\mathbf{u}}_1 + \ldots + \dot{\mathbf{u}}_n = \mathbf{b},\ \overline{\mathbf{Y}}_1'\dot{\mathbf{u}}_1 \geqq \mathbf{0}, \ldots, \overline{\mathbf{Y}}_n'\,\dot{\mathbf{u}}_n \geqq \mathbf{0}\right\}. \tag{H.18}$$

$\dot{\mathsf{U}}$ is therefore a polyhedral convex set.

H.5. Generator Sets

Let $\mathsf{X}(\dot{\mathbf{u}})$ denote the set of those OCI programs which may be composed from the sector programs feasible under the evaluable central program $\dot{\mathbf{u}} = [\dot{\mathbf{u}}_1', \ldots, \dot{\mathbf{u}}_n']'$. Then

$$\mathsf{X}(\dot{\mathbf{u}}) = \mathsf{X}_1(\dot{\mathbf{u}}_1) \times \ldots \times \mathsf{X}_n(\dot{\mathbf{u}}_n) =$$
$$= \left\{\begin{bmatrix}\mathbf{x}_1\\ \vdots \\ \mathbf{x}_n\end{bmatrix} : \mathbf{x}_1 \in \mathsf{X}_1(\dot{\mathbf{u}}_1), \ldots, \mathbf{x}_n \in \mathsf{X}_n(\dot{\mathbf{u}}_n)\right\}. \tag{H.19}$$

* See A. I. GOLDMAN and A. W. TUCKER [46], Corollary 1B, p. 60.

** GOLDMAN [45], pp. 44–49. $\mathbf{Y}_i$ is the matrix consisting of the extreme points of Y_i. If Y is bounded, then by definition $\overline{\mathbf{Y}}_i = \mathbf{0}$. Otherwise $\overline{\mathbf{Y}}_i$ is the matrix consisting of the extreme points of the set $\overline{\mathsf{Y}}_i$, which consists of the probability vectors $\overline{\mathbf{y}}_i$ satisfying the reduced homogeneous system $\overline{\mathbf{y}}_i A_i \geqq \mathbf{0}$, $\overline{\mathbf{y}}_i \geqq \mathbf{0}$.

The (proper or improper) subset U of the set U of all evaluable central programs, is said to *generate* X, or, in other words, U *is the generating set of* X, if

$$\mathsf{X} = \bigcup_{\mathbf{u} \in \mathsf{U}} \mathsf{X}(\mathbf{u}). \tag{H.20}$$

For the case of $\mathsf{U} = \dot{\mathsf{U}}$ (H.20) is valid, i.e. the non-empty polyhedral convex set $\dot{\mathsf{U}}$ of all evaluable central programs generates the set X of the feasible OCI programs. This may be proved in two steps:

(1) From (H.5) $\mathsf{X} \neq \mathsf{O}$. Let $\mathbf{x} = [\mathbf{x}_1', \dots, \mathbf{x}_n']' \in \mathsf{X}$, and let the components $\dot{\mathbf{u}}_1 = \mathbf{A}_1\mathbf{x}_1, \dots, \dot{\mathbf{u}}_{n-1} = \mathbf{A}_{n-1}\mathbf{x}_{n-1}$, $\dot{\mathbf{u}}_n = \mathbf{b} - (\dot{\mathbf{u}}_1 + \dots + \dot{\mathbf{u}}_{n-1})$ be defined. Obviously $\mathbf{x}_i \in \mathsf{X}_i(\dot{\mathbf{u}}_i)$, so that $\mathsf{X}_i(\dot{\mathbf{u}}_i) \neq \mathsf{O}$, $i = 1, \dots, n$, and consequently, because of (H.15) $\dot{\mathbf{u}} = [\dot{\mathbf{u}}_1', \dots, \dot{\mathbf{u}}_n']'$ is an evaluable central program, so that $\dot{\mathsf{U}}$ is a *non-empty* set. Moreover $\mathbf{x} \in \mathsf{X}(\dot{\mathbf{u}})$ and since the above construction provides such a central program $\dot{\mathbf{u}} \in \dot{\mathsf{U}}$ for each OCI program $\mathbf{x} \in \mathsf{X}$, it hence follows that $\mathsf{X} \subset \subset \bigcup_{\mathbf{u} \in \dot{\mathsf{U}}} \mathsf{X}(\dot{\mathbf{u}})$.

(2) If $\dot{\mathbf{u}} = [\dot{\mathbf{u}}_1', \dots, \dot{\mathbf{u}}_n']' \in \dot{\mathsf{U}}$ and $\mathbf{x}_i \in \mathsf{X}_i(\dot{\mathbf{u}}_i)$ i.e. $\mathbf{A}_i\mathbf{x}_i \leqq \dot{\mathbf{u}}_i$, $\mathbf{x}_i \geqq \mathbf{0}$, $i = 1, \dots, n$, then because of the constraint vector partitioning condition under (H.8), $\mathbf{A}_1\mathbf{x}_1 + \dots + \mathbf{A}_n\mathbf{x}_n \leqq \dot{\mathbf{u}}_1 + \dots + \dot{\mathbf{u}}_n = \mathbf{b}$, $\mathbf{x} = [\mathbf{x}_1', \dots, \mathbf{x}_n']' \geqq \mathbf{0}$, so that $\mathbf{x} \in \mathsf{X}$. Hence $\mathsf{X}(\dot{\mathbf{u}}) \subset \mathsf{X}$, and thus $\bigcup_{\dot{\mathbf{u}} \in \dot{\mathsf{U}}} \mathsf{X}(\dot{\mathbf{u}}) = \subset \mathsf{X}$.

From (1) and (2), $\mathsf{X} = \bigcup_{\dot{\mathbf{u}} \in \dot{\mathsf{U}}} \mathsf{X}(\dot{\mathbf{u}})$.

The generating property (H.20) may also be possessed by a non-empty polyhedral convex proper subset U of the set $\dot{\mathsf{U}}$ of all the evaluable central programs.

In the case of a matrix $\mathbf{A}$ of special form, cf. Dantzig [27] and Dantzig and Wolfe [28], (H.7) may assume the form

$$\mathbf{A}_1^{\#}\mathbf{x}_1 + \dots + \mathbf{A}_n^{\#}\mathbf{x}_n \leqq \mathbf{b}^{\#} \tag{H.21}$$

$$\begin{aligned} \mathbf{A}_1^0\mathbf{x}_1 \quad & \leqq \mathbf{b}_1^0 \\ \ddots \quad & \quad \vdots \\ \mathbf{A}_n^0\mathbf{x}_n & \leqq \mathbf{b}_n^0 \end{aligned} \tag{H.22}$$

$$\mathbf{x}_1 \geqq \mathbf{0}, \dots, \mathbf{x}_n \geqq \mathbf{0} \tag{H.23}$$

$$\mathbf{c}_1'\mathbf{x}_1 + \dots + \mathbf{c}_n'\mathbf{x}_n \longrightarrow \max! \tag{H.24}$$

Here $\mathbf{A}_i^0\mathbf{x}_i \leqq \mathbf{b}_i^0$ contains those conditions of the OCI problem which only refer to the ith sector. These conditions may be called the *special sector conditions* of the *i*th sector. It is useful here also to put the central program in the form

$$\mathbf{u} = \begin{bmatrix}\mathbf{u}_1\\ \vdots \\ \mathbf{u}_n\end{bmatrix} \qquad \mathbf{u}_i = \begin{bmatrix}\mathbf{u}_i^{\#}\\ \mathbf{u}_{i1}^0 \\ \vdots \\ \mathbf{u}_{in}^0\end{bmatrix}, \qquad i = 1,\dots, n \tag{H.25}$$

and in this case the constraint vector partitioning condition is expressed by the equations

$$\begin{aligned} \mathbf{u}_1^{\#} + \dots + \mathbf{u}_n^{\#} &= \mathbf{b}^{\#} \\ \mathbf{u}_{1i}^0 + \dots + \mathbf{u}_{ni}^0 &= \mathbf{b}_i^0, \qquad i = 1,\dots, n. \end{aligned} \tag{H.26}$$

Let $\dot{\mathsf{U}}$ stand for the set of all the evaluable central programs, and U denote that subset of $\dot{\mathsf{U}}$, in which each sector "gets" in full the bounds occurring in its special sector conditions, that is, let

$$\mathsf{U} = \left\{\mathbf{u} = \begin{bmatrix}\mathbf{u}_1\\ \vdots \\ \mathbf{u}_n\end{bmatrix} : \mathbf{u} \in \dot{\mathsf{U}},\ \mathbf{u}_1 = \begin{bmatrix}\mathbf{u}_1^{\#}\\ \mathbf{b}_1^0 \\ \mathbf{0} \\ \vdots \\ \mathbf{0}\end{bmatrix}, \dots, \mathbf{u}_n = \begin{bmatrix}\mathbf{u}_n^{\#}\\ \mathbf{0} \\ \vdots \\ \mathbf{0} \\ \mathbf{b}_n^0\end{bmatrix}\right\}. \tag{H.27}$$

It is obvious that U is a non-empty polyhedral convex subset of $\dot{\mathsf{U}}$, which does not necessarily contain every evaluable central program, e.g. in the case of $\mathbf{b}^{\#} \geqq \mathbf{0}$, $\mathbf{b}_i^0 > \mathbf{0}$ $(i = 1,\dots, n)$, $\mathsf{U} \subset \dot{\mathsf{U}}$, but $\mathsf{U} \neq \dot{\mathsf{U}}$.

H.6. The Two-level Problem

Let U be a non-empty convex polyhedral subset of $\dot{\mathsf{U}}$, such that it generates X. Let us fix U and let its elements be called *feasible central programs.* For any feasible central program, $\mathbf{u} = [\mathbf{u}_1',\dots, \mathbf{u}_n']'$, the *sector-optima*

$$\varphi_i(\mathbf{u}_i) = \max_{\mathbf{x}_i \in \mathsf{X}_i(\mathbf{u}_i)} \mathbf{c}_i' \mathbf{x}_i = \min_{\mathbf{y}_i \in \mathsf{Y}_i} \mathbf{y}_i' \mathbf{u}_i, \qquad i = 1,\dots, n \tag{H.28.}$$

and their sum, the *overall optimum*

$$\varphi(\mathbf{u}) = \varphi_1(\mathbf{u}_1) + \dots + \varphi_n(\mathbf{u}_n) \tag{H.29}$$

under $\mathbf{u}$ may be defined.

These are quasi-linear, continuous concave functions of $\mathbf{u}$. For if $\mathbf{y}_{i1},\ldots,\mathbf{y}_{iN}$ denote the extreme points of Y_i, i.e. if $\mathbf{Y}_i = [\mathbf{y}_{i1},\ldots,\mathbf{y}_{iN_i}]$ may be written in (H.16), then, because $\mathbf{u}$ is evaluable,

$$\varphi_i(\mathbf{u}_i) = \min_{\mathbf{y}_i \in \mathsf{Y}_i} \mathbf{y}_i'\mathbf{u}_i = \min \{\mathbf{y}_{i1}'\mathbf{u}_i, \ldots, \mathbf{y}'_{iN_i}\mathbf{u}_i\}, \tag{H.30}$$

so that φ_i is the lower envelope of a finite number of linear functions ($i = 1,\ldots, n$). The same is true for $\varphi(\mathbf{u})$, the sum of the φ_i's.

The *two-level problem* obtained from the OCI problem by means of the sector decomposition (H.6) and choice of the set of feasible central programs as above, is understood to mean the following problem.

(1) At the "*central level*", to determine the feasible central program which yields the maximum overall optimum, in other words, to solve the concave programming problem

$$\mathbf{u} \in \mathsf{U}, \ \varphi(\mathbf{u}) \to \max! \tag{H.31}$$

and to determine the set

$$\mathsf{U}^* = \{\mathbf{u}^* : \varphi(\mathbf{u}^*) = \max_{\mathbf{u} \in \mathsf{U}} \varphi(\mathbf{u})\} \tag{H.32}$$

consisting of the *optimal central programs*.

(2) At the "*sector level*", in each sector to determine the optimal sector program corresponding to the optimal central program component, i.e. for each $\mathbf{u}^* = [\mathbf{u}_1^{*\prime}, \ldots, \mathbf{u}_n^{*\prime}]' \in \mathsf{U}^*$, to solve the sector problems

$$\mathbf{A}_i\mathbf{x}_i \leqq \mathbf{u}_i^*, \ \mathbf{x}_i \geqq \mathbf{0}, \ \mathbf{c}_i'\mathbf{x}_i \to \max!, \tag{H.33}$$

thus to determine the sets $\mathsf{X}_i^*(\mathbf{u}_i^*)$ for $i = 1,\ldots, n$, defined in (H.11).

(3) To compose the OCI program which may be obtained from the optimal sector programs under the optimal central program, in other words to determine the union of the sets

$$\mathsf{X}^*(\mathbf{u}^*) = \mathsf{X}_1^*(\mathbf{u}_1^*) \times \ldots \times \mathsf{X}_n^*(\mathbf{u}_n^*) = \\ = \left\{\begin{bmatrix}\mathbf{x}_1^* \\ \vdots \\ \mathbf{x}_n^*\end{bmatrix} : \mathbf{x}_1^* \in \mathsf{X}_1^*(\mathbf{u}_1^*), \ldots, \mathbf{x}_n^* \in \mathsf{X}_n^*(\mathbf{u}_n^*)\right\}, \tag{H.34}$$

i.e. the set $\bigcup_{\mathbf{u}^* \in \mathsf{U}^*} \mathsf{X}^*(\mathbf{u}^*)$.

The relation between the OCI problem and the two-level problem defined above, is shown by the following theorem:

THEOREM 1. *Any two-level problem derived from a solvable OCI problem is itself also solvable, and its solution is equivalent to the solution of the problem:*

$$U^* \neq O \quad \text{and} \quad X^* = \bigcup_{\mathbf{u}^* \in U^*} X^*(\mathbf{u})^*. \tag{H.35}$$

The maximum value of the overall optimum is equal to the optimum of the OCI problem:

$$\max_{\mathbf{u} \in U} \varphi(\mathbf{u}) = \max_{\mathbf{x} \in U} \mathbf{c}'\mathbf{x} = \Phi\,. \tag{H.36}$$

Proof. The statements of the theorem may be read from the following sequence of relations:

$$\Phi = \max_{\mathbf{x} \in X} \mathbf{c}'\mathbf{x} = \max \{\mathbf{c}'\mathbf{x} : \mathbf{x} \in \bigcup_{\mathbf{u} \in X} X(\mathbf{u}) = \max_{\mathbf{u} \in U}\ (\max_{\mathbf{x} \in X(\mathbf{u})} \mathbf{c}'\mathbf{x}) =$$
$$= \max_{\mathbf{u} \in U} \left\{ \sum_{i=1}^{n} \max_{\mathbf{x}_i \in X_i(\mathbf{u})_i} \mathbf{c}_1'\mathbf{x}_i \right\} = \max_{\mathbf{u} \in X} \varphi(\mathbf{u})\,. \tag{H.37}$$

H.7. Derived Polyhedral Game

The objective function of the concave programming problem to be solved at the "central level" in the two-level problem is the overall optimum $\varphi(\mathbf{u})$. This function is only given in implicit form by the data of the OCI problem and its decomposition into sectors. The two-level problem is put into a form in which it may more easily be solved. Let V denote the set of feasible *sector shadow price system teams* according to (H.12):

$$V = Y_1 \times \ldots \times Y_n = \{\mathbf{v} = \begin{bmatrix} \mathbf{y}_1 \\ \vdots \\ \mathbf{y}_n \end{bmatrix} : \mathbf{y}_1 \in Y_1, \ldots, \mathbf{y}_n \in Y_n\}\,. \tag{H.38}$$

Then the following expression is obtained for the overall optimum:

$$\varphi(\mathbf{u}) = \sum_{i=1}^{n} \varphi_i(\mathbf{u}_i) = \sum_{i=1}^{n} \min_{\mathbf{y}_i \in Y} \mathbf{y}_i' \mathbf{u}_i =$$
$$= \min_{\mathbf{y}_i \in Y_i} \sum_{i=1}^{n} \mathbf{y}_i' \mathbf{u}_i = \min_{\mathbf{v} \in V} \mathbf{v}'\mathbf{u}\,, \quad i = 1, \ldots, n. \tag{H.39}$$

Hence, according to (H.36), the following may be written for the OCI optimum:

$$\Phi = \max_{\mathbf{u} \in \mathsf{U}} \min_{\mathbf{v} \in \mathsf{V}} \mathbf{v}'\mathbf{u}. \tag{H.40}$$

Let us therefore define a polyhedral game* in the following terms: Let U be the set of strategies of the maximizing, and V of the minimizing player, and the homogeneous bilinear function $\mathbf{v}'\mathbf{u}$ ($\mathbf{u} \in \mathsf{U}$, $\mathbf{v} \in \mathsf{V}$) be the pay-off function of the game. The maximizing player may be identified with the "centre", the minimizing player with the "team of sectors"**. Consequently we may speak of a *central strategy* in place of the feasible central program, *sector strategy* in place of the feasible sector shadow price system team, and in the case of both strategies we may consider the various *sector components* of the strategy. The game which has thus been defined is called the *polyhedral game derived from the two-level problem* or *from the OCI problem* through the given decomposition of sectors and the given choice of the set of feasible central programs, in symbols: (U, V). What the relation (H.40) expresses, is that the optimum of the OCI problem is the max-min (lower) value of the polyhedral game derived from it. The connection between the OCI problem, the two-level problem and the polyhedral game derived from it, is contained in the following theorem:

THEOREM 2. *A polyhedral game derived from a solvable OCI problem is itself solvable and its value equals the OCI optimum. The optimal strategies of the "central player" are the optimal central programs appearing in the corresponding two-level problem. Among the optimal strategies of the "sector-team player" there is always a strategy whose sector components are equal – the necessary and sufficient condition for a sector strategy whose sector components are equal to be optimal, is that it should be the optimal counter-strategy to some central strategy***. In an optimal sector strategy whose sector components are equal, this common sector component forms an optimal OCI shadow price system and vice versa: a sector strategy made up of any optimal OCI shadow price system as its equal sector component, is optimal in the derived polyhedral game.*

Proof. (1) In the case of a solvable OCI problem the OCI optimum Φ exists and is finite, while according to (H.40) it is equal to the max-min

* See P. WOLFE [179]. In this case $m = n$, $X = \mathsf{U}$, $Y = \mathsf{V}$, $A = \mathbf{E}$ = identity matrix.

** See the definition of a "person", e.g. by J. C. C MCKINSEY [124], p. 4, §. 3.

*** $\hat{\mathbf{v}} \in \mathsf{V}$ is an optimal counter-strategy to the central strategy $\mathbf{u} \in \mathsf{U}$, if $\hat{\mathbf{v}}'\mathbf{u} = \min_{\mathbf{v} \in \mathsf{V}} \mathbf{v}'\mathbf{u} = \varphi(\mathbf{u})$.

value of the polyhedral game (U, V). From this it follows according to the theorem of Wolfe [177], that Φ is at the same time also the min-max (upper) value of this game,

$$\Phi = \max_{\mathbf{u} \in \mathsf{U}} \min_{\mathbf{v} \in \mathsf{V}} \mathbf{v}'\mathbf{u} = \min_{\mathbf{v} \in \mathsf{V}} \sup_{\mathbf{u} \in \mathsf{U}} \mathbf{v}'\mathbf{u}\,, \tag{H.41}$$

so that (U, V) is solvable, and its value is Φ, and both players have optimal strategies.

(2) Since according to (H.39) $\varphi(\mathbf{u})$ is the minimum of the pay-off function $\mathbf{v}'\mathbf{u}$ on the set V, the set consisting of the optimal strategies of the central player equals the set U^* in (H.32).

(3) Using the notation of (H.3)–(H.12) it will first be shown that

$$\mathsf{Y}_1^*(\mathbf{u}_1) \cap \ldots \cap \mathsf{Y}_n^*(\mathbf{u}_n) = \begin{cases} \mathsf{Y}^* & \text{if } \mathbf{u} \in \mathsf{U}^* \\ \bigcirc & \text{if } \mathbf{u} \notin \mathsf{U}^*\,, \end{cases} \tag{H.42}$$

so that an optimal counter-strategy the sector-components of which are equal exists only as a counter-strategy against some optimal central strategies, but then always exists, and the common sector component is an optimal OCI shadow price system. As the first part of the proof of (H.42) it can be shown that for $\mathbf{y}^* \in \mathsf{Y}^*$, $\mathbf{u}^* \in \mathsf{U}^*$ it is true that $\mathbf{y}^* \in \mathsf{Y}_i^*(\mathbf{u}_i^*)$ $(i = 1, \ldots, n)$. For if the opposite were the case, then we would have

$$\Phi = \varphi(\mathbf{u}^*) = \sum_{i=1}^{n} \varphi_i(\mathbf{u}_i^*) = \sum_{i=1}^{n} \min_{\mathbf{y}_i \in \mathsf{Y}_i} \mathbf{y}_i'\mathbf{u}_i^* < \sum_{i=1}^{n} \mathbf{y}^{*\prime}\mathbf{u}_i^* =$$

$$= \mathbf{y}^{*\prime} \sum_{i=1}^{n} \mathbf{u}_i^* = \mathbf{y}^{*\prime}\,\mathbf{b} = \Phi \quad ,$$

which is impossible. As the second part of the proof of (H. 42) it can be shown that in the reverse case, for $\hat{\mathbf{y}} \in \mathsf{Y}_i^*\,(\hat{\mathbf{u}}_i)$ $(i = 1, \ldots, n)$, it is true that $\hat{\mathbf{y}} \in \mathsf{Y}^*$ and $\hat{\mathbf{u}} \in \mathsf{U}^*$. For let $\mathbf{y} \in \mathsf{Y}$ be arbitrary; then

$$\mathbf{y}'\mathbf{b} = \mathbf{y}' \sum_{i=1}^{n} \hat{\mathbf{u}}_i = \sum_{i=1}^{n} \mathbf{y}'\hat{\mathbf{u}}_i \geqq \sum_{i=1}^{n} \min_{\mathbf{y}_i \in \mathsf{Y}_i} \mathbf{y}_i'\,\hat{\mathbf{u}}_i$$

$$= \sum_{i=1}^{n} \varphi_i(\hat{\mathbf{u}}_i) = \varphi(\hat{\mathbf{u}}) = \sum_{i=1}^{n} \hat{\mathbf{y}}'\hat{\mathbf{u}}_i = \hat{\mathbf{y}}' \sum_{i=1}^{n} \hat{\mathbf{u}}_i = \hat{\mathbf{y}}'\mathbf{b},$$

so that $\mathbf{y}'\mathbf{b} \geqq \hat{\mathbf{y}}'\mathbf{b}$ holds i.e. $\hat{\mathbf{y}} \in \mathsf{Y}^*$. It follows furthermore, that $\varphi(\hat{\mathbf{u}}) = = \hat{\mathbf{y}}'\mathbf{b} = \Phi$, so that $\hat{\mathbf{u}} \in \mathsf{U}^*$. (H.42) has thus been proved. To complete the proof of Theorem 2 it is now only necessary to show that for any optimal OCI shadow price system $\mathbf{y}^*$, the sector strategy $\tilde{\mathbf{v}}^* = [\mathbf{y}^*, \ldots, \mathbf{y}^{*\prime}]'$ with equal sector components $\mathbf{y}^*$ is an optimal one. For this it is sufficient to prove that $\tilde{\mathbf{v}}^*$, together with any optimal central strategy $\mathbf{u}^* \in \mathsf{U}^*$, forms a saddle-point of the function $\mathbf{v}'\mathbf{u}$ in (U, V). For let $\mathbf{u}^* = [\mathbf{u}_1^{*\prime}, \ldots, \mathbf{u}_n^{*\prime}]'$ be an optimal central strategy, and $\mathbf{u} = [\mathbf{u}_1', \ldots, \mathbf{u}_n']' \in \mathsf{U}$ as well as $\mathbf{v} = [\mathbf{y}_1', \ldots, \mathbf{y}_n']' \in \mathsf{V}$ be arbitrary. Then

$$\tilde{\mathbf{v}}^{*\prime}\mathbf{u} = \sum_{i=1}^{n} \mathbf{y}^{*\prime}\mathbf{u}_i = \mathbf{y}^{*\prime} \sum_{i=1}^{n} \mathbf{u}_i = \mathbf{y}^{*\prime}\mathbf{b} = \Phi = \mathbf{y}^{*\prime} \sum_{i=1}^{n} \mathbf{u}_i^* =$$

$$= \sum_{i=1}^{n} \mathbf{y}^{*\prime}\mathbf{u}_i^* = \tilde{\mathbf{v}}^{*\prime}\mathbf{u}^* \leqq \sum_{i=1}^{n} \mathbf{y}_i' \mathbf{u}_i^* = \mathbf{v}'\mathbf{u}^*,$$

so that

$$\tilde{\mathbf{v}}^{*\prime}\mathbf{u} \leqq \tilde{\mathbf{v}}^{*\prime}\mathbf{u}^* \leqq \mathbf{v}'\mathbf{u}^*, \qquad (\mathbf{u} \in \mathsf{U}, \mathbf{v} \in \mathsf{V}).$$

Theorem 2 is thus proved.

H.8. Regularity

The OCI problem has thus been reduced to the solution of the polyhedral game (U, V) derived from it. A method was now sought for its solution, which would utilize the decomposition of the problem, and be built up of partial computations that can take place separately at the centre and in the sectors. For this it is necessary to introduce some regularity conditions. It will be shown in section H.12 that all linear programming problems can be decomposed in such a way that the polyhedral game derived from them should be regular in the sense treated below.

Let first the concept of an *evaluable sector strategy* (or an *evaluable sector shadow price system team*) be defined. They are understood to mean a sector strategy $\mathbf{v} \in \mathsf{V}$, against which there exists an optimal central counter-strategy; in other words one where the linear program

$$\mathbf{u} \in \mathsf{U}, \ \mathbf{v}'\mathbf{u} \rightarrow \max! \qquad \text{(H.43)}$$

is solvable. Let a derived polyhedral game (U, V) be called *regular* if all its sector strategies are evaluable. Consider here, that according to the definition of a two-level problem every element of an evaluable central strategy, i.e. a central program $\mathbf{u}$ for which the linear program

$$\mathbf{v} \in \mathsf{V}, \ \mathbf{v}'\mathbf{u} \to \min! \tag{H.44}$$

is solvable. In the case of a regular polyhedral game therefore, there is an optimal counter-strategy to each strategy of both players.

It thus follows that all regular polyhedral games are strategically reducible* to a matrix game**. For let $\mathsf{U} = \mathbf{U}^{\Delta} + \overline{\mathbf{U}}^{<}$, and $\mathsf{V} = \mathbf{V}^{\Delta} + \overline{\mathbf{V}}^{<}$ be the canonical decompositions of the strategy sets concerned. The elements of U are then of the form $\mathbf{u} = \mathbf{Up} + \lambda\overline{\mathbf{U}}\overline{\mathbf{p}}$ (where $\mathbf{p}$ and $\overline{\mathbf{p}}$ are probability vectors and λ is a non-negative number), while the elements of V are of the form $\mathbf{v} = \mathbf{Vq} + \mu\,\overline{\mathbf{V}}\overline{\mathbf{q}}$ (where $\mathbf{q}$ and $\overline{\mathbf{q}}$ are probability vectors and μ is a non-negative number) so that the objective function of the program problems (H.43)–(H.44) may be written in the form

$$\mathbf{v}'\mathbf{u} = (\mathbf{q}'\mathbf{V}' + \mu\,\overline{\mathbf{q}}'\overline{\mathbf{V}}')(\mathbf{Up} + \lambda\overline{\mathbf{U}}\overline{\mathbf{p}}) = \mathbf{q}'\mathbf{V}'\mathbf{Up} + \lambda\mathbf{q}'\mathbf{V}'\mathbf{Up} + \\ + \mu\overline{\mathbf{q}}'\overline{\mathbf{V}}'\mathbf{Up} + \lambda\mu\overline{\mathbf{q}}'\overline{\mathbf{V}}'\overline{\mathbf{U}}\overline{\mathbf{p}}. \tag{H.45}$$

Hence

$$\sup_{\mathbf{u}\in\mathsf{U}} \mathbf{v}'\mathbf{u} = \sup_{\mathbf{p},\lambda,\overline{\mathbf{p}}} (\mathbf{q}'\mathbf{V}' + \mu\,\overline{\mathbf{q}}'\overline{\mathbf{V}}')(\mathbf{Up} + \lambda\,\overline{\mathbf{U}}\overline{\mathbf{p}}) = \\ = \max_{\mathbf{p}} (\mathbf{q}'\mathbf{V}'\mathbf{U}' + \mu\,\overline{\mathbf{q}}\,\overline{\mathbf{V}}'\mathbf{U})\mathbf{p} + \\ + \sup_{\lambda\geqq 0} \lambda\cdot\{\max_{\mathbf{p}} (\mathbf{q}'\mathbf{V}'\mathbf{U} + \mu\,\overline{\mathbf{q}}'\overline{\mathbf{V}}'\overline{\mathbf{U}})\overline{\mathbf{p}}\}. \tag{H.46}$$

Since any $\mathbf{v}$ is evaluable, the sum according to (H.46) is finite for any choice of $\mathbf{q}$, μ and $\overline{\mathbf{q}}$. It hence also follows that for any choice of $\mathbf{q}$, μ, $\overline{\mathbf{q}}$,

$$\max_{\overline{\mathbf{p}}} (\mathbf{q}'\mathbf{V}'\mathbf{U} + \mu\,\overline{\mathbf{p}}'\overline{\mathbf{V}}'\overline{\mathbf{U}})\overline{\mathbf{p}} \leqq 0 \quad \text{i.e. } \mathbf{q}'\mathbf{V}'\overline{\mathbf{U}} + \mu\,\overline{\mathbf{p}}'\overline{\mathbf{V}}'\overline{\mathbf{U}} \leqq \mathbf{0} \tag{H.47}$$

holds. Choosing $\mu = 0$, for all values of $\mathbf{q}'$ we have $\mathbf{q}'\mathbf{V}'\overline{\mathbf{U}} \leqq \mathbf{0}$, i.e.

$$\mathbf{V}'\overline{\mathbf{U}} \leqq \mathbf{O}. \tag{H.48}$$

* A game is said to be *strategically reducible* to another game, if the latter is solvable and its every solution (optimal strategy-pair) is a solution of the original game, too.

** For a definition of the matrix game see e.g. p. 17 of S. KARLIN [63].

On the other hand $\mathbf{q}'\mathbf{V}'\mathbf{U} \leqq \mathbf{0}$ must hold for any $\mathbf{q}'$ otherwise if μ was chosen to be sufficiently large and positive, (H.47) would not be valid. Thus

$$\overline{\mathbf{V}}'\overline{\mathbf{U}} \leqq \mathbf{O}. \qquad \text{(H.49)}$$

A similar argument will show upon the analysis of (H.44) that

$$\overline{\mathbf{V}}'\mathbf{U} \geqq \mathbf{O} \qquad \text{(H.50)}$$

and

$$\overline{\mathbf{V}}'\overline{\mathbf{U}} \geqq \mathbf{O}. \qquad \text{(H.51)}$$

Summarizing, from (H.49) and (H.51) we have

$$\mathbf{V}'\overline{\mathbf{U}} \leqq \mathbf{O}, \quad \overline{\mathbf{V}}'\overline{\mathbf{U}} = \mathbf{O}, \quad \overline{\mathbf{V}}'\mathbf{U} \geqq \mathbf{O}. \qquad \text{(H.52)}$$

Note that it follows from the above conditions, which are equivalent to the regularity of the polyhedral game, that for any strategy $\mathbf{u} = \mathbf{Up}+\lambda\overline{\mathbf{U}}\overline{\mathbf{p}} \in \mathsf{U}$ it is possible to find a strategy, namely $\mathbf{u}^{\triangle}=\mathbf{Up} \in \mathsf{U}^{\triangle}$ for which

$$\mathbf{v}'\mathbf{u} \leqq \mathbf{v}'\mathbf{u}^{\triangle} \quad \text{for all} \quad \mathbf{v} \in \mathsf{V}, \qquad \text{(H.53)}$$

while for any strategy $\mathbf{v} = \mathbf{Vq} + \mu\overline{\mathbf{V}}\overline{\mathbf{q}} \in \mathsf{V}$ it is possible to find a strategy, namely $\mathbf{v}^{\triangle} = \mathbf{Vq} \in \mathsf{V}^{\triangle}$, for which

$$\mathbf{v}'\mathbf{u} \geqq \mathbf{v}^{\triangle\prime}\mathbf{u} \quad \text{for all} \quad \mathbf{u} \in \mathsf{U}. \qquad \text{(H.54)}$$

In other words the elements of U outside $\mathsf{U}^{\triangle}$ and the elements of V outside $\mathsf{V}^{\triangle}$ may be dominated (in the broader sense) by elements within $\mathsf{U}^{\triangle}$ and $\mathsf{V}^{\triangle}$. The polyhedral game (U, V) is therefore strategically reducible to the polyhedral game $(\mathsf{U}^{\triangle}, \mathsf{V}^{\triangle})$, and this in turn is isomorphic with the matrix game having a pay-off matrix $\mathbf{V}'\mathbf{U}$.

H.9. Fictitious Play

It should be pointed out that the matrix game $\mathbf{V}'\mathbf{U}$ is only stated in an implicit form, since the pay-off matrix $\mathbf{V}'\mathbf{U}$ is not directly known, the only available fact being that $\mathbf{U}$ and $\mathbf{V}$ are the matrices composed by the extreme vectors of the convex polyhedral sets U and V, defined by the constraint systems of the centre and the sectors, respectively. If, therefore, it is intended to find a solution of a regular polyhedral game

(U, V) by solving the matrix game with the pay-off matrix $\mathbf{V}'\mathbf{U}$, then for this reason itself – apart from the difficulties of a computing problem of at least the same size as the original OCI problem – it is impossible to apply direct computing procedures.

It is possible, on the other hand, to use the *fictitious play* method of Brown and Robinson*. According to the above, against each central strategy $\mathbf{u} \in \mathsf{U}$ of the regular polyhedral game (U, V), it is possible to find an optimal counter-strategy $\mathbf{v}^*(\mathbf{u}) \in \mathbf{V}^\Delta$, while against each sector strategy $\mathbf{v} \in \mathsf{V}$ it is possible to find an optimal counter-strategy $\mathbf{u}^*(\mathbf{v}) \in \mathbf{U}^\Delta$, for which

$$\mathbf{v}^*(\mathbf{u})'\mathbf{u} = \min_{\mathbf{v} \in \mathsf{U}} \mathbf{v}'\mathbf{u} \quad \text{and} \quad \mathbf{v}'\mathbf{u}^*(\mathbf{v}) = \max_{\mathbf{u} \in \mathsf{V}} \mathbf{v}'\mathbf{u} \tag{H.55}$$

hold. The determination of $\mathbf{v}^*(\mathbf{u})$ is called the *regular evaluation* of $\mathbf{u}$, the determination of $\mathbf{u}^*(\mathbf{v})$ that of $\mathbf{v}$. (Both kinds of regular evaluation imply the solution of a linear programming problem.) The *regular fictitious play* of the regular polyhedral game (U, V) is understood to mean the construction, according to the rule stated below, of the strategy sequences $\mathbf{u}^*\langle 1\rangle, \mathbf{u}^*\langle 2\rangle, \ldots, \mathbf{u}^*\langle N\rangle, \ldots$ within $\mathbf{U}^\Delta$ and $\mathbf{v}^*\langle 1\rangle, \mathbf{v}^*\langle 2\rangle, \ldots, \mathbf{v}^*\langle N\rangle, \ldots$ within $\mathbf{V}^\Delta$.

Phase 1.

Step I: Select any central strategy $\mathbf{u}^{(1)} \in \mathbf{U}^\Delta$.

Step II: By definition $\mathbf{u}^*\langle 1\rangle = \mathbf{u}^{(1)}$.

Step III: (The regular evaluation of $\mathbf{u}^*\langle 1\rangle$). Determine $\mathbf{v}^{(1)} = \mathbf{v}^*(\mathbf{u}^*\langle 1\rangle)$.

Step IV: By definition $\mathbf{v}^*\langle 1\rangle = \mathbf{v}^{(1)}$.

Next the process goes on for Phases 2, 3, ...

Phase N. $(N = 2, 3, \ldots)$.

Step I. (The regular evaluation of $\mathbf{v}^*\langle N-1\rangle$): Determine $\mathbf{u}^{(N)} = \mathbf{u}^*(\mathbf{v}^*\langle N-1\rangle)$.

Step II. ("Mixing" with the term of the previous phase): Compute $\mathbf{u}^*\langle N\rangle = [(N-1)/N]\,\mathbf{u}^*\langle N-1\rangle + (1/N)\,\mathbf{u}^{(N)}$.

Step III. (The regular evaluation of $\mathbf{u}^*\langle N\rangle$): Determine $\mathbf{v}^{(N)} = \mathbf{v}^*(\mathbf{u}^*\langle N\rangle)$.

Step IV. ("Mixing" with the term of the previous phase): Compute $\mathbf{v}^*\langle N\rangle = [(N-1)/N]\,\mathbf{v}^*\langle N-1\rangle + (1/N)\,\mathbf{v}^{(N)}$.

* G. W. Brown [16], [17]; J. Robinson [150]. For a detailed discussion: S. Karlin [63], pp. 179–189.

Since all regular polyhedral games are strategically reducible to a matrix game, "max" may be written for "sup" in the minimax relation (H.41). From this relation, on the basis of the definitions of the regular evaluations, it may easily be deduced that the *upper optimum*

$$\Phi^*\langle N\rangle = \max_{\mathbf{u}\in U} \mathbf{v}^*\langle N-1\rangle'\mathbf{u} = \max_{\mathbf{u}\in \mathbf{U}\Delta} \mathbf{v}^* \langle N-1\rangle'\mathbf{u} = \mathbf{v}^*\langle N-1\rangle'\mathbf{u}^{(N)}$$

in the *N*th phase (N = 2, 3,. . .) yields an upper estimate, the *lower optimum*

$$\varphi^*\langle N\rangle = \min_{\mathbf{v}\in V} \mathbf{v}'\mathbf{u}^*\langle N\rangle = \min_{\mathbf{v}\in \mathbf{V}\Delta} \mathbf{v}'\mathbf{u}^*\langle N\rangle = \mathbf{v}^{(N)'}\,\mathbf{u}^*\langle N\rangle$$

in the *N*th phase ($N = 1, 2, 3,\ldots$) a lower estimate for the OCI optimum Φ, i.e.

$$\Phi^*\langle N\rangle \geqq \Phi \quad (N = 2, 3,\ldots), \quad \varphi^*\langle N\rangle \leqq \Phi \quad (N = 1,2,\ldots). \tag{H.56}$$

For

$$\Phi^*\langle N\rangle = \max_{\mathbf{u}\in U} \mathbf{v}^*\langle N-1\rangle'\,\mathbf{u} \geqq \min_{\mathbf{v}\in V}\,\max_{\mathbf{u}\in U}\,\mathbf{v}'\mathbf{u} = \Phi \tag{H.57}$$

and

$$\varphi^*\langle N\rangle = \min_{\mathbf{v}\in V} \mathbf{v}'\mathbf{u}^*\langle N^*\rangle \leqq \max_{\mathbf{u}\in U}\,\min_{\mathbf{v}\in V} \mathbf{v}'\mathbf{u} = \Phi\,. \tag{H.58}$$

Since, moreover, the series also imply, on account of their construction, the fictitious play of the matrix game with the pay-off matrix **V′U**, the Brown–Robinson theorem is valid, so that

$$\lim_{N\to\infty} \Phi^*\langle N\rangle = \lim_{N\to\infty} \varphi^*\langle N\rangle = \Phi \tag{H.59}$$

and the limit points of the sequences $\mathbf{u}^*\langle N\rangle$ and $\mathbf{v}^*\langle N\rangle$ are optimal central and sector strategies.

H.10. The Termination of the Iteration: δ-optimal Solution

The *δ-termination* of the iteration of regular fictitious play, where δ is an arbitrary small positive number, is understood to mean the following termination of the above infinite procedure. Let N_δ be the smallest, positive integer for which

$$\Phi^*\langle N_\delta\rangle - \varphi^*\langle N_\delta\rangle \leqq \delta \qquad \text{or } \Phi^*\langle N_\delta + 1\rangle - \varphi^*\langle N_\delta\rangle \leqq \delta \quad \text{(H.60)}$$

holds. According to (H.56) and (H.59), such an N_δ may be found for any arbitrarily small positive number δ. Then:

(1) The iteration is terminated at Step II of Phase N_δ, or Step I of phase $N_\delta + 1$, according to whether the first or the second inequality in (H.60) has been satisfied.

(2) The linear programming problems

$$\mathbf{A}_i\,\mathbf{x}_i \leqq \mathbf{u}_i^*\langle N\rangle,\ \mathbf{x}_i \geqq \mathbf{0}, \qquad \mathbf{c}_i'\mathbf{x}_i \rightarrow \max!,\ i = 1,\ldots,n \qquad \text{(H.61)}$$

in the sectors are solved.

(3) From the optimal sector programs $\mathbf{x}^{\delta *}$ thus obtained, the feasible OCI program $\mathbf{x}^{\delta *} = [\mathbf{x}_1^{\delta *\prime},\ldots,\mathbf{x}_n^{\delta *\prime}]'$ is composed. Since

$$\mathbf{c}'\mathbf{x}^{\delta *} = \sum_{i=1}^{n} \mathbf{c}_i'\mathbf{x}_i^{\delta *} = \sum_{i=1}^{n} \mathbf{y}_i^*(\mathbf{u}_i^*\langle N_\delta\rangle)'\,\mathbf{u}_i^*\langle N_\delta\rangle =$$
$$= \mathbf{v}^*(\mathbf{u}^*\langle N_\delta\rangle)'\,\mathbf{u}^*\langle N_\delta\rangle = \varphi^*\langle N_\delta\rangle,$$

according to (H.60)

$$\Phi - \delta \leqq \mathbf{c}'\mathbf{x}^{\delta *} \leqq \Phi. \qquad \text{(H.62)}$$

(H.62) is briefly referred to as the fact that $\mathbf{x}^{\delta *}$ is a *δ-optimal* OCI program.

H.11. The "Equalization" of the Shadow Prices

As a supplementary instance, take the case where the polyhedral game (U, V) may be solved uniquely for the sector-team player. It thus follows that its reduced version, the matrix game with the pay-off matrix $\mathbf{V}'\mathbf{U}$, also possesses this property, so that according to the previously quoted Brown–Robinson theorem the sequence $\mathbf{v}^*\langle N\rangle$ is convergent and its limit is the unique optimal sector-team strategy. On the basis of part (3) of Theorem 2, this is no other than that sector shadow price system team whose every sector component is, in consequence of the above conditions, the unique optimal OCI shadow price system.

The results obtained in sections H.8–H.11 may be summarized as follows:

THEOREM 3. *In the case of a regular polyhedral game derived from a solvable OCI problem the latter may be solved through regular fictitious* *play to any required degree of accuracy, in the sense that for an arbitrarily small positive δ the δ-termination of regular fictitious play leads to a δ-optimal OCI program. If, at the same time, the derived regular polyhedral game may be uniquely solved for the sector-team player, the sector components of the mixed sector strategy series obtained in the course of regular fictitious play are equalized, i.e. they converge towards a common limit which is the optimal OCI shadow price system.*

H.12. A General Decomposition and Embedding Technique for Solving an Arbitrary Solvable Linear Programming Problem by the Use of the Method of Two-level Programming

(1) The matrix $\mathbf{A}$ is, after carrying out some necessary column changes, decomposed into parts $\mathbf{A}_1, \ldots, \mathbf{A}_n$ whose row vectors have components of constant sign. More exactly, if

$$\mathbf{A} = [\mathbf{A}_1, \ldots, \mathbf{A}_n], \quad \mathbf{A}_i = \begin{bmatrix} \mathbf{a}'_{i1} \\ \vdots \\ \mathbf{a}'_{im} \end{bmatrix}, \; i = 1, \ldots, n, \qquad \text{(H.63)}$$

then it is required that all the vectors $\mathbf{a}'_{ik}$ $(1 \leqq i \leqq n,\ 1 \leqq k \leqq m)$ be either $\mathbf{0}'$, or else non-negative or non-positive vectors differing from $\mathbf{0}'$. This means that the index sets $\mathsf{I}^+_k\ \mathsf{I}^0_k, \mathsf{I}^-_k$ $(k = 1, \ldots, m)$ and K^+_i, K^0_i, K^-_i, $(i = 1, \ldots, n)$ may be defined by the following relations*:

$$\begin{aligned} \mathbf{a}_{ik} &\geq \mathbf{0} \quad \text{if} \quad i \in \mathsf{I}^+_k \\ \mathbf{a}_{ik} &= \mathbf{0} \quad \text{if} \quad i \in \mathsf{I}^0_k \qquad k = 1, \ldots, m, \\ \mathbf{a}_{ik} &\leq \mathbf{0} \quad \text{if} \quad i \in \mathsf{I}^-_k \end{aligned} \qquad \text{(H.64)}$$

and

$$\begin{aligned} \mathbf{a}_{ik} &\geq \mathbf{0} \quad \text{if} \quad k \in \mathsf{K}^+_i \\ \mathbf{a}_{ik} &= \mathbf{0} \quad \text{if} \quad k \in \mathsf{K}^0_i \qquad i = 1, \ldots, n. \\ \mathbf{a}_{ik} &\leq \mathbf{0} \quad \text{if} \quad k \in \mathsf{K}^-_i \end{aligned} \qquad \text{(H.65)}$$

* For a vector $\mathbf{a}$, the relation $\mathbf{a} \geq \mathbf{0}$ means the every component of $\mathbf{a}$ is non-negative but there is at least one component which is strictly positive, i.e. $\mathbf{a} \geqq \mathbf{0}$. but $\mathbf{a} \neq \mathbf{0}$. The relation $\mathbf{a} \leq \mathbf{0}$ is used in a similar sense.

(2) A primal auxiliary variable is introduced for each sector, i.e. the OCI problem is embedded into a new problem characterized by the element $\mathbf{A}^0$, $\mathbf{x}^0$ and $\mathbf{c}^0$ where

$$\mathbf{A}^0 = [\mathbf{A}_1^0, \ldots, \mathbf{A}_n^0]$$

$$\mathbf{A}_i^0 = \begin{bmatrix} \mathbf{a}_{i1}^{0\prime} \\ \vdots \\ \mathbf{a}_{im}^{0\prime} \end{bmatrix} \qquad \mathbf{a}_{ik}^{0\prime} = \begin{cases} [-1, \mathbf{a}_{ik}'] & \text{if } k \in \mathrm{K}_i^- \\ [0 \quad \mathbf{a}_{ik}'] & \text{otherwise} \end{cases}$$

$$\mathbf{x}^{0\prime} = [\mathbf{x}_1^{0\prime}, \ldots, \mathbf{x}_n^{0\prime}]', \qquad \mathbf{x}_i^0 = [\mathbf{x}_i', \mathbf{x}_i^0]'$$

$$\mathbf{c}^{0\prime} = [\mathbf{c}_1^{0\prime}, \ldots, \mathbf{c}_n^{0\prime}], \qquad \mathbf{c}_i^{0\prime} = [-c_0, \mathbf{c}_i']. \tag{H.66}$$

The number c_0 must be chosen sufficiently large. It is enough for example if

$$c_0 > \min_{\mathbf{y} \in \mathbf{Y}^\Delta} \mathbf{1}' \, \mathbf{y}. \tag{H.67}$$

The ith sector problem in its primal and dual version is now as follows ($\mathbf{u}_i = [u_{i1}, \ldots, u_{im}]'$ and $\mathbf{y}_i = [y_{i1}, \ldots, y_{im}]'$):

$$\begin{aligned} \mathbf{a}_{ik}' \mathbf{x}_i &\leqq u_{ik} && \text{for } k \in \mathrm{K}_i^+ \\ x_i^0 + (-\mathbf{a}_{ik})' \mathbf{x}_i &\geqq -u_{ik} && \text{for } k \in \mathrm{K}_i^- \\ \mathbf{x}_i &\geqq 0 \end{aligned} \tag{H.68}$$

$$-c_0 x_i^0 + \mathbf{c}_i' \mathbf{x}_i \rightarrow \max!.$$

$$\begin{aligned} \sum_{k \in \mathrm{K}_i^+} \mathbf{a}_{ik} \, y_{ik} - \sum_{k \in \mathrm{K}_i^-} (-\mathbf{a}_{ik}) \, y_{ik} &\geqq \mathbf{c}_i \\ \sum_{k \in \mathrm{K}_i^-} y_{ik} &\leqq c_0 \\ y_{ik} \geqq 0 \qquad (k \in \mathrm{K}_i^+ \cup \mathrm{K}_i^-) \end{aligned} \tag{H.69}$$

$$\sum_{k \in \mathrm{K}_i^+} u_{ik} \, y_{ik} - \sum_{k \in \mathrm{K}_i^-} (-u_{ik}) \, y_{ik} \rightarrow \min!$$

(3) The central program is constrained by the following conditions ($\mathbf{b} = [b_1, \ldots, b_m]'$):

$$\sum_{i \in I_k^+} u_{ik} - \sum_{i \in I_k^-} (-u_{ik}) = b_k$$

$$\sum_{i \in I_k^-} (-u_{ik}) \leqq u_k^0 \qquad \text{(H.70)}$$

$$u_{ik} \geqq 0 \text{ for } i \in I_k^+, \; - u_{ik} \geqq 0 \text{ for } i \in I_k^-, \; k = 1, \ldots, m.$$

The number u_k^0 must be chosen to be sufficiently large. If N_k denotes the largest of the absolute values of the negative coefficients in the kth row of the matrix **A**, then it is enough that

$$u_k^0 > \max \{ -b_k, N_k \cdot \max_{\mathbf{x} \in \mathbf{X}^\Delta} \mathbf{1}'\mathbf{x} \}, \qquad k = 1, \ldots, m. \qquad \text{(H.71)}$$

(4) The two-level problem and polyhedral game derived from the new OCI problem by this decomposition under the above conditions will be regular in the sense of (H.8), so that the algorithm outlined in (H.2)–(H.11), will be applicable to it. In the case of the choices (H.67) and (H.71), moreover, the optimal primal programs of the new OCI problem will have $x_1^0 = \ldots x_n^0 = 0$, in other words these are essentially optimal in the original problem as well.

Central programming, i.e. maximization under the conditions (H.70) with an objective function formed by shadow price coefficients is thus broken up into "microprogramming problems" which may be solved very easily. For if i^+ and i_k^- are indices defined by the relations

$$y_{i_k^+,k} = \max_{i \in I_k^+} y_{ik}, \qquad y_{i_k^-,k} = \min_{i \in I^-} y_{ik} \qquad \text{(H.72)}$$

then the "optimal" central program with the shadow prices y_{ik} is as follows:

(i) For all those indices k where $y_{i_k^+,k} \geqq y_{i_k^-}$, is the case,

$$u_{ik} = \begin{cases} u_k^0 + b_k, & \text{if } \quad i = {}_k^+ \\ -u_k^0, & \text{if } \quad i = i_k^- \\ 0 & \text{otherwise.} \end{cases} \qquad \text{(H.73)}$$

(ii) For all those indices k, where $y_{\iota^+,k} < y_{i_k^-,k}$ is the case,

$$u_{ik} = \begin{cases} \max \{0, b_k\}, & \text{if } \quad i = i_k^+ \\ \min \{0, b_k\}, & \text{if } \quad i = i_k^- \\ 0 & \text{otherwise.} \end{cases} \qquad \text{(H.74)}$$

REFERENCES

This list should not be considered a full bibliography either of long-term planning, or calculations of the economic efficiency of investments, or of mathematical programming. It contains only the works to which reference is made in this book.

In the case of articles in periodicals, the number before the year refers to the volume, the numbers after the year to the pages. In the case of those periodicals whose pages are not numbered consecutively through the year, the number in which the cited paper appeared has also been given. This reference follows after the year, preceded by the abbreviation "No.", or else the date of publication has been given.

BOOKS, ARTICLES, PAPERS

1. Ackoff, R. L. (ed.), *Progress in Operations Research*, Vol. 1, New York – London: Wiley, 1961.
2. Arnoff, E. L. and Sengupta, S. S., "Mathematical programming", see ref. 1., 105–210.
3. Arrow, K. J., "Alternative approaches to the theory of choice in risk-taking situations", *Econometrica*, 19 (1951) 404–437.
4. Arrow, K. J. and Debreu, G., "Existence of an equilibrium for a competitive economy", *Econometrica*, 22 (1954) 265–290.
5. Arrow, K. J., Hurwicz, L. and Uzawa, H., *Studies in Linear and Non-Linear Programming*, Stanford: Stanford University Press, 1958.
6. Arrow, K. J., Chenery, H. B., Minhas, B. S. and Solow, R. M., "Capital–labour substitution and economic efficiency", *The Review of Economics and Statistics*, 43 (1961) 225–250.
7. Arrow, K. J. and Hurwicz, L., "Decentralization and computation in resource allocation", *Essays in Economics and Econometrics*, Chapel Hill, N. C.: University of North Carolina Press, 1960.
8. Augustinovics, M., "The chessboard-type table for the year 1965", see ref. 109., 182–192.
9. Baumol, W. J., *Economic Theory and Operational Analysis*, Englewood Cliffs: Prentice Hall, 1962.
10. Berk, J. M. and Haselbarth, J. E., "Cost capacity data", *Chemical Engineering*, 67 (1960, 12 Dec.) 172; 68 (1961, 23 Jan.) 161.

11. BODEWIG, E., *Matrix Calculus*, Amsterdam: North-Holland Publ. Co., 1956.
12. BOGNÁR, J., *Kereslet és keresletkutatás a szocializmusban* (Demand and demand-research under socialism), Budapest: Közgazdasági és Jogi Könyvkiadó, 1961.
13. BOULDING, K. E., "Welfare Economics", see ref. 50, 1–36.
14. BRÓDY, A., "Az ágazati kapcsolatok mérlege és a közvetett beruházások" (The input–output table of the economy, and indirect investments), *Közgazdasági Szemle*, 7 (1960) 561–580.
15. BRÓDY, A., *Az ágazati kapcsolatok modellje* (The model of input–output tables), Budapest: Akadémiai Kiadó, 1964.
16. BROWN, G. W., "Some notes on computation of games solutions", RAND Corporation D–436, 1949.
17. BROWN, G. W., "Iterative solution of games by fictitious play", see ref. 69, 374–376.
18. CHARNES, A. and LEMKE, C. E., *Minimization of Non-Linear Separable Functions*, Pittsburgh: Carnegie Institute of Technology, 1954.
19. CHARNES, A., COOPER, W. W. and HENDERSON, A., *An Introduction to Linear Programming*, New York: Wiley, 1953.
20. CHERNOFF, H., "Rational selection of decisions functions", *Econometrica*, 22 (1954) 422–443.
21. CHURCHMAN, C. W., ACKOFF, R. L. and ARNOFF, E. L., *Introduction to Operations Research*, New York: Wiley, 1957.
22. COURTILLOT, M., "Programmation linéaire. Étude de la modification de tous les paramètres", *Comptes Rendus de Séances de l'Académie des Sciences*, 247 (1958) 670–673.
23. CRAMÉR, H., *Mathematical Methods of Statistics*, Princeton: Princeton University Press, 1957.
24. CSEPINSZKY, A., "Some problems of the interdependence of the producing branches in agriculture", see ref. 109, 112–121.
25. CSIKÓS NAGY, B., *A szocialista árképzés* (Socialist price fixing), Budapest: Közgazdasági és Jogi Könyvkiadó, 1961.
26. CUKOR, GY. and ROMÁN, Z., "Az ágazati kapcsolatok mérlegének felhasználása az ipar ágazati szerkezetének vizsgálatára és tervezésére" (Utilization of the input–output balance of the economy to examine and plan the sectoral pattern of industry), *Magyar Tudományos Akadémia Közgazdaságtudományi Intézetének Közleményei*, (1960) No. 9.
27. DANTZIG, G. B., "On the significance of solving linear programming problems with some integer variables", *Econometrica*, 28 (1960) 30–44.
28. DANTZIG, G. B. and WOLFE, P., "Decomposition principle for linear programs", *Operations Research*, 8 (1960) 101–111.
29. DANTZIG, G. B. and WOLFE, P., "The decomposition algorithm for linear programs", *Econometrica*, 29 (1961) 767–778.
30. DAVIES, M. and VERHULST, M. (eds.), *Operational Research in Practice*, London: Pergamon, 1958.
31. DEAN, J., *Managerial Economics*, Englewood Cliffs: Prentice Hall, 1959.
32. DEÁK, A., *Egyes vegyi folyamatok termelési költségeinek elemzési módszere* (A method for the analysis of the production costs of certain chemical processes), Manuscript dissertation for a Candidate's degree, Budapest, 1962.
33. DEÁK, J. and NEMES, F., "A beruházások utólagos vizsgálata" (The subsequent examination of investments), *Figyelő*, 5 (1961) No. 23.

34. DEÁK, J., "A termelés közvetlen és közvetett állóeszközigényességi mutatójáról" (On the index of the direct and indirect fixed capital requirements of production), *Pénzügyi Szemle*, 7 (1963) No. 7, 13–21.
35. DEBREU, G., *Theory of Value*, New York: Wiley, 1959.
36. DOMAR, E. D., *Essays in the Theory of Economic Growth*, New York: Oxford University Press, 1957.
37. DORFMAN, R., SAMUELSON, P. A. and SOLOW, R. M., *Linear Programming and Economic Analysis*, New York: McGraw-Hill, 1958.
38. DOUGLAS, P. H., *The Theory of Wages*, New York: Macmillan, 1934.
39. DÖME, J., HOÓS, J. and KATÓCS, A., "A szintétikus anyagmérleg" (The synthetic material balance), *Közgazdasági Szemle*, 11 (1964) 899–911.
40. FRISCH, R., *A Survey of Types of Economic Forecasting and Programming, and a Brief Description of the Channel Model*, Oslo: University of Oslo, 1961.
41. FRISS, I. (ed.), *A Magyar Tudományos Akadémia Közgazdaságtudományi Intézetének Évkönyve* (Yearbook of the Institute for Economics of the Hungarian Academy of Sciences) *III*. 1960–1961, Budapest: Közgazdasági és Jogi Könyvkiadó, 1962.
42. GANCZER, S., *Árszámítások modern matematikai módszerekkel* (Price calculations by modern mathematical methods). Manuscript dissertation for a Candidate's degree, Budapest, 1962.
43. GASS, S. I., *Linear Programming*, New York: McGraw-Hill, 1958.
44. GERLE, GY., "A beruházások gazdaságosságának vizsgálata" (Examination of the economic efficiency of investments), Published in: *Beruházások gazdasági hatékonysága* (Economic efficiency of investments), Budapest: Közgazdasági és Jogi Könyvkiadó, 1959.
45. GOLDMAN, A. I., "Resolution and separation theorems for polyhedral convex tests", see ref. 93, 41–51.
46. GOLDMAN, A. I. and TUCKER, A. W., "Theory of linear programming", see ref. 93, 53–97.
47. HADLEY, G., *Linear Programming*, Reading–London: Addison-Wesley, 1962.
48. HALEY, B. F. (ed.), *A Survey of Contemporary Economics*, Homewood: Irwin, 1952.
49. HAVAS, P., "Az ágazati kapcsolatok mérlegének felhasználása exportgazdaságossági számításokhoz" (Utilization of the input–output table for calculations of the economic efficiency of exports), *Statisztikai Szemle*, 38 (1960) 352–363.
50. HAVAS, P., "Az exportgazdaságosság átlagos színvonala és határértékei" (The mean level and boundary values of the economic efficiency of exports), *Közgazdasági Szemle*, 9 (1962) 1346–1364.
51. HAYEK, F. A. (ed.), *Collectivist Economic Planning*, London: Routledge, 1935.
52. HICKS, J. R., *Value and Capital*, Oxford: Clarendon Press, 1957.
53. HICKS, J. R., "Thoughts on the theory of capital – The Corfu conference", *Oxford Economic Papers*, 12 (1960) 123–132.
54. HOCH, R., "Az indifferencia felületekről szóló tanítás elméleti alapjainak bírálata" (Critique of the theoretical basis of the indifference-curve analysis), see ref. 44., 331–362.
55. HOUTHAKKER, H. S., "The present state of consumption theory", *Econometrica*, 29 (1961) 704–740.
56. HURWICZ, L., "Optimality criteria for decision making under ignorance", *Cowles Commission Discussion Paper, Statistics* (1951), No. 370.

57. HURWICZ, L., "Programming in linear spaces", see ref. 5, 38–102.
58. ISARD, W., SCHOOLER, E. W. and VIETORISZ, T., *Industrial Complex Analysis and Developments. A Case Study of Refinery-Petrochemical-Synthetic Fibre Complexes*, New York: Wiley, 1959.
59. JÁVORKA, E. and BERÉNYI, J., *Jövedelmek a munkabéren felül* (Incomes above wages), Budapest: Kossuth Könyvkiadó, 1960.
60. KÁDÁR, I., "On the application of the input–output table in building industry", see ref. 109, 235–243.
61. KÁDAS, K., *Az emberi munka termelékenységének statisztikai vizsgálata a magyar gyáriparban. A Cobb–Douglas-féle statisztikai törvény kiegészítése* (Statistical examination of the productivity of human labour in Hungarian factory industry. A supplement to the Cobb–Douglas statistical law), Budapest: Hornyánszky, 1944.
62. KANTOROVICH, L. V., *Ekonomicheski raschet nailuchshego ispolzovania resursov* (Economic calculation of the optimal utilization of resources), Moscow: Izd. AN SSSR, 1959.
63. KARLIN, S., *Mathematical Methods and Theory in Games, Programming and Economics*, Reading – London: Addison—Wesley, 1959.
64. KATAOKA, S., "A stochastic programming model", *Econometrica*, 31 (1963) 181–196.
65. KHACHATUROV, T., "Problemi ekonomicheskoy effektivnosti kapitalovlozheni v sotsialisticheskom khozyaystve" (Problems of the economic effectiveness of capital investments under a socialist economy), *Voprosi Ekonomiki* (1957) No. 2, 106–121.
66. KHACHATUROV, T., "Ekonomicheskaya effektivnost kompleksnoi mekhanizatsii i avtomatizatsii proczvodstva" (Economic effectiveness of the complex mechanization and automation of industry), *Voprosi Ekonomiki* (1959) No. 12, 61–74.
67. KNIGHT, F. H., *Risk, Uncertainty and Profit*, Boston: Houghton-Mifflin, 1921.
68. KOOPMANS, T. C., "Analysis of production as an efficient combination of activities", see ref. 69, 33–97.
69. KOOPMANS, T. C. (ed.), *Activity Analysis of Production Allocation*, New York – London: Wiley–Chapman, 1951.
70. KORNAI, J., *A gazdasági vezetés túlzott központosítása*, Budapest: Közgazdasági és Jogi Könyvkiadó, 1957.
71. KORNAI, J., *Overcentralization in Economic Administration* (English translation of ref. 70.), Oxford: Oxford University Press, 1959.
72. KORNAI, J., "A műszaki fejlesztés és a beruházások gazdaságosságának számítása" (Technical development and the calculation of the economic efficiency of investments), *Közgazdasági Szemle*, 7 (1960) 670–684.
73. KORNAI, J., "Egy iparág optimális beruházási tervének meghatározása lineáris programozással" (Determining the optimal investment plan of a sector of industry by linear programming), *Közgazdasági Szemle*, 8 (1961) 570–585.
74. KORNAI, J., *A központi és ágazati programozások összekapcsolása* (Linking up central and sectoral programming), Manuscript, Budapest: Magyar Tudományos Akadémia Számítástechnikai Központja, 1961.
75. KORNAI, J., *A beruházások matematikai programozása* (The mathematical programming of investments), Budapest: Közgazdasági és Jogi Könyvkiadó, 1962.

76. KORNAI, J., HOLLÓ, J., MARCSÁNYI, Z., SIMÁN, M., RIMLER, J. and WELLISCH, P., *A ruházati ipar ágazati kapcsolatainak mérlege* (Input – output table of the garment industry), Duplicated, Budapest: Textilipari Kutató Intézet, 1962.
77. KORNAI, J., KOTÁNYI, F., PAPP, Z., PÉCSI, J., SZABÓ, L. and WELLISCH, P., *A pamutszövőipar optimális beruházási programjának meghatározása* (Determination of the optimal investment program of the cotton weaving industry), Duplicated, Budapest: Textilipari Kutató Intézet, 1960.
78. KORNAI, J. and LIPTÁK, TH., *A nyereségérdekeltség matematikai vizsgálata* (Mathematical investigation of the profit-sharing incentives), Budapest: Közgazdasági és Jogi Könyvkiadó, 1959.
79. KORNAI, J. and LIPTÁK, TH., "A mathematical investigation of some economic effects of profit sharing in socialist firms", *Econometrica*, 30 (1962), 140–161.
80. KORNAI, J. and LIPTÁK, TH., *Kétszintű tervezés* (Two-level planning), Duplicated, Budapest: Magyar Tudományos Akadémia Számítástechnikai Központja, 1962.
81. KORNAI, J. and LIPTÁK, TH., "Kétszintű tervezés: Játékelméleti modell és iteratív számítási eljárás népgazdasági távlati tervezési feladatok megoldására" (Two-level planning. A game theory model and iterative computing procedure for solving long-term planning problems of the national economy), *A Magyar Tudományos Akadémia Matematikai Kutató Intézetének Közleményei*, 7 (1962) 577–621.
82. KORNAI, J. and LIPTÁK, TH., "Two-level planning", *Econometrica*, 33 (1965) 141–169.
83. KORNAI, J., LIPTÁK, TH. and VIDOS, T., *Gazdasági számítás a magyar műszálgyártás fejlesztési programjának meghatározására* (Economic calculations to determine the development program of Hungarian man-made fibres production), Duplicated, Budapest: Szerves Vegyipari és Műanyagipari Kutató Intézet, 1960.
84. KORNAI, J. and MARTOS, B., "The application of the input – output table to determine the optimum development program of the aluminium industry", see ref. 109, 193–203.
85. KORNAI, J., TARDOS, M., VERDEN, F. and FREY, T., *A magyar műszálgyártás fejlesztésének matematikai programozása* (Mathematical programming of the development of Hungarian man-made fibres production), Duplicated, Budapest: Magyar Tudományos Akadémia Számítástechnikai Központja, 1963.
86. KORNAI, J. and WELLISCH, P., "A kalkulatív kamatláb és bértarifa a hosszúlejáratú gazdaságossági számításokban" (Computational rate of interest and wage rate in long-run efficiency calculations), *Közgazdasági Szemle*, 10 (1963) 1456–1475; 11 (1964) 76–91.
87. KORNAI, J. and WELLISCH, P., "Protsentnaya stavka v perspektivnikh racherakh po ekonomicheskoy effektivnosti", *On Political Economy and Econometrics – Essays in Honour of Oskar Lange*, Warszawa: PWN – Polish Scientific Publishers, 1964, 247 – 286.
88. KOROTKHEVICH, V. C., "Razvitie proizvodstva sinteticheskikh kauchukov" (Development of the manufacture of artificial rubbers), *Zh. Vses. Khim. Obshchestva. im. D. I. Mendeleeva*, 6 (1961) No. 1, 69 – 74.
89. KÖLBEL, H. and SCHULZE, J., *Projektierung und Vorkalkulation in der chemischen Industrie*, Berlin – Göttingen – Heidelberg: Springer, 1960.
90. KREKÓ, B., *Lineáris programozás* (Linear programming), Budapest: Közgazdasági és Jogi Könyvkiadó, 1962.

91. KREKÓ, B., *Mátrixszámítás* (Matrix calculus), Budapest: Közgazdasági és Jogi Könyvkiadó, 1964.
92. KUHN, H. W. and TUCKER, A. W., "Nonlinear programming", see ref. 137, 481–492.
93. KUHN, H. W. and TUCKER, A. W. (eds.), *Linear Inequalities and Related Systems*, Princeton: Princeton University Press, 1956.
94. KÜNZI, H. P. and KRELLE, W., *Nichtlineare Programmierung*, Berlin – Göttingen – Heidelberg: Springer, 1962.
95. LANGE, O., *Price Flexibility and Employment*, Bloomington: Principia, 1944.
96. LANGE, O., *Introduction to Econometrics*, Oxford – Warszawa: Pergamon – PWN, 1962.
97. LANGE, O., *Ekonomia Polityczna* (Political Economics) Vol. I, Warszawa: PWN. 1959.
98. LENIN, V. I., "Agrarii vopros i 'kritiki Marksa' " (The agrarian problem and the "critics of Marx"), *Sochinenia*, Vol. 5, 87–202, Moscow: Gospolitizdat, 1949.
99. LEONTIEF, W., *The Structure of American Economy*, 1919–1939, New York: Oxford University Press, 1953.
100. LEONTIEF, W. (ed.), *Studies in the Structure of the American Economy*, New York: Oxford University Press, 1953.
101. LERNER, A. P., *The Economics of Control*, New York: MacMillan, 1947.
102. LIPTÁK, TH., Kétszintű tervezés—Módosított matematikai rész (Two-level planning – Modified mathematical part), Duplicated, Budapest: Magyar Tudományos Akadémia Számítástechnikai Központja, 1962.
103. LIPTÁK, TH., "Two-level programming", *Colloquium on Applications of Mathematics to Economics, Budapest, 1965*. Budapest: Akadémiai Kiadó, (1965.) 243–253.
104. LIPTÁK, TH. and NAGY, A., *A magyar pamutszövet-kivitel rövidle'áratú optimumszámításának modellje* (Model of the short-term optimum calculation of Hungarian cotton fabric exports), Duplicated, Budapest: Hungarotex – Magyar Kereskedelmi Kamara, 1962. A shortened publication in English: "A short-run optimization model of Hungarian cotton fabric exports", *Economics of Planning*, 3 (1963) 117–140.
105. LIPTÁK, TH. and NAGY, A., *A külkereskedelmi optimumszámítások eredményének összehasonlítása hányad- és összeg-típusú célfüggvény alkalmazása esetén* (Comparison of the results of foreign trade optimum calculations using objective functions of the quotient and sum types), Duplicated, Budapest: Magyar Kereskedelmi Kamara, 1963.
106. LUCE, R. D. and RAIFFA, H., *Games and Decisions*, New York: Wiley, 1958.
107. LUKÁCS, L., "Összefüggések a beruházások gazdaságossága és az érdekeltség között" (Relations between the economic efficiency of investments and incentives), see ref. 41, 237–248.
108. LUKÁCS, O., "Az első magyar ágazati kapcsolati mérleg összeállítása és felhasználása" (Compilation and utilization of the first Hungarian input-output table), *Közgazdasági Szemle*, 7 (1960) 168–175.
109. LUKÁCS, O. (ed.), *Input – Output Tables, Their Compilation and Use*, Budapest: Akadémiai Kiadó, 1962.
110. LUKÁCS, O., "Hungarian input—output tables and the statistical basis of their compilation", see ref. 109, 19–27.
111. LUTZ, F. and LUTZ, V., *The Theory of the Investment of the Firm*, Princeton: Princeton University Press, 1951.

112. Macskássy, H. and Vidos, T., *A műanyagok szerepe hazánk és a világ anyaggazdálkodásában* (The role of synthetics in the material economy of Hungary and the world), Manuscript, Budapest: Szerves Vegyipari és Műanyagipari Kutató Intézet, 1960.
113. Magyar, J., *A saját források szerepe a beruházások finanszírozásában* (The part of own resources in financing investments), Duplicated, Budapest: Magyar Beruházási Bank, 1963.
114. Malinvaud, E., "Programmes d'expansion et taux d'intérêt", *Econometrica*, 27 (1959) 215–227.
115. Malinvaud, E., *Decentralised Procedures for Planning*, Duplicated, Cambridge: International Economic Association, 1963.
116. Malishev, I. S., *Obshchestvenni uchet truda i tseni pri sotsialisme* (The social registration of labour and prices under socialism), Moscow: Sotsekgiz, 1960.
117. Mandel, M., Szunyogh, Z. and Varga, J., "A termelő beruházások gazdaságossági számításának módszere" (Method for calculating the economic efficiency of productive investments), *Közgazdasági Szemle*, 5 (1958) 257–272.
118. Markowitz, H. M., *Portfolio Selection*, New York – London: Wiley–Chapman, 1959.
119. Martos, B., Kornai, J. and Nagy, A., "Lineáris programozási modell a magyar alumíniumipar távlati tervezéséhez" (A linear programming model for the long-term planning of the Hungarian Aluminium industry), Budapest: *Magyar Tudományos Akadémia Számítástechnikai Központjának Tájékoztatója* (1961), No. 7, 53–74.
120. Máriás, A., *A termelés mennyisége és a termelési költségek közötti összefüggések iparvállalatokban* (The relations between the output volume and production costs of industrial firms), Manuscript dissertation for a Candidate's degree, Budapest, 1962.
121. Marx, K., *Das Kapital*, Vols. I—III, Berlin: Dietz, 1948.
122. Massé, P., "Économie et stratégie", see ref. 30, 114–131.
123. McKenzie, L., "Turnpike theorems for a generalized Leontief model", *Econometrica*, 31 (1963) 165–180.
124. McKinsey, J. C. C., *Introduction to the Theory of Games*, New York: McGraw-Hill, 1952.
125. Mendershausen, H., "On the significance of Professor Douglas' production function", *Econometrica*, 6 (1938) 143–153.
126. Merk, G., "Wahrscheinlichkeitstheorie und Investitionstheorie", *Weltwirtschaftliches Archiv*, 81–1 (1958) 66–78.
127. Milnor, J., "Games against Nature", see ref. 165, 49–59.
128. Montias, J. M., "On the consistency and efficiency of central plans", *The Review of Economic Studies*, 29 (1962) 280–290.
129. Morva, T., *A társadalmi termék-mérleg szerepe a népgazdasági tervezésben* (The role of the social product balance in planning), Manuscript dissertation for a Candidate's degree, Budapest, 1962.
130. Mstislavsky, P., "A beruházások hatékonyságának néhány kérdéséről" (On some problems of the economic efficiency of investments), *Magyar – Szovjet Közgazdasági Szemle*, 3 (1949) 724–727.
131. Nagy, T. and Esze, Zs., "A többcsatornás ipari termelői ártípus" (The multichannel type industrial producers' price), *Közgazdasági Szemle*, 10 (1963) 15–29.

132. NEMCHINOV, V. S., "Stoimost i tsena pri sotsializme" (Value and price under socialism), *Voprosy Ekonomiki* (1960) No. 12, 85–103.

133. NEMCHINOV, V. S. (ed.), *Primenenie matematiki v ekonomicheskikh issledovaniakh*, Vol. I, (The application of mathematics to economic research), Moscow: Izdatelstvo sotsialno-ekonomicheskoy literatury, 1961.

134. NEMÉNYI, I. (ed.), *A beruházások és felújítások finanszírozása* (The financing of investments and up-dating), Budapest: Közgazdasági és Jogi Könyvkiadó, 1959.

135. NEUMANN, J., "A model of general economic equilibrium", *The Review of Economic Studies*, 13 (1945–46) 1–9.

136. NEUMANN, J. and MORGENSTERN, O., *Theory of Games and Economic Behaviour*, Princeton: Princeton University Press, 1953.

137. NEYMANN, F. (ed.), *Proceedings of the Second Berkeley Symposium on Mathematical Statistics and Probability*, Berkeley – Los Angeles: University of California Press, 1951.

138. NOVOZHILOV, V. V., "Izmerenie zatrat i ikh rezultatov v sotsialisticheskom khozyaystve" (The measurement of costs and their consequences in a socialist economy), see ref. 138, 42–213.

139. NYITRAI, V., "Inversion of the input–output table", see ref. 109, 81–88.

140. PAJESTKA, J., *Zatrudnienie i inwestycje a wzrost gospodarczy* (Employment, investments and economic growth), Warszawa: Panstwowe Wydawnictwo Naukowo, 1961.

141. PETERS, S. M., *Plant Design and Economics for Engineers*, New York: Mc Graw–Hill, 1958.

142. PIGOU, A. C., *The Economics of Welfare*, London: Macmillan, 1946.

143. RÁCZ, A. and ÚJLAKI, L., "Az ágazati kapcsolatok 1957. évi mérlegének inverze" (The inverse of the 1957 input–output table), *Statisztikai Szemle*, 38 (1960), 1216–1230.

144. RÁCZ, A. and ÚJLAKI, L., "A népgazdasági költségszint és termelékenység alakulásának elemzése az ágazati kapcsolatok mérlege alapján" (Analysis of the level of costs and of productivity of the national economy by input–output tables), *Statisztikai Szemle*, 40 (1962) 533–549, 643–658.

145. RÁCZ, J., *Állóalap-számítások a hosszútávlati tervezésben* (The calculation of fixed capital in long-term planning), Duplicated, Budapest: Magyar Tudományos Akadémia Közgazdaságtudományi Intézete, 1962.

146. RADNER, R., "Paths of economic growth that are optimal with regard only to final states: A turnpike theorem", *Review of Economic Studies*, 28 (1961) 98–104.

147. RADNÓTI, É., *A fogyasztási szerkezet sajátosságai a háztartásstatisztikai adatok tükrében és azok felhasználása a keresleti prognózis készítésénél* (Peculiarities of the pattern of consumption in the light of the figures of household statistics, and their utilization in preparing demand forecasts), Duplicated, Budapest: Magyar Tudományos Akadémia Közgazdaságtudományi Intézete, 1962.

148. RÉNYI, A., *Valószínűségszámítás* (Theory of probability), Budapest: Tankönyvkiadó, 1954.

149. RIMLER, J., "A ruházati ipar ágazati kapcsolatainak mérlegéről" (On the input-output table of the garment industry), *Ipari és Építőipari Statisztikai Értesítő*, 12 (1961) 446–452.

150. ROBINSON, JULIA, "An iterative method of solving a game", *Annals of Mathematics*, 54 (1961) 296–301.

151. Sadowski, W., "W sprawie ekonometrycznej koncepcji wzrostu gospodarczege" (On the problem of the econometric conception of economic growth), *Ekonomista* (1962) 824–835.

152. Samuelson, P. A., *Foundations of Economic Analysis*, Cambridge: Harvard University Press, 1948.

153. Savage, L. J., *The Foundations of Statistics*, New York: Wiley, 1954.

154. Schneider, E., *Wirtschaftlichkeitsrechnung*, Tübingen–Zürich: Mohr – Polygraphischer Verlag, 1957.

155. Shackle, G. L. S., *Expectation in Economics*, Cambridge: Cambridge University Press, 1952.

156. Simon, Gy. and Kondor, Gy., "A külkereskedelmi kapcsolatok optimalizálása" (The optimization of foreign trade relations), *Közgazdasági Szemle*, 7 (1960) 822–839.

157. Simon, Gy. and Kondor, Gy., "Partial input–output tables and some questions of their combined application", see ref. 109, 124–134.

158. Simon, Gy. and Kondor, Gy., "A gazdasági optimumszámítások problémái Kantorovics és Novozsilov műveiben" (The problems of economic optimum calculations in the works of Kantorovich and Novozhilov), *Magyar Tudományos Akadémia Közgazdaságtudományi Intézetének Tájékoztató Közleményei*, (1963) No. 2.

159. Simon, Gy. and Kondor, Gy., *A gazdasági hatékonyság értékelésének néhány problémája* (Some problems of the evaluation of economic efficiency), Duplicated, Budapest: Magyar Tudományos Akadémia Közgazdaságtudományi Intézete, 1963.

160. Solow, R. M., "A contribution to the theory of economic growth", *Quarterly Journal of Economics*, 70 (1956) 65–94.

161. Solow, R. M., "Technical change and the aggregate production function", *The Review of Economics and Statistics*, 30 (1957) 312–320.

162. Stepankov, A., "O metodike opredelenia ekonomicheskoy effektivnosti kapitalnykh vlozheni v promyshlenosti SSSR" (On the methods of determining the economic effectiveness of capital investments in Soviet industry), *Voprosy Ekonomiki* (1960) No. 6, 93–100.

163. Strumilin, S. G., "Faktor vremeni v proyektirovkakh kapitalnykh vlozheni" (The time factor in planning capital investments), *Izvestia Akademii Nauk*, (1946) No. 3, 195–215.

164. Theil, H., *Economic Forecast and Policy*, Amsterdam: North-Holland Publishing Co., 1958.

165. Thrall, R. M., Coombs, C. H. and Davis, R. L. (eds.), *Decision Processes*, New York: Wiley, 1954.

166. Tinbergen, J., *Econometrics*, Philadelphia: Blakiston, 1951.

167. Tinbergen, J. and Bos, H. C., *Mathematical Models of Economic Growth*, New York, McGraw–Hill, 1962.

168. Trzeciakowski, W., "A külkereskedelem optimalizálása a tervgazdaságban" (The optimization of foreign trade in a planned economy), *Közgazdasági Szemle*, 9 (1962) 577–588.

169. Turánszky, M., "A beruházások gazdaságosságának fogalma és értékelése" (The concept and evaluation of the economic efficiency of investments), Published in: *Beruházások gazdasági hatékonysága* (Economic efficiency of investments), Budapest: Közgazdasági és Jogi Könyvkiadó, 1959.

170. Újlaki, L., "Az ágazati kapcsolatok mérlege a távlati tervezésben" (Input-output tables in long-run planning), *Figyelő*, 8 (1964) No. 30.
171. Uzawa, H., "Neutral inventions and the stability of growth equilibrium", *The Review of Economic Studies*, 28 (1961) 117–124.
172. Varga, J., "Felhalmozás és gazdaságosság" (Accumulation and economic efficiency), *Közgazdasági Szemle*, 6 (1959) 522–536.
173. Vázsonyi, A., *Scientific Programming in Business and Industry*, New York: Wiley, 1958.
174. Viner, J., "Cost curves and supply curves", *Zeitschrift für Nationalökonomie*, 3 (1931) 23–46.
175. Waelbroeck, J., "La grande controverse sur la planification et la théorie économique mathématique contemporaine", *Cahiers de l'ISEA* (1964, février) No. 146, 3–24.
176. Wald, A., *Statistical Decision Functions*, New York: Wiley, 1950.
177. Weckstein, R. S., "On the use of the theory of probability in economics", *The Review of Economic Studies*, 20–3 (1952–1953) 191–198.
178. Williams, R., "Six-tenths factor. Aids in approximating costs", *Chemical Engineering*, 54 (1947) No. 12, 124.
179. Wolfe, P., "Determinateness of polyhedral games", see ref. 93, 195–198.

OFFICIAL MATERIALS AND PUBLICATIONS

180. Akademii Nauk SSSR (Academy of Sciences of the USSR), *Tipovaya metodika opredelenia ekonomicheskoy effektivnosti kapitalnykh vlozheni i novoy tekhniki v narodnom khozhyaistve SSSR* (Standard methods for determining the economic effectiveness of capital investments and new techniques in the national economy of the USSR), Moscow: Gosplanizdat, 1960.
181. Tsentralnoje statisticheskoje upravlenie (Central Statistical Authority), *Narodnoje khozyaistvo SSSR v 1960 godu* (The national economy of the USSR in 1960), Moscow: Gosstatizdat, 1961.
182. Federal Trade Commission, *Economic Report on Antibiotic Manufacture*, Washington: United States Government Printing Office, 1958.
183. Komisja Planowania Przy Radzie Ministrów (Planning Commission of the Council of Ministers), *Instrukcja ególna w sprawie metodyki badan ekonomicznej efektywnosci inwestycji* (General instructions on the methodology of the economic efficiency investigation of investments), Warszawa: 1960.
184. Központi Statisztikai Hivatal (Central Statistical Office), *Adatok és adalékok a népgazdaság fejlődésének tanulmányozásához. 1949—1955* (Facts and figures for studying the development of the national economy. 1949–1955), Budapest, 1957.
185. Központi Statisztikai Hivatal (Central Statistical Office), *Statisztikai Évkönyv, 1957* (Statistical Yearbook, 1957), Budapest, Statisztikai Kiadó V, 1958.
186. Központi Statisztikai Hivatal (Central Statistical Office), *Az ágazati kapcsolatok mérlege, 1957* (The input–output table, 1957), Budapest, 1959.
187. Központi Statisztikai Hivatal (Central Statistical Office), *A magyar népgazdaság ágazati kapcsolatainak mérlege, 1959* (The input–output table of the Hungarian national economy, 1959), Budapest, 1961.

188. Központi Statisztikai Hivatal (Central Statistical Office), *Statisztikai Évkönyv, 1961* (Statistical yearbook, 1961), Budapest: Statisztikai Kiadó V, 1962.

189. Központi Statisztikai Hivatal (Central Statistical Office), *Ipari termelői és fogyasztói árak és árarányok vizsgálata* (Examination of industrial, producers' and consumers' prices and price ratios), Budapest, 1963.

190. Központi Statisztikai Hivatal (Central Statistical Office), "A népgazdaság állóeszközei 1959–61" (The fixed capital of the national economy, 1959–61), *Statisztikai Időszaki Közlemények*, (1963) No. 53.

191. Központi Statisztikai Hivatal (Central Statistical Office), *A magyar népgazdaság ágazati kapcsolatainak mérlege az 1961. évben* (The input-output table of the Hungarian national economy, 1961), Budapest, 1964.

192. Magyar Gazdaságkutató Intézet (Hungarian Economic Research Institute) *Különféle textilipari nyersanyagok termelése és áralakulása* (Output and price trends of various raw materials of the textile industry), Budapest, 1943.

193. Magyar Kereskedelmi Kamara (Hungarian Chamber of Commerce), *Tőkés árupiacok. A világ műanyagtermelésének fejlődése* (Capitalist commodity markets. Development of the world's synthetic material output), Duplicated, Budapest, 1960.

194. Országos Árhivatal (Price Control Board), "Az értékár-, a termelési ár és a többcsatornás ipari ártípusszámítások az 1959 évi ÁKM 77 termelő ágazatra egyszerűsített változatával" (Computations for industrial price systems of "value type", "production price type" and "multi-channel type" by the input-output table of the year 1959, aggregated to 77 productive branches), *Árpolitikai jelentés* (1964) No. 6.

195. Országos Tervhivatal – Pénzügyminisztérium – Építésügyi Minisztérium (National Planning Board – Ministry of Finance – Ministry of Building), *Beruházási Kódex* (Investment Code), Budapest, 1963.

196. Statistisches Bundesamt, "Grosshandelspreise. Grundstoffe", *Preise, Löhne, Wirtschaftsrechnungen* (1954–1960) Reihe 9, Teil II–III.

197. *A Magyar Szocialista Munkáspárt VII. Kongresszusa* (Seventh Congress of the Hungarian Socialist Workers' Party), Budapest: Kossuth, 1959.

198. "A Marx Károly Közgazdaságtudományi Egyetem 1960 évi tudományos ülésszaka" (The 1960 Scientific Session of the Karl Marx Economics Faculty), *Közgazdasági Szemle*, 7 (1960) 1087–1104.

199. "Markets for materials", *Modern Plastics*, 37 (1959) 89–112.

200. "Prices", *Chemical and Engineering News* (permanent feature), 1950–1960.

AUTHOR INDEX

The numbers in italics indicate the page numbers of References

Ackoff, R. L. *507*, *508*
Allais, M. 258
Arnoff, E. L. 140, *507*, *508*
Arrow, K. J. 91, 150, 163, 186, 260, 382, *507*
Augustinovics M. xi, 34, *507*

Barone, E. 381
Baumol, W. J. 85, 160, *507*
Berényi, J. 482, *510*
Berk, J. M. 101, *507*
Bliss, C. J. xi
Bodewig, E. 17, *508*
Bognár, J. 396, *508*
Bos, H. C. 402, *515*
Boulding, K. E. 385, 410, *508*
Bródy, A. xi, 18, 28, 220, 223, 225, *508*
Brown, G. W. 501, 502, 503, *508*
Bulgakov, N. S. 262

Cauchy, A. L.
Charnes, A. 68, 92, *508*
Chenery, H. B. *507*
Chernoff, H. 150, 186, *508*
Churchman, C. W. 400, *508*
Clark, J. B. 256, 257
Cobb, C. W. 256, 260, 265, 268, 457, 474
Coombs, C. H. *515*
Cooper, W. W. *508*
Courtillot, M. 147, *508*
Cramér, H. 135, 136, 168, *508*
Csepinszky, A. *508*
Csikós Nagy, B. 313, *508*
Cukor, Gy. XI 220, *508*

Dantzig, G. B. 86, 344, 372, 381, 492, *508*
Davies, M. *508*
Davis, R. L. *515*
Dean, J. 85, 101, 285, 291, *508*
Deák, A. 97, *508*
Deák, J. 129, 219, *508*, *509*
Debreu, G. 382, 413, *507*, *509*
Desroussaux, J. 258
Domar, E. D. 468, *509*
Dorfman, R. 28, 258, 410, *509*
Douglas, P. H. 256, 260, 265, 268, 457, 474, *509*
Döme, J. 38, *509*

Esze, Zs. 210, 482, 484, *513*

Földeák, J. 74
Frey, T. 51, 68, 74, 429, *511*
Frisch, R. 344, 350, 376, *509*
Friss, I. *509*
Frivaldszky, S. 371
Fülöp, S. 51
Futó, L. 74

Ganczer, S. 226, 310, *509*
Gass, S. 68, 144, 321, 353, 431, *509*
Gerle, Gy. 485, *509*
Goldman, A. I. 489, 491, *509*

Hadley, G. 68, *509*
Haley, B. F. *509*
Haselbarth, J. E. 101, *507*
Havas, P. 222, 306, 307, *509*
Hayek, F. A. 377, *509*
Henderson, A. *508*
Hicks, J. R. 174, 257, *509*
Hoch, R. 413, *509*
Holló, J. *511*
Hoós, J. *509*
Houthakker, H. S. 414, *509*
Hurwicz, L. 160, 382, 410, *507*, *509*, *510*

Isard, W. 101, *510*

Jávorka, E. 482, *510*

Kádár, I. *510*
Kádas, K. 457, *510*
Kantorovich, L. V. 269, 344, 423, 479, 484, *510*
Karlin, S. 68, 89, 353, 358, 410, 413, 499, 501, *510*
Kataoka, S. 172, *510*
Katócs, A. *509*
Khachaturov, T. 448, 478, 485, *510*
Knight, F. H. 173, *510*
Kondor, Gy. 269, 315, 343, 423, 477, 479, 485, *515*
Koopmans, T. C. 385, 410, *510*
Kornai, J. 185, 227, 343, *510*, *511*, *513*
Korotkhevich, V. C. 108, *511*
Kotányi, F. 51, *511*
Kováts, G. 74
Kölbel, H. 101, *511*
Krekó, B. 17, 68, 353, *511*, *512*
Krelle, W. 91, *512*
Kuhn, H. W. 91, 410, *512*
Künzi, H. P. 91, *512*

Lange, O. 28, 174, *512*
Laplace, P. S.
Lemke, C. E. 92
Lenin, V. I. 262, *512*
Leontief, W. 28, *512*
Lerner, A. P. 385, *512*
Lipták, Th. xi, 74, 97, 162, 343, 411, 444, 487, *511*, *512*
Luce, R. D. 150, 160, *512*
Lukács, L. 109, 132, *512*
Lukács, O. *512*
Lutz, F. 216, 450, *512*
Lutz, V. 216, 450, *512*

Macskássy, H. 285, *513*
Magyar, J. *513*
Malinvaud, E. 266, 344, 381, *513*
Malishev, I. S. 481, 485, *513*
Mandel, M. 282, 478, *513*
Marcsányi, Z. 51, *511*
Markowitz, H. M. 195, *513*
Martos, B. xi, 76, 220, *511*, *513*
Máriás, A. 97, *513*
Marx, K. *513*
Massé, P. 51, *513*
McKenzie, L. 258, *513*
McKinsey, J. C. C. 496, *513*
Megyeri, E. 481
Mendershausen, H. 268, *513*
Merk, G. 162, *513*
Milnor, J. 150, 160, *513*
Minhas, B. S. *507*
Montias, J. M. 117, *513*
Morgenstern, O. 150
Morva, T. 34, *513*
Mstislavsky, P. 480, *513*

Nagy, A. xi, 411, *512*, *513*
Nagy, T. xi, 210, 482, 484, *513*
Nemchinov, V. S. 482, 484, *514*
Neményi, I. 60, *514*
Nemes, F. *508*
Neumann, J. von 150, 258, 266, 271, *514*
Neymann, F. *514*
Novozhilov, V. V. 479, *514*
Nyilas, A. 457
Nyitrai, V. 30, *514*

Pajestka, J. 474, 475, *514*
Papp, Z. *511*
Pareto, V. 410
Pécsi, J. 51, *511*
Peters, S. M. 101, *514*
Phelps, E. S. 258
Pigou, A. C. 223, *514*

Rácz, A. 30, 222, *514*
Rácz, J. 457, 459, 462, 463, 464, 465, *514*
Radner, R. 258, *514*
Radnóti, É. *514*
Raiffa, H. 150, 160, 512
Rényi, A. 135, 136, *514*
Rimler, J. *511*, *514*
Robinson, Joan 258
Robinson, Julia 501, 502, 503, *514*
Román, Z. 220, *508*

Sadowski, W. 474, *515*
Samuelson, P. A. 258, 385, 414, *509*, *515*
Savage, L. J. 150, 186, *515*
Schneider, E. 450, *515*

Schooler, E. W. *510*
Schulze, J. 101, *511*
Sengupta, S. S. 140, *507*
Shackle, G. L. S. 162, *515*
Simán, M. *511*
Simon, Gy. 269, 315, 343, 423, 477, 479, 484, *515*
Solow, R. M. 237, 258, 260, 474, *507*, *509*, *515*
Somogyi, M. 457
Stepankov, A. 481, *515*
Strumilin, S. G. 480, *515*
Swan, T. 258
Szabó, L. 51, *511*
Szunyogh, Z. *513*

Tardos, M. 74, 283, 292, 434, *511*
Tarlós, B. 74
Tarnay, Gy. 371
Theil, H. 298, *515*
Thrall, R. M. *515*
Tinbergen, J. 268, 402, *515*
Trzeciakowski, W. 344, 424, *515*
Tucker, A. W. 91, 410, 489, 491, *509*, *512*
Turánszky, M. 23, 479, 480, 484, 485, *515*

Újlaki, L. 30, 38, 222, *514*, 516
Uzawa, H. 237, *507*, *516*

Varga, J. 478, *513*, *516*
Vázsonyi, A. 92, *516*
Verden, F. 74, *511*
Verhulst, M. *508*
Vidos, T. 74, 283, 285, *513*
Vietorisz, T. *510*
Viner, J. 223, *516*

Waelbroeck, J. 381, *516*
Wald, A. 150, 410, *516*
Walras, L. 382
Weckstein, R. S. 162, *516*
Weizsäcker, C. C. von 258
Wellisch, P. xi, 51, 74, 188, 234, 453, 457, *511*
Williams, R. 101, *516*
Wolfe, P. 344, 372, 381, 496, *508*, *516*

SUBJECT INDEX

The following index is not complete; it is confined to listing, in alphabetic order, the notions employed in the work in a special sense (and printed in spaced letters where they first occur or are defined in the text). The page numbers refer to the place where the notion in question is defined and explained in detail.

The abbreviation (TP) which follows some of the notions refers to the fact that the notion in question was given a special interpretation in Chapter 24, in connection with two-level planning.

acceptable hypothesis 235
accounting for domestic input 208
— — foreign-trade input 208
— period 449
— principle 207
accumulation share 255
activity 55
—, export (TP) 349
—, import (TP) 349
—, investment (TP) 348
—, reproductive (TP) 348
actual price 26
addressee 6
admissible program, economico-politically 417
allocation programming problem, primary 241
— — —, secondary 243
auxiliary plan equation 15
— — figures 13
average efficiency of production fund 261
— productivity of labour 263

balance, product 6
—, specified 10
—, synthetic 5
basic price system 225
bounded import activity 349

centre (TP) 346
characteristic of model 141
— value 144
— —, qualitative 144
— —, quantitative 144
chessboard balance 34
choice based on simple ranking 113
closing of the calculation (TP) 358
complete imputation 265
— system of preferences 413
completion period 448
computational 26
— evaluation 26
— —, official 26
— pay-roll tax 210
— price 26
— rate of interest 214
— rental on capital 209
— wage factor 209
— — rate 243
consistency analysis 335
constraint 58
constraint-constant 67
constructed unit 400
conventional unit 400
cost degression 94
—, depending on the program 65
— discounted 449
—, investment 24

cost, isocost-line of 244
—, operation 24
— progression 91
currency exchange, rate of 25

data presented in "from-to" form 151
datum interval 151
decision problem 51
degression, cost 94
δ-optimal (TP) 356
direct material input coefficient 29
— production fund coefficient 219
— wage coefficient 222
divisibility 86
documented plan equation 14
— — figures 13
domination 114
dual parametric programming 321

economic administration 413
— policy 393
— —, aims of 393
— —, requirement of 401
— —, target of 401
— —, weight of the aim of 398
economico-political effect 410
— requirement, efficient according to 410
economico-politically admissible program 417
effect vector 411
efficiency of production fund 238
— — — —, average 261
— — — —, marginal 238
efficient program 410
elasticity of the national income with respect to the labour force 259
— — — — — — — — — —| production fund 259
examination of terminability (TP) 358
exogenous bound 14
export activity (TP) 349
— price 208
extensive utilization 464
external consumption (TP) 347
— input 30
— — coefficient 31

feasible program 68
final output 29

fixed capital 24
foreign currency return (TP) 352
foreign-trade price 208
framework 140
"from-to" form, data presented in 151

gross investment 59
— output 28

hazard, strategy of 174
hypothesis, acceptable 235
—, provisional 235
—, unacceptable 235

identity interval 144
— —, qualitative 144
— —, quantitative 144
import activity (TP) 349
— —, bounded 349
— —, unbounded (TP) 349
— price 208
imputation 247
—, complete 265
index of economic efficiency 23
— system 5
indirect material input coefficient 29
— requirements 29
inner square of technological matrix 29
input—output table 28
internal rental on capital 250
inverse matrix 29
investment activity (TP) 348
— cost 24
— —with interest added 448
isocost-line 244
isoquant curve 239

labour, average productivity of 263
— force coefficient (TP) 351
— —, marginal productivity of 238
—, technical equipment of 260
long-term input functions 325
loose target of economic policy 405
lower optimum (TP) 358

machine group 56
maintenance input 216
manpower quota (TP) 347
marginal efficiency 238
— productivity 238

marginal rate of substitution 239
material input coefficient (TP) 351
— — —, direct 29
— — —, indirect 29
— quota (TP) 347

national income, elasticity of, with respect to the labour force 259
— —, — —, — — — — production fund 259
normal price 289
novelty price 285

objective function 64
official computational evaluation 26
— — prices 26
— plan 61
operation cost 24
— —, proportional 441
optimal program 68
optimum, lower 358
—, upper 358
output coefficient (TP) 350
overall central information problem (TP) 344
over-tight target of economic policy 405

parameter 142
parametric programming 142
— —, dual 321
pay-roll tax, computational 210
period (TP) 347
—, completion 448
permit paper 22
phase (TP) 358
plan coordination 17
— directive 45, 347
— equation, auxiliary 15
— figure 320, 347
— —, auxiliary 13
— —, documented 13
— term (TP) 347
planners 417
possible program 416
preference relation 413
preferences, complete system of 413
price, actual 26
—, computational 26
—, export 208
price, foreign-trade 208
—, import 208
—, normal 289
—, novelty 285
—, official computational 26
—, shadow 338
— system, basic 225
primary allocation program 241
priority material 440
— product 6
product 6, 346
— balance 6
production function 237
— fund 24
— —, average efficiency of 261
— — coefficient 219
— —, marginal efficiency of 238
program 58
—, cost depending on 65
—, δ-optimal (TP) 356
—, economico-politically admissible 417
—, efficient 410
—, feasible 68
—, optimal 68
—, possible 416
programming, dual parametric 321
—, parametric 142
—, safety 172
— scope 53
— surplus 421
progression, cost 91
proportional operation cost 441
provisional hypothesis 235

qualitative characteristic value 144
— identity interval 144
quality parameter of the technical level 259
quantitative characteristic value 144
— identity interval 144

rate of currency exchange 25
— — interest 214
rational computational rental on capital 243
— — wage rate 243
realization coefficient 129
renewal 9
rent on capital 24
rental formula 447

rental on capital 24
— — —, internal *250*
— — —, rational 243
reproductive activity (TP) 348
return, foreign currency (TP) 352
risk-indefference, strategy of 173

safety factor 172
— level 157, 172
— programming 172
— ranking 159
— strategy 173
— value 172
secondary allocation programming problem 243
sensitivity analysis 140
set of possible programs 416
shadow price 338
slack variable 67
special constraint (TP) 351
— optimum component (TP) 362
specified balance 10
standard distribution 255
step (TP) 359
strategy of hazard 174
— — limited safety 173
— — maximum safety 174
— — risk-indefference 173
—, safety 173
structural decision ix
structure ix
— of the program 143
substitution, marginal rate of 239
supply task (TP) 347
synthetic balance 5

technical equipment of labour 260
— level, quality parameter of 259
technological coefficient (TP) 28
— matrix, inner square of 29
— variant 56
terminability, examination of (TP) 358
terminal year 50
tight target of economic policy 405
total contents 32
— — coefficient 31
— domestic input-content 305
— material input coefficient 30
— system of preferences 413
traditional methods of planning 3
two-level planning (TP) 344

unacceptable hypothesis 235
unbounded import activity (TP) 349
uncertainty bonus 157, 174
—, grade of 152
— penalty 157, 173
upper optimum (TP) 358

variables 55

wage coefficient, direct 222
— factor, computational 209
— rate 243
— —, computational 243
working capital 24
— hypothesis 235
— —, acceptable 235
— —, provisional 235
— —, unacceptable 235